Optoelectronic Semiconductor Devices

Optoelectronic Semiconductor Devices

David Wood

Prentice Hall
New York   London   Toronto   Sydney   Tokyo   Singapore

First published 1994 by
Prentice Hall International (UK) Limited
Campus 400, Maylands Avenue
Hemel Hempstead
Hertfordshire, HP2 7EZ
A division of
Simon & Schuster International Group

© Prentice Hall International (UK) Limited 1994

Printed and bound in Great Britain by
Redwood Books, Trowbridge, Wiltshire.

Library of Congress Cataloging-in-Publication Data

Available from the publisher

British Library Cataloguing in Publication Data

A catalogue record for this book is available from
the British Library
ISBN 0-13-638750-0

2   3   4   5   98   97   96

For Frances and Stephanie

Contents

Preface

In preparing this book, the aim was to describe optoelectronic devices in detail from a semiconductor physics point of view. The demand for this kind of text has become clear from the increasing importance of light emitters and detectors in undergraduate courses. The combination of a treatment of semiconductor theory with detailed accounts of optoelectronic devices, as well as the techniques available for making them, provides the individuality of the book. The text differs from many others on semiconductor devices in that there is no treatment here of field effect or bipolar transistors. It also differs from the many books containing descriptions of optoelectronic devices in that these are usually discussed from a communications viewpoint.

Each device is first described in its basic form, and then the various specialist improvements are introduced, showing how the impressive performance of modern devices has not been built up overnight but has taken many years to develop. After the introductory material, extensive use is made of references to provide the reader with directions for their own line of interest. All chapters provide conceptual and numerical problems as well as worked examples. The academic level of this book is set at that of final year undergraduate/early postgraduate.

Chapter 1 is a brief summary of the salient points of semiconductor physics relevant to the book, and Chapter 2 covers the basic properties of semiconductor junctions. The level provided is that necessary to understand the devices in this book. The familiar reader may well miss out these first two chapters if they are happy with their own understanding, as the material is likely to have been covered in more detail at an earlier stage in their education.

Light emitting devices, the LED and semiconductor laser, are introduced in Chapters 3 and 4 respectively. Chapter 3 describes the light emission process, its problems and limitations, structures and reliability, as well as introducing some electronics in drive circuitry. Chapter 4 takes the reader from the LED to a laser through the concept of stimulated emission. The structure of a modern diode laser is gradually unveiled through the early part of the chapter, and the last two thirds is devoted to the many different types of semiconductor laser available, whether single frequency, quantum well, visible emission, high power, etc.

Chapters 5–7 describe semiconductor light detectors. The simplest type, the photoconductor, is introduced in Chapter 5 along with problems associated with optical detection from a device point of view, namely noise and sensitivity. Chapter 6 summarizes the reverse biased PIN diode, its operation, structure and integration into a monolithic detector/amplifier. The avalanche photodiode described in Chapter 7 is a reverse biased diode with internal gain. Comparisons are then made between the avalanche and PIN diode as a detector element.

How all these devices are made forms an important part of the book. Chapter 8 covers all the aspects of making semiconductors and their associated junctions. The creation of single crystal wafers is described, and subsequent work is concentrated on the processes that have enabled so much progress to be made in optoelectronic devices, i.e. those based on epitaxy. Doping and wet etching techniques conclude this chapter. Once the semiconductors have been made, they need to be patterned, etched and metallized. Although wet etching is included in Chapter 8, the increasingly important process of dry etching is described in detail in Chapter 9, as is lithography and metallization. Chapter 10 concludes this book with subjects that are often overlooked but which nonetheless are vital to the reliability of modern optoelectronics, namely packaging and testing.

Besides the previously mentioned emphasis on a semiconductor physics approach, other 'slants' to this book are discussions of III–V rather than II–VI devices and communication, rather than general, applications. This keeps a reasonable control on the direction of the book.

Many people have helped with the preparation of this text, and deserve a special mention at this point. My thanks first of all go to Professor John Wilson of the University of Northumbria at Newcastle for encouraging me to present ideas to Prentice-Hall International, and to PHI for welcoming them. I am also very grateful to the many individuals and organizations who have allowed me to use their original material in this book, without which it would be significantly worse off. In particular, the following people have provided original drawings or photographs; Joe Mun and Steve Clements of BNR-Europe, Alan Bussell of Balzers High Vacuum, Keith Vanner of GEC-Marconi Materials Technology, G Borghs of IMEC, Nick Ward of Leybold, Allan Goodbrand of Oxford Plasma Technology, Jack Jewell of Photonics Research, Gary Wilkinson of Shipley Europe and Brian Miller of VG Semicon. A special thanks is given to Joe Mun, for letting me work in semiconductor processing and find out how it was really done. Further, my appreciation goes to all the students at the University of Durham who have seen parts of the text and made useful suggestions and comments. Thank you must also be said to the University itself, for providing an excellent environment in which to write a book.

The book was prepared in LaTeX at the University of Durham; thanks go to many people for help in learning how to use this typesetting facility. Richard Fidczuk, senior production editor at PHI, has also been very helpful in this respect. Thanks especially to my wife Elaine, Mrs. Sybil Lyons and Mrs. Sylvia Mellanby for help in preparing this text; it has taken a long time and a lot of effort, especially by my mother-in-law, Sybil, who has shown tremendous devotion to this work.

Finally, the biggest and most individual thank you of all goes to Elaine, just for being there.

David Wood
University of Durham
December 1993

1

Basics

An appreciation of crystal structure is crucial to understanding how any solid state device works, though as with most aspects of advanced topics there is no limit to the kind of detail potentially involved. Here we put an artificial limit to this knowledge, this limit being the basic minimum sufficient to understand the working of the devices mentioned in this book. It is assumed that the reader has had an introduction to the physical structure of semiconductors, and this chapter is intended to reinforce the salient points of such a course. There are many suitable textbooks which go into more detail, from an introductory level, e.g. [1], to a more advanced treatise, e.g. [2]. Here we restrict ourselves to a description of the type of bond found in semiconductors, how atoms are bonded to form structures, how to describe these structures in terms of Miller indices and how defects can affect device properties.

$E-k$ diagrams are then reviewed; these give the basis from which all device action is subsequently described, i.e. energy bands and the Fermi level. The effects of doping are then discussed, and the chapter ends with a description of the various current carrying mechanisms present in a semiconductor.

1.1   Crystal structure

The physical way in which atoms come together to form a crystal structure determines the properties of the material. In a single crystal there is a periodicity to the lattice that extends right through the material. This is an ideal case, and sometimes there may be many periodicities to the structure. The material is then said to be polycrystalline, and grain boundaries exist between different periodic structures. An extreme case of polycrystalline material is where the periodic structure extends for only a few atoms. Such a material is called amorphous, and the structure has only short range order: it may even have none at all. Single crystal material is the most difficult to grow, and hence is the most expensive. Polycrystalline and amorphous materials find uses where cost considerations outweigh those of device efficiency, e.g. for large area solar cells. For all of the devices we will be discussing in later chapters the assumption is made that the structure is single crystal.

1.1.1   Diamond and zincblende

Semiconductors are covalently bonded and always form a tetrahedral structure. The reason for this can be seen by considering Figure 1.1. Only the four outer electrons in silicon or germanium contribute to the bond, and these interact with one another to produce an elongated electron cloud associated with each electron. These clouds all point away from the nucleus and arrange themselves with the greatest possible angle between them, i.e. $109° 28'$, to form the tetrahedral shape. Adjacent atoms then contribute electrons to the clouds and the tetrahedral structure is repeated through the crystal, as in Figure 1.2(a). This is known as a diamond structure. Dissimilar atoms, such as In and P, bond in a similar fashion, now known as a zincblende structure and shown in Figure 1.2(b), despite the electron contributions from each atom being unequal. An atom of indium acts as the central point of a tetrahedron bonding to four phosphorus atoms; similarly one phosphorus atom bonds to four atoms of indium. Most of the compound semiconductors form the zincblende structure, but a few of the II–VI compounds crystallize in a slightly different form known as wurtzite, in which the tetrahedral bonding is maintained but the two interlocking sublattices are hexagonal rather than face-centred cubic (fcc). Silicon carbide is an interesting material, in that it can take either the zincblende or wurtzite form, and any one of the many combinations in between. The behaviour of this material is thus related to its polytype, i.e. its crystal structure: this will be clearly demonstrated in Chapter 3 on light emitting diodes, where the different polytypes give rise to different coloured devices.

Whatever the structure, the tetrahedrally bonded atoms extend through space to form a crystal lattice. The basic arrangement of atoms, i.e. that which cannot be simplified any further and which is periodically repeated to form the lattice, is called the unit cell. Obviously different lattice structures have different unit cells, but there are only fourteen different unit cells known in nature. These are described by their geometric shape; three are cubic, two tetragonal, four orthorhombic, two monoclinic, one triclinic and two trigonal. Details of how these are formed by stretching the different axes of a cube or by altering its internal angles are given in [3]. The unit cell of most interest here is the face-centred cubic (fcc), or cubic F, as shown in Figure 1.3. This has an atom at each corner of a cube, along with one at the centre of each of the six faces. The dimension of the cube is called the lattice constant, a, and is typically of the order of a few angströms. Each corner atom has one-eighth of its volume in the cube, and each face atom one-half. The unit cell thus contains four atoms.

The diamond structure belongs to the face-centred cubic family, although at first sight this may not necessarily be obvious. However, close inspection of Figure 1.2(a)

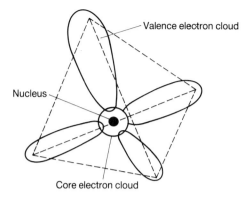

Figure 1.1 Tetrahedral structure of valence electron clouds in a covalently bonded atom.

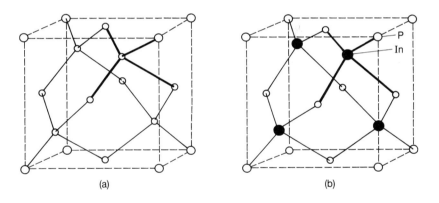

Figure 1.2 (a) Diamond, and (b) zincblende structure of covalently bonded semiconductors.

will show that diamond is composed of two separate fcc sublattices, displaced from one another by one-quarter of a body diagonal of the cube. This can perhaps be more readily appreciated by considering the zincblende structure of Figure 1.2(b). Unlike the diamond structure, where each sublattice consists of identical atoms, the sublattices in zincblende consist of different atoms, in this case one sublattice of indium and one of phosphorus.

Example 1.1

Calculate the fraction of a unit cell that is occupied by atoms in the face-centred cubic structure, if each atom can be represented by a hard sphere.

Solution: Each corner sphere has 1/8 of its volume inside the unit cell; eight corners ≡ 1 sphere. Each face sphere has 1/2 its volume inside the unit cell; six faces ≡ 3 spheres. Total ≡ 4 spheres.

From Figure 1.3, for a cell of lattice constant a a face diagonal is $\sqrt{2}a$ across – this represents the radius of 4 spheres.

The total volume occupied by the spheres is then

$$4 \times \frac{4}{3}\pi \times \left(\frac{\sqrt{2}a}{4}\right)^3 = 0.74a^3. \tag{1.1}$$

The volume of the unit cell is a^3, and so the fraction occupied is 0.74.

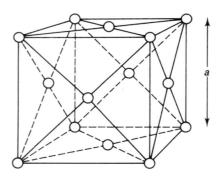

Figure 1.3 The face-centred cubic (fcc) unit cell.

1.1.2   Miller indices

From Figure 1.3 it can be seen that the arrangement of atoms, and their associated spacings, along the face of a cube is different from that across the body of the cube. This explains why the crystal properties along a particular plane are different from that along another plane with a dissimilar atomic layout. This leads on to the observation that electrical, and hence device, properties are dependent on crystal orientation.

We would like to have a method to define a particular orientation of a crystal but without giving its position in space. Thus there is no need for a reference point within the crystal, and the orientation specified can be applied anywhere in the structure. Such a method is provided by the use of Miller indices, which are based on intercepts of a plane with Cartesian x, y and z axes. The method of determining Miller indices can be explained by considering the example of Figure 1.4. The crystal plane intercepts the x, y and z axes at $a/2$, $b/3$ and $c/4$ respectively. To determine the Miller indices:

1. Find the intercepts as a fraction, or multiple, of the unit distance on each axis. In this case these are $a/2$, $b/3$ and $c/4$.
2. Remove these unit distances to leave $\frac{1}{2}$, $\frac{1}{3}$ and $\frac{1}{4}$. Note that for a cubic structure the unit distance along each axis is identical.
3. Take the reciprocals of these fractions to give 2, 3 and 4.
4. Reduce these numbers to the three smallest integers having the same ratio. In this case 2,3,4 cannot be reduced any further, but results such as 2,2,2 and 4,6,8 could be reduced to 1,1,1 and 2,3,4 respectively.
5. Remove the commas and enclose the result in parentheses to give (234). (234) are the Miller indices of the plane described in Figure 1.4, and all parallel planes.

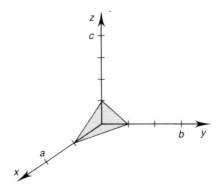

Figure 1.4 A (234) crystal plane.

Figure 1.5 gives the Miller indices of some important planes in a cubic crystal structure, including how they are derived from the process outlined above. Because the Miller indices assume no reference point, it is clear that any one of the six faces of the cube in Figure 1.5(a) can be considered to be (100). For instance the top face of the cube, which has Miller indices (001), looks identical to the chosen front face. Thus there are six planes; (100), (010), (001) and ($\bar{1}$00), (0$\bar{1}$0), (00$\bar{1}$) – the bar is meant to indicate a minus direction: this is achieved by moving the origin of the coordinate axis to another corner of the cube. These six planes form the {100} family of planes.

Miller indices can also be used to denote crystallographic directions, e.g. the [100] direction is the x-axis, and is perpendicular to the (100) plane. In a similar way to a family of planes, $\langle 100 \rangle$ denotes a family of crystallographic directions; in this case [100], [010], [001], [$\bar{1}$00], [0$\bar{1}$0] and [00$\bar{1}$].

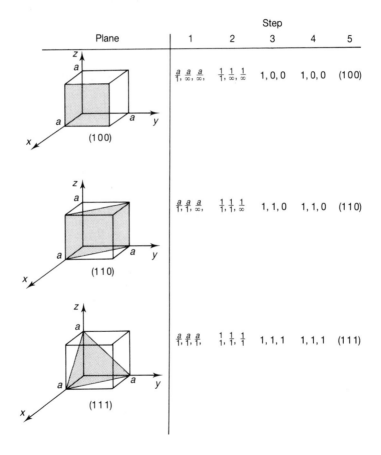

Figure 1.5 Three important planes in a cubic crystal and their associated Miller indices.

1.1.3   Defects

No matter what the crystal structure involved, no lattice is perfect. The nature of defects, their understanding and control is a major part of producing optimum working devices. The major types of defects found in semiconductors are shown in Figure 1.6. A vacancy, or Schottky defect, is a gap in the structure formed by the absence of an atom. In the case of silicon this is represented as V_{Si}. This vacancy can have electrical properties, as it distorts the electron distribution of neighbouring atoms. An interstitial, or Frenkel defect, occurs when an atom has managed to locate itself in the middle of the lattice structure; this physically distorts the lattice and similarly it distorts the neighbouring electron distributions. In the case of silicon this type of defect is denoted by Si_i. An edge dislocation occurs when a column of atoms comes to an abrupt end; attempts by neighbouring atoms to form columns below this fault result in strain in the structure. Two edge dislocations of a similar nature produce a stacking fault, and a grain boundary, mentioned earlier, is shown as a line denoting a change in direction of the crystal lattice.

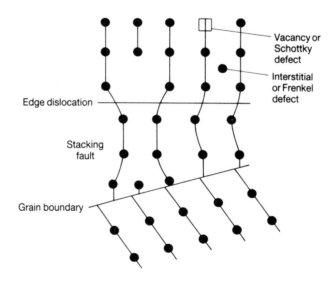

Figure 1.6 Common defects in semiconductor crystals.

Other defects also exist. One of these is the antisite defect in a compound semiconductor; for GaAs, for instance, this would manifest itself as a gallium atom located on an arsenic site, or an arsenic atom on a gallium site, represented by Ga_{As} and As_{Ga} respectively.

1.2   Energy bands and the semiconductor

It is said that the early part of the 20th century will be remembered as the golden age of physics, as at last the mysteries of atomic structure were beginning to be unravelled (to a level appropriate to most other disciplines even to this day) and radical ideas on the relationship between waves and particles were proposed. Atomic structure and quantum mechanics revolutionized ideas about conduction in solids; modern electronic devices all have their roots in these early concepts.

1.2.1   Energy bands and E–k diagrams

To separate an energy level of an isolated atom into closely spaced sublevels, some external field must be applied. This is the principle behind the Zeeman and Stark effects, where the application of a magnetic or electric field respectively across a gas manifests itself as a splitting of the spectral lines associated with that gas. However, atoms are sufficiently far apart in a gas for their effect on each other to be negligible. In a solid it is the interaction of closely spaced atoms that leads to a splitting of energy levels. As all the levels are split this gives the formation of energy bands, each band being a collection of closely spaced sublevels as in Figure 1.7. We can extend our ideas by considering atoms in a crystal. Here the structure repeats itself in a periodic fashion, and a simplified solution is obtained using the Kronig–Penney model [4], which takes a one-dimensional array of atoms and assigns a potential box at each atom. The solution leads to the concept of ranges of allowed energies, or bands, separated by ranges of forbidden energies, or band gaps. Discontinuities occur between energy bands and gaps when

$$k = \pm \frac{n\pi}{a} \tag{1.2}$$

where k is the wavevector and n is a number. The E–k curve, known as a dispersion curve, then looks as in Figure 1.8, with each part of the curve separated into distinct Brillouin zones. Because of the periodicity of the solution which forms this curve it is customary to shift all Brillouin zones into the first, by moving the curve by an integral multiple of π/a. This gives a reduced zone representation of the E–k diagram, with the advantage that the allowed and forbidden regions are much easier to see, as in Figure 1.9.

In all solids the lower energy bands are full. The two highest energy bands, namely the valence and conduction bands, and their associated band gap are crucial in determining the electronic properties of a solid. When an electron reaches the conduction band, it is free to move through the crystal and hence contribute to conduction. The more electrons that there are in the conduction band, the greater the conductivity of the material. Semiconductors have a larger band gap than metals. In the case of gallium arsenide, $E_g = 1.42$ eV as in Figure 1.10(a). Thus few electrons can enter the conduction band, and the valence band remains nearly

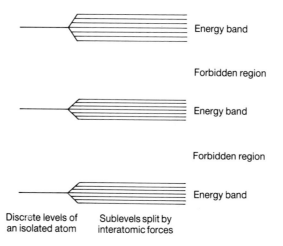

Figure 1.7 The creation of energy bands and forbidden regions.

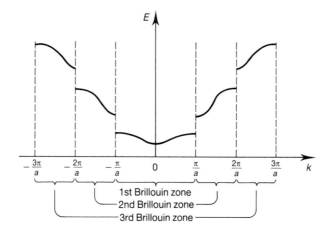

Figure 1.8 The $E-k$ diagram of the Kronig–Penney model and the associated Brillouin zones.

full. Another semiconductor such as silicon is shown in Figure 1.10(b). Here E_g = 1.11 eV, but the $E-k$ diagram has a different shape to that of gallium arsenide. For silicon, the top of the valence band does not have the same value of k as the bottom of the conduction band; an electron would have to gain energy and be associated with a change in wavevector to transfer to the conduction band. A semiconductor having an $E-k$ relationship similar to silicon is called an indirect (gap) semiconductor; gallium arsenide is a direct (gap) semiconductor because of

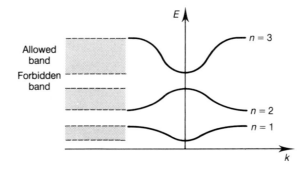

Figure 1.9 Reduced zone representation of an $E–k$ diagram.

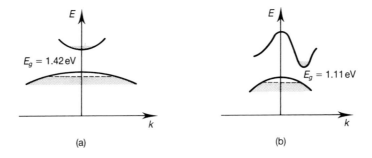

Figure 1.10 $E–k$ relationships for an (a) direct, and (b) indirect gap semiconductor.

its $E–k$ properties. The significance of direct and indirect semiconductors will be addressed in more detail when devices are discussed in Chapters 3–7.

1.3   Conduction in semiconductors

We will now see what determines the transfer of electrons from the valence to the conduction band, and what effect that has on electrical properties.

1.3.1 Fermi–Dirac distribution

Fermi–Dirac statistics describe electrons in a solid. The probability $F(E)$ of a particular energy level E being occupied is given by [5]

$$F(E) = \frac{1}{\exp\left[\frac{(E-E_f)}{kT}\right] + 1} \qquad (1.3)$$

where k is Boltzmann's constant and E_f is a particular energy value known as the Fermi level. At absolute zero $F(E)$ is a step function as shown in Figure 1.11. A definition of E_f is that the Fermi level is that energy level below which all states are occupied and above which all states are empty at absolute zero. As the temperature is increased the shape of the diagram changes, and E_f goes from 1 to 0 over a range of about $4kT$. Note that the trace always passes through $F(E) = 0.5$ at $E = E_f$, however. Thus we can alternatively define the Fermi level as that energy level which has an occupational probability of 0.5 at all temperatures. Subsequent sections will show the importance of the Fermi level, as it is used to characterize the electron distribution and hence the device operation.

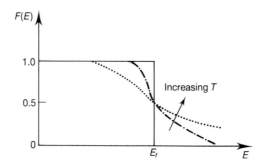

Figure 1.11 The Fermi–Dirac distribution and its dependence on temperature.

1.3.2 Density of states and effective mass

Having obtained from (1.3) the probability of a particular energy level, or state, being occupied, we now have to determine how many energy states exist per unit volume of momentum space, known as the density of states function $Z(E)$. This is done by considering an electron moving in a portion of crystal momentum space. By looking at the change in momentum associated with each energy state, and equating this with the volume of momentum space needed for an energy state [6],

$Z(E)$ is given by

$$Z(E) = 4\pi \left(\frac{2m_e^*}{h^2}\right)^{3/2} E^{1/2} \tag{1.4}$$

where m_e^* is the electron effective mass. This is not the same as the electron rest mass, m_o, but is a measure of the effect of crystal structure on m_o. The numerical value of effective mass is dependent on the individual semiconductor.

1.3.3   Intrinsic semiconductor

A simplified way of showing E–k diagrams is shown in Figure 1.12. This method has achieved universal acceptance and greatly eases the understanding of electron transitions and hence device operations. The ordinate still has units of electron energy, and although the abscissa has no physical meaning it is often used as a coordinate of 'distance'. This is particularly true of junction regions, where a notion of 'near to' or 'far from' the junction adds further to device comprehension.

Imagine an electron gaining sufficient energy to be promoted from an energy state in the valence band to one in the conduction band. This leaves an unoccupied state in the valence band, which may be filled by an electron of the same energy moving from a neighbouring part of the lattice. This can occur under the influence of an applied electric field (Figure 1.12(b)–(d)). This will in turn leave an unoccupied state which may be filled by another neighbouring electron. Thus we can think of an unoccupied state, or hole, moving through the lattice in the opposite direction to the valence band electron motion. The hole is an absence of negative charge; it can be thought of as positively charged. As the promoted electron is free to move in the conduction band, giving conduction by negative charges, so the subsequent hole is free to move in the valence band, leading to conduction by positive charges.

Every promoted electron creates a hole, and so it follows that the number of holes in the valence band equals the number of electrons in the conduction band. It also follows that as $F(E)$ represents the probability of a state being occupied by an electron, $1 - F(E)$ represents the probability of a state being unoccupied by an electron, i.e. occupied by a hole. It should also follow that as $F(E)$ has symmetry about the value E_f, then the value of E_f should lie in the middle of the band gap, shown in Figure 1.12(e) as a dotted line.

We are now in a position to calculate the number of electrons in the conduction band of a semiconductor; this number, known as the carrier concentration, n, determines how well the material will conduct. n is found by multiplying the density of states function by the probability of a state being occupied, and then integrating the result over all the energy levels available to a conduction band electron. Thus

$$n = \int_{E_c}^{\infty} F(E) Z(E) \, \mathrm{d}E. \tag{1.5}$$

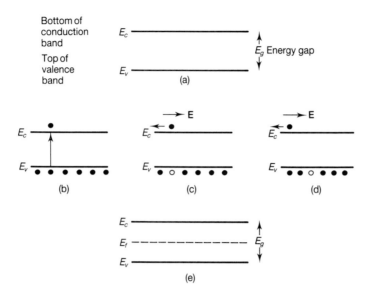

Figure 1.12 Simplified energy band diagrams, showing (a) basic structure, (b) promotion of an electron, creating (c) a hole in the valence band, (d) electron and hole motion, and (e) position of the Fermi level.

From (1.3) and (1.4) this becomes

$$n = \int_{E_c}^{\infty} 4\pi \left(\frac{2m_e^*}{h^2}\right)^{3/2} \frac{(E - E_c)^{1/2}\, \mathrm{d}E}{\exp\left[\frac{E - E_f}{kT}\right] + 1} \tag{1.6}$$

where the level at the top of the conduction band is given the value ∞ – although physically incorrect, mathematically it is a good approximation because the Fermi–Dirac distribution term is an exponentially decaying function, and thus the precise value of this energy level is unimportant as long as it is well above E_c. E_c rather than 0 is chosen as the bottom level of integration as we are only interested in conduction band electrons; thus the $E^{1/2}$ term in the density of states function is modified to $(E - E_c)^{1/2}$. Integration of (1.6) gives

$$n = 2\left(\frac{2\pi m_e^* kT}{h^2}\right)^{3/2} \exp\left(\frac{E_f - E_c}{kT}\right), \tag{1.7}$$

and similarly for a p-type semiconductor

$$p = 2\left(\frac{2\pi m_h^* kT}{h^2}\right)^{3/2} \exp\left(\frac{E_v - E_f}{kT}\right) \tag{1.8}$$

where m_h^* is the hole effective mass. Equations (1.7) and (1.8) can be used to plot carrier concentrations as a function of energy, as shown in Figure 1.13.

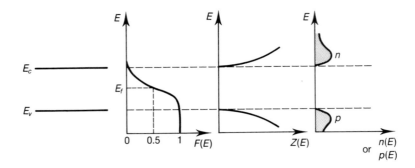

Figure 1.13 The dependence of F, Z, n and p on energy levels in an intrinsic semiconductor.

Here we have found the carrier concentrations in a semiconductor, n and p, in terms of the material parameters when free electrons and holes are created solely by electron promotion from the valence to conduction band. Such a semiconductor is called intrinsic, because all the carriers are generated by the atoms of the host material.

It is perhaps trivial to note that

$$n_i^2 = np \qquad (1.9)$$

where n_i is the intrinsic carrier concentration, but this law of mass action has important consequences. One that can be deduced straightaway is that from (1.7), (1.8) and (1.9)

$$n_i = 2 \left(\frac{2\pi kT}{h^2} \right)^{3/2} (m_e^* m_h^*)^{3/4} \exp \left(\frac{-E_g}{2kT} \right) . \qquad (1.10)$$

This gives a value for n_i without the need to calculate the position of the Fermi level. The law of mass action will be used again later.

1.3.4   Extrinsic semiconductor

We will now see how the carrier concentration can be greatly increased by doping with some external element, giving an extrinsic semiconductor. Consider Figure 1.14. This shows a silicon lattice, into which dopant impurities arsenic and gallium have been added. Arsenic (group V) has five outside electrons for four bonding sites – hence one electron is totally free from any particular bond. Only a small amount of energy is required to produce a free electron and an arsenic ion – the free electron is said to be donated to the crystal lattice, and the arsenic ion is known as a donor. Gallium (group III) has three outside electrons for four bonding sites

– hence one site has an electron vacancy, i.e. a hole. An electron from somewhere else in the lattice must be accepted into this vacancy to create a gallium ion and a stable bond. The hole, as shown earlier, can then be thought of as moving off into the lattice. In a similar way to the arsenic ion, a gallium ion in silicon is known as an acceptor.

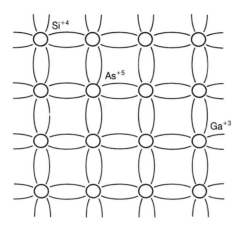

Figure 1.14 The effect of dopants on bonding in a silicon lattice.

The energy levels associated with donors and acceptors are not found in the silicon lattice, but are in the forbidden region, as shown in Figure 1.15(a). The difference between a donor level and the conduction band, or the valence band and an acceptor level, is equivalent to the ionization energy of the associated impurity level. The ionization energies involved are low, and so all dopants added to a semiconductor can readily be activated to contribute either an electron or hole to the lattice. In addition the intrinsic carrier concentration is low (for instance Si: $n_i = 1.4 \times 10^{10}$ cm^{-3} and GaAs: $n_i = 1.8 \times 10^6$ cm^{-3} [7] compared with an atomic density of 4.9×10^{22} cm^{-3} and 4.4×10^{22} cm^{-3} respectively), and so adding only a small amount of dopant to a semiconductor drastically changes its conductivity, and extrinsic carriers becomes the dominant source of conduction in such materials. Thus for an extrinsic type semiconductor the electron density $n = N_D$, the donor concentration. If we let

$$N_c = 2 \left(\frac{2\pi m_e^* kT}{h^2} \right)^{3/2} \tag{1.11}$$

in (1.7), where N_c is known as the effective density of states in the conduction band, then

$$n = N_D = N_c \exp \left(\frac{E_f - E_c}{kT} \right) . \tag{1.12}$$

Example 1.2

Determine the electron effective mass in GaAs if the conduction band effective density of states is 4.7×10^{17} cm^{-3} at 293 K.

Solution: from equation (1.11)

$$m_e^* = \left(\frac{N_c}{2}\right)^{2/3} \frac{h^2}{2\pi kT} = 0.07 m_0 \tag{1.13}$$

where m_0 is the rest mass of an electron.

Similarly for p-type material

$$p = N_A = N_v \exp\left(\frac{E_v - E_f}{kT}\right) \tag{1.14}$$

where p, N_A and N_v are the hole density, the acceptor concentration and the effective density of states in the valence band respectively. From (1.12) and (1.14)

$$E_f = E_c + kT \log_e \frac{N_D}{N_c} \tag{1.15}$$

$$\text{and} \quad E_f = E_v - kT \log_e \frac{N_A}{N_v}. \tag{1.16}$$

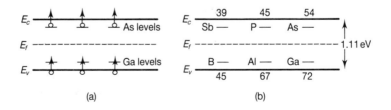

Figure 1.15 (a) Donor and acceptor levels in the band gap. (b) Typical values for dopants in silicon (the numbers represent the energy difference in meV between the band edge and the dopant level).

Notice now that the position of the Fermi level depends on the doping density. Also notice that in Figure 1.15(a) donor and acceptor levels are shown as discrete, and not as continuous bands. This is because the doping concentrations are usually so low that ions can be considered as discrete entities. If the doping level is raised until $N_D > N_c$, (1.15) shows that for an n-type semiconductor E_f will eventually reside in the conduction band as in a metal. What is happening now is that the fifth electron orbits of the donors overlap with those of neighbouring donors, making the impurity states part of a single system, i.e. a band. This donor band extends into the conduction band, forming a continuous allowed system. Highly doped semiconductors fulfilling this criteria are labelled n^+ or p^+, have a conductivity constant with temperature over a wide range because of the overlapping bands, and are given the name degenerate.

Example 1.3

If the intrinsic carrier concentration of GaAs is 1.8×10^6 cm^{-3} at 293 K, calculate the p concentration if this semiconductor is doped n-type with 10^{11} dopants cm^{-3}, assuming complete ionization. Also calculate the Fermi level in this material.

Solution: from equation (1.9)

$$p = \frac{3.2 \times 10^{12}}{10^{11}} = 32 \text{ cm}^{-3}. \tag{1.17}$$

From (1.15)

$$E_f = E_c + 293k \log_e \left(\frac{10^{11}}{4.7 \times 10^{17}} \right) = E_c - 0.39 \text{ eV}, \tag{1.18}$$

i.e. the Fermi level is 390 meV below the bottom of the conduction band.

The carrier concentrations can now be expressed in terms of the intrinsic carrier concentration and the Fermi level. If we let

$$\exp \left(\frac{E_f - E_c}{kT} \right) = \exp \left(\frac{E_f - E_i}{kT} \right) \exp \left(\frac{E_i - E_c}{kT} \right) \tag{1.19}$$

then (1.12) becomes

$$n = n_i \exp \left(\frac{E_f - E_i}{kT} \right) \tag{1.20}$$

because $n = n_i$ when $E_f = E_i$. Similarly

$$p = p_i \exp \left(\frac{E_i - E_f}{kT} \right). \tag{1.21}$$

As can be seen from (1.20) and Figure 1.16, there is an exponential increase in n_i with temperature. Eventually n_i will be nearly equal to n, making intrinsic carriers the main conduction medium. If the temperature is lowered, extrinsic conduction is dominant right down to the freeze-out region, in which there is not sufficient thermal energy in the lattice to promote electrons from donor levels to the conduction band. Consequently the carrier concentration rapidly drops in this region.

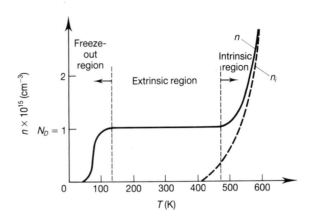

Figure 1.16 The carrier concentration in silicon as a function of temperature for a donor concentration of 10^{15} cm^{-3}.

It is usual to dope a semiconductor, or at least any active part of a device, with just one dominant type of impurity. This leads to a situation where the majority of the current is carried by electrons or holes for n- and p-type respectively. For n-type, electrons are termed the majority carriers, with holes the minority carriers. The roles are reversed for a p-type semiconductor. Although minority carriers have a low number density, they have a crucial role to play in the operation of solid state optoelectronic devices, as we shall see in later chapters.

1.3.5   Photoconductivity

Up to now it has been assumed that the promotion of an electron to the conduction band involves the supply of thermal energy. Whilst this is true, energy can also be supplied in the form of a photon of the appropriate frequency given by

$$h\nu = \frac{hc}{\lambda} \geq E_g .\tag{1.22}$$

Photons possessing this characteristic will be readily absorbed; those of a lower energy cannot be absorbed by a band to band transition and thus the material will remain transparent to such photons. The cut-off criterion is quite sharp, and leads to a fundamental absorption edge in the semiconductor as shown in Figure 1.17. Practical curves differ from the ideal case because of the additional, and comparatively random, thermal energy available to an electron. For most practical cases, the cut-off wavelength is taken to be when the absorption has fallen to half of its maximum value.

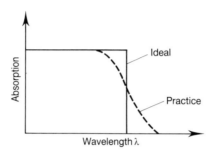

Figure 1.17 The fundamental absorption edge in a semiconductor.

The increase in carriers gives an increase in conductivity which can be detected in an external circuit by treating the photoconductor as a resistor – more details are given in Chapter 5. There will be an equal increase in the number of electrons and holes in the conduction and valence bands respectively for any photoconductor, but for a material that is already an extrinsic semiconductor the relative increase in majority carrier concentration will be small.

1.3.6 Recombination

Just as a photon can be absorbed by a semiconductor to create an electron–hole pair, so such a pair can recombine to liberate either a photon or thermal energy in the form of phonons. This is the basis of all light emitting processes in semiconductors. In a semiconductor electron–hole pairs are being generated and others are recombining all the time. The recombining of a generated carrier after having spent some time contributing to conduction leads to the concept of carrier lifetime, the average time spent by a free carrier before recombining to become bound. In thermal equilibrium the generation rate g_i equals the recombination rate r_i, being proportional to both the electron and hole equilibrium concentrations n_0 and p_0:

$$g_i = r_i = Bn_0p_0 \tag{1.23}$$

where B is a constant. Equilibrium will be upset by shining light on the semiconductor, where the new generation rate $g_0 + g_i$ will be larger than r_i. Excess carrier concentrations will be given by Δn and Δp ($\Delta n = \Delta p$). The recombination rate will also increase:

$$r_0 + r_i = B(n_0 + \Delta n)(p_0 + \Delta p). \tag{1.24}$$

The net change in hole concentration is given by

$$\frac{dp}{dt} = g_0 + g_i - (r_0 + r_i). \tag{1.25}$$

After a certain time a new steady state will be reached, where there is no net increase in carrier concentrations, i.e. $dp/dt = 0$. In this case, from (1.23), (1.24) and (1.25)

$$g_0 = B(n_0 + \Delta n)(p_0 + \Delta p) - Bn_0 p_0. \tag{1.26}$$

If we assume that the semiconductor is n-type, i.e. $n \gg p$ and the product $\Delta n \Delta p$ is negligible compared to the other terms, (1.26) simplifies to

$$g_0 \simeq Bn_0 \Delta p = \frac{p - p_0}{1/Bn_0} \tag{1.27}$$

where p is the optically generated hole concentration. $1/Bn_0$ has units of time, and is known as the minority carrier lifetime τ_p. As the semiconductor has now reached a steady state, we can say that

$$g_0 = r_0 = \frac{p - p_0}{\tau_p}. \tag{1.28}$$

Note that τ_p is expressed in terms of the majority carrier concentration. A similar expression to (1.28) can be found to express the electron lifetime in p-type material. This lifetime can be measured from the Haynes–Schockley experiment [8] or from a photoconductive decay experiment, as shown in Figure 1.18. Here a semiconductor is uniformly illuminated, the illumination removed and the decay time constant measure from an oscilloscope display. From (1.28)

$$p = p_0 + \tau_p g_0. \tag{1.29}$$

If the illumination is switched off at $t = 0$, then $p(t = 0) = p_0 + \tau_p g_0$ and $p(t = \infty) = p_0$. Equation (1.25) can now be solved for the time dependent case. Thus

$$\frac{dp}{dt} = g_i - (r_0 + r_i) \tag{1.30}$$

which from (1.23), (1.24) and the simplifying assumptions used to get (1.27) becomes

$$\frac{dp}{dt} = -\frac{p - p_0}{\tau_p}. \tag{1.31}$$

This has a solution given by

$$p(t) = p_0 + \tau_p g_0 \exp\left(-t/\tau_p\right) \tag{1.32}$$

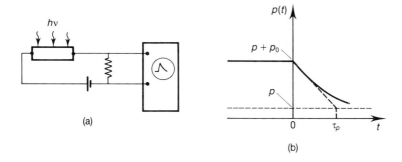

(a)

(b)

Figure 1.18 The measurement of minority carrier lifetime using photo-conductivity. (a) Experimental set-up. (b) Observation of hole decay.

using the boundary conditions for p mentioned above.

The discussion of recombination has so far centred on direct mechanisms, where an electron 'falls' straight into the valence band. For indirect gap semiconductors, such as silicon, this mechanism is unlikely because electrons at the bottom of the conduction band in such materials have a non-zero value of crystal momentum with respect to the top of the valence band. The dominant recombination mechanism in silicon is an indirect transition via localized energy states in both the valence band and the forbidden region. Recombination via this type of process can rapidly confuse the calculation of carrier lifetime, as there are many more steps to consider.

1.3.7 Traps

There are energy levels in the band gap which are neither donors nor acceptors – such centres capture one or other type of carrier, for later release by thermal emission. Such centres are called traps, and their effect is such that the carrier lifetime, and hence conductivity, are reduced. Examples of simple traps in silicon are shown in Figure 1.19. Arsenic and gallium ions are donors and acceptors respectively, whereas a vacant site serves to trap electrons. Similarly a silicon interstitial atom is a hole trap. It is clear that traps are usually undesirable elements to be avoided or, more realistically, minimized, as they can have a detrimental effect on device properties if present in large numbers. Control of traps is a major consideration in the growth of semiconductor materials (Chapter 8).

1.4 Carrier transport

Now that some of the mechanisms for creating electrons and holes have been discussed, the movement of these carriers needs to be looked at in more detail. There

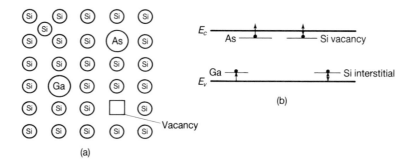

Figure 1.19 Typical dopants and traps in a silicon lattice. (a) Lattice structure. (b) Energy levels.

are three types of motion to be considered: thermal, drift and diffusion. Thermal motion gives a random velocity caused by treating the electrons (or holes) as behaving as a gas and finding the mean thermal velocity associated with temperature ($v_{th} = (3kT/m)^{1/2}$ from kinetic theory). This random effect will produce no net current as the overall velocity is zero.

A drift current is caused by carriers acquiring a velocity v in an electric field E. This is generally given by the equation

$$v = \mu E \tag{1.33}$$

for both electrons and holes where μ is known as the mobility. Consider an electric field applied to the semiconductor as in Figure 1.20. Electrons and holes, being oppositely charged, will move in opposite directions. But the currents will move in the same direction, regardless of the sign of the charge carrier. This apparently confusing result can be resolved by considering again the illusion of hole movement; electrons in the valence band are moving in the same direction as those in the conduction band.

Equation (1.33) is only valid for certain values of electric field. In many cases an upper limit is reached for the carrier drift velocity in a high field – this is considered in more detail in section 6.2.1.

1.4.1 Mobility and conductivity

The derivation of (1.33) follows from a consideration of electron mechanics, and the mobility μ is a product of three terms:

$$\mu = \frac{e\tau_{th}}{m^*} \tag{1.34}$$

where τ_{th} is the mean lifetime between collisions. It can be seen from (1.34) that mobility depends on effective mass, and hence μ_e and μ_h will be different. All

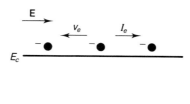

Figure 1.20 The movement of carriers under the influence of an electric field.

Semiconductor	μ_e (cm^2/Vs)	μ_h (cm^2/Vs)
Si	1350	480
Ge	3900	1900
GaAs	8500	480
InP	4600	150
GaP	450	150
InAs	3300	460
CdTe	1050	100

Table 1.1 Room temperature mobilities of commonly used intrinsic semiconductors.

semiconductors in common use have $\mu_e > \mu_h$, as shown in Table 1.1. These values should be considered as nominal, as true values for any material will depend on the success of the growth.

It can readily be seen from (1.33) that a high value of mobility will give a high carrier velocity, implying a fast device. Mobility is thus the ease with which a carrier moves through the material. Mobility can be reduced by causing collisions, i.e. introducing scattering centres such as ionized impurities, where Coulombic interactions with the carriers deflect the electron or hole from its original path. The decrease in mobility with doping density can be seen in Figure 1.21 for GaAs. This type of graph is usually described by an empirical relationship [9].

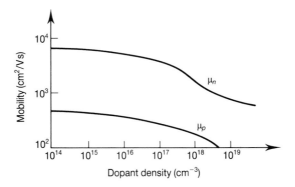

Figure 1.21 The dependence of mobility on doping density for GaAs.

Increasing the temperature gives an increase in lattice vibrations, again causing more scattering. The resultant drift mobility is a combination of two terms:

$$\frac{1}{\mu} = \frac{1}{\mu_L} + \frac{1}{\mu_I} \tag{1.35}$$

$$\text{lattice} \qquad \text{impurity}$$

$$\text{scattering} \quad \text{scattering}$$

$$\text{where} \quad \mu_L \propto T^{-3/2} \tag{1.36}$$

$$\text{and} \quad \mu_I \propto \frac{T^{3/2}}{N_I} \tag{1.37}$$

where N_I is the impurity concentration. The effect of lattice and impurity scattering can be seen in Figure 1.22. It should be noted that there is an alternative mobility parameter, the Hall mobility, derived from the Hall effect. Values of mobility measured this way do not turn out to be significantly different from those of the drift mobility.

Conductivity, σ, in a semiconductor is defined as

$$\sigma = ne\mu_e + pe\mu_p . \tag{1.38}$$

For an extrinsic semiconductor one carrier type usually dominates, e.g.

$$\sigma \simeq ne\mu_e \tag{1.39}$$

for an n-type semiconductor. It can be seen from (1.12) that there is a direct increase in n with doping density N_D. Figure 1.21 shows that there is a slow decrease in μ with N_D. Thus the net result of doping is to increase the conductivity σ. A plot of conductivity against temperature is a combination, using (1.38), of carrier concentration (Figure 1.16) and mobility (Figure 1.22) plots against temperature. A general shape of such a graph is given in Figure 1.23, showing the regions where different effects predominate.

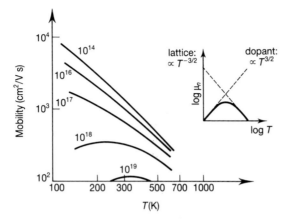

Figure 1.22 The effect of temperature and doping density on mobility for n-type silicon.

Example 1.4

What is the resistivity of intrinsic GaAs at room temperature?

Solution: from example 1.3, $n_i = 1.8 \times 10^6$ cm^{-3}. From (1.38) and Table 1.1

$$\sigma = 1.8 \times 10^6 \times e \times (8500 + 480) = 2.6 \times 10^{-9} \ (\Omega \, \text{cm})^{-1}.$$
$$\text{Resistivity,} \ \rho = 1/\sigma = 3.9 \times 10^8 \ \Omega \, \text{cm}. \tag{1.40}$$

The drift current density J_n is related to the conductivity σ by

$$J_n = \sigma E = ne\mu_e E \tag{1.41}$$

for electrons, and similarly

$$J_p = \sigma E = pe\mu_h E \tag{1.42}$$

for holes.

1.4.2 Diffusion

For a uniform distribution of carriers drift would form the only contribution to the current. However, an uneven distribution will cause diffusion of carriers to try

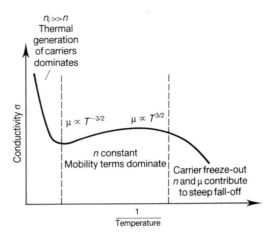

Figure 1.23 The dependence of conductivity on temperature for a non-degenerate semiconductor.

and create an equilibrium, rather like diffusion of different gas molecules or, as we shall see in section 8.6, diffusion of dopants in a semiconductor. This movement of carriers will cause a current to flow, known as the diffusion current. We will see that diffusion current is really a result of the thermal velocity generating a net component because of an electron concentration gradient.

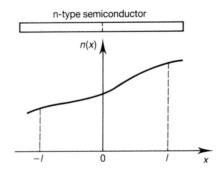

Figure 1.24 The principle of diffusion current in a semiconductor.

Consider an n-type semiconductor sample having an electron concentration varying along its length as in Figure 1.24. The electrons will have a thermal velocity v_{th} giving a random motion with mean free path l, and mean free time between collisions τ_{th} (hence $v_{th} = l/\tau_{th}$). Electrons at $x = l$ can move equally to the left or right, and in a time τ_{th} half of them will have crossed the plane given by $x = 0$. This leads to an average electron flow rate R_r crossing this plane from the right given by

$$R_r = \frac{1}{2} n(l) \, v_{th} . \tag{1.43}$$

There is a similar flow rate from left to right across $x = 0$ given by

$$R_l = \frac{1}{2} n(-l) \, v_{th} . \tag{1.44}$$

The net rate of carrier flow across the plane is then

$$R = R_l - R_r = \frac{1}{2} v_{th} \left(n(-l) - n(l) \right) \tag{1.45}$$

where R is chosen from left to right, and hence is a positive number. If the electron density function $n(x)$ satisfies the conditions for a Taylor series, and assuming that second and higher order derivatives can be ignored, then (1.45) becomes

$$R = \frac{1}{2} v_{th} \left[\left(n(0) - l\frac{\mathrm{d}n}{\mathrm{d}x} \right) - \left(n(0) + l\frac{\mathrm{d}n}{\mathrm{d}x} \right) \right] \tag{1.46}$$

$$= -D_n \frac{\mathrm{d}n}{\mathrm{d}x} \tag{1.47}$$

where $D_n = l v_{th}$ and is known as the electron diffusivity, or diffusion coefficient, or diffusion constant. Because each electron has a charge given by $-e$, the diffusion current density J_n is given by

$$J_n = e D_n \frac{\mathrm{d}n}{\mathrm{d}x} . \tag{1.48}$$

A similar analysis for a hole concentration gradient leads to a similar value for hole diffusion current density:

$$J_p = -e D_p \frac{\mathrm{d}p}{\mathrm{d}x} . \tag{1.49}$$

If, in addition to a concentration gradient, there is an applied field, then both drift ((1.41) and (1.42)) and diffusion will contribute to the current:

$$\text{for n-type} \quad J_n = e\mu_e n E + e D_n \frac{\mathrm{d}n}{\mathrm{d}x} \tag{1.50}$$

$$\text{and for p-type} \quad J_p = e\mu_h p E - e D_p \frac{\mathrm{d}n}{\mathrm{d}x} \tag{1.51}$$

because electrons and holes give the same current directions for the same applied field, but opposite currents for the same concentration gradient. Total current density is given simply by

$$J = J_n + J_p . \tag{1.52}$$

A treatment of the thermal motion of electrons by the kinetic theory of gases yields

$$\frac{1}{2}m_e^* v_{th}^2 = \frac{1}{2}kT \tag{1.53}$$

for the case of one dimensional electron motion, as in the case studied above. If (1.34) is combined with $v_{th} = l/\tau_{th}$ and (1.53), then

$$lv_{th} = \frac{kT}{e}\mu_e, \tag{1.54}$$

and as we have seen when deriving (1.47) $D_n = lv_{th}$. Thus we have a relationship between diffusivity, mobility and temperature given by

$$D_n = \frac{kT}{e}\mu_e \tag{1.55}$$

and similarly for holes

$$D_p = \frac{kT}{e}\mu_h. \tag{1.56}$$

Equations (1.55) and (1.56) are known as the Einstein relations.

1.4.3   The continuity equation

For a complete picture of carrier dynamics in semiconductors, the processes of drift, diffusion, generation and recombination must be combined into one study: the resultant is know as the continuity equation. If we consider the net flow of electrons into an infinitesimal slice of semiconductor as in Figure 1.25, it can be seen that there are four contributions to the net carrier density.

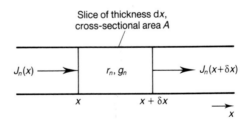

Figure 1.25 The contributions to current density in an infinitesimal semi-conductor slice of thickness dx.

Two are additive:

(i) the number of electrons flowing into the slice at x,
(ii) the generation rate within the slice,

and two are subtractive:

(iii) the number of electrons flowing out of the slice at $x + \mathrm{d}x$,
(iv) the recombination rate within the slice.

Summing these components together results in a expression for the rate of change of electron density within the slice:

$$\frac{\partial n}{\partial t} A\,\mathrm{d}x \quad = \quad \left[\frac{J_n(x)A}{-e} - \frac{J_n(x+\mathrm{d}x)A}{-e} \right] + (g_n - r_n)A\,\mathrm{d}x \qquad (1.57)$$

$$\qquad\qquad\qquad \text{(i)} \qquad\qquad \text{(ii)} \qquad\qquad \text{(iii)} \quad \text{(iv)}$$

where g_n and r_n are electron generation and recombination rates respectively. Again, if $J_n(x+\mathrm{d}x)$ can be expressed as a Taylor series, then (1.57) can be simplified to

$$\frac{\partial n}{\partial t} \quad = \quad \frac{1}{e}\frac{\partial J_n(x)}{\partial x} + (g_n - r_n) \qquad (1.58)$$

which is the electron continuity equation. If we have a situation where low level injection of minority carriers is occuring in a p-type semiconductor, then (1.50) and (1.58) can be combined to give

$$\frac{\partial n_p}{\partial t} \quad = \quad n_p\mu_e \frac{\partial E}{\partial x} + \mu_e E \frac{\partial n_p(x)}{\partial x} + D_n \frac{\partial^2 n_p(x)}{\partial x^2} + g_n - r_n\,. \qquad (1.59)$$

For holes, (1.58) and (1.59) become

$$\frac{\partial p}{\partial t} \quad = \quad -\frac{1}{e}\frac{\partial J_p(x)}{\partial x} + (g_p - r_p) \qquad (1.60)$$

$$\text{and} \quad \frac{\partial p_n}{\partial t} \quad = \quad -p_n\mu_h \frac{\partial E}{\partial x} - \mu_h E \frac{\partial p_n(x)}{\partial x} + D_p \frac{\partial^2 p_n(x)}{\partial x^2} + g_p - r_p \qquad (1.61)$$

where the sign reversals compared to the electron equation are because of the positive charge on the hole. The solution of (1.59) and (1.61), together with Poisson's equation in the same region, is given by the boundary conditions. Solutions are generally difficult and physical approximations are a useful starting point before any algebra is attempted. An example is shown in Figure 1.26(a), showing excess carriers being injected at one end of a p-type semiconductor sample of infinite length. If there is no applied field the first two terms on the right hand side of (1.59) disappear. The term g_n will also disappear if we are dealing with a slice of material well away from the injecting edge. For a steady state situation, where a concentration gradient away from the surface exists, $\partial n_p/\partial t = 0$ and (1.59) simplifies to

$$\frac{\mathrm{d}n_p}{\mathrm{d}t} \quad = \quad 0 \quad = \quad D_n \frac{\mathrm{d}^2 n_p(x)}{\mathrm{d}x^2} - r_n \qquad (1.62)$$

where partial derivatives are no longer required because the time variation of this equation is zero. From (1.28) and (1.62) we have the final version of the electron continuity equation

$$D_n \frac{\mathrm{d}^2 n_p(x)}{\mathrm{d}x^2} = \frac{\Delta n_p(x)}{\tau_n}. \tag{1.63}$$

At $x = 0$, i.e. the injecting surface, $n_p = n_p(0)$, and, at $x = \infty$, $n_p = n_p$, the carrier concentration without any injection. The solution of (1.63) is then

$$n_p(x) = n_p + (n_p(0) - n_p)\exp(-x/L_n) \tag{1.64}$$

where $L_n = \sqrt{D_n \tau_n}$ and is known as the diffusion length. It can be shown that L_n represents the average distance an electron can travel before recombining, i.e. the distance covered in an average time τ_n [10]. Figure 1.26(b) shows the variation of $n_p(x)$ against x, showing a characteristic decay length of L_n. There is a similarly defined diffusion length L_p for holes.

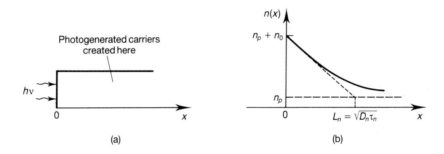

(a)   (b)

Figure 1.26 The use of the continuity equation to determine carrier diffusion lengths. (a) Carrier injection at one end of an infinite sample. (b) Diffusion length calculation.

1.5   Problems

1. Assume that an atom can be represented by a hard sphere. Calculate the fraction of a unit cell that is occupied by atoms in the diamond structure. Recalculate the fraction for the case of:

   (i) a simple cubic,

   (ii) a body-centred cubic, i.e. a simple cubic with one additional atom at the centre of the cube.

2. If the lattice constants of Si and GaAs are 5.43 Å and 5.63 Å respectively, find the density of the two materials.

3. Draw a cubic lattice and all the [111] family of directions.
4. Calculate the number of atoms per unit area in the crystal planes (100), (110) and (111) for silicon.
5. Consider the effect of Fermi level E_f and temperature T on the probability $F(E)$ of finding an electron in a state kT above the conduction band of a semiconductor. Calculate:

   (i) $F(E)$ if $T = 300$ K and E_f is incremented in 50 meV steps from 50 meV to 500 meV below the bottom of the valence band.

   (ii) $F(E)$ if E_f is 150 meV below the bottom of the conduction band and T is raised in 50 K steps from 50 K to 500 K.

   Draw appropriate graphs of these results. (Note: although E_f has a temperature dependence as seen by combining (1.7) and (1.8), assume in part (ii) that it remains fixed. The idea of this question is to show the power of the exponential functions extensively used in semiconductor calculations.)
6. Comment on the relative values of free and effective electron masses. What does this tell you about the nature of conduction band electrons and valence band holes?
7. What would happen to the nature of a semiconductor if it was doped, for example, n-type at a doping density equivalent to the effective density of states in the conduction band? What would happen if an attempt was made to dope with a higher density?
8. What would happen if a GaAs crystal was doped with silicon? Does it depend on where the dopant finally comes to rest in the crystal?
9. What happens to the nature of a semiconductor material if the temperature is raised such that the intrinsic carrier concentration is greater than the doping density? How would this affect the operation of a semiconductor device which relied on different doping profiles in different parts of the structure?
10. In what temperature range would you calculate 'freeze-out' to occur with arsenic doped silicon?
11. What is the resistivity of intrinsic Si at room temperature?
12. Calculate the minority carrier lifetime if a Haynes–Schockley experiment shows that the maximum amplitudes of the minority carrier signal differ by a factor 10 at $t_1 = 10$ μs and $t_2 = 20$ μs, assuming that the signal 'in the dark' has already been subtracted when calculating the maximum amplitudes.

1.6   References

1. M N Rudden and J Wilson, *Elements of Solid State Physics*, Wiley, 1980.
2. N W Ashcroft and N D Mermin, *Solid State Physics*, Holt, Rinehart and Winston, 1976.
3. A Nussbaum, *Semiconductor Device Physics*, Prentice-Hall, 1962.

4. A Bar-Lev, *Semiconductors and Electronic Devices*, 2nd ed., Prentice-Hall International, 1984, p. 65.

5. M W Zemansky, *Heat and Thermodynamics*, 5th ed., McGraw Hill, 1968, p. 323.

6. S M Sze, *Semiconductor Devices – Physics and Technology*, Wiley, 1985, p. 15.

7. D R Wight, 'The Physical and Electronic Properties of GaAs', in *Gallium Arsenide: Materials, Devices and Circuits*, M J Howes and D V Morgan, eds, Wiley, 1985, p. 11.

8. A Bar-Lev, *Semiconductor and Electronic Devices*, 2nd ed., Prentice-Hall International, 1984, p. 49.

9. R S Muller and T I Kamins, *Device Electronics for ICs*, Wiley, 1977, p. 26.

10. B G Streetman, *Solid State Electronic Devices*, 2nd ed., Prentice-Hall International, 1980, p. 119.

2

Junctions

In the last chapter we saw how carriers in a semiconductor behaved under the influence of various external constraints; an applied electric field, for example. We assumed, in discussing any particular material, that the material was homogeneous throughout, whether as an n- or p-type semiconductor, Si or GaAs, etc. Now we will look at what happens when two dissimilar materials come together to form a junction.

The properties of junctions are the basis of practically all semiconductor devices, including optoelectronic ones. The only important exception is the photoconductor (Chapter 5); LEDs, lasers, and photodiodes are all centred around junction properties.

The most common junction, and hence the one introduced first, is the pn junction. This is where n- and p-type material of the same semiconductor meet (strictly it should be called a homojunction, signifying the use of the same semiconductor, but often the prefix is left off). It is important to note that this cannot be formed simply by placing n- and p-type material together; the lattice structure must have continuity for the band diagrams (subsequently described) to be valid. Junctions are formed by introducing dopants of opposite polarity into p- or n-material; the junction is formed where p-material becomes n-type – see Figure 2.1(b) (the principles of dopant incorporation are discussed in sections 8.6 and 8.7. The density of the introduced dopant must be greater that that of the host dopant to cause type-conversion (change of conductivity type) of that part of the semiconductor.

Another important system is the metal-semiconductor junction. Here lattice continuity is impossible, as the materials are entirely different and the junction is not formed by doping, but usually by some deposition process (see Chapter 9). Heterojunctions are introduced at appropriate points in each device's chapter, and the principles of this type of structure are discussed in detail in section 4.2.

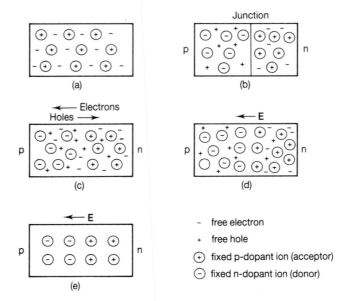

Figure 2.1 The formation of a pn junction. (a) n-type semiconductor. (b) After p-type dopant incorporation. (c) Carrier diffusion with fixed dopants. (d) Net electric field opposes further carrier motion. (e) Formation of a depletion or space charge region.

2.1   The pn junction

2.1.1   Equilibrium

Equilibrium in this case refers to the condition of no applied bias, and the junction maintained at a constant temperature. If a situation as in Figure 2.1(b) exists, where a continuous material has electron and hole concentrations that suddenly become discontinuous, then it is clear that diffusion of carriers (holes to n-type, electrons to p-type) will occur across the junction because of the concentration discontinuity. The ionized impurity concentrations are also discontinuous, but the dopants are fixed in the lattice: they are not free to move, and remain immobile despite the free carrier movement. This arrangement of free carriers and fixed dopants soon builds up a region of space charge in the junction region, positive on the n-side and negative on the p-side (Figure 2.1(c)). An electric field is then set up in a direction to oppose any further carrier motion (Figure 2.1(d)). The original carrier diffusion down a concentration gradient causes a (diffusion) current, which is then balanced by (drift) current in the opposing direction, with all free charges swept out of the junction region because of the net field.

Equilibrium is reached when the magnitudes of these two currents are equal; no further net carrier movement across the junction then occurs. A region of space charge is now formed in the junction region, which is depleted of free carriers – Figure 2.1(e) (hence the common term depletion region used to describe this phenomenon). The depletion region, and hence its associated electric field, extend only a short distance either side of the original junction (as we shall see, distances less than 1 μm are involved). The bulk of the semiconductor remains unaffected by the creation of the junction, and retains its original conductivity type and carrier density. For these reasons a pn junction is often represented as in Figure 2.2.

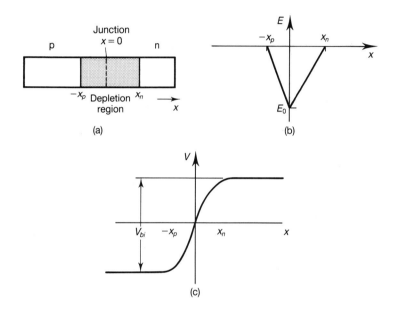

Figure 2.2 Electrostatic consideration of a pn junction. (a) Depletion region with $N_A \gg N_D$. (b) Electric field associated with the pn junction. (c) Potential built in to the junction as a result of the electric field. (Note: if the n-region is drawn on the left-hand side of the junction, i.e. for $x < 0$, the signs of V are reversed; hence dV/dx becomes negative and E (= $-dV/dx$) becomes positive.)

Now we should consider what happens to the energy bands within the semiconductor. It is important to remember that we are considering the junction as part of one semiconductor structure. Thus the probability of finding an electron of any particular energy must be the same throughout the structure; otherwise electrons would flow to those regions of higher probability but of the same energy. But we have said that in equilibrium no net current will flow. Equation (1.3) relates the probability $F(E)$ of a particular energy level E being occupied to the position of the Fermi level; if the probability is the same throughout the material, the Fermi level must likewise remain constant throughout the n- and p-regions, including the junction area. As we have said, the bulk of the n- and p-regions are unaffected by the carrier movement in the depletion region; their band diagrams will resemble those of n- or p-type semiconductors (Figure 2.3(a)). The junction region, however, must accomodate the change from both n-type to bulk p-type whilst maintaining a constant Fermi level; the only way this can be accomodated is by bending the conduction and valence bands in the depletion region, as in Figure 2.3(b). There will be a potential difference, V_{bi}, shown in Figures 2.2(c) and 2.3(b), between the conduction bands of the n- and p-type materials (the same potential difference also exists between the valence bands). This is known as the built-in, contact or diffusion voltage (or potential), and it can be seen that it acts as a potential barrier to further electron transport from n to p regions, or for the holes from p to n regions.

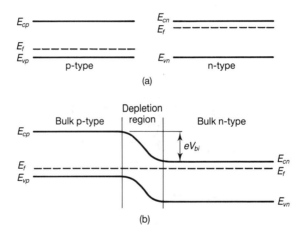

Figure 2.3 Band diagrams of a pn junction in equilibrium. (a) Bulk semiconductor band structure. (b) Band structure in the depletion region.

We can calculate a value for V_{bi} by first considering the equation relating the electron concentration to the difference between the Fermi level and the conduction band. Thus (1.12) becomes

$$n_{n0} \;=\; N_c \exp\left(\frac{E_f - E_{cn}}{kT}\right) \tag{2.1}$$

$$\text{and} \quad n_{p0} \;=\; N_c \exp\left(\frac{E_f - E_{cp}}{kT}\right) \tag{2.2}$$

for electron concentration in the n and p regions respectively, where the extra '0' subscript is used to denote equilibrium values. N_c is the same in both equations because we are concerned with the same semiconductor throughout. N_c and E_f can then be eliminated from both these equations to give

$$E_{cp} - E_{cn} = kT \log_e \frac{n_{no}}{n_{po}} .$$
(2.3)

As we have already noted (Figure 2.3(b))

$$E_{cp} - E_{cn} = e V_{bi},$$
(2.4)

and so from (2.3) and (2.4)

$$V_{bi} = \frac{kT}{e} \log_e \frac{n_{no}}{n_{po}} .$$
(2.5)

If (1.14) is used as the starting point, (2.5) becomes

$$V_{bi} = \frac{kT}{e} \log_e \frac{p_{po}}{p_{no}} .$$
(2.6)

Alternatively, a consideration of either of the continuity equations, along with Poisson's equation in one dimension

$$\frac{\mathrm{d}E}{\mathrm{d}x} = -\frac{\mathrm{d}^2V}{\mathrm{d}x^2} = \frac{\rho}{\epsilon\epsilon_0} = \frac{e(N_D - N_A)}{\epsilon\epsilon_0}$$
(2.7)

in the junction region, leads to [1]

$$V_{bi} = \frac{D_p}{\mu_h} \log_e \frac{N_A N_D}{n_i^2} = \frac{D_n}{\mu_e} \log_e \frac{N_A N_D}{n_i^2} .$$
(2.8)

Consideration of (1.9), (1.12), (1.14), (1.55) and (1.56) will show that the forms of the built-in voltage expressed in the above equations are all equivalent.

Example 2.1

Calculate the room temperature value of the built-in potential at a GaAs pn junction, with a doping density of 10^{15} cm^{-3} on either side.

Solution: from (2.6) and (2.8)

$$V_{bi} = \frac{293k}{e} \log_e \left(\frac{10^{15} \times 10^{15}}{(1.8 \times 10^6)^2} \right)$$
$$= 1.02 \text{ V}.$$
(2.9)

2.1.2   Depletion layer width

This can be found by solving (2.7) and assuming that the junction is abrupt, i.e. the doping densities are as in Figure 2.4(a). Then, for the p-side of the depletion region $(-x_p \leq x < 0)$

$$\frac{\mathrm{d}E}{\mathrm{d}x} = -\frac{e}{\epsilon\epsilon_0}N_A \tag{2.10}$$

and for the n-side $(0 < x \leq x_n)$

$$\frac{\mathrm{d}E}{\mathrm{d}x} = \frac{e}{\epsilon\epsilon_0}N_D . \tag{2.11}$$

If $E = 0$ at both $x = -x_p$ and $x = x_n$, and $E = E_0$ at $x = 0$, then (2.10) becomes

$$\int_0^{E_0} \mathrm{d}E = -\frac{eN_A}{\epsilon\epsilon_0} \int_{-x_p}^0 \mathrm{d}x \tag{2.12}$$

$$\text{or} \quad E_0 = -\frac{eN_A}{\epsilon\epsilon_0} x_p \tag{2.13}$$

$$\text{and similarly} \quad E_0 = \frac{eN_D}{\epsilon\epsilon_0} x_n . \tag{2.14}$$

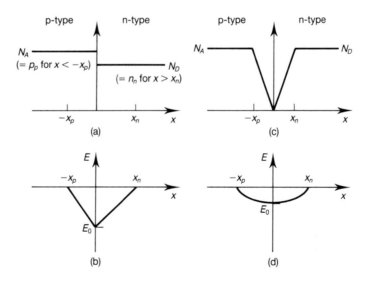

Figure 2.4 Doping profiles (a and c) and electric field (b and d) of two common junction types. (a) and (b) Abrupt junction. (c) and (d) Linearly graded junction.

Integrating (2.13) and (2.14) with respect to x gives the potential in each region:

$$V_p = \frac{eN_A}{2\epsilon\epsilon_0}x_p^2 \qquad (2.15)$$

$$\text{and} \quad V_n = \frac{eN_D}{2\epsilon\epsilon_0}x_n^2. \qquad (2.16)$$

As $V_p + V_n = V_{bi}$, the built-in potential, and $x_p + x_n = w$, the total depletion region width, (2.15) and (2.16) can be rearranged to give V_{bi} in terms of w:

$$V_{bi} = \frac{eN_A}{2\epsilon\epsilon_0}x_p(x_p + x_n), \qquad (2.17)$$

$$\text{because} \quad N_A x_p = N_D x_n \qquad (2.18)$$

is a condition of space charge neutrality, i.e. equal numbers of positive and negative charges exist in the junction region. Equation (2.18) can be rearranged to give x_p in terms of the depletion width and doping densities to give

$$x_p = \frac{wN_D}{N_A + N_D} \qquad \text{and} \qquad x_n = \frac{wN_A}{N_A + N_D}. \qquad (2.19)$$

Equations (2.17) and (2.19) can then be combined to give

$$V_{bi} = \frac{e}{2\epsilon\epsilon_0}\frac{N_A N_D}{N_A + N_D}w^2 \qquad (2.20)$$

$$\text{or} \quad w = \left(\frac{2V_{bi}\epsilon\epsilon_0(N_A + N_D)}{eN_A N_D}\right)^{1/2}. \qquad (2.21)$$

Example 2.2

Calculate the width of the depletion region for the junction illustrated in example 2.1.

Solution: in this example it is easier to work in SI units. From (2.21)

$$w = \left(\frac{2 \times 1.02 \times 13.1 \times \epsilon_0\,(2 \times 10^{21})}{e \times 10^{21} \times 10^{21}}\right)^{1/2}$$

$$= 1.7 \ \mu\text{m}. \qquad (2.22)$$

Hence w, x_p and x_n are all proportional to $V_{bi}^{1/2}$ for an abrupt junction. The same analysis on a linearly graded junction, with the doping densities as in Figure

2.4(c), would give a $V_{bi}^{1/3}$ dependency. Equations (2.13), (2.14), (2.19) and (2.21), along with the expressions derived in section 2.1.1, provide useful information as the maximum electric field, the extent of the depletion region either side of the junction and the built-in potential can all be obtained from a knowledge of the doping densities and the relative permittivity ϵ of the semiconductor.

The space charge distribution in an abrupt junction resembles that of a parallel plate capacitor, and so there is a junction capacitance C_j associated with the depletion region. This is given by

$$C_j = \left| \frac{\mathrm{d}Q}{\mathrm{d}V} \right| \tag{2.23}$$

because the charge on each side of the depletion region varies non-linearly with the applied voltage; hence $C = |Q/V|$ is not valid in this case. If the junction has an area A, then

$$|Q| = eAx_n N_D = eAx_p N_A . \tag{2.24}$$

From (2.19) and (2.24)

$$|Q| = \frac{eAwN_A N_D}{N_A + N_D} . \tag{2.25}$$

From (2.21) and (2.25)

$$Q = A\left[2e\epsilon\epsilon_0 V_{bi}\left(\frac{N_A N_D}{N_A + N_D}\right)\right]^{1/2} \tag{2.26}$$

and hence from (2.23) and (2.26)

$$C_j = \frac{A}{2}\left[\frac{2e\epsilon\epsilon_0}{V_{bi}}\left(\frac{N_A N_D}{N_A + N_D}\right)\right]^{1/2} = \frac{\epsilon\epsilon_0 A}{w} \tag{2.27}$$

which is identical to the form of the capacitance of a parallel plate capacitor.

Example 2.3

Find the capacitance per unit area of the diode illustrated in example 2.2.

Solution: from (2.27)

$$\frac{C}{A} = \frac{13.1 \times \epsilon_0}{1.7 \times 10^{-6}}$$
$$= 6.8 \times 10^{-5} \text{ F m}{-2}. \tag{2.28}$$

In familiar units the capacitance per unit area is 6.8 nF cm^{-2}.

2.1.3   Bias conditions

The application of an external bias to a pn junction upsets the previously discussed equilibrium. Carriers are now being injected at both ends of the semiconductor, and so the Fermi level is no longer constant throughout the material. The depletion region, as we saw in section 2.1.1, has no free carriers and hence is highly resistive compared to the rest of the semiconductor. Because of this all of the applied bias can be considered to be dropped across the depletion region. Thus the effect of an applied voltage V is to adjust the Fermi level in the depletion region by an amount eV, and the conduction and valence bands bend according to the magnitude of V.

There are many factors to consider when applying bias to a pn junction which result, as we shall see, in different formulae for the operating current as a function of applied voltage. In section 2.1.5 we will look at the causes of current on reverse bias, but we start in section 2.1.4 by looking at the forward biased current mechanisms, diffusion and generation–recombination.

2.1.4   Forward bias

2.1.4.1   Diffusion current

Consider Figure 2.5(a), which shows a junction under forward bias. This arrangement means that electrons are being injected into the n-semiconductor (similarly holes are being injected into the p-material). The conduction and valence bands bend accordingly, the overall effect being the reduction in the barrier height from eV_{bi} to $e(V_{bi} - V)$, as shown in Figure 2.5(b). The excess electron concentration on the n-side, and the lowering of the barrier height, combine to make it easier for electrons to diffuse from n to p; for similar reasons holes can diffuse more easily from p to n. On crossing the junction these previously majority carriers now become minority carriers, creating new minority carrier concentration gradients with peak values of n_p and p_n as in Figure 2.5(c). The diffusion currents created by this carrier movement are quite large, but the drift currents across the potential barrier are relatively unaffected by forward (or reverse) bias.

We can calculate the new minority carrier concentrations, and hence derive an expression for the current under forward bias, by rearranging (2.5) to give for an applied voltage V

$$n_p = n_{n0} \exp\left(\frac{-e(V_{bi} - V)}{kT}\right) \tag{2.29}$$

$$= n_{p0} \exp\left(\frac{eV}{kT}\right). \tag{2.30}$$

The change in electron concentration, $\Delta n(x)$, as a function of distance from the junction, is given by

$$\Delta n(x) = n_p(x) - n_{p0} \tag{2.31}$$

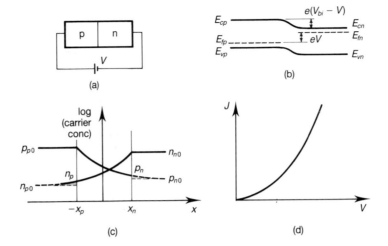

Figure 2.5 Characteristics of a pn junction under forward bias: (a) biasing arrangement, (b) band diagram, (c) carrier concentration, and (d) $I–V$ curve.

and so $\Delta n(0) = n_p - n_{po}$. $\qquad(2.32)$

From (2.30) and (2.32)

$$\Delta n(0) = n_{po}\left[\exp\left(\frac{eV}{kT}\right) - 1\right]. \qquad(2.33)$$

From our definition of diffusion length, (1.64), and (2.31)

$$\Delta n(x) = \Delta n(0)\exp\left(\frac{-x}{L_n}\right). \qquad(2.34)$$

Differentiating this gives

$$\frac{\mathrm{d}\Delta n(x)}{\mathrm{d}x} = -\frac{\Delta n(0)}{L_n}\exp\left(\frac{-x}{L_n}\right). \qquad(2.35)$$

As $\dfrac{\mathrm{d}\Delta n(x)}{\mathrm{d}x} = \dfrac{\mathrm{d}n(x)}{\mathrm{d}x}$, $\qquad(2.36)$

we can use our equation for electron diffusion current density, (1.47), to give

$$J_n = \frac{eD_n\Delta n(0)}{L_n}\exp\left(\frac{-x}{L_n}\right). \qquad(2.37)$$

Equations (2.33) and (2.37) can be combined to give, at $x = 0$

$$J_n = \frac{eD_n}{L_n}n_{po}\left[\exp\left(\frac{eV}{kT}\right) - 1\right]. \qquad(2.38)$$

A similar analysis for holes, starting from (2.6), would lead to a value for hole diffusion current density J_p given by

$$J_p = \frac{eD_p}{L_p} p_{no} \left[\exp\left(\frac{eV}{kT}\right) - 1 \right]. \tag{2.39}$$

The total diffusion current density is thus

$$J = J_n + J_p = J_s \left[\exp\left(\frac{eV}{kT}\right) - 1 \right], \tag{2.40}$$

$$\text{where} \quad J_s = \frac{eD_p}{L_p} p_{no} + \frac{eD_n}{L_n} n_{po}. \tag{2.41}$$

For large values of V the term -1 inside the brackets becomes negligible, and thus under forward bias there is a near exponential increase in current with applied voltage:

$$J = J_s \exp\left(\frac{eV}{kT}\right) \tag{2.42}$$

as shown in Figure 2.5(d). This means that a forward biased junction conducts very readily.

Example 2.4

Find the value of V in (2.40) which means that the approximation in (2.42) is accurate to within 1% at room temperature.

Solution: from (2.40) and (2.42), the approximation is true when

$$\frac{J}{1.01 J} = \frac{\exp(eV/kT) - 1}{\exp(eV/kT)}$$

$$\text{or} \quad 1.01 = 0.01 \exp\left(\frac{eV}{kT}\right)$$

$$\text{and so} \quad V = \frac{kT}{e} \log_e 101$$

$$= 0.12 \text{ V}. \tag{2.43}$$

So the term 'large' in the condition placed on V in (2.40) means greater than the value calculated here.

2.1.4.2   Generation–recombination current

The current generating process alluded to in the last section is the dominant one on forward bias, and as we shall soon see for all but low values of bias it can be assumed to be the only mechanism. There is a second process besides diffusion, however; although this does occur for all values of forward (and indeed reverse) bias, its numerical value is only significant for low forward voltages. The current is due to generation and recombination within the depletion region. Generation and recombination processes were described in section 1.3.6, and the four possible transitions are shown in Figure 2.6:

   (a) electron capture at an empty centre,
   (b) electron emission from an occupied centre,
   (c) hole capture at an occupied centre, and
   (d) hole release from an empty centre.

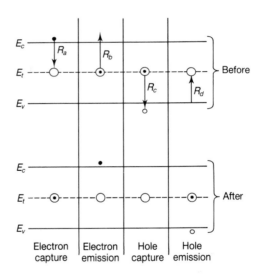

Figure 2.6 The generation and recombination processes in a semiconductor.

   For any centre of energy E_t within the band gap and concentration N_t, the rate R_a of capture of electrons by process (a) is given by

$$R_a = c_n n N_t \left(1 - F\left(E_t\right)\right) \tag{2.44}$$

where $F(E_t)$ is the Fermi–Dirac distribution function and is given by (1.3) (and hence $1 - F(E_t)$ is the probability of a trap being unoccupied), and c_n is known as the capture coefficient of electrons, a product of the thermal velocity v_{th} and the electron capture cross-section σ_{cn} (typical values of c_n are $\sim 10^{18}$ cm^3 s^{-1}).

Because only one electron can occupy a given centre, R_a is proportional to the number of unoccupied centres, which is the product $N_t(1 - F(E_t))$.

For process (b), the rate R_b of electron emission is given by

$$R_b = e_n N_t F(E_t) \,. \tag{2.45}$$

Similarly for the processes (c) and (d), the capture and emission rates of holes (R_c and R_d respectively) are given by

$$R_c = c_p p N_t F(E_t) \tag{2.46}$$
$$\text{and} \quad R_d = e_p p N_t (1 - F(E_t)) \tag{2.47}$$

where c_p and e_p are the hole capture and emission coefficients respectively.

Under thermal equilibrium the number of emitted electrons must equal that of captured holes, i.e. $R_a = R_b$. Thus from (2.44) and (2.45)

$$c_n n (1 - F(E_t)) = e_n F(E_t) \,. \tag{2.48}$$

Using (1.20) for the electron concentration in thermal equilibrium, and (1.3) for the Fermi–Dirac distribution, yields

$$e_n = c_n n_i \exp\left(\frac{E_t - E_i}{kT}\right) \,. \tag{2.49}$$

A similar calculation for holes in processes (c) and (d) gives

$$e_p = c_p n_i \exp\left(\frac{E_i - E_t}{kT}\right) \,. \tag{2.50}$$

If we introduce some non-equilibrium phenomena, such as generation of electron–hole pairs across the band gap, then the conditions of (2.49) and (2.50) do not apply. If the generation rate can be represented by G, then in a steady state the number of electrons in the conduction band, or holes in the valence band, must be constant, i.e.

$$G = R_a - R_b \tag{2.51}$$
$$\text{and} \quad G = R_c - R_d \,. \tag{2.52}$$

This is known as the principle of detailed balance. Combining (2.51) and (2.52) with (2.44)–(2.47) gives

$$c_n n (1 - F(E_t)) - e_n F(E_t) = c_p p F(E_t) - e_p (1 - F(E_t)) \,. \tag{2.53}$$

For simplicity's sake, it is usual at this stage to assume the capture coefficients c_n and c_p are equal and can be represented by c_0. If this is done, (2.53) can be isolated in terms of $F(E_t)$ by using (2.49) and (2.50) and the trigonometrical relationship $\cosh x = (e^x + e^{-x})/2$. $F(E_t)$ then becomes

$$F(E_t) = \frac{n + n_i \exp((E_i - E_t)/kT)}{n + p + 2n_i \cosh((E_t - E_i)/kT)} \,. \tag{2.54}$$

In the steady state $G = U$, the recombination rate, and so, using (2.49)–(2.54),

$$U = c_0 N_t \left[n \left(1 - F(E_t)\right) - n_i \, \exp\left(\frac{E_t - E_i}{kT}\right) F(E_t) \right] . \tag{2.55}$$

With some intermediate arithmetic, this finally becomes

$$U = \frac{c_0 N_t \left(pn - n_i^2\right)}{n + p + 2n_i \, \cosh\left(\left(E_t - E_i\right)/kT\right)} . \tag{2.56}$$

For an equilibrium situation $np = n_i^2$, and hence the net recombination rate is zero. However, under forward bias the carrier concentration increases, such that $np > n_i^2$. The excess carriers will attempt to regain their previous equilibrium via recombination, and so we expect the dominant generation–recombination mechanism under forward bias to be the capture process. If we consider the n-side of the semiconductor, then using (2.30) gives

$$n_p p_n \;=\; n_{no} p_{no} \, \exp\left(\frac{eV}{kT}\right) \tag{2.57}$$

$$\;=\; n_i^2 \, \exp\left(\frac{eV}{kT}\right) \tag{2.58}$$

where we have assumed that $n_n \sim n_{no}$, which will be valid under most situations. From (2.56) and (2.58)

$$U = \frac{c_0 N_t n_{no} p_{no} \left[\exp\left(eV/kT\right) - 1 \right]}{n_{no} + p_{no} + 2n_i \, \cosh\left(\left(E_t - E_i\right)/kT\right)} . \tag{2.59}$$

The maximum value of U is when the denominator of (2.59) is a minimum. For any semiconductor n_i is fixed, and the cosh function is fixed for a given trap level. Therefore $n_{no} + p_{no}$ must be a minimum; as their product is a constant it follows from simple calculus that $n_{no} + p_{no}$ is a minimum when $n_{no} = p_{no}$. This condition occurs when E_i is halfway between E_{fp} and E_{fn} in the depletion region. At this point

$$n_{no} = p_{no} = n_i \, \exp\left(\frac{eV}{2kT}\right) . \tag{2.60}$$

Combining (2.59) and (2.60) gives

$$U_{max} = \frac{c_0 N_t n_i \left[\exp\left(eV/kT\right) - 1 \right]}{2 \left[\exp\left(eV/2kT\right) + 1 \right]} \tag{2.61}$$

if we simplify the arithmetic by making $E_t = E_i$. For values of $V \geq 4kT/e$, (2.61) can be further simplified to

$$U_{max} = \frac{c_0 N_t n_i}{2} \, \exp\left(\frac{eV}{2kT}\right) . \tag{2.62}$$

The recombination current density J_{gr} is defined by

$$J_{gr} = \int_0^w eU \, \mathrm{d}x \,. \tag{2.63}$$

Substituting (2.62) in (2.63) gives

$$J_{gr} = \frac{ewn_i}{2\tau} \exp\left(\frac{eV}{2kT}\right) \tag{2.64}$$

$$\text{or} \quad J_{gr} = J_R \exp\left(\frac{eV}{2kT}\right) \tag{2.65}$$

$$\text{where} \quad J_R = \frac{ewn_i}{2\tau} \tag{2.66}$$

and τ is known as the effective recombination lifetime, given by

$$\tau = \frac{1}{c_o N_t} \,. \tag{2.67}$$

The total forward current is the sum of (2.42) and (2.65):

$$J = J_s \exp\left(\frac{eV}{kT}\right) + J_R \exp\left(\frac{eV}{2kT}\right) \tag{2.68}$$

as shown in Figure 2.7. As can be seen, the diffusion current dominates over the generation–recombination current at all but low values of applied bias because of the difference in the exponential multiplier. In general, the total forward current J can be written as

$$J \propto \exp\left(\frac{eV}{nkT}\right) \tag{2.69}$$

where n is known as the ideality factor. When diffusion current dominates, (2.42) applies and $n = 1$. When the recombination current dominates, generally for low values of forward bias, (2.65) applies and $n = 2$. n obviously varies between these two extremes for all real diodes. The roll-off from the $n = 1$ curve at high values of forward bias is largely due to the series resistance of the diode.

2.1.5   Reverse bias

2.1.5.1   Diffusion current
When $V = 0$ (2.40) will show that the I–V plot of a pn junction passes through the origin. Situations analagous to the forward bias characterisitics are shown for the case of reverse bias in Figures 2.8(a)–(d). The Fermi level is raised on the p-side, because electrons are being injected from the external source into this region. The barrier height becomes $e(V_{bi} + V)$, where V is the magnitude of the reverse bias. There will be no diffusion of electrons from n to p (or from p to n either because, despite electron injection at the p-side, they are still minority carriers

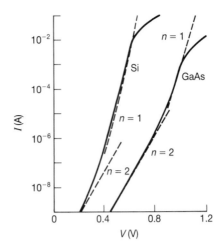

Figure 2.7 The forward I–V characteristics of Si and GaAs pn junction diodes.

in p as Figure 2.8(c) shows). For similar reasons there will be no diffusion of holes across the junction, and hence the only movement of minority carriers across the junction comes from the drift of minority carriers under the influence of the external bias. Thus drift causes a minority carrier extraction around the depletion region, characterized by the carrier diffusion length – Figure 2.8(c). The drift of carriers must be supplied from the minority carrier concentrations which, as we can see from the biasing conditions, are replenished at either end of the semiconductor. Thus diffusion of carriers to the vicinity of the depletion region supplies the drift mechanism; we can thus use the same arguments as previously to define the total current density under reverse bias. A similar derivation to that of (2.40) gives

$$J = J_n + J_p = J_s \left[\exp\left(\frac{-eV}{kT}\right) - 1 \right]. \tag{2.70}$$

For large values of reverse bias the exponential term becomes negligible, unlike the case for forward bias and (2.40). Under these conditions the reverse current becomes

$$J = -J_s \tag{2.71}$$

and hence leads to the characteristics in Figure 2.8(d), where for large values of reverse bias the current density approaches a (small) saturation value J_s. Thus, unlike the case for forward bias, a pn junction under reverse bias conducts very poorly.

Although the current across the pn junction is caused by drift of minority carriers, the fact that the minority carrier concentrations are replenished by diffusion to

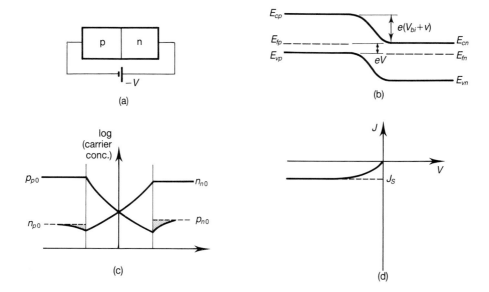

Figure 2.8 The characteristics of a pn junction under reverse bias: (a) biasing arrangement, (b) band diagram, (c) carrier concentration, and (d) *I–V* curve (diffusion current only).

the junction region causes this mechanism also to be known as a diffusion current. This is initially confusing, but will be a useful distinction from 'true' drift current in reverse biased photodetectors where, as we shall see in Chapter 6, carriers are generated within the depletion region by photon absorption and then immediately separated by the electric field.

2.1.5.2 *Generation–recombination current*

Because for reverse bias $np < n_i^2$ within the depletion region, the dominant mechanisms from Figure 2.6 are now emission of electrons and holes, the opposite of a forward biased junction. Substitution of $np < n_i^2$ into (2.56) leads to a negative recombination rate $-U$, i.e. a positive generation rate G. The resulting current is then a generation current on reverse bias, instead of a recombination current on forward bias. If $n_i > p$ and $n_i > n$ then (2.56) can be simplified to

$$G = \frac{c_0 N_t n_i}{2 \cosh\left((E_t - E_i)/kT\right)} \ . \tag{2.72}$$

Again, this reaches a maximum at $E_t = E_i$ as for the forward biased diode. G falls off exponentially as E_t moves away from E_i, and so only those centres with $E_t \sim E_i$ contribute significantly to the generation rate. Doping silicon with gold is an efficient way of doing this. The total current due to generation is then

$$J_{gr} = \int_0^w eG \, dx \tag{2.73}$$

$$= \frac{ewn_i}{\tau} \tag{2.74}$$

where τ in this case is the effective generation lifetime. The total reverse current is then the sum of (2.42) and (2.74):

$$|J| = J_s + \frac{ewn_i}{\tau} . \tag{2.75}$$

If one carrier dominates, e.g. $N_A \gg N_D$, then (2.41) and (2.75) give

$$|J| = \frac{eD_p}{L_p} p_{no} + \frac{ewn_i}{\tau}$$

$$= e\sqrt{\frac{D_p}{\tau_p}} \frac{n_i^2}{N_D} + \frac{ewn_i}{\tau} . \tag{2.76}$$

If n_i is large, such as for small band gap materials such as germanium, the diffusion current dominates and the reverse current saturates at $|J| = J_s$. However, if n_i is small, the generation current may dominate as in wider gap semiconductors such as GaAs. This is considered in more detail in section 6.2.2.1, where the total reverse current represents a dark current in a pn junction used as a photodetector. Temperature effects are also considered in the same section. The reverse bias characteristics of a pn junction are shown in Figure 2.9.

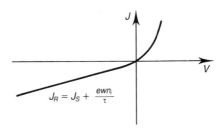

Figure 2.9 Reverse bias characteristics of a pn junction.

Example 2.5

Use the following data to determine the relative magnitudes of the diffusion and generation currents in a reverse biased n⁺p GaAs diode at room temperature: D_p

$= 70$ cm^2/s and $\tau_p = 1.5$ ns for a doping density N_D of 10^{18} cm^{-3}. Assume the effective generation time is 50 ns, and the p-doping density is 10^{15} cm^{-3}.

Solution: from examples 2.1 and 2.2 the depletion region width can be calculated as 1.3 μm. From (2.76)

$$\frac{J_s}{J_{gr}} = \frac{\sqrt{70/1.5 \times 10^{-9}} \times 1.8 \times 10^6 \times 50 \times 10^{-9}}{10^{18} \times 1.3 \times 10^{-4}}$$

$$= 1.5 \times 10^{-10}, \tag{2.77}$$

i.e. in this case the generation current is the dominant factor on reverse bias.

2.1.6 Depletion width and capacitance under bias

The equations derived in section 2.1.2 for depletion layer width (2.21) and depletion layer capacitance (2.27) are modified under the influence of an external bias by replacing V_{bi} by $(V_{bi} - V)$ for forward bias, and by $(V_{bi} + V)$ for reverse bias. Thus (2.21) becomes

$$w = \left(\frac{2(V_{bi} - V)\epsilon\epsilon_0(N_A + N_D)}{eN_AN_D}\right)^{1/2} \tag{2.78}$$

under forward bias, and

$$w = \left(\frac{2(V_{bi} + V)\epsilon\epsilon_0(N_A + N_D)}{eN_AN_D}\right)^{1/2} \tag{2.79}$$

under reverse bias. Similarly (2.27) becomes

$$C_j = \frac{A}{2}\left(\frac{2\epsilon\epsilon_0}{V_{bi} - V}\left(\frac{N_AN_D}{N_A + N_D}\right)\right)^{1/2} \tag{2.80}$$

under forward bias, and

$$C_j = \frac{A}{2}\left(\frac{2\epsilon\epsilon_0}{V_{bi} + V}\left(\frac{N_AN_D}{N_A + N_D}\right)\right)^{1/2} \tag{2.81}$$

under reverse bias. It can be seen that the effect of reverse bias is to increase the depletion layer width and reduce its capacitance, a consequence we shall return to later in Chapter 6 on pin diodes.

Example 2.6

Calculate the percentage change in capacitance of the junction in example 2.3 under an applied reverse bias of –5 V.

Solution: from (2.81)

$$\frac{C}{A} = \frac{1}{2}\left(\frac{2 \times 13.1 \times \epsilon_0}{1.02 + 5}\left(\frac{10^{21} \times 10^{21}}{2 \times 10^{21}}\right)\right)^{1/2}$$
$$= 2.8 \times 10^{-5}\ \text{Fm}^{-2}. \tag{2.82}$$

In familiar units the capacitance is 2.8 nF cm^{-2} – a reduction of 59%.

2.1.7   Transient behaviour

Most solid state devices, and this is especially true of optoelectronic ones, are used for modulation purposes rather than for the steady state operations outlined in section 2.1.3. Some understanding of transient behaviour is therefore necessary, but a complete treatment is mathematically very lengthy and beyond the scope of this book. Further details are provided in [2] and [3], but only a basic description of the phenomena involved is presented here.

Under forward bias, the minority carrier distributions will be as in Figure 2.5(c), and described by (2.34). There is thus a charge stored in each of the neutral p and n regions, given by integrating the excess carrier concentration in each region. For electrons in the p-region

$$Q_n = e \int_{x_p}^{\infty} \Delta n(x)\mathrm{d}x \tag{2.83}$$

where the integration limit of ∞ implies considering the whole of the bulk semiconductor. From (2.33), (2.34) and (2.83)

$$Q_n = e \int_{x_p}^{\infty} n_{po}\left[\exp\left(\frac{eV}{kT}\right) - 1\right]\exp\left(-\frac{(x - x_p)}{L_n}\right)\mathrm{d}x \tag{2.84}$$
$$= eL_n n_{po}\left[\exp\left(\frac{eV}{kT}\right) - 1\right]. \tag{2.85}$$

There is a similar expression for the hole charge stored in the n-region

$$Q_p = eL_p p_{no}\left[\exp\left(\frac{eV}{kT}\right) - 1\right]. \tag{2.86}$$

Storage of charge on both sides of the depletion region leads to an additional capacitance term. This is known as the charge storage or diffusion capacitance, C_d, the latter term denoting the cause of the phenomenon. C_d is given by

$$C_d = A\left(\frac{dQ_n}{dV} + \frac{dQ_p}{dV}\right), \tag{2.87}$$

where A is the cross-sectional area of the device. Often the semiconductor is doped p$^+$n or n$^+$p so that $p_{no} \gg n_{po}$ or $n_{po} \gg p_{no}$ respectively. For the former case the term dQ_n/dV can be ignored in (2.87), and the diffusion capacitance becomes, using (2.86),

$$C_d = \frac{Ae^2 L_p p_{no}}{kT} \exp\left(\frac{eV}{kT}\right). \tag{2.88}$$

For the case of reverse bias (2.88) shows that C_d is negligible. However C_d dominates C_j for forward bias because of its exponential dependence on V. For small changes in the current, we can find the a.c. conductance G of the diode. From (2.40)

$$G = \frac{dI}{dV} = A\frac{dJ}{dV} \tag{2.89}$$

$$= \frac{eA}{kT}J_s \exp\left(\frac{eV}{kT}\right) \tag{2.90}$$

$$= \frac{eI}{kT}. \tag{2.91}$$

Thus the a.c. component of current i is given by

$$i = G_v + C_d\frac{dv}{dt} \tag{2.92}$$

where v is the a.c. component of applied voltage.

For switching applications the transition between forward and reverse bias should be short. If we suddenly switch a diode from forward to reverse bias at time $t=0$ there will be an initial current I_R flowing due to the charge storage in the diode. A transient time, t_0, is used as a figure of merit for the subsequent current decay and is defined as the time taken for the reverse current to fall to 10% of its original value (Figure 2.10). For electrons in the p-region of a n$^+$p junction (2.38) and (2.85) can be combined to give

$$Q_n = \frac{L_n^2}{D_n}J_n. \tag{2.93}$$

From (1.63) and (2.93)

$$Q_n = \tau_n J_n = \tau_n\frac{I_n}{A}. \tag{2.94}$$

As t_0 depends on the time taken to remove this excess charge, it can be seen that the transient time is a function of carrier lifetime; reducing this is usually accomplished by introducing recombination centres that have energy levels near the middle of the band gap.

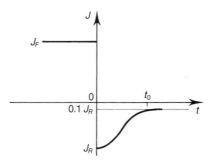

Figure 2.10 Transient time of a pn diode.

2.1.8   Reverse breakdown

Let us consider a pn junction under reverse bias, where the applied voltage is such that the energy band diagram of Figure 2.8(b) is modified to that of Figure 2.11(a), where E_{vp} is at a higher energy than E_{cn}. This aligns the many empty energy states above E_{cn} with the many full states below E_{vp}. If the barrier separating these two regions, i.e. the depletion region, is narrow, then there is a finite probability that electrons can tunnel from p to n, creating majority carriers on either side of the junction. This tunnelling is a quantum mechanical effect resulting from the finite probability of finding an electron outside a potential well [4]. As can be seen from Figure 2.11(b) for a junction where one side is heavily doped, tunnelling only occurs for high values of doping coupled with high applied fields, and is then not as common a cause of breakdown as the avalanche effect; this is considered separately in Chapter 7 as it forms the basis of a complete family of photodetectors. Nevertheless, either mechanism can give an enormous increase in conduction, as shown in Figure 2.11(c). This effect is the basis of the Zener diode used as a voltage regulator as in Figure 2.11(d). Any increase in applied bias above a certain value results in a large current being passed through the reverse biased diode, keeping the voltage at the output constant. Electron tunnelling is considered in more detail in section 2.2.3, where it is an important factor in the ohmic contact.

2.2   Metal–semiconductor junctions

These fall into two categories; Schottky, where the $I–V$ characteristics are similar to that of a pn junction, and ohmic, where the $I–V$ trace follows Ohm's law. A Schottky, or rectifying contact, is used in the metal–semiconductor photodiode and as the gate in a MESFET amplifier integrated on the same chip as the optoelectronic device. Ohmic contacts are, for optoelectronic purposes, far more common

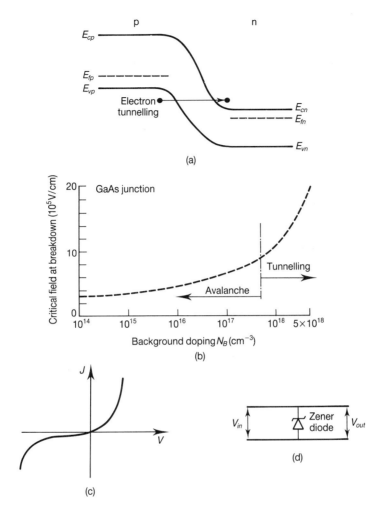

Figure 2.11 Electron tunnelling and the Zener effect. (a) Principle of electron tunnelling. (b) Doping and electric field ranges for Zener and avalanche breakdown. (c) *I–V* characteristic. (d) Zener diode as a voltage regulator.

and form the connection between the device and the 'hard wiring' of associated circuitry.

2.2.1   The Schottky barrier

Metal–semiconductor junctions can only be formed by bringing dissimilar materials together and creating a junction region between them. The effects of interface traps, surface states and impurities then become important, as a discussion in section 9.2.9 shows. Thus it is valid, as in Figure 2.12, to discuss the band diagrams before and after the contact has been made. The term χ in Figure 2.12(a) is known as the semiconductor electron affinity, and $e\phi_n$ represents the energy required to remove an electron completely from an n-type semiconductor, i.e. the work function. The metal work function, $e\phi_m$, is defined similarly to that of the semiconductor and is measured from E_{fm} to the vacuum level.

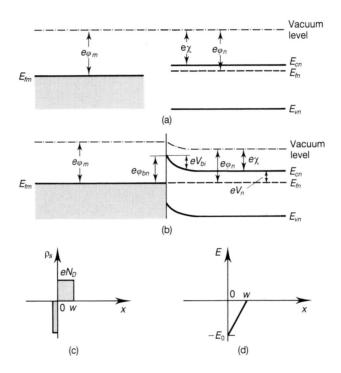

Figure 2.12 The metal–n-type semiconductor junction with no applied bias for $\phi_m > \phi_n$. (a) Band diagrams of metal and n-type semiconductor (separated). (b) Band diagram of metal–n-type semiconductor junction. (c) Charge distribution. (d) Electric field representation.

As with the pn system, at a metal–semiconductor junction the Fermi levels equalize, and all other bands bend accordingly. The only levels of significance in this procedure are E_{cn} and E_{vn}, which must bend upwards at the junction (Figure 2.12(b)) for a system where $\phi_m > \phi_n$. To achieve this electrons must be transferred from semiconductor to metal, creating a depletion region in the near surface of the semiconductor and excess negative charge on the metal side, as in Figure 2.12(c), resulting in an electric field distribution as shown in Figure 2.12(d). The effect is similar to that of the p^+n junction, and the depletion region width w can be calculated in the same way from (2.21) assuming that $N_A \gg N_D$.

The electron barrier height ϕ_{bn} is given by

$$\phi_{bn} = \phi_m - \chi . \tag{2.95}$$

For a p-type semiconductor with $\phi_m < \phi_p$, Figure 2.12(b) is modified to that of Figure 2.13. Here a positive and a negative charge on the metal and semiconductor sides respectively are required to equalize the Fermi levels. Similarly to (2.95) the hole barrier height is

$$\phi_{bp} = E_g - (\phi_m - \chi) . \tag{2.96}$$

The application of an external bias to a metal–semiconductor junction will alter the relative position of the Fermi levels, and hence the energy bands in the semiconductor. This is similar to the effect in a pn junction but with one important exception; we saw that in a pn system current transport is dominated by minority carriers, but in a metal–semiconductor system thermionic emission of majority carriers over the potential barrier is the major source of current flow. Consider Figure 2.14. In equilibrium, with no applied bias, there are two drift currents, of equal magnitude but opposite directions, which flow across the junction because of the built-in electric field – this again is similar to a pn junction. The current densities will be proportional to the electron concentration n in the junction region, i.e.

$$J_{sm} = J_{ms} = Cn \tag{2.97}$$

where C is a constant. Note that the arrows represent current flow; because we are dealing with electrons, the charge flow is in the opposite direction. At the surface of the semiconductor, (1.12) becomes

$$n = N_c \exp\left(-\frac{e\phi_{bn}}{kT}\right) , \tag{2.98}$$

and so combining the last two equations gives

$$J_{sm} = J_{ms} = CN_c \exp\left(-\frac{e\phi_{bn}}{kT}\right) . \tag{2.99}$$

For $V > 0$, i.e. the application of a forward bias to the junction, the built in potential V_{bi} is lowered by V; however, the barrier height ϕ_{bn} is unaltered (Figure 2.14(b)). This has the effect of increasing the electron density at the semiconductor

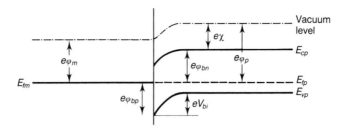

Figure 2.13 Band diagram of a metal–p-type semiconductor for $\phi_m < \phi_p$.

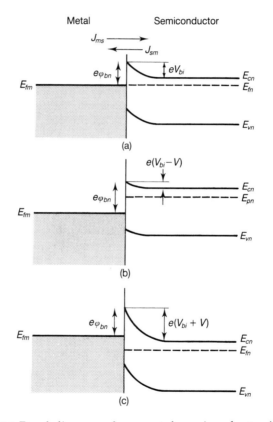

Figure 2.14 Band diagrams for a metal–semiconductor junction with an applied bias: (a) $V = 0$, (b) $V > 0$, and (c) $V < 0$.

surface, thereby increasing J_{sm}, but J_{ms} remains as before. There is a net current flow across the barrier given by

$$J = J_{sm} - J_{ms}$$

$$= \ CN_c \ \exp\left(-\frac{e(\phi_{bn} - V)}{kT}\right) - CN_c \ \exp\left(-\frac{e\phi_{bn}}{kT}\right)$$

$$= \ CN_c \ \exp\left(-\frac{e\phi_{bn}}{kT}\right)\left[\exp\left(\frac{eV}{kT}\right) - 1\right]. \tag{2.100}$$

This can be simplified to

$$J \ = \ J_s\left[\exp\left(\frac{eV}{kT}\right) - 1\right] \tag{2.101}$$

$$\text{where} \quad J_s \ = \ CN_c \ \exp\left(-\frac{e\phi_{bn}}{kT}\right). \tag{2.102}$$

CN_c is found to be equal to $\mathcal{A}^{**}T^2$, where $\mathcal{A}^{**}$ is the effective Richardson constant, and depends on the effective mass m^* of the carriers. It is given by [5]

$$\mathcal{A}^{**} \ = \ \frac{4\pi m^* e k^2}{h^3}. \tag{2.103}$$

For reverse bias, i.e. $V < 0$, again J_{ms} is unaltered, but J_{sm} is smaller than in the equilibrium case. The net effect is that (2.101) becomes

$$J \ = \ J_s\left[\exp\left(-\frac{eV}{kT}\right) - 1\right]. \tag{2.104}$$

Equations (2.101) and (2.104) are similar to the $I-V$ characteristics obtained for a pn junction, (2.40) and (2.70). They can similarly be simplified for large magnitudes of V, and similarly have an ideality factor (usually between 1.0 and 1.3 for a metal–semiconductor junction) introduced into the denominator of the exponential term. The current carrying mechanisms are very different, however, and the constant J_s is derived from totally different physical parameters in either case.

2.2.2   Measurement of barrier parameters

The barrier height ϕ_{bn} is an important characteristic of a Schottky contact, as it determines when any applied forward bias V is large enough to cause significant conduction. If we introduce the ideality factor into (2.101), and assume V is large, then the $I-V$ characteristics become

$$I \ = \ I_s \exp\left(\frac{eV}{nkT}\right) \tag{2.105}$$

$$\text{or} \quad \log_e I \ = \ \log_e I_s \ + \ \frac{eV}{nkT}. \tag{2.106}$$

If we plot $\log_e I$ vs V, a straight line of slope e/nkT and y-intercept $\log_e I_s$ is obtained, as in Figure 2.15. The ideality factor n is thus

$$n \ = \ \frac{e}{kT} \times \frac{1}{\text{gradient}} \tag{2.107}$$

and from (2.102)

$$\log_e I_s = -\frac{e\phi_{bn}}{kT} + \log_e\left(A\,\mathcal{A}^{**}T^2\right) \tag{2.108}$$

where A is the junction area. Therefore

$$\phi_{bn} = \frac{kT}{e}\log_e\frac{A\,\mathcal{A}^{**}T^2}{I_s}. \tag{2.109}$$

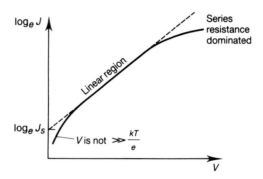

Figure 2.15 *I–V* characteristics of a forward biased Schottky diode.

Figure 2.15 also shows two other regions of the *I–V* curve. In the lower area the exponential characteristics are not apparent because the –1 term in (2.101) is still important; above a certain value of V the current is limited by the series resistance of the semiconductor material associated with the diode.

2.2.3   The ohmic contact

This form of metal–semiconductor junction is far more common in optoelectronic devices than the Schottky contact. Ohmic contacts to both p- and n-type materials are needed to connect external circuitry with the active region of a device. Unlike a Schottky contact, which shows rectifying behaviour, an ohmic contact needs to have a linear *I–V* characteristic for both biasing directions and the contact resistance at the junction needs to be as small as possible, although the achievement of zero resistance is impossible.

In section 2.2.1 we noted the material conditions necessary for a Schottky contact: $\phi_m > \phi_n$ for an n-type semiconductor and $\phi_m < \phi_p$ for p-type. For ohmic contacts these requirements are reversed, i.e. $\phi_m < \phi_n$ for n-type and $\phi_m > \phi_p$ for p-type. The associated band diagrams are shown in Figure 2.16. For the n-type case, the Fermi levels are equalized by transferring electrons from the metal to the semiconductor. There is thus no depletion at the junction, and because of the charge transfer the conduction band minimum is lowered. There is then only a small barrier to further electron flow from metal to semiconductor, easily overcome by an external bias. A similar situation occurs for the contact to the p-type material, where holes readily flow from the metal to the semiconductor.

In the above mentioned cases thermionic emission is again the cause of current flow. The specific contact resistance R_{sc} is defined as

$$R_{sc} = \left[\frac{\partial J}{\partial V} \right]_{V=0}^{-1} \tag{2.110}$$

which, from (2.101), becomes

$$R_{sc} = \frac{k}{e\mathcal{A}^{**}T} \exp\left(\frac{e\phi_{bn}}{kT} \right). \tag{2.111}$$

It is clear from Figures 2.16(b) and (d) that the barrier height needs to be as low as possible. For most III–V semiconductors, as we shall see in section 9.2.9, the bending of the bands at the surface is not as great as would be preferred because of the problem of surface state pinning. Thermionic emission is thus seldom exploited, and an alternative current mechanism, tunnelling, is used. As we saw in section 2.1.8 and Figure 2.11(a), a heavily doped semiconductor will make a narrow barrier width. Ohmic contacts can thus be formed by introducing a heavily doped region close to the semiconductor surface, as shown in Figure 2.17. There is then a finite probability that electrons can tunnel across the narrow barrier and into the main part of the metal or semiconductor. From a consideration of the properties of a tunnel diode [6] it can be shown that the tunnelling current I is given approximately by

$$I = \exp\left[-2w \left(\frac{2m_e^*(e\phi_{bn} - eV)}{\hbar^2} \right)^{1/2} \right]. \tag{2.112}$$

Equation (2.27) gives a value for the depletion layer width w by approximating the system to a p$^+$n junction:

$$w = \left(\frac{2(V_{bi} - V)\epsilon\epsilon_0}{eN_D} \right)^{1/2}$$

$$\simeq \left(\frac{2(\phi_{bn} - V)\epsilon\epsilon_0}{eN_D} \right)^{1/2} \tag{2.113}$$

for a heavily doped junction with V_n small, i.e. $\phi_{bn} \simeq V_{bi}$. Substituting (2.113) in (2.112) gives

$$I = \exp\left[-\frac{2}{\hbar} \left(\frac{m_e^*\epsilon\epsilon_0}{N_D} \right)^{1/2} (\phi_{bn} - V) \right]. \tag{2.114}$$

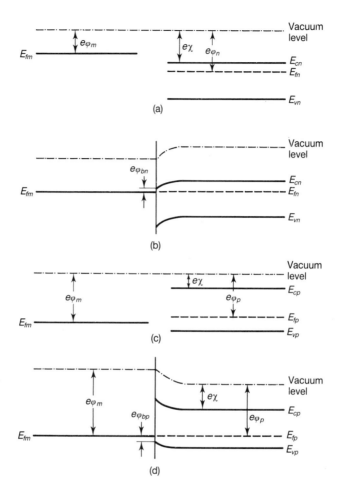

Figure 2.16 The formation of metal–semiconductor ohmic contacts. (a) Metal and n-type semiconductor before contact, (b) in equilibrium after contact. (c) Metal and p-type semiconductor before contact, (d) in equilibrium after contact.

From (2.110) and (2.114)

$$R_{sc} = \exp\left[\frac{2}{\hbar}\left(\frac{m_e^* \epsilon \epsilon_0}{N_D}\right)^{1/2} \phi_{bn}\right],$$ (2.115)

showing that for a tunnelling contact the specific contact resistance depends strongly on the barrier height and doping density, i.e. low barrier heights and high doping concentrations must both be used to make a successful ohmic contact.

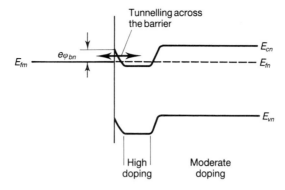

Figure 2.17 The tunnelling process in a metal–n-type semiconductor contact.

2.2.4 Measurement of contact resistance

There are several ways of doing this, the best method being dependent on the contact geometry (size, shape and planarity) and the metal and semiconductor material parameters. A description of a common technique, the transmission line, is given here, and for a fuller review of all the techniques the reader is referred to [7].

A series of identically sized ohmic contacts are spaced on the surface of a semiconductor by ever increasing distance, as shown in Figure 2.18(a). The area around the contact pattern is isolated, $w_1 \simeq w_2$ and $w_1 \gg l$. The use of these restrictions and a semi-insulating substrate under the contact pattern (with $w_1 \gg z$, the thickness of the conducting part of the semiconductor) effectively confines current flow to the x-dimension only. A voltage is applied across two adjacent contacts. The current can be measured, giving a value for the total resistance R in the circuit. This is repeated for all adjacent contacts, leading to a specific value of R for each value of l. The contact arrangement of Figure 2.18(b) has an equivalent circuit as shown in Figure 2.18(c). If the metal used for the ohmic contact is highly conductive, all current flow between adjacent contacts will occur at the contact edges, irrespective of where the contact probes are placed. This happens very rarely, as most good ohmic contacts are formed with poorly conducting metals. The use of another metal of good conductivity on top of the ohmic metal alleviates this problem. Thus for any pair of contacts, R can be simplified to be the sum of the probe contacts resistances R_p, the ohmic contact resistances R_c and the sheet resistance R_s in the region (Figure 2.18(d)). Thus

$$ R = 2R_p + 2R_c + \frac{R_s l}{w} . \tag{2.116}$$

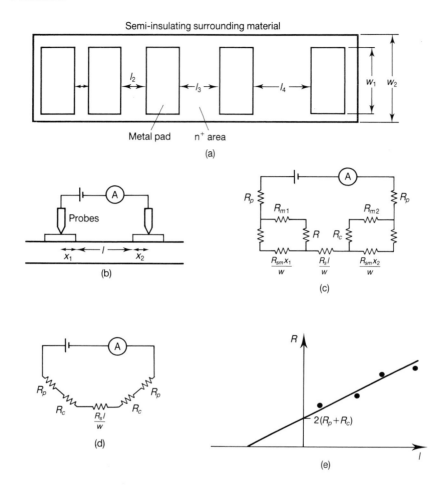

Figure 2.18 Contact resistance measured by the transmission line method. (a) Contact pattern design. (b) Probing arrangement. (c) Equivalent circuit. (d) Simplified equivalent circuit. (e) Typical plot.

A plot of R vs l will give a graph as in Figure 2.18(e), which has a slope R_s/w and

$$R = 2(R_p + R_c) \tag{2.117}$$

when $l = 0$. $2R_p$ can be found by measuring the resistance through the circuit when the two probes are touched together. Subtracting this figure from (2.117) gives a value for R_c, the contact resistance. Any figure quoted is usually normalized to a contact width w_1, e.g. $R_c = 2\,\Omega$ for $w_1 = 0.1\,\mathrm{mm}$ becomes $R_c = 0.2\,\Omega\,\mathrm{mm}$. The relationship between contact resistance R_c and specific contact resistance R_{sc}

is given by

$$R_c = \left(\frac{R_{sc}R_s}{w}\right)^{1/2} \tag{2.118}$$

if we make the assumption that the sheet resistance of the semiconductor under the contact area is identical to that between the contacts, i.e. $R_{sm} = R_s$ in Figure 2.18(c).

2.3 Problems

1. Sketch the distribution of electric field E across an abrupt pn junction, assuming that one side is far more heavily doped than the other. Compare it to the case of a junction where the doping densities are equal.

2. Show how the doping density on both sides of the type of junction in problem 1, called a p^+n junction, can be obtained from the dependence of built-in potential V_{bi} on depletion region width w.

3. Consider a p^+n junction in silicon, in equilibrium with a p-side doping density of 10^{17} acceptors cm^{-3} and on the n-side 10^{15} donors cm^{-3}. Calculate the room temperature values of:

    (i) built-in voltage V_{bi},

    (ii) depletion region width,

    (iii) the part of V_{bi} dropped on the p-side of the depletion region,

    (iv) the hole carrier concentration at the metallurgical junction between the n and p semiconductors.

    Hence calculate the hole drift current density at the metallurgical junction and prove that the diffusion current density has equal magnitude. Discuss possible heating effects in the pn junction as a result of these current densities. Use the following data for silicon: $n_i = 1.45 \times 10^{10}$ cm^{-3}, $\epsilon = 11.9$ and $\mu_p = 200$ cm^2/Vs at 10^{17} acceptors cm^{-3}.

4. Explain how the effect of applied bias on capacitance can be used to measure the doping concentrations within a semiconductor. Give an additional example of this bias–capacitance relationship.

5. Consider a pn junction under forward bias. Illustrate how the electron current J_n and the hole current J_p vary as a function of distance, from the p-type semiconductor through the depletion region to the n-type. Carefully explain all the important features of this diagram, and use it to justify why the total current J on forward bias is the sum of J_n at the p-edge of the depletion region and J_p at the n-edge.

6. The nature of the Fermi level in the depletion region of a biased pn junction has been deliberately left out of all diagrams. Considering that such a device

is in a non-equilibrium state, propose arguments that illustrate the form that E_f takes under these conditions.

7. Consider a particular pn junction with p- and n-side doping of $N_A = 5 \times 10^{17}$ cm^{-3} and $N_D = 5 \times 10^{15}$ cm^{-3} respectively. Calculate the room temperature minority carrier concentrations at the edges of the depletion layer for an applied forward bias of 0.55 V. Hence estimate the ratio of the drift currents on the n-side of the depletion layer.

8. For the same diode as in problem 7, calculate the value of applied bias necessary to give a forward current of 2 mA. Assume that for this diode the cross-sectional area is 0.03 cm^2, $\tau_n = \tau_p = 1\,\mu s$, and at these doping densities μ_n on the p-side $= 300$ cm^2/Vs and μ_p on the n-side $= 600$ cm^2/Vs.

9. Consider the reverse bias characteristics of the same diode as problem 7. Calculate the reverse saturation electron and hole current components, and hence compare the total reverse current with that obtained for a forward bias of 0.8 V.

10. Compare the roles of majority and minority carriers in pn junctions with their roles in Schottky junctions. Hence explain why Schottky diodes are faster switching devices than pn junctions.

11. Given that ϕ_{bn} for a W–n-type Si contact has a value of 0.66 V, calculate the contact potential, depletion region width and maximum electric field strength if the silicon doping density is 10^{17} cm^{-3}.

12. Consider two diodes of the same cross-sectional area of 0.02 cm^2. One diode is a pn junction, with n- and p-side doping of $N_D = 3 \times 10^{16}$ cm^{-3} and $N_A = 5 \times 10^{18}$ cm^{-3} respectively, and a minority carrier lifetime $\tau_p = 1\,\mu s$. The other is the Schottky diode of problem 11. Assuming that the diodes are both at 300 K, and the effective Richardson constant $\mathcal{A}^{**}$ has a value of 110 A K^{-2} cm^{-2},

   (i) calculate the current in both diodes for a forward bias of 0.3 V,

   (ii) what bias is needed on the pn junction diode to make it equal to that of the Schottky diode at 0.3 V?

13. The following measurements were taken of the forward characteristics of a Au–GaAs Schottky diode; 0.43 nA at 0.2 V, 9.5 nA at 0.3 V, 210 nA at 0.4V and 4600 nA at 0.5 V.

   (i) From a suitable graph calculate the room temperature ideality factor n at 300 K. Also calculate the barrier height ϕ_{bn}, assuming that the gold contact is a rectangle of $1 \times 100\,\mu m$.

   (ii) Show that the minority carrier current in such a diode is negligible compared to that of the majority carriers, for a semiconductor doping density $N_D = 10^{16}$ cm^{-3}.

   Use the following data for GaAs: $\mathcal{A}^{**} = 8.1$ A K^{-2} cm^{-2}, $n_i = 1.8 \times 10^6$ cm^{-3} at 300 K, and, at $N_D = 10^{16}$ cm^{-3}, $D_p = 10$ cm^2 s^{-1} and $L_p = 1.0 \times 10^{-4}$ cm.

14. Calculate the maximum dopant concentration required to give an ohmic contact between a metal of work function $\phi_m = 3.8$ eV and GaAs, with a band gap $E_g = 1.42$ eV and an electron affinity $\chi = 3.58$ eV.

2.4 References

1. A Bar-Lev, *Semiconductors and Electronic Devices*, 2nd. ed., Prentice-Hall International, 1984, p. 100.
2. R H Kingston, 'Switching Time in Junction Diodes and Junction Transistors', *Proc. IRE* **42**, 829 (1954).
3. B G Streetman, *Solid State Electronic Devices*, 2nd ed., Prentice-Hall International, 1980, p. 166.
4. See [3], p. 42.
5. D L Pulfrey and N G Tarr, *Introduction to Microelectronic Devices*, Prentice-Hall International, 1989, p. 277.
6. S M Sze, *Semiconductor Devices – Physics and Technology*, Wiley, 1985, p. 224.
7. R E Williams, *Gallium Arsenide Processing Techniques*, Artech House, 1984, p. 241.

3

Light emitting diodes

The light emitting diode or LED is now a familiar item, but it is worth remembering important dates in the development and application of these devices. Silicon carbide was the first material noted to emit 'cold' light – the term 'cold' is used to differentiate the emission process from black body radiation, which is attributed to the material heating up when a current passes. It was not until 1940, sixteen years later, that the light emitting region was identified as a pn junction [1]. Work in the early 1950s reported light emission from several materials using point contact metal–semiconductor diodes: GaP [2], GaAs, GaSb, InP [3] and Ge and Si [4] – perhaps surprisingly as we shall see later on in this chapter. It was several years later before material quality improved to the point of being able to reliably produce pn junctions, especially in compound semiconductors – and this step was necessary before LEDs could be made useful, as a metal, if in the form of a blanket contact covering all of the semiconductor surface, would absorb most of the light being emitted or, if a point contact, would lead to too low a light output. The coincidence of reasonable yields from both integrated circuit and visible (red) LED manufacture in the early 1970s saw the appearance of digital watches and elementary hand-held calculators with LED displays. Within a short space of time device yields improved through a greater understanding of contamination and the need for purity, leading to dramatic reductions in price. LED displays were, and still are, power hungry, and for a battery powered device this is an important consideration. The maturity of low power liquid crystal displays (LCDs) in the mid-1970s saw the virtual disappearance of LED watches and calculators by the end of the decade.

If that had been the only market LEDs would no longer be made today. But obviously this is not the case: an LED display is much in demand where clarity is more important than power consumption, LEDs are used as indicators in place of incandescent bulbs, they are often used as the light source in a 'laser' printer and, of greatest interest to us here, LEDs are widely used in fiber optic based communication systems.

The choice of material dictates the colour of the emitted light. Obviously for displays and indicators visible LEDs are needed, whereas, for fiber optic communication, advantage needs to be taken of low loss and low dispersion windows in the fiber, and the availability of suitable detectors. Early LEDs for this application operated at around $0.85\,\mu$m, in the near infra-red, because the technology was available to make emitters and detectors at this wavelength. However this is not an ideal wavelength for fiber-based communication, because the minimum attenuation of a glass fiber is typically at $1.55\,\mu$m (Figure 3.1), and for zero material dispersion $1.3\,\mu$m is chosen [5].

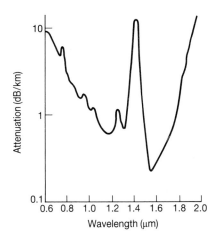

Figure 3.1 Attenuation characteristic for a typical optical fiber.

This chapter is intended to give an introduction to the properties and operating characteristics of LEDs, as well as show how they are driven and the future use of these devices which dictates the direction of current research. There are several texts available (e.g. [6]–[8]) that are devoted solely, or largely, to the LED for the reader needing a more advanced treatment.

3.1 Recombination

The light emitting process which forms the operation of an LED is, in its simplest terms, a variation on the theme of luminescence, where a material emits cold light under the influence of various stimuli. For a modern LED, it is the junction depletion region of a pn semiconductor structure that emits light when a forward biased current passes through the device, a process known as injection or junction electroluminescence. This is different from 'ordinary' electroluminescence (the Destriau effect) in that the latter involves light emitted from bulk material when a high voltage is applied across it; injection electroluminescence involves low voltages across a junction. How light is emitted from an LED by the various recombination mechanisms in the depletion region is now discussed.

3.1.1   Spontaneous emission

In section 2.1 we introduced the concept of a pn junction. We saw how charge transport mechanisms dictated current flow under forward or reverse bias conditions, and introduced the terms depletion region and its associated width and capacitance. We have also come across direct and indirect semiconductors (section 1.2.1), carrier lifetime (section 1.3.6) and diffusion length (section 1.4.3). All are important considerations in the basic understanding of spontaneous emission. The various recombination mechanisms are now discussed.

3.1.1.1   Band to band recombination

Under forward bias (Figure 3.2) electrons are injected from the n-side and holes from the p-side of a pn junction. The built-in potential of the junction is lowered by an amount equal to the applied potential V, and the injected carriers can pass across the junction into the region of opposite conductivity where they become excess minority carriers. For an LED the aim is to get the excess carriers to recombine quickly, i.e. a short minority carrier lifetime and diffusion length are required. The recombination process shown in Figure 3.2 produces a photon with energy $h\nu$ nearly equal to the band gap – it actually is given by

$$h\nu = E_g + kT \tag{3.1}$$

because if the expression inside the integral of (1.6) is differentiated, it leads to an equation for n_{max} in terms of E, i.e. the most probable energy an electron in the conduction band can have, which is $E_c + kT/2$. Similarly the most probable energy of a hole is $E_v - kT/2$. For most practical purposes we can ignore the kT term and leave it as

$$h\nu = E_g. \tag{3.2}$$

Example 3.1

Calculate the photon wavelength associated with the band gap of GaAs (1.42eV) at room temperature.

Solution: from (3.2)

$$\lambda = \frac{hc}{1.42 \times e} = 870\,\text{nm}. \tag{3.3}$$

In terms of an E–k diagram, the band to band transition is as shown in Figure 3.3. For a direct gap semiconductor (Figure 3.3(a)) no change in crystal momentum is involved, and so the transition is characterized by a high probability and short minority carrier lifetime. An indirect semiconductor, such as represented by Figure 3.3(b), must involve at least one phonon in the recombination process to conserve momentum (the term $\pm E_p$ should be added to (3.2); although E_p is generally small, around 0.01 eV, its effect obviously becomes significant for a very small band gap semiconductor). The direct transition involves just two particles, electron and hole; the indirect transition involves at least three. Thus the latter has a much lower probability of occurrence, characterized by the recombination rate term B in (1.23). Table 3.1 [9] lists the value of B for commonly used direct and indirect semiconductors. From this it can be seen why indirect materials including silicon make poor LEDs: the recombination rate is too low.

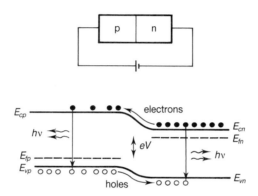

Figure 3.2 The pn junction under forward bias showing injection electroluminescence.

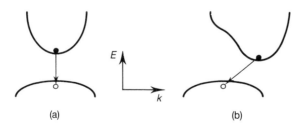

Figure 3.3 (a) Direct, and (b) indirect transitions between the conduction and valence bands.

Semiconductor	Recombination constant B (cm^3 s^{-1}) at or near room temperature
Si	1.79×10^{-15}
Ge	5.25×10^{-14}
GaP	5.37×10^{-14}
GaAs	7.21×10^{-10}
GaSb	2.39×10^{-10}
InP	1.26×10^{-9}
InAs	8.50×10^{-11}
InSb	4.58×10^{-11}

Table 3.1 Recombination constant for various common semiconductors.

We have only considered one type of transition, however, and the other mechanisms are now discussed which can lead to some efficient LEDs made from indirect starting material.

3.1.2   Other dopant centres

A donor state contributes electrons to the conduction band, and so clearly such a state can also act to receive conduction band electrons. The emitted energy would be quite small, however, and probably in the form of phonons. Such a level only becomes useful if the electron subsequently recombines with a valence band hole, as in Figure 3.4(a). A similar situation applies to holes (Figure 3.4(b)) and transitions between a donor and an acceptor state (Figure 3.4(c)) – for the latter case it must be remembered that the two states must be close together in the lattice, or the transition is unlikely to occur because of the large number of phonons that would need to be involved.

The case of GaAs doped with silicon is interesting. Silicon in this material acts as an amphoteric dopant, i.e. depending on process conditions it can lead to n- or p-type. In the junction region in a GaAs:Si pn diode, the random distribution of the ionized impurities will shift the relative positions of the valence and conduction bands (up and down respectively). This effectively shrinks the band gap, and the resultant emission from the junction is at 1.31 eV (940 nm), not, as might be expected from a consideration of the bulk value of the band gap, 1.42 eV (870 nm) [10].

3.1.3   Isoelectronic centres

In section 1.3.4 we introduced the idea of external doping of a semiconductor. We saw that introducing an atom from a different group in the periodic table to the host atoms introduced donor or acceptor states in the forbidden band. For example, gallium (group III) is an acceptor and arsenic (group V) is a donor in silicon (group IV). If, however, we dope with an element from the same group in the periodic table a different type of state is created. An important example of this is GaP (III–V) doped with nitrogen (group V). In this case nitrogen doesn't introduce either an acceptor or donor state because it has the same number of outer shell electrons as phosphorus (hence the term isoelectronic). It therefore doesn't contribute to conduction, but because it is a different atom to the host it introduces a shallow level below the conduction band which localizes an electron. This subsequently attracts a hole to form a bound exciton, which recombines radiatively to give green emission of 50 meV less energy than the band gap.

Another interpretation of the GaP:N system can be found using Heisenberg's Uncertainty Principle. One representation of this equation is

$$\Delta p \, \Delta x \geq \hbar \qquad\qquad (3.4)$$

where p is momentum and x is position. Because the position of a localized state due to any nitrogen atom is well known (each one could in theory be identified), then Δx is small. If so, Δp is large. The k in an E–k diagram is just a representation of crystal momentum, and so a large uncertainty in p will give a similar uncertainty associated with k for a nitrogen level. This means that the wave function of the level spreads out in k-space, and has a finite value directly above the top of the valence band. An electron dropping from the conduction band to the nitrogen level has a finite probability of appearing directly above the top of the valence band, as in Figure 3.4(d). Thus the indirect semiconductor looks like a direct gap material. This is an example of efficient LED action from an indirect gap semiconductor; doping GaP with zinc and oxygen is similarly successful.

3.1.4   Non-radiative recombination

This is essentially an electron losing energy by emitting phonons rather than photons. An example is the initial transition from conduction band to donor level as in Figure 3.4(a). Other non-radiative centres occur within the forbidden band which capture electrons via phonon emission: examples include crystal lattice defects and deep level impurities. An electron captured by one of these centres can then recombine with a valence band hole, again with the emission of phonons. Thus via at least two transitions an electron has fallen from the conduction band to the valence band, but all the released energy has been dissipated in the host material as vibrational energy, i.e. heat.

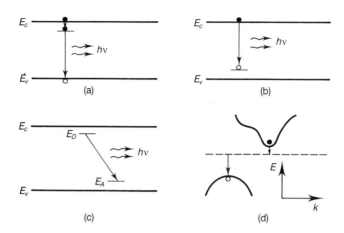

Figure 3.4 Recombination at (a) donor centre, and (b) acceptor centre. (c) Donor to acceptor recombination. (d) *E–k* diagram of an isoelectronic centre.

3.2   Output spectrum

The choice of LED is determined by its particular application; obviously visible of a particular colour for display purposes, and infra-red for optical communication because of the fiber characteristics as shown in Figure 3.1. Other applications such as optocouplers, or as light sources in some 'laser' printers are not particularly colour dependent; ease of manufacture and high power output respectively are the major considerations for these devices.

3.2.1   Choice of semiconductor

The eye's response to electromagnetic radiation in the 'visible' part of the spectrum is not constant [11]; for most people colour sensitivity peaks around 555 nm (2.23eV) – hence green LEDs appear brighter than others for the same power output. High efficiency red LEDs have been made, but blue devices still tend to be of low output.

Table 3.2 lists the common semiconductors used to produce light in the visible and infra-red parts of the spectrum. Cross-sections of the devices are given in section 3.5.1.

3.2.1.1   Infra-red

Most attention here is centred around devices operating at 0.8–0.95 μm, and 1.3 and 1.55 μm; these are the three areas of interest for optical communication. The

Material	Wavelength (nm)
InAsSbP/InAs	4200
InAs	3800
InGaSaP/GaSb	2000
GaSb	1800
$In_{1-x}Ga_xAs_{1-y}P_y$	1100–1600
$In_{0.53}Ga_{0.47}As$	1550
$In_{0.73}Ga_{0.27}As_{0.63}P_{0.37}$	1300
GaAs:Er, InP:Er	1540
Si:C	1300
GaAs:Yb, InP:Yb	1000
$Al_xGa_{1-x}As$:Si	650–940
GaAs:Si	940
$Al_{0.11}Ga_{0.89}As$:Si	830
$Al_{0.4}Ga_{0.6}As$:Si	650
$GaAs_{0.6}P_{0.4}$	660
$GaAs_{0.4}P_{0.6}$	620
$GaAs_{0.15}P_{0.85}$	590
$(Al_xGa_{1-x})_{0.5}In_{0.5}P$	655
GaP	690
GaP:N	550–570
GaN	340, 430, 590
SiC	400–460
BN	260, 310, 490

Table 3.2 Common III–V materials used to produce LEDs and their emission wavelengths.

former region is also used in many optocoupler devices (0.94 μm). Devices operating at 2 μm and above are used in more specialist applications such as impurity monitoring in gases or liquids; impurities can act as strong absorption centres for infra-red wavelengths and this can readily be monitored by a fall in received signal intensity. Because the bandgap is so narrow, cooling of the devices is necessary to narrow the spectral bandwidth – this can also shift the peak intensity wavelength.

A simple GaAs:Si pn junction usually suffices for 940 nm, but for shorter wavelengths a heterojunction (section 3.5.4) $Al_xGa_{1-x}As$/GaAs device is needed. One great advantage of this system is that both AlAs and GaAs have similar lattice constants (5.66 Å and 5.65 Å respectively) so that heterostructures with variable values of x can be grown without too much concern for lattice strain. This type of junction technology is now very mature, with the structures having been grown by a variety of epitaxial techniques from liquid phase epitaxy (LPE) through to more modern methods such as molecular beam epitaxy (MBE). Attention is now focussed on preparing these devices on Si substrates, using epitaxial techniques (see Chapter 8) to grow an initial seeding layer of GaAs on Si, on top of which is grown the diode structure, e.g. [12].

Lattice matching is however a problem for $In_{1-x}Ga_xAs_{1-y}P_y$ devices, and this is considered in more detail in section 4.2.5 when discussing semiconductor lasers. As with the GaAs/AlGaAs system, the growth of InGaAsP on silicon substrates has received attention; an example is [13], where an InGaAsP/InP LED emitting at 1.15 μm was made.

More recent studies have suggested that emission at 1.3 μm and 1.54 μm can be obtained from simpler materials. By taking a carbon rich silicon wafer and selectively implanting opposite sides a pn junction can be obtained. If the wafer is then irradiated with a controlled amount of high energy electrons optically active Si–C complexes occur which give a much stronger luminescent output than unirradiated silicon [14]. Rare earth doping of fibers has received much attention in order to generate a fiber laser, but it also has been used to produce infra-red luminescence peaks in GaAs. Besides the characteristic broad spectrum centred around 0.9 μm, Er^+ doping in GaAs produces an output peak at 1.54 μm [15]. Similar results can be seen for InP and for Yb^+ doping [16] – output at 1.0 μm. The great problem with these structures is the low output level at room temperature; although luminescence can be readily observed at 77 K, Er^+ doped signals fall by a factor of around 20 in raising the diode to room temperature, whilst Yb^+ signals disappear altogether.

3.2.1.2   Red

From a display point of view these are the most familiar of LEDs. A standard red LED will have an emission wavelength of 660 nm, and consists of a pn junction of $GaAs_{0.6}P_{0.4}$ grown on a GaAs substrate. The n doping is produced using tellurium in the growth and the p-region produced by zinc diffusion.

690 nm radiation can be produced from a GaP:ZnO/GaP:Te pn junction grown on a GaP substrate. These devices are brighter than standard LEDs because the substrate and epitaxial layers are transparent to the 690 nm radiation (see section 3.3.4 on coupling parameters and external efficiency). However, because the eye is less sensitive to this radiation such devices are not particularly advantageous.

High brightness LEDs based on $Al_{0.4}Ga_{0.6}As:Zn/Al_{0.7}Ga_{0.3}As:Te$ heterostructures on a GaAs substrate are becoming increasingly popular. They can be up to ten times as bright as a standard LED, and use the GaAs/AlGaAs lattice system where minimal mismatching occurs.

Increasingly, the use of polymer optical fibers is becoming attractive to local area networks (LANs). These materials have two transmission windows; one at 570 nm in the green and the other at 655 nm in the red. Because a device made using an $Al_{0.4}Ga_{0.6}As/Al_{0.3}Ga_{0.7}As$ junction relies on indirect transitions, some speed limitations may affect the incorporation of these types of LEDs in a LAN system. For this reason a diode based on an $(Al_xGa_{1-x})_{0.5}In_{0.5}P$ lattice matched to GaAs (with x variable within the structure) has attracted a lot of interest in this type of application [17].

As will be shown later in section 3.3.3 crystalline silicon makes a poor light emitter. However, devices based on a junction of indium tin oxide (ITO)/porous silicon/p-type silicon have demonstrated electroluminescence in the 0.6–0.9 μm region [18, 19]. Porous silicon has a structure exactly as it sounds, where large volumes of a crystal are etched away leaving a sponge-like structure to the remaining material. If the pore size is large enough, the remaining silicon is small enough (~ 50 Å across, several microns long) for the structure to resemble a series of free standing quantum wires (see section 4.5 on quantum well lasers). Quantum confinement effects on band structure can then be exploited, which are thought to be the mechanism behind a widening of the band gap into the visible region. Because porous silicon has a high resistivity, most of the applied bias is dropped across this region of the junction. Electrons and holes are injected into the porous silicon from the ITO and p-type silicon respectively by tunnelling. Recombination, and hence light emission, then occurs. The quantization of the conduction and valence bands in the porous silicon leads to a direct recombination process, despite the indirect nature of bulk silicon.

3.2.1.3 *Orange and yellow*

As can be seen from Table 3.2, the difference between producing 620 nm orange or 590 nm yellow radiation using a $GaAs_{1-y}P_y$ system is to use $y = 0.6$ and $y = 0.85$ for the former and latter respectively. A pn junction is formed by initially growing an n-layer on a GaP substrate (used instead of the GaAs for red LEDs because the values of y chosen here make lattice matching easier for GaP). Both yellow and orange LEDS are made from indirect gap material, and so the material is additionally doped with nitrogen to form an isoelectronic centre for increased efficiency (see section 3.1.3). A p-region is then formed by zinc diffusion. Yellow LEDs have been made in SiC (the first such device) from the 6H hexagonal phase – nitrogen doping provides n conduction, while B or B/Al diffusion gives a p-region. In fact, by using these same dopants with the different crystal structures (polytypes) of silicon carbide, different colour LEDs can be made. This is shown in Figure 3.5(a) [20]. The fact that there is the same energy difference between band gap and peak intensity wavelength implies that the same recombination mechanism occurs in all polytypes, despite the different colours. The spectra of SiC are complicated even further by considering Figure 3.5(b), which shows the main recombination centres in the 6H phase [21].

SiC is a difficult material both to grow and to work with (it is extremely hard), and its use in all but blue LEDs had temporarily disappeared until the late 1980s.

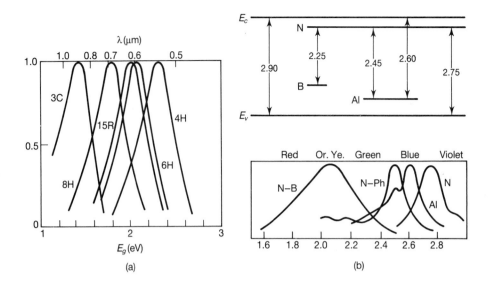

Figure 3.5 (a) Emission characteristics of the various polytypes of SiC (©AIME: reproduced by kind permission). (b) Main recombination centres in the 6H phase of SiC (©Pergamon Press Ltd.: W von Munch, W Kurzinger and I Pfaffeneder, 'Silicon Carbide Light Emitting Diodes with Epitaxial Junctions', *Solid State Electron.* **19**, 871 (1976), reproduced by kind permission).

However, work on amorphous SiC:H thin film LEDs (TFLEDs) based on a PIN structure has attracted interest as an alternative to liquid crystal devices (LCDs) for flat panel displays [22]; the ability to tune the display colour using integrated multilayer structures is a distinct advantage of TFLEDs.

3.2.1.4   Green

Green is produced from a pn junction in GaP. As mentioned in section 3.1.2 nitrogen doping in the n-region forms an isoelectronic centre to increase the emission efficiency, while a subsequent diffusion of zinc creates a p-zone. Such a device has an emission wavelength peak intensity at 565–570 nm, where it nearly coincides with the eye's maximum sensitivity; this means that they appear very bright. The peak emission and intensity can vary with the nitrogen doping level, as the latter dictates the number of junction region recombination centres (increasing doping means that the recombination occurs with increasing probability at lower energy, i.e. higher wavelength, nitrogen–pair centres). Nitrogen free diodes, emitting at 555 nm can also be made but with lower efficiency than the N doped diodes.

3.2.1.5 Blue

As already mentioned and shown in Figure 3.5(b), Al- or N-doped SiC can produce blue LEDs. Suitable doping with both can not only produce blue emission, but also a pn junction as well. SiC is an indirect semiconductor and hence devices are of low efficiency, and radiative recombination only occurs via donors and acceptors not isoelectronic traps as in GaP:N, for instance.

Gallium nitride is another wide band gap semiconductor but it has been unable to be produced as a bulk single crystal (due partly to a high, and unknown, melting point). The material can be deposited epitaxially, e.g. by metalorganic vapour phase epitaxy (MOVPE), and is n-type in the undoped state. Zinc or magnesium doping are used to dope GaN p-type, but usually result in a high resistivity material. Until recently this inhibited the formation of blue LEDs in GaN. Devices in GaN have high forward voltages (5–10 V) and low forward currents (a few mA) compared to standard LEDs. However, MOVPE has been used [23] to grow n-type GaN and, using magnesium, dope it p-type. A subsequent low energy electron beam irradiation (LEEBI) is then used to make the p-material low resistivity. Forward voltages are as low as 3 V, with the light emission peaking in the ultra violet at 3.35 eV (370 nm) and with a broad violet peak centred at 2.9 eV (427 nm). The research into blue LEDs is stimulated by the need for a blue laser; optical storage devices need as low a wavelength as possible so that diffraction limiting effects on information packing density can be minimized. Now that a pn LED can be formed in GaN, it is possible to develop the material to form a blue semiconductor laser; this material has already been photopumped by a HeCd laser and shown stimulated emission (at 83 meV lower than the peak of spontaneous emission [24]).

Boron nitride has the highest band gap of all III–V semiconductors, 6.4 eV (194 nm). This is an extremely difficult material to grow and dope, but an LED in this material has been made [25]. Because of its high band gap it can operate at a temperature as high as 650 °C; broad band luminescence is observed, with peaks at 4.77 eV (260 nm), 4.00 eV (310 nm) and 2.53 eV (490 nm).

3.2.2 Spectral width

Although an LED has a peak spectral intensity at a wavelength given by

$$\lambda \;=\; \frac{hc}{E} \tag{3.5}$$

where E is the energy in joules of the photon associated with the recombination transition, a simple differentiation will show that there is a spread of wavelength $\Delta\lambda$ associated with a spread of energy ΔE:

$$\Delta\lambda \;=\; \frac{-1}{hc}\,\lambda^2\,\Delta E. \tag{3.6}$$

ΔE represents the spread of likely available energies of an electron/hole in a particular band/impurity state and is given by kT from (3.1). $\Delta\lambda$ on either side of the wavelength peak thus has a dependence on λ^2 and T. The spectral half-width of the intensity is given by $|2\Delta\lambda|$.

Example 3.2

Calculate the spectral half-width at room temperature of an infra-red LED of peak wavelength 850 nm.

Solution: from (3.6)

$$2\Delta\lambda = \frac{2 \times (8.5 \times 10^{-7})^2 \times 293 \times k}{hc} = 43\,\text{nm}. \tag{3.7}$$

Unfortunately the relationship given in (3.6) does not quite work in practice, and experimental data show that

$$\Delta\lambda = \frac{Nk}{hc}\lambda^2 T, \tag{3.8}$$

where the term N (ideally $= 1$) is a factor varying between 0.75 and 1.75, depending on the material involved [26] and the doping density [27]; for instance $\Delta\lambda$ from a InGaAsP/InP diode is greater than that from an AlGaAs/GaAs diode of the same wavelength, and increasing the doping density in InGaAsP/InP diodes increases $\Delta\lambda$. This observation is also dependent on which is the 'p' and which is the 'n' of InGaAsP/InP [28]. The exact origins of these phenomena are complex and relate to defects, compositional deviation at interfaces and band tail effects at high doping densities. Output spectra of LEDs are further complicated by the appearance of emissions at wavelengths other than the peak; there can be several recombination centres in a LED junction other than the dominant one.

3.3   Operating parameters

3.3.1   Forward characteristics

We saw in section 2.1.4 how the $I-V$ relationship of a forward biased diode is the sum of two terms, one due to diffusion current and the other to generation–recombination current within the depletion region. The total current density is given by (2.68) and shown in Figure 2.7.

For an LED, the diffusion current will lead to efficient injection of majority carriers to the opposite side of the junction. There they will recombine as excess minority carriers to give an emission characteristic of transitions already described previously in this chapter. Generation–recombination current, however, is mostly non-radiative for two reasons:

(i) The concentrations n and p in the depletion region are greater than equilibrium, and so recombination dominates generation,

(ii) most recombination in the depletion region occurs via traps, which are at their most efficient in this region where their energy value is at the centre point of the band gap.

An optimized LED should have a minimum value of J_R, obtained by decreasing the number of traps, which usually means improving the material quality. Surface recombination can be minimized by making the device's junction as far into the bulk of the material as possible.

Also to be considered in designing a device is the injection ratio, defined as electron current divided by hole current. Equation (2.40) shows that diffusion current is made up of two terms. Because of the dependence of diffusivity D on mobility μ, carriers of high mobility, usually electrons, will produce a greater contribution to diffusion current than those of lower mobility. Where $\mu_e > \mu_h$, therefore, electron injection is more efficient and devices should be doped to give an n$^+$p junction. However, fabrication procedures (section 3.5) dictate that this is not always possible, such as when p-type substrates are not available.

3.3.2   Temperature dependence

There is a T term in both of the exponentials of (2.68), giving an obvious temperature dependence of J. But the terms J_s and J_R are also temperature sensitive. Assuming complete ionization, we can see from (1.9) and (2.41) that

$$J_s = en_i^2 \left[\frac{D_p}{L_p N_D} + \frac{D_n}{L_n N_A} \right], \tag{3.9}$$

and from (1.10) for n_i and (1.55) and (1.56) for D_n and D_p respectively, the temperature dependence of J_s can be seen (the situation is further complicated by D_n and D_p having temperature dependent mobility terms). So the temperature sensitivity of J_s is largely dependent on that of n_i^2. However, as (2.66) shows, J_R has a temperature dependence given by the n_i term. So, for a given change in operating temperature, there will be a much greater change in J_s than in J_R. This is shown in Figure 3.6, which also shows that, in the normal operating area of the diode, the forward bias needed to produce a given current density decreases with increasing temperature.

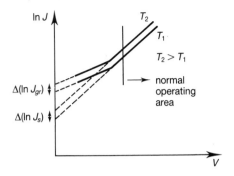

Figure 3.6 The temperature dependence of the $I-V$ characteristic of a pn diode.

3.3.3 Internal efficiency

This can be quantified in several ways, although the definition is always the same; it is the ratio of the number of photons created in the junction region to the number of electron–hole pairs in that region. Thus this efficiency η_i can be expressed in terms of the relative recombination rates for radiative (r_r) and non-radiative transitions (r_{nr}). If, for both transitions,

$$\Delta r \;=\; r - r_0 \tag{3.10}$$

where r_0 represents a thermal equilibrium value, and r represents an operating recombination rate, then

$$\eta_i \;=\; \frac{\Delta r_r}{\Delta r_r + \Delta r_{nr}} \,. \tag{3.11}$$

The value of r is related to the change in equilibrium carrier concentration in the depletion region by (1.31)

$$\Delta r \;=\; \frac{\mathrm{d}p}{\mathrm{d}t} = \frac{p - p_0}{\tau} \tag{3.12}$$

for both r_r and r_{nr}, with a similar equation for the electron concentration. The negative sign has been removed from (1.31) because an operational LED has a greater recombination rate than a generation rate. From (3.11) and (3.12) η_i becomes

$$\eta_i \;=\; \frac{\tau_{nr}}{\tau_r + \tau_{nr}} \,. \tag{3.13}$$

Thus for a high internal efficiency $\tau_{nr} \gg \tau_r$, implying a device with a low concentration of trapping centres in the depletion region; this usually means that a material of a low defect density is needed.

Section 1.3.6 looked at the generation-recombination situation under one particular non-equilibrium condition, i.e. the absorption of photons in a semiconductor. A pn junction under forward bias is also a non-equilibrium case, and (1.23) can be suitably modified to give a value for Δr_r on the p-side of

$$\Delta r_r = B(n_0 + p_0 + \Delta n)\Delta n \qquad (3.14)$$

because, as said above, in this case the recombination rate is positive. From (3.12) and (3.14)

$$\tau_r = \frac{1}{B(n_0 + p_0 + \Delta n)}. \qquad (3.15)$$

For τ_r to be large, $n_0 = p_0 = n_i$ because this represents the minimum value of the product $n_0 + p_0$. Thus long lifetimes are obtained in intrinsic material – not much use for an LED, where (3.13) suggests that τ_r should be as small as possible. For material doped such that $p_0 \gg n_0$, then

$$\tau_r = \frac{1}{B\,N_A} \qquad (3.16)$$

for conditions of low injection ($\Delta n \ll p_0$), and for high injection currents

$$\tau_r = \frac{1}{B\,\Delta n}. \qquad (3.17)$$

Δn is in this case a function of position within the depletion region, and τ_r becomes difficult to quantify. For both (3.16) and (3.17), however, τ_r is a function of the recombination constant B, which tends to be many orders of magnitude higher for direct gap materials than for indirect ones, as shown in Table 3.1. From this, and (3.13) and (3.17), a direct gap material should show a greater internal efficiency than an indirect one. A good demonstration of this effect is shown in Figure 3.7, where the transition from the direct to indirect form of $GaAs_{1-y}P_y$ gives a drop in efficiency of more than two orders of magnitude [29].

Example 3.3

Calculate the recombination lifetime in GaAs and Si for a doping density of 5×10^{18} cm^{-3} on the n$^+$ side of an n$^+$p junction. Hence calculate the internal efficiency if the non-radiative lifetime of each diode is 2 ns.

Solution: from (3.16) and Table 3.1

$$\tau_r = \frac{1}{7.2 \times 10^{-10} \times 5 \times 10^{18}} = 278\,\text{ps} \quad \text{for GaAs,} \quad \text{and}$$

$$\tau_r = \frac{1}{1.8 \times 10^{-15} \times 5 \times 10^{18}} = 111\,\mu\text{s} \quad \text{for Si.} \qquad (3.18)$$

From (3.13)

$$\eta_i = \frac{2 \times 10^{-9}}{2 \times 10^{-9} + 2.78 \times 10^{-10}} = 0.88 \quad \text{for GaAs, and}$$

$$\eta_i = \frac{2 \times 10^{-9}}{2 \times 10^{-9} + 1.11 \times 10^{-4}} = 1.8 \times 10^{-5} \quad \text{for Si.} \tag{3.19}$$

It is then clear that crystalline silicon makes a very poor LED.

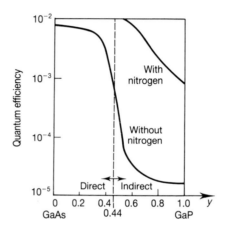

Figure 3.7 A comparison of the efficiencies of the direct and indirect forms of GaAs$_{1-y}$P$_y$ (©AIP: reproduced by kind permission).

The internal efficiency can also be expressed in terms of a power, as opposed to a quantum, efficiency by comparing the output power Φ emitted from the junction for a given input electrical power IV;

$$\eta_i = \frac{IV}{\Phi}. \tag{3.20}$$

Because in this case Φ is difficult to measure, (3.20) is more useful in its external efficiency form, where the output power can be readily calculated as in the next two sections.

3.3.4 Coupling characteristics and external efficiency

Once photons have been generated in the depletion region of an LED, they must be released to the outside world to be of any use. The external quantum efficiency

η_e is then given by the ratio of the power emitted by the surface of the LED to the input power. Consider Figure 3.8, which shows the various mechanisms by which a photon can be lost on its way from the junction to the emitting surface of the LED, using the case of GaAsP on a GaAs substrate as an example:

(i) absorption in the material. This can be at any one of several trapping centres and, for LEDs that rely on band to band recombination, by a similar process to band to band generation. The magnitude of this phenomenon is related to the absorption coefficient for a given photon wavelength, and the mechanisms are discussed in more detail in section 6.1.1. Absorption can be minimized by making the junction close to the emitting surface.

(ii) Absorption in the substrate area, where the band gap decreases with increasing depth. The use of a different substrate, such as GaP, will enable photons to be reflected off the bottom metal contact and hence increase their probability of escaping from the emitting surface.

(iii) Reflection at the surface. Because there is a refractive index mismatch at the semiconductor/air interface, photons incident at angles greater than the critical angle θ_c will be reflected back into the bulk semiconductor; in this case the semiconductor refractive index n_2 is ~ 3.45, leading to θ_c of 17°.

(iv) Transmission losses at the interface. These occur because the transmission coefficient from Fresnel's equations is given by

$$T \;=\; \frac{4n_1 n_2}{(n_1 + n_2)^2}\,,\tag{3.21}$$

where n_1 is the refractive index of the outside medium.

Combining (iii) and (iv), we can think of a cone of angle of incidence limited by θ_c, giving a distribution of emitted radiation into a 90° angle, i.e. a hemisphere. In solid angle terms, the fraction F_{sp} of photons emitted from the interface into the air, compared to those incident on the interface from the semiconductor is

$$F_{sp} \;=\; \frac{T\,\Omega_i}{\Omega_e}\tag{3.22}$$

where Ω_i and Ω_e are the incident and emitted solid angles respectively. The term F_{sp} is used to distinguish this particular transmission factor for spontaneous emission from that used in Chapter 4 for stimulated emission, F_{st}. From the definition of solid angle as

$$\Omega \;=\; 2\pi\,(1 - \cos\,\theta)\tag{3.23}$$

where θ is the semi-vertical angle subtended at the apex of a cone, F_{sp} is given by

$$F_{sp} \;=\; \frac{T\,(1 - \cos\theta_c)}{(1 - \cos 90°)}\,.\tag{3.24}$$

Example 3.4

Calculate the Fresnel transmission coefficient and hence the transmission factor for an LED of material refractive index 3.45.

Solution: from (3.21) and (3.24)

$$T = \frac{4 \times 3.45 \times 1}{(3.45 + 1)^2} = 0.70 \tag{3.25}$$

$$\text{and} \quad F_{sp} = \frac{T (1 - \cos 17°)}{(1 - \cos 90°)} \sim 0.03. \tag{3.26}$$

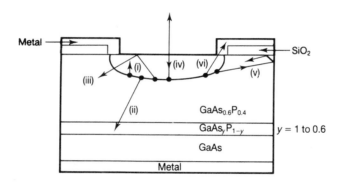

Figure 3.8 Mechanisms of photon loss within the bulk of an LED.

Clearly the reduction in internal reflection is a major issue. The use of materials of lower refractive index helps in increasing both T and θ_c. A non-planar hemispherical emitted surface can be formed, either in the LED material itself, or in an encapsulating material and is used to great effect in modern LEDs (see section 3.5). Etching of the emitting surface to produce a series of irregularities in the incident angle is also useful.

(v) Reflection at the top metal semiconductor interface.

(vi) Absorption in the top contact metal.

(v) and (vi) are minimized by having as small an area as possible of top metal contact, consistent with fabrication technology and the maximum current density able to be supported by the metal. All the factors (i) to (vi) are involved in making the external efficiency much less than the internal one, and section 3.5.5 looks at fabrication techniques aimed at increasing the external efficiency of LEDs.

An LED surface is a Lambertian emitter. Consider a plane material emitting light perpendicular to its surface with an intensity I_0. At an angle θ with the normal the intensity is a function of that angle (Figure 3.9). If this is so, then the intensity distribution is also a function of $\cos \theta$. In practice this dependence turns out to be a power law, and hence

$$I(\theta) \;=\; I_0 \cos^x \theta \qquad\qquad (3.27)$$

where x is a number. If $x = 0$, then $I(\theta) = I_0 =$ a constant, and the emitter is said to be isotropic. If $x = 1$, then $I(\theta) = I_0 \cos \theta$, and the emitter is said to be a perfect Lambertian. Often $x > 1$, and the drop in intensity with viewing angle is very pronounced, leading to the familiar uncertainty with reading an LED display at near grazing angles of incidence.

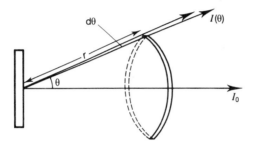

Figure 3.9 Emission from a plane surface.

To estimate the total intensity emitted from the material, we have to assess contributions for all angles of view ($0 \le \theta \le \pi/2$). This is done by taking a solid angle approach, and integrating the intensity emitted into each ring of plane angle $d\theta$. Such a ring is shown in Figure 3.9 and it has a radius of $r \sin \theta$ and width $r d\theta$. The surface area dA of such a ring is given by

$$dA \;=\; 2\pi r^2 \sin \theta \, d\theta \qquad\qquad (3.28)$$

giving a solid angle $d\Omega$ ($= dA/r^2$ as shown in Figure 3.10) subtended at $d\theta$ equal to

$$d\Omega \;=\; 2\pi \sin \theta \, d\theta . \qquad\qquad (3.29)$$

The power radiated into this solid angle is given by

$$I(\theta)d\Omega \;=\; I_0 \cos^x \theta d\Omega \qquad\qquad (3.30)$$

and obviously depends on the value of x. For an isotropic emitter ($x = 0$) the total intensity emitted, Φ, is given by

$$\Phi \;=\; \int_0^{\pi/2} I_0 2\pi \sin \theta \, d\theta. \qquad\qquad (3.31)$$

This readily reduces to

$$\Phi = 2\pi I_0. \tag{3.32}$$

For a perfect Lambertian emitter ($x = 1$), there is an additional $\cos\theta$ term in (3.32), leading to

$$\Phi = \pi I_0. \tag{3.33}$$

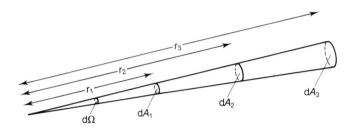

Figure 3.10 Solid angle geometry.

How an angular dependence comes about should readily be seen from discussions in this section. Why the dependence is a cosine function is discussed in section 9.2.4, where a similar function is derived for evaporation from a metal source; the mathematics of light emission from an LED surface are identical.

3.4 Drive circuitry

Whatever the values of the internal and external efficiencies of an LED, it is normally assumed that this is a constant independent of the current passing through the device. Thus a plot of forward current (related to the number of electrons) vs output power (related to the number of photons) for an ideal LED should be a straight line as in Figure 3.11. However, red LEDs show a fall in output power with current, as in Figure 3.11 [30]. This is due to the large current heating the device, specifically the junction region. As the temperature rises the injection efficiency improves, but the light generation efficiency decreases [31]. This usually results in a decrease in quantum efficiency, with a temperature coefficient of about $-1\%/^\circ$C. The various types of drive electronics to take account of this and to exploit the other features of LEDs are now described.

3.4.1 Basic operation

Besides Figure 3.11, electrical characteristics (Table 3.3) and the *I–V* curve (Figure 3.12(a)) need to be considered in devising drive electronics. Table 3.3 shows typical

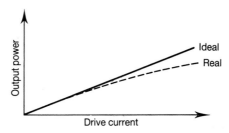

Figure 3.11 Output power vs drive current for an LED.

characteristics of both normal and high radiance LEDs, and Figure 3.12(a) shows typical $I-V$ characteristics of a visible LED. Only the blue LEDs have turn-on voltages out to 5 V – most colours need a voltage in the range 1.8–2.4 V, with infra-red diodes needing less ($\sim$ 1.3–1.5 V). As can be seen, the current is very sensitive to voltage fluctuations, and hence so is the light output from the LED. To limit the current through the device an in line series resistor can be used as in Figure 3.12(b). The light vs current characteristics (Figure 3.11) should be used to select an operating current, from which an operating forward voltage (Figure 3.12(a)) can be chosen. Given the nature of the power supply, the value of R can be readily calculated.

Example 3.5

If a 5 V supply is to be used to drive an LED requiring a forward voltage drop of 2.1 V to provide 30 mA, calculate the nearest preferred value for an appropriate series resistance.

Solution:

$$R = \frac{(5 - 2.1)}{30 \times 10^{-3}} = 97\,\Omega. \tag{3.34}$$

The nearest preferred value would be 100 Ω.

Switching the LED on or off can be obtained using the circuit of Figure 3.12(c). In this case the value of R_2 is determined by the current across the base-emitter junction; a value of 1–10 kΩ is typical of R_2.

Parameter	Normal LEDs	High radiance LEDs
Forward voltage drop (V)	1.3–5.0	1.3–5.0
Forward current (mA)	20–200	20–200
Ouput power (mW)	1–3	1–20
Rise time (10%–90%, ns)	5–50	2–20
Frequency response (–3 dB, MHz)	7–70	18–175
Non-linearity (%)	0.03–1	0.3–3
Operating temperature (°C)	–55 – +150	–40 – +90

Table 3.3 Some important operating characteristics of LEDs.

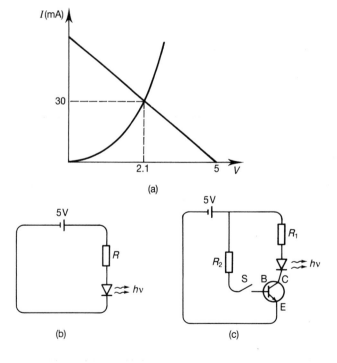

Figure 3.12 (a) Typical $I-V$ characteristic of an LED. (b) Use of a resistor as a current limiter. (c) Switching an LED.

3.4.2　Constant light output

As has been shown, the light output from an LED is dependent on the forward current, which in turn is dependent on the forward voltage. For the circuits shown in Figures 3.12(b) and (c), any variation in V will produce a corresponding variation in light output. Temperature effects that vary I for a given V will also affect the LED output.

A single constant current supply is shown in Figure 3.13(a). For a given LED current, the voltage drop across both the LED and resistor R_2 can readily be calculated. Suppose a small increase in $+V$ produces more current at the base T_1: then T_1 becomes more conducting and increases the current available to the base of T_2 and the resistor/LED combination. However, T_2 now becomes more conducting, and hence the base current of T_1 is reduced, leading to a restabilization of the current through the LED.

Example 3.6

In Figure 3.13(a), assume the LED current is 25 mA, the base current into T_1 is negligible by comparison, the current gain of T_1 is 125 and the minimum value of $+V$ is 5 V. Calculate the nearest preferred value of R_1.

Solution: all of the 25 mA through the LED goes through T_1 and R_2, and the forward voltage drop across R_2 if $R_2 = 50\,\Omega$ is 1.4 V. Assuming a base-emitter voltage drop of 0.7 V for T_1, and an LED forward voltage of 2 V, then the voltage dropped across R_1 is $(5 - 2 - 0.7 - 1.4) = 0.9$ V. For a current gain of 125 and a collector current of 25 mA, the base current of T_1 needs to be 0.2 mA. Therefore the value of R_1 should be 4500 Ω, or 4.7 kΩ for a preferred value.

A more sophisticated current control is shown in Figure 3.13(b), where the LED output is monitored by a photodiode, and the output from this fed into a differential amplifier to limit the effect of fluctuations in input voltage. A variation on this theme is often used for driving laser diodes, and is also quite useful in low frequency modulation circuits. However, at high drive frequencies phase shifts present a problem and other designs are usually adopted.

As already mentioned LED output decreases with increasing temperature. Thus any effort to temperature compensate an LED output would try to raise the LED current with rising ambient temperature. The way this is implemented depends on the drive circuit in question [32], but all exploit the temperature coefficient of the built-in voltage of a silicon pn junction (about 2.5 mV/°C). A simple example is shown in Figure 3.14. Assuming that the value of the collector–emitter voltage V_{CE} for the transistor is negligible when turned on, the current through the resistor

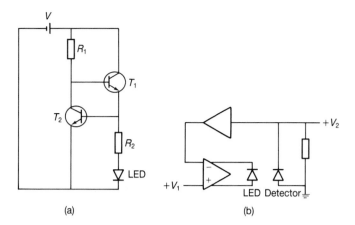

(a)   (b)

Figure 3.13 Two methods of constant current control for an LED (see text for details).

R, and hence through the LED, is given by

$$I_{LED} = \frac{V - V_{LED} - 3V_{bi}}{R} \tag{3.35}$$

where V_{bi} is the built-in voltage of any one of the pn junction diodes. For a given temperature change ΔT

$$\frac{\Delta I_{LED}}{\Delta T} = \frac{\Delta V}{R} - \frac{\Delta V_{LED}}{R} - \frac{3\Delta V_{bi}}{R}. \tag{3.36}$$

Example 3.7

Assuming that ΔV is a constant with T, and that $\Delta V_{LED} = \Delta V_{bi}$, calculate the value of resistance R for which the temperature coefficient of an LED is 1 mA/°C (take the temperature coefficient of V_{bi} in silicon to be -2.5 mV/°C).

Solution:

$$\frac{\Delta I_{LED}}{\Delta T} = -\frac{4\Delta V_{bi}}{R}$$

$$1\,\text{mA/°C} = \frac{10\,\text{mV/°C}}{R},$$

giving $R = 10\,\Omega$. \hfill (3.37)

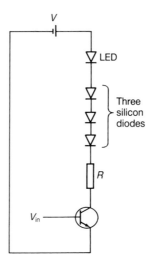

Figure 3.14 Temperature compensation circuit for an LED.

3.4.3 Equivalent circuit of an LED

In a simple analysis an LED is just a semiconductor junction as far as a consideration of circuit elements is concerned. As shown in Figure 3.15, the junction region itself has a resistance R_D (defined in (3.6)) and capacitance C_D (defined as dV/dI at the operating point) related to the additional free carriers stored in the region outside the diffusion layer in order to supply a current I, and a capacitance C_j, the junction capacitance as defined in (2.27). The elements R_p, R_n, L_p, L_n represent the resistances and inductances associated with the bulk material, metal–semiconductor contacts and leads from the n and p-type regions. A simple analysis ignores these latter terms and reduces the element to just R_D, C_D and C_j. C_j dominates C_D on reverse bias but on forward bias C_j is negligible in comparison and R_D is just a few ohms [33]. Thus the equivalent circuit, on forward bias, can be reduced to just two elements.

The flaw in assuming an LED to be just another pn junction is that it takes no account of the optical properties of the device. A model has been proposed [34] that takes account of this, and incorporates the effect of non-linearities in internal quantum efficiency and recombination rate, as well as including the parasitic resistance and capacitances mentioned above. Non-radiative recombination currents are also included.

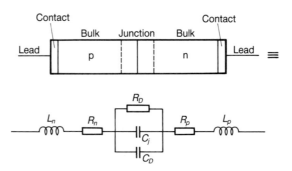

Figure 3.15 Equivalent circuit of an LED.

3.4.4   Modulation effects

Only in the cases of indicators or displays are LEDs driven in a d.c. mode; for most communication purposes modulation is employed, representing either a high frequency analog signal or a high bit rate digital one. Obviously an LED cannot respond instantaneously to a forward current because of the finite value of the recombination time. This is not important for low frequency signals, where the period is significantly greater than the decay time, but it places an upper limit on analog signal frequency or the bit rate of a digital signal. To discuss both of these, we first need to take the current continuity equation (1.58) and insert a net recombination term from (3.12). Rearranging in terms of the current flux, the net result is

$$\frac{-\partial J_p}{\partial x} \;=\; e\left[\frac{\partial \Delta p_n(x,t)}{\partial t} + \frac{\Delta p_n(x,t)}{\tau_p}\right] \tag{3.38}$$

where we have assumed a p^+n junction construction so that we can assume one dominant current carrier to simplify the mathematics. To find the current i_p through the diode, the current density needs to be integrated over the whole n region. If A is the cross-sectional area, then

$$\begin{aligned} i_p \;&=\; -A \int_{J_p(x_n)}^{J_p(\infty)} \mathrm{d}J_p \\ &=\; A[J_p(x_n) - J_p(\infty)]. \end{aligned} \tag{3.39}$$

Far from the junction region, i.e. at infinity, J_p is zero because all the current will be carried by electrons. Equation (3.39) can then be combined with (3.38) to give

$$i_p \;=\; Ae \int_{x_n}^{\infty}\left[\frac{\Delta p(x,t)}{\tau_p} + \frac{\partial \Delta p_n(x,t)}{\partial t}\right]\mathrm{d}x\,. \tag{3.40}$$

From (2.34), $\Delta p_n(x,t)$ is given by

$$\Delta p_n(x,t) \;=\; \Delta p_n(x_n,t)\, \exp\left[\frac{x - x_n}{L_p}\right]. \tag{3.41}$$

These two equations (3.40) and (3.41) will now be applied to determine the effects of applying first an analog and then a digital signal to an LED. The analysis is simplified by noting two further equations; it can readily be seen that the integral in (3.40), when multiplied by the constant Ae, is just the time-varying charge density in the n-region. Thus

$$i_p = \frac{Q_p(t)}{\tau_p} + \frac{\partial Q_p(t)}{\partial t}. \tag{3.42}$$

We can use the results of the last three equations (3.40)–(3.42) to get a value for $Q_p(t)$:

$$Q_p(t) = Ae L_p \Delta p_n(x,t). \tag{3.43}$$

3.4.4.1 Analog signal

Rarely is a pure analog waveform used in driving an LED; for one thing the diode would only conduct on the positive half of the signal! Standard practice is to apply a constant d.c. voltage V and superimpose an a.c. voltage V_1 ($= V_{AC} \exp(\jmath\omega t)$) on this.

To find the excess charge as a function of time, we can use (2.30) and (2.32):

$$\Delta p_n(x_n, t) = p_{no} \exp\left(\frac{eV}{kT}\right). \tag{3.44}$$

For the input signal $V + V_1$, (3.44) becomes

$$\Delta p_n(x_n, t) = p_{no} \exp\left(\frac{e(V + V_1)}{kT}\right). \tag{3.45}$$

If V_1 is small, such that $eV_1 \ll kT$, then the two voltage terms can be split and the latter term treated as a factor in a binomial expansion of which only the first two terms are needed. Equation (3.45) then becomes

$$\Delta p_n(x_n, t) = p_{no} \exp\left(\frac{eV}{kT}\right) \exp\left(\frac{eV_1}{kT}\right)$$

$$\text{and hence} \quad \Delta p_n(x_n, t) = p_{no} \exp\left(\frac{eV}{kT}\right) \left(1 + \frac{eV_1}{kT}\right). \tag{3.46}$$

We can now use (3.42) and (3.43) in conjunction with (3.46) to get a value of the current through the device:

$$\begin{aligned}
i_p &= \frac{Ae L_p \Delta p_n(x,t)}{\tau_p} + \frac{\partial(Ae L_p \Delta p_n(x,t))}{\partial t} \\
&= \frac{Ae L_p}{\tau_p}\left(p_{no} \exp\left(\frac{eV}{kT}\right)\left(1 + \frac{eV_1}{kT}\right)\right) \\
&\quad + Ae L_p \frac{\partial\left(p_{no} \exp\left((eV/kT)\right)\left(1 + (eV_1/kT)\right)\right)}{\partial t} \\
&= \frac{Ae L_p}{\tau_p} p_{no} \exp\left(\frac{eV}{kT}\right)\left[1 + \frac{eV_1}{kT} + \frac{e\tau_p}{kT}\frac{\partial V_1}{\partial t}\right]. \tag{3.47}
\end{aligned}$$

If we denote the constant current part i_{DC} by

$$i_{DC} = \frac{AeL_p}{\tau_p} p_{no} \exp\left(\frac{eV}{kT}\right) \tag{3.48}$$

then (3.47) can be written as

$$i_p = i_{DC} + \frac{ei_{DC}}{kT}V_1 + \frac{\tau_p ei_{DC}}{kT}\frac{\partial V_1}{\partial t}. \tag{3.49}$$

ei_{DC}/kT represents the conductance G of the device, and combining (2.41), (2.42) and (2.88) gives

$$\frac{\tau_p ei_{DC}}{kT} = C_d, \tag{3.50}$$

where C_d is the diffusion capacitance. Equation (3.49) can then be written as

$$i_p = i_{DC} + GV_1 + C_d\frac{\partial V_1}{\partial t}. \tag{3.51}$$

This has now to be related to the output optical power. This can be expressed as an integral over the whole radiating area:

$$P(x,t) = \int_0^\infty h\bar{\nu}\frac{\Delta p_n(x,t)}{\tau_p}\,dx \tag{3.52}$$

per unit area, which assumes that the LED output is optically symmetric with an average optical frequency of $\bar{\nu}$. It is evident that the emitted power is proportional to the excess carrier density, or the steady state excess charge. If we assume the latter can be given by

$$Q_{po}(t) = Q_{po}\exp[\jmath(\omega t - \phi)], \tag{3.53}$$

$$\text{then when}\quad i_p = i_o\exp(\jmath\omega t), \tag{3.54}$$

and using (3.42), i_o becomes

$$i_o = \left(\frac{Q_{po}}{\tau_p} + \jmath\omega Q_{po}\right)\exp(-\jmath\phi). \tag{3.55}$$

$$\text{Hence}\quad |Q_{po}| = \frac{i_o\tau_p}{(1 + (\omega\tau_p)^2)^{1/2}} \tag{3.56}$$

$$\text{or}\quad |Q_{po}| = \frac{Q_0}{(1 + (\omega\tau_p)^2)^{1/2}} \tag{3.57}$$

where $Q_0 = i_o\tau_p$, and represents the static excess charge at $\omega = 0$. From the dependency on charge described in (3.52) it is clear that the output power has a similar equation relating it to signal frequency:

$$P(x,t) = \frac{P_0}{[1 + (\omega\tau_p)^2]^{1/2}}. \tag{3.58}$$

This is shown in Figure 3.16, where the output power response is normalized to P/P_0 [35]. Clearly a device with a low value of minority carrier lifetime is required for the best high frequency response. As the total minority carrier lifetime τ_p is made up from radiative τ_{pr} and non-radiative τ_{pnr} components by

$$\frac{1}{\tau_p} = \frac{1}{\tau_{pr}} + \frac{1}{\tau_{pnr}} \tag{3.59}$$

it is important to realize the effects of changing τ_{pr} or τ_{pnr} to produce the minimum in τ_p. For instance, reducing τ_{pnr} will produce a reduction in internal efficiency η_i (3.10), and hence lead to a fall in optical power available at all frequencies – this is shown in Figure 3.17. It is therefore evident that the reduction in τ_p should be achieved by minimizing τ_{pr}, which gives the best high frequency response and the maximum efficiency. Equations (3.16) and (3.17) imply that high doping levels are needed to obtain this – this is true up to the solubility limit of dopants in the semiconductor, when the non-radiative lifetime starts to decrease. This phenomenon is considered further when discussing heterostructures in section 3.5.3.

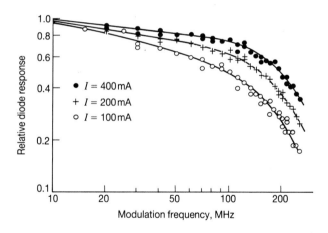

Figure 3.16 The normalized response of an LED as a function of signal driving frequency (©1976 RCA: reproduced by kind permission of General Electric).

Example 3.8

Calculate the 3 dB (half power) frequency of the GaAs LED in example 3.3.

Solution: from (3.58), some rearrangement of the arithmetic will give

$$f = \frac{3}{2\pi\tau_p}. \tag{3.60}$$

Using example 3.3 and (3.59)

$$\frac{1}{\tau_p} = \frac{1}{2.78 \times 10^{-10}} + \frac{1}{2 \times 10^{-9}}$$

$$\text{giving } \tau_p = 2.44 \times 10^{-10} \text{ s.}$$

$$\text{Hence } f = 1.96 \times 10^9 \text{ Hz.} \tag{3.61}$$

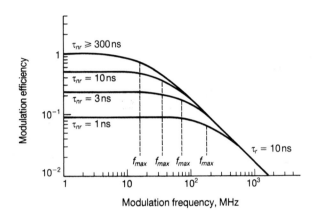

Figure 3.17 Effect of non-radiative recombination time on an LED's frequency response.

3.4.4.2   *Digital signal*

In this case the input is not a sinusoidal function, but a square wave with a maximum current of $i = i_0$ and a minimum of $i = 0$. If we assume that at time $t = 0$ the current is switched from i_0 to 0, there will be an excess charge in the device which will start to decay. Equation (3.42) then becomes

$$0 = \frac{Q_p(t)}{\tau_p} + \frac{\partial Q_p(t)}{\partial t}. \tag{3.62}$$

This can be solved to give

$$Q_p(t) = Q_p(0)\exp(-t/\tau_p)$$

$$= i_0\tau_p\exp(-t/\tau_p). \tag{3.63}$$

This gives an exponential decay in charge density which, again using (3.52), will give a similar response to the form of the optical power output.

When the current changes from $i = 0$ to i_0 a similar thing happens; this time it takes a finite time for the excess charge to build up. These effects are shown in Figure 3.18, and again emphasize the point about requiring an LED with a short recombination time for an adequate response to, in this case, a high bit rate digital signal.

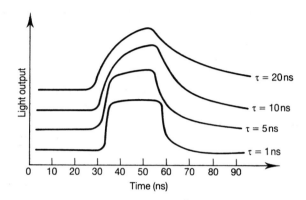

Figure 3.18 Effect of recombination time on diode response to a 25 ns square wave.

3.5   Construction

As with all semiconductor devices, an LED was initially a simple structure but, as device understanding progressed, became more complicated in order to exploit the particular features of this device for any given application. Common to all devices is the need to consider efficiency, reliability and manufacturing technology in the final design and construction. Highlighted in this section are the key points of how LEDs have evolved since their popularity began in the late 1960s. All the individual techniques of crystal growth and doping (Czochralski, epitaxy, diffusion, etc.), device fabrication (lithography, metallization, etc.) and packaging and testing are described in Chapters 8, 9 and 10 respectively.

3.5.1   Basic surface emitting devices

A surface emitting device was described in the consideration of coupling characteristics and external efficiency (section 3.3.4). All display and a lot of communication

LEDs are surface emitters, where the light is picked up in a direction perpendicular to the junction interface.

3.5.1.1   Standard red LED

Such a device is shown in Figure 3.19 and, after Table 3.2, consists of an active region of doped GaAsP. The process starts with a doped substrate of 200 μm LEC pulled GaAs. This material is usually n-type, and doped with Si or Te to a concentration of about 2×10^{17} cm^{-3}. It is cut 2° off the (100) plane in a [110] direction to minimize dislocations in the subsequent epitaxial layer. Because there is a lattice mismatch between GaAs and GaAsP, the layer of GaAs$_{0.6}$P$_{0.4}$ cannot be grown directly on to the substrate. Rather, vapour phase epitaxy (VPE) is used to grow a series of layers of GaAs$_{1-y}$P$_y$, starting with $y = 0$ and gradually increasing this value until a layer of GaAs$_{0.6}$P$_{0.4}$ is reached. This method gradually reduces the lattice parameter ensuring a smooth transition of minimum dislocation density from GaAs to GaAs$_{0.6}$P$_{0.4}$ over about 40 μm. The active layer of GaAs$_{0.6}$P$_{0.4}$ is around 50 μm, and doped n-type to a value of $\sim 10^{17}$ cm^{-3} using tellurium. A photolithographically defined silicon dioxide or nitride layer is then used as a diffusion mask against the p-dopant, usually zinc, which is diffused into the GaAs$_{0.6}$P$_{0.4}$ with a junction depth of about 5 μm and a surface concentration of 10^{19} cm^{-3}. An alloy of AuGe and Ni is used for the (unmasked) n-type ohmic contact and, for the (masked) p-type contact, either Al or AuZn is used. The wafer of LEDs is then scribed and broken into individual die, which are then soldered onto a lead frame header and wire bonded. Because the light emitting junction is only ~ 5 μm of GaAs$_{0.6}$P$_{0.4}$ away from the p-contact, and ~ 50 μm of the same semiconductor plus ~ 200 μm of GaAs away from the n-contact, it follows that most of the light is emitted from the p-doped surface. Hence the chips are mounted p-face up. Plastic encapsulation using the familiar red tinted dome completes the fabrication and packaging cycle.

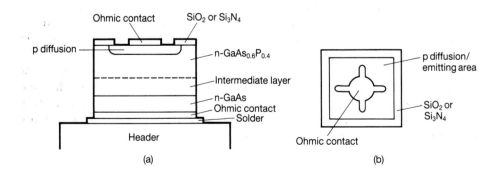

Figure 3.19 (a) Cross-section, and (b) top view of a typical GaAsP red LED.

3.5.1.2 Other standard types

It would not be particularly instructive to go through every other type of LED mentioned in Table 3.2; listed here are just a few types covering the infra-red, yellow and green ranges. The infra-red AlGaAs LED is shown in Figure 3.20(a) [36]. Although the GaAs diode is simpler, the AlGaAs types have found favour in communication because their band gap is tunable to take advantage of lower wavelengths (around 880 nm) where silicon photodetector sensitivity is higher. On top of a GaAs substrate is grown an n-doped layer of $Al_xGa_{1-x}As$. Doping is provided by silicon, and $x = 0.3$ provides a direct gap material in the AlGaAs. There are no lattice matching problems in the AlAs–GaAs system because the lattice constants are so similar (5.66 Å and 5.65 Å respectively). Subsequent layers of $Al_xGa_{1-x}As$ reduce x from 0.3 to 0.08 over a thickness of about 50 μm. The growth temperature has to be below 820 °C for the silicon to produce n-type material with liquid phase epitaxy (LPE). Above this temperature, Si doping produces p-type material and the rest of the $Al_xGa_{1-x}As$ layer is then grown, gradually reducing x from 0.08 to zero over about 130 μm. The p-type ohmic contact (AuZn) is then applied, and the GaAs substrate removed. The reason for this is that increasing the Al content of $Al_xGa_{1-x}As$ increases the band gap. As shown in Figure 3.20(b), light emitting from the junction will be strongly absorbed if it moves to a region of low aluminium concentration ('to the right'). However, if it moves 'to the left' the $Al_xGa_{1-x}As$ is transparent, but the GaAs substrate is not. The GaAs is therefore removed, n-type ohmic contacts (AuGe/Ni) are made and the rest of the device processing is as for the standard red LED.

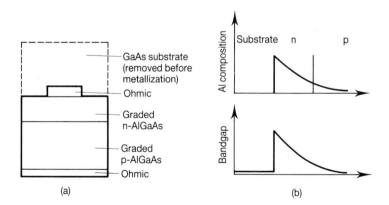

Figure 3.20 Graded AlGaAs LED.

A cross-section of a green LED is shown in Figure 3.21(a). The device is a simple structure formed by growing an epitaxial doped GaP layer on top of a GaP substrate followed by a diffusion stage. The substrate is Czochralski grown, and doped n-type with sulphur to a density of $\sim 10^{18}$ cm^{-3}. It is cut 5° off the (100) axis towards the [110] direction before a VPE layer, again of sulphur doped GaP, is grown. The carrier concentration is less, about 1×10^{17} cm^{-3}, and the thickness is about 50 μm. The final layer is nitrogen doped GaP, n-type with a high doping density of 2×10^{19} cm^{-3}. Masked zinc diffusion, as for the red LED, produces the p-type doping. The rest of the processing is as for the other LEDs, except that an alloy of Au/Te/Ni is usually a better ohmic contact to n-type GaP than AuGe/Ni. Somewhat brighter LEDs can be made using an LPE growth technique, with a cross-section as shown in Figure 3.21(b). The higher brightness is largely attributed to the better quality LPE material, with fewer dislocations giving a proportionate reduction in non-radiative recombination centres [37]. Yellow LEDs have a very similar structure to those of standard red LEDs, as shown by the cross-section of the former in Figure 3.22. The important differences are that the starting substrate is GaP and the epitaxial material is GaAs$_{0.15}$P$_{0.85}$ for yellow, and GaAs substrates with GaAs$_{0.6}$P$_{0.4}$ epitaxy for red. The change of y in GaAs$_{1-y}$P$_y$ produces the shift in characteristic emission and, because for yellow LEDs the epitaxial material is more like GaP than GaAs, it is easier to grow it on a GaP substrate, with the reverse being true for a red LED (orange LEDs, formed in GaAs$_{0.4}$P$_{0.6}$, are also grown on GaP substrates).

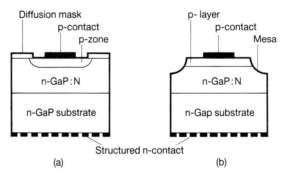

Figure 3.21 (a) Diffused, or (b) mesa etched green GaP LED.

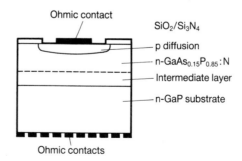

Figure 3.22 Yellow GaAsP LED.

3.5.2   Burrus type LED

All the LEDs discussed in section 3.5.1 are fabricated so that the light is taken out perpendicular to the junction in a direction away from the substrate; the exception to this is the infra-red LED, where the substrate is etched away.

An alternative approach is the Burrus type LED [38], shown in Figure 3.23. There are two important differences in this structure from the basic LED. First, the device is 'upside down' compared to those described in the last section, with a deeply etched well in the substrate to allow light to get out by this exit. Second, the p-type contact is defined in a small area on the axis of the etched well. This leads to current confinement in a small area of the junction, with the result that it is substantially only this 'active region' that is emitting light. Although this leads to a high current density, and hence heating effects, the use of the p-contact as a thermal path to the heat sink minimizes the temperature rise of the junction. This is important for three reasons:

(i) the band gap changes with temperature, with a temperature rise leading to a shift in the emission peak to a higher wavelength. This effect has a coefficient of about 2 Å K^{-1} for direct gap materials and 0.9 Å K^{-1} for indirect gap emitters.

(ii) Increasing the temperature gives a fall in output power, as detailed in section 3.4.

(iii) As most device failure mechanisms are temperature driven, undue heating will lead to a much shortened device life. Compensation circuits have been designed to stabilize LED output with varying temperature [39].

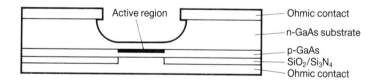

Figure 3.23 Burrus–type LED.

The Burrus LED is used for communication type LEDs, i.e. infra-red devices, where the confined active area and etched well couple light fairly efficiently into an optical fiber via some refractive index matching epoxy.

3.5.3   Double heterostructures

A homojunction has the same material on both sides of a pn junction; the visible LEDs described in section 3.5.1 are examples of this. A heterojunction has dissimilar materials on either side of the pn divide; because the value of x in the $Al_xGa_{1-x}As$ system, described as the infra-red LED in section 3.5.1, changes through the device this is a heterojunction system, although normally heterojunction refers to an abrupt interface between two materials of noticeably dissimilar band gaps, rather than the small change given in this example.

The reasons for introducing heterojunctions into optical devices are to control both the injection currents and refractive indices, leading to optical activity in one well defined region. Heterojunctions can be formed by materials of different band gaps with either similar or dissimilar doping types.

Double heterojunction (DH) devices are more common than single heterojunction (SH), and are considered in detail in section 4.2. A typical example of a DH LED is shown in Figure 3.24, where the structure (Figure 3.24(a)) is fabricated from a Burrus type LED. The DH structure is formed around the 2 μm thick n or p $Al_yGa_{1-y}As$ or GaAs layer. As an example, let this layer be n-type GaAs – we then have what is known as an NnP structure (where the capital letters denote material of a higher bandgap relative to the lower case material – if the central region was p-type GaAs, the structure would be NpP). Because the material on either side of the GaAs has a higher band gap (Figure 3.24(b)), light generated in the GaAs will pass unabsorbed through the AlGaAs. It can then be picked up efficiently by the optical fiber. Because of the refractive index comparisons of GaAs and AlGaAs (Figure 3.24(c)) the two regions of AlGaAs also act as optical confinement elements for photons generated in the GaAs region that are incident on the GaAs/AlGaAs interface at an angle. This is exploited in the edge emitting LED described in the next section and especially in the semiconductor laser.

3.5.4   Edge emitting LED

So far we have only considered light emitted in a direction perpendicular to the active junction region. Figure 3.25 shows a device, again made using a double heterostructure system, that takes the light out parallel to the junction, at the edge of the structure. This edge emitting LED is very similar in its stripe geometry construction to semiconductor lasers (see section 4.3) and as we shall see it has different characteristics to a surface emitting LED.

The stripe geometry of the p-contact metal is of importance. Its area defines the active region of the underlying junction. Because the active region is highly absorbing of its own generated radiation, it is often the case that a restricted length p-stripe is used to limit internal losses. But because the two layers on either side of the active region act as waveguides for the LED active region, the latter can be made very thin ($\sim$ 0.05–0.1 μm) to minimize absorption. Longer stripe regions can then be used to encourage superradiant emission – that which occurs just before full laser emission, where part of the output is stimulated emission (further discussion is given in section 4.1.3.5). One facet of the device should be of high optical quality (the output end), sometimes with an antireflection coating, and the

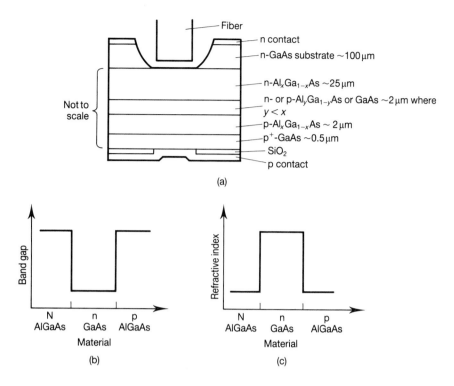

Figure 3.24 The double heterostructure NnP LED: (a) Burrus-type construction, (b) band gap vs composition, (c) refractive index vs composition.

other is usually etched, again to mitigate against laser action. Another technique is to use an integrated absorber and rear window built into the structure, as shown in Figure 3.25(b). Here the rear window of InP reduces reflection at the waveguide edge, and by electrically isolating the rear portion of the InGaAsP from the active part, an unpumped (i.e. takes no current) region is integrated into the structure which acts as an absorbing medium [40]. Comparisons have been made between the characteristics of surface (SLED) and edge-emitting (ELED) devices [41, 42]. These can be summarized as:

(i) as shown in Figure 3.26(a), an SLED has a two-dimensional angular Lambertian distribution to the emission, with a full width, half power beamwidth of 120°. This gives a spherical radiation pattern. However, for an ELED (Figure 3.26(b)), the transverse waveguide has the effect of containing most of the emitted radiation in a narrow angle ($\theta = 30°$) in the plane perpendicular to the junction, although in the parallel plane the profile is still Lambertian with a 120° beamwidth.

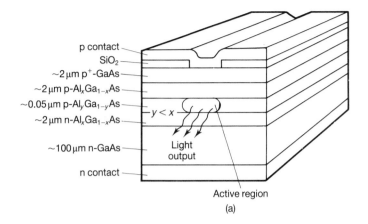

p contact
SiO₂
~2 µm p⁺-GaAs
~2 µm p-Al$_x$Ga$_{1-x}$As
~0.05 µm p-Al$_y$Ga$_{1-y}$As
~2 µm n-Al$_x$Ga$_{1-x}$As
~100 µm n-GaAs
n contact

$y < x$

Light output

Active region

(a)

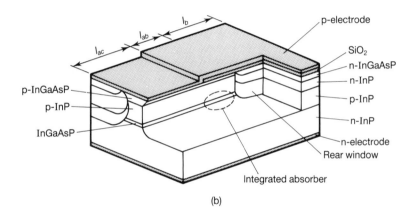

l_b
l_{ab}
l_{ac}

p-electrode
SiO₂
n-InGaAsP
n-InP
p-InGaAsP
p-InP
p-InP
n-InP
InGaAsP
n-electrode
Rear window
Integrated absorber

(b)

Figure 3.25 (a) The edge emitting LED (ELED). (b) An ELED with a rear window and integrated absorber (©AIP: reproduced by kind permission).

(ii) Because of these emission characteristics, ELEDs couple their output much more efficiently to fibers of low numerical aperture (NA) or to external lenses.

(iii) Because the active region of an ELED is much thinner than that of an SLED, the non-radiative lifetime of minority carriers is reduced which, via (3.58) and Figure 3.16 increases the modulation bandwidth of an ELED compared to its equivalent SLED by a factor of 5–6 (Figure 3.27(a)).

(iv) However, the smaller active region of the ELED gives a fall in total power compared to an SLED (although at lower current densities – Figure 3.27(b)).

The combination of all these characteristics leads to the conclusion that edge emitters are preferred for an optical communication system with data rates of between

20 and 200 Mbit/s, which use low numerical aperture (NA) fibers. However, systems using low data rates over short distances (using high NA fibers) would incorporate surface LEDs.

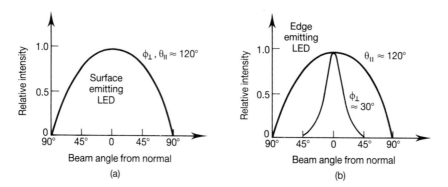

Figure 3.26 Angular distribution of output intensity from (a) a surface emitting LED, and (b) an edge emitting LED (©1979 IEEE: reproduced by kind permission).

3.5.5 Coupling methods

Section 3.3.4 discussed the effect of diode design on the external efficiency of the device, i.e. the amount of light generated at the junction which can be accessed. Assuming that the factors (i), (ii), (v) and (vi) listed in that section have been optimized, then factors (iii) and (iv), i.e. reflection and transmission losses respectively, can be minimized by one of the following:

(i) geometrical techniques to ensure that most of the emitted light from the junction arrives within the critical angle θ_c at the semiconductor–air interface,

(ii) increasing the value of θ_c by encapsulating the semiconductor in a medium with a refractive index value between that of air and the semiconductor,

(iii) coating the semiconductor with a dielectric antireflection film of suitable refractive index and thickness.

The geometrical designs of LEDs were generated very early on in device development. Figure 3.28 shows several examples, and Table 3.4 lists their relative merits [43]. Note that, for all these designs, only 50% of the generated light is directed towards the emitting surface; hence the maximum theoretical value of radiant flux is 0.5, representing 100% external efficiency. Not suprisingly, the flat diode is the least efficient in terms of both radiant flux and radiant intensity. The hemisphere, Weierstrasse sphere, and paraboloid geometries have a higher efficiency than that

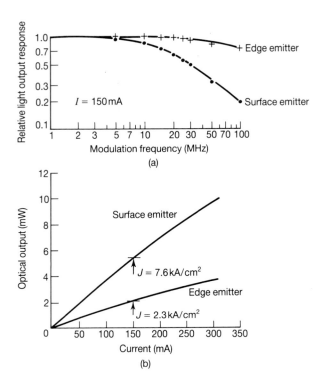

Figure 3.27 SLED vs ELED comparison of (a) modulation bandwidth, and (b) output power (©1979 IEEE: reproduced by kind permission).

of the truncated cone, but the latter can more efficiently couple its radiant flux to detectors of a similar area. The highest radiant intensity is given by the truncated ellipsoid but this is highly directional.

All the designs in Table 3.4 can be fabricated in the LED material (Figure 3.29(a)) or in other materials deposited on the semiconductor (Figure 3.29(b)). Transparent plastics find uses here, despite their comparatively low refractive indices (1.4–1.8). Low melting point arsenic–chalcogen–halogen glasses with $n = 2.4$–2.9 can also be used [44].

Example 3.9

Calculate the change in critical angle for a coating of $n = 1.8$ on the LED of example 3.4. Hence determine the increase in external efficiency achieved using such a coating.

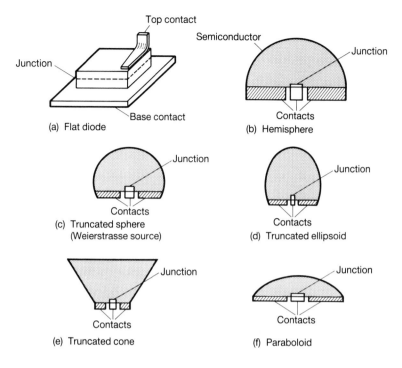

Figure 3.28 Various geometrical designs of an LED (©1972 IEEE: reproduced by kind permission).

Solution: using the familiar equation for critical angle, and the same method as example 3.4, gives

$$
\begin{aligned}
\theta_c &= 31°, \\
T &= \frac{4 \times 3.45 \times 1.8}{(1.8 + 3.45)^2} = 0.90, \\
F_{sp} &= 0.90\,(1 - \cos 31°) = 0.13,
\end{aligned}
\tag{3.64}
$$

an increase of ~ 4.3 in transmission into the coating.

To minimize reflectivity losses, we have to consider the reflection coefficient R given by Fresnel's equations for a semiconductor of $n = n_1$ and external medium $n = n_3$:

$$
R = \frac{(n_1 - n_3)^2}{(n_1 + n_3)^2}.
\tag{3.65}
$$

Geometry	Radiant flux	Maximum radiant intensity $\theta = 0°$	Average radiant intensity $\theta = 26°$
Flat plane diode area emission	0.013	0.0042	0.0039
Hemisphere	0.34	0.054	0.054
Weierstrasse sphere	0.34	1.4	0.52
Truncated ellipsoid	0.25	9.8	0.39
Truncated cone	0.20	0.063	0.059
Paraboloid: $R_j/F_p = 0.1$	0.34	0.84	0.52
Paraboloid: $R_j/F_p = 0.05$	0.34	3.3	0.52

Table 3.4 Figure of merit for various LED geometries per unit internal light flux generation ($n = 3.6$). Note: for the paraboloid sources, R_j and F_p are the junction area and the focal length of the paraboloid respectively.

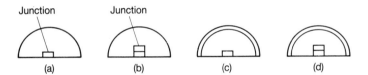

Figure 3.29 Various means of producing a hemispherical LED: (a) shaping the semiconductor material, (b) encapsulating a junction, (c) and (d) are as (a) and (b) respectively but with the addition of a thin dielectric coating.

When an additional material of thickness t and refractive index n_2 is placed directly on top of the shaped semiconductor, as shown in Figure 3.29(c), R becomes

$$R = \frac{(n_1 n_3 - n_2^2)^2}{(n_1 n_3 + n_2^2)^2}. \tag{3.66}$$

Clearly R becomes zero when

$$n_1 n_3 = n_2^2 \tag{3.67}$$

for a reflection at the n_1/n_2 interface, and

$$n_2 t = \frac{\lambda}{4}(2l - 1) \tag{3.68}$$

at the n_2/n_3 interface, where l is a positive integer. n_2 is in the range of 1.8–1.9, readily obtainable from the SiO_xN_y (silicon oxynitride) range of materials, and easily deposited.

Example 3.10

What is the thickness of silicon oxynitride required to act as an effective anti-reflection coating at 1300 nm, if the dielectric refractive index is 1.85?

Solution: from (3.68)

$$t = \frac{1.3 \times 10^{-6}}{4 \times 1.85} = 176 \,\text{nm}, \tag{3.69}$$

or, when $l = 2$, 527 nm ($l = 3$, 878 nm, etc.).

Figure 3.29(d) shows a combination of both encapsulating plastic and antireflection coating; obviously in this case the value of n_2, and hence t, will change because the value of n_1 has changed from the semiconductor case of Figure 3.29(c).

The consideration of coupling efficiency is very important for communication type LEDs. Having designed a device to a particular specification as regards wavelength, current density, etc., it is very wasteful not to consider the output coupling. Because communication LEDs are not usually made to the squarely symmetric design of display LEDs (more usual is the stripe geometry) modifications have to be made to the arguments developed above. For instance, a stripe geometry SLED with a buried cylindrical lens is shown in Figure 3.30 [45], with this type of lens performing a similar function to that shown in Figure 3.29(a).

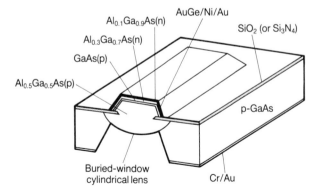

Figure 3.30 A stripe geometry SLED with a buried cylindrical lens (©Physical Society of Japan: reproduced by kind permission).

Most of the interest of LEDs to communication has centred on the use of multimode fibers. However, there is a use for LEDs in local loop applications using single mode fibers (SMF), and hence the coupling characteristics of this system have attracted attention. By considering the LED as an ensemble of antennae, radiating in a mutually incoherent fashion, it is possible to come up with a general equation [46] for the coupling efficiency η of an LED to a SMF

$$\eta = A \frac{\int \int_{-\infty}^{\infty} dx\, dy\, E_t^2(x,y)\, N(x-\alpha, y-\beta)}{\int \int_{-\infty}^{\infty} dx\, dy\, \int_0^{2\pi} \int_0^{\pi/2} d\theta\, d\phi\, \sin\theta\, F(\phi,\theta)\, N(x,y)} \qquad (3.70)$$

$$\text{where} \quad A = \frac{2\pi^2 nT}{k_0^2 N_0} \left(\frac{\epsilon_0}{\mu_0} \right)^{1/2} \qquad (3.71)$$

and the functions $N(x,y)$ and $F(\phi,\theta)$ give the spatial and angular dependencies respectively of the radiated light intensity, α and β represent the light source centre in the x–y coordinate system, E_t is the value of the transverse electric field component of the fundamental propagation mode in the fiber (LP_{01}), n is the glass refractive index and k_0 the free space wave vector. ϵ_0 and μ_0 are respectively the free space values of permittivity and permeability and T is the Fresnel transmission coefficient. N_0 is known as the normalization constant of the fundamental mode. Equation (3.70) can be reduced to individual expressions for SLEDs and ELEDs. For SLEDs

$$\eta = T \frac{m+1}{2} \frac{\lambda_0^2}{\pi A_s} \qquad (3.72)$$

where A_s is the area of the light emitting surface, λ_0 the free space wavelength and $m = 1$ for a Lambertian emitter. For ELEDs

$$\eta = T \frac{(\mu + \nu + 2)}{2\pi^2} \frac{\lambda_0^2}{[(2r_0^2 + L^2)(2r_0^2 + W^2)]^{1/2}} S_x S_y \qquad (3.73)$$

where μ and ν are respectively the transverse and lateral power distribution coefficients, $2W$ and $2L$ are respectively the transverse and lateral $1/e^2$ full widths of the near field, r_0 is the $1/e$ mode field radius and S_x and S_y are sensitivity functions given by

$$S_x = \exp\left(\frac{-2\alpha^2}{2r_0^2 + L^2} \right) \qquad (3.74)$$

$$\text{and} \quad S_y = \exp\left(\frac{-2\beta^2}{2r_0^2 + W^2} \right) \qquad (3.75)$$

where α and β again represent the light source centre.

When the LED source is smaller than the fiber core, lenses can be used to increase the coupling efficiency. For an ELED with an ideal lens, an extra term M^2 is introduced into the numerator of (3.73) and as a prefix to the L^2 and W^2 terms; M represents the lens magnification.

A coherent mode approach to the coupling problem of LEDs to SMF [47] gives the same answer as (3.72) for SLEDs (ELEDs were not considered). The effect of lens imperfections on LED coupling to SMFs has also been considered [48].

3.6   Reliability and degradation

LEDs in common use today are now so reliable, and generally cheap to replace if they fail, that they tend to be taken for granted. It is important though, that for any new LED or new application, the failure of the device must not be the limiting factor on the overall acceptance of the system containing the LED. This is especially true where the upheaval involved in replacing a buried component would be considerable.

As the development of LEDs has occurred over a similar timescale to that of silicon ICs, experience gained from the manufacture of the latter has been applied to the former. This is particularly true for cleanliness and a contamination free environment, which have proved to have a dramatic effect on yield and reliability. But, aside from these 'housekeeping' issues, empirical observations have found several important features of LED degradation. These are extensively discussed in [49], and a summary is given here:

(i) degradation only occurs under forward bias, and increases with the operating current density J as J^m $(1.5 < m < 2)$,

(ii) the degradation slows down with time, but increases with temperature, according to

$$P = P_0 \exp(-\beta t) \qquad (3.76)$$

where β is a temperature dependent degradation rate, given by

$$\beta = \beta_0 \exp\left(\frac{-E_A}{kT}\right) \qquad (3.77)$$

where β_0 is a constant and E_A is an activation energy [50]. Typical results are shown in Figures 3.31(a) and (b); the latter also shows the importance of contamination, where the removal of unwanted copper from the processing environment caused a large increase in device operating time [51],

(iii) infra-red emitters usually degrade slower than visible LEDs [52],

(iv) there is an increase in non-radiative recombination during the degradation,

(v) dark line and/or dark spot defects, representing crystal faults, can occur at high current densities.

Typical values of E_A and β_0 are 0.56–0.65 eV and 93 h^{-1} for AlGaAs/GaAs LEDs [53] and 0.9–1.0 eV and 1.8×10^7 h^{-1} for InGaAsP/InP devices [50].

Example 3.11

Calculate the expected operational lifetime of an InGaAsP LED at 30 °C, if the device is unacceptable for use once $P = 0.5P_0$. Use a value of E_A of 0.97 eV.

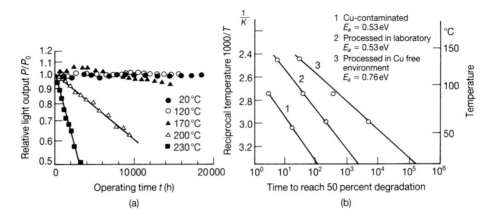

Figure 3.31 Effect on degradation of an LED of time, temperature and contamination ((a) is ©1981 IEEE: reproduced by kind permission).

Solution: from (3.76) and (3.77)

$$\beta = 1.8 \times 10^7 \exp\left(\frac{-0.97e}{303k}\right) = 1.32 \times 10^{-9}\,\mathrm{h}^{-1},$$

$$t = \frac{-1}{1.32 \times 10^{-9}} \log_e 0.5 = 5.2 \times 10^8\,\mathrm{h} \qquad (3.78)$$

or $\sim 60,000$ years. Calculations like this involve two exponentials, and so the end results will be markedly affected by the precise values of the numbers used. However, it can be seen why the reliability should be taken for granted.

Various mechanisms and models for the observed degradation characteristics have been put forward. As degradation occurs at comparatively low junction temperatures, with values of E_A in the range of 0.5–1.0 eV, the well known thermally activated rate processes in III–V semiconductors cannot be responsible because phenomena such as defect formation, annihilation and self-diffusion have much higher values of $E_A \sim 2.6$ eV. Also, any mechanism has to explain the current dependency, i.e. the need for a presence of a large non-equilibrium free carrier concentration. Models have been proposed, with recombination enhanced diffusion [54, 55] being a likely cause of LED degradation. Besides the semiconductor based mechanisms, mechanical processes can also affect device reliability. Sawing damage and stress inducing encapsulants are the other most obvious sources of problems, with both leading to the movement and multiplication of dislocations, and hence nonradiative transitions or even dark lines or spots. Saw damage can be alleviated by a subsequent etch, and a low stress encapsulant, e.g. [56], not only minimizes dislocation formation, but also removes the stress-associated problems of bond wire breakage and corrosion.

3.7   Integration

The integration of LEDs can be split into two distinct technology routes:

(i) the fabrication and addressing of LED arrays,

(ii) the integration of an LED with other circuit elements on the same chip.

Progress in both these areas is briefly discussed here.

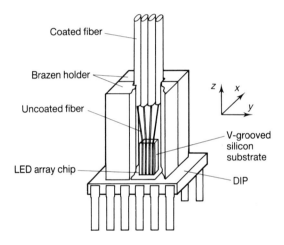

Figure 3.32 A packaged LED array (©Physical Society of Japan: reproduced by kind permission).

3.7.1   LED Arrays

The first array of this type was reported in 1978 [57] when 10 DH AlGaAs high radiance LEDs were integrated on a GaAs substrate. The array has all 10 diodes in a line, with a glass lens bonded on to each diode, ready for optical connection to a 10 core optical fiber. A similar structure for a 1×4 array is shown in Figure 3.32 [58]. Other arrays of LEDs have been designed and fabricated, and in different materials such as InGaAsP/InP emitting at 1.3 μm [59]. These developments have rapidly led to the integration of both LED and matching photodiode arrays [60]. The surface emitting LEDs used in this package are shown in Figure 3.33(a), with the 12 channel fiber to LED alignment shown in Figure 3.33(b). Figures 3.33(c), (d) and (e) show similar cross-sections for the photodiode array, alignment of the fiber block and the PIN diode package respectively.

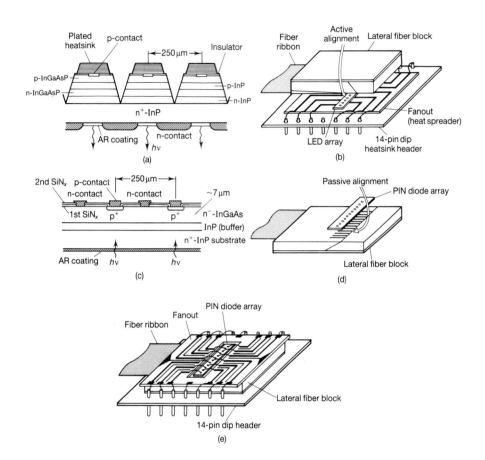

Figure 3.33 LED arrays: (a) SLEDs used in array, (b) fiber to LED alignment, (c) pin diodes used in array, (d) fiber to PIN diode alignment, and (e) PIN diode package (©1987 IEEE: reproduced by kind permission).

The limitation on array size using monolithic integration (i.e. all devices on the same chip) is quality and uniformity of the starting material. What may be a good yield for small individual LEDs soon becomes unacceptable for a large array. An alternative is to take individual LEDs and connect them together. Most packaging and bonding methods have been unable to produce acceptable yields over a large area, but the microbump bonding method (see Chapter 10) can be used to great effect; [61] reports A4 sized arrays of LEDs and driver chips with yields of 9.8%, with the poor devices caused by environmental dirt producing bonding failure.

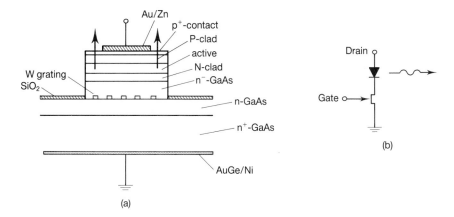

Figure 3.34 A vertically integrated GaAs/AlGaAs LED and GaAs MES-FET (©Physical Society of Japan: reproduced by kind permission).

3.7.2 Integration with other devices

This can be further subdivided into two distinct areas: integration using either the same material, or different materials for the LED and other devices, usually an FET. For integration using the same material, a particularly elegant technique uses vertical integration of a GaAs/AlGaAs LED with a MESFET, as shown in Figure 3.34 [62]. The embedded tungsten grating acts as the gate contact for the MESFET.

As is described in section 8.5.6, the growth of III–V semiconductors on silicon substrates can have many advantages. An example is the use of a GaAs layer to grow a GaAs/AlGaAs LED, whilst the Si layer can be used for a familiar MOSFET driver circuit. This has been done for both single and multiple FET drivers, with LED modulation rates exceeding 100 MHz [63].

3.8   Problems

1. Why is LED emission 'cold' light?
2. What differentiates injection luminescence from electroluminescence?
3. Why is it that only the junction region of an LED is considered to emit light? Doesn't radiative recombination also occur in the bulk semiconductor?

4. Why are direct gap semiconductors far more efficient LEDs than indirect materials?

5. Why does nitrogen doping in some III–V compounds create an isoelectronic centre?

6. Why is the internal efficiency of an LED much greater than the external efficiency?

7. Compare the radiative minority carrier lifetimes in InP and Ge, when the minority carriers are electrons injected into the p-region with a doping density of 10^{18} cm^{-3}. Assume the electron density is small compared with the majority carrier density. If the non-radiative minority carrier lifetime is 2 ns for each material, calculate the internal efficiency of each semiconductor as an LED.

8. What output power, measured at the junction, would an InP LED, as described in problem 7, give for a forward voltage of 1.8 V at 80 mA? Assuming that this power is radiated symmetrically about the junction, and the device is planar, calculate the amount of light reaching the surface of the p-region if it is 3 μm thick and the absorption coefficient is 5×10^5 m^{-1}. Use the following simplifying assumptions: all light radiated into the n-region is lost, all light entering the p-region eventually reaches the surace by internal reflection and the path length taken by these reflections is the same as that of light emitted from the surface.

9. Explain why an LED made from a poor quality crystal will not be a very efficient device.

10. Distinguish between the terms 'low' and 'high' when applied to LED injection currents.

11. For the same device as in problems 7 and 8, calculate the ratio of the power emitted from the surface to that reaching it for the following two conditions:

    (i) emission into air,

    (ii) emission into a dielectric of refractive index $n = 1.6$,

    if the refractive index of GaAs is 3.45.

12. For a planar LED emitting into air, determine

    (i) the optical loss, in dB, in coupling the output light to a fiber of coupling efficiency $\eta_c = 0.04$, assuming that the fiber has a larger diameter than the LED and the fiber and LED are in close proximity,

    (ii) the loss, in dB, relative to the internally generated optical power of problem 8 when coupling the LED to the fiber with a small air gap.

13. Combine the answers of problems 7, 8, 11 and 12 to determine the maximum length of fiber that can be used to couple the LED to a receiver of sensitivity −60 dB, for the two cases of an LED with and without a dielectric coating. 0 dB is referenced to 1 mW of power.

14. Consider an LED where the radiative minority carrier lifetime is much less than the equivalent non-radiative lifetime, and is equal to 3 ns. Under d.c.

conditions the optical output power is 150 μW. What is the optical output power when the device is modulated at (i) 1 MHz, (ii) 50 MHz, and (iii) 500 MHz with an r.m.s. drive current equivalent to the d.c. drive current. What are the 3 dB optical and electrical bandwidths of the device?

15. An LED has its output power proportional to the diffusion current only. If the recombination current dominates over the diffusion current in such a device, show how the output radiant flux depends on the forward current.

16. Calculate the series resistor needed to operate a typical red LED from a 5 V power supply.

17. What would you expect to happen if several LEDs, of the same type but chosen at random, were connected in a parallel array?

18. An AlGaAs LED based communication system is made with a careful calculation of its performance, and then a 5 dB margin added for the fall in LED output with time. If the diode has an initial output power of 5 mW and works at a constant temperature of 40 °C, estimate the operational lifetime of the system if all the other components have a negligible age-related degradation. For such diodes $E_A = 0.57$ eV and $\beta_0 = 93$ h^{-1}. Calculate the improvement in operational lifetime if the diode is replaced by one based on InGaAsP/InP, with $E_A = 1.0$ eV and $\beta_0 = 1.8 \times 10^7$ h^{-1}. 0 dB is referenced to 1 mW.

3.9   References

1. For a review and list of references for this work see K Lehovec, C A Accardo and E Jamgochian, 'Injected Light Emission of Silicon Carbide Crystals', *Phys. Rev.* **83**, 603 (1951).

2. G A Wolff, R A Hebert and J D Broder, 'Electroluminescence of GaP', *Phys. Rev.* **100**, 1144 (1955).

3. R Braunstein, 'Radiative Transitions in Semiconductors', *Phys. Rev.* **99**, 1892 (1955).

4. J R Haynes and H B Briggs, 'Radiation Produced in Germanium and Silicon by Electron–Hole Recombination', Proc. Am. Phys. Soc. meeting, Columbus, Ohio, USA, 20–22 March, 1952, *Phys. Rev.* **86**, 647 (1952).

5. J Wilson and J F B Hawkes, *Optoelectronics: an Introduction*, 2nd ed., Prentice-Hall International, 1989, p. 333.

6. E W Williams and R Hall, *Luminescence and the Light Emitting Diode*, Vol. 13 of Int. Series on Science of the Solid State, B R Pamplin, ed., Pergamon, 1978.

7. H Kressel and J K Butler, *Semiconductor Lasers and Heterojunction LEDs*, Series on Quantum Electronics – Principles and Applications, Y-H Pao and P Kelley, eds, Academic Press, 1977.

8. K Gillesen and W Schairer, *Light Emitting Diodes – an Introduction*, Prentice-Hall International, 1987.

9. Y P Varshni, 'Band to Band Radiative Recombination in Groups IV, VI and III–V Semiconductors (I)', *Phys. Stat. Sol.* **19**, 459 (1967).

10. See [8], p. 171.

11. W D Wright, *The Measurement of Colour*, 2nd ed., Hilger and Watts, 1958, p. 53.

12. S Sakai, S S Chang and R V Ramaswamy, '$Al_{0.3}Ga_{0.7}As/Al_{0.05}Ga_{0.95}As$ Light Emitting Diodes on GaAs-coated Si Substrates Grown by Liquid Phase Epitaxy', *Appl. Phys. Lett.* **53**, 1201 (1988).

13. M Razeghi, R Blondeau, M Defour, F Omnesan and P Maurel, 'First Room Temperature CW Operation of a GaInAsP/InP Light Emitting Diode on a Silicon Substrate', *Appl. Phys. Lett.* **53**, 854 (1988).

14. L T Canham, K G Barraclough and D J Robbins, '1.3 μm Light Emitting Diode from Silicon Electron Irradiated at its Damage Threshold', *Appl. Phys. Lett.* **51**, 1509 (1987).

15. A Rolland, A Le Corre, P N Favennec, M Gauneau, B Lambert, D Lecrosnier, H L'Haridon, D Moutonnet and C Rochaix, 'Erbium Doped GaAs Light Emitting Diode at 1.54 μm', *Elec. Lett.* **24**, 956 (1988).

16. W H Haydl, H D Muller and H Ennen, 'Ytterbium Doped InP Light Emitting Diode at 1.0 μm', *Appl. Phys. Lett.* **49**, 870 (1985).

17. B V Dutt, J H Racette, S J Anderson, F W Scholl and J R Shealy, 'Al-GaInP/GaAs Red Edge Emitting Diodes for Polymer Optical Fiber Applications', *Appl. Phys. Lett.* **53**, 2091 (1988).

18. A Richter, P Steiner, F Kozlowski and W Lang, 'Current Induced Light Emission from a Porous Silicon Device', *IEEE Electron. Dev. Lett.* **12**, 691 (1991).

19. N Koshida and H Koyama, 'Visible Electroluminescence from Porous Silicon', *Appl. Phys. Lett.* **60**, 347 (1992).

20. M R Lorenz, 'The Generation of Visible Light from P-N Junctions in Semiconductors', *Trans. Metall. Soc. AIME* **245**, 539 (1969).

21. W von Munch, W Kurzinger and I Pfaffeneder, 'Silicon Carbide Light Emitting Diodes with Epitaxial Junctions', *Solid State Electron.* **19**, 871 (1976).

22. S M Paasche, T Toyama, H Okamoto and Y Hamakawa, 'Amorphous SiC Thin Film p-i-n Light Emitting Diode using Amorphous-SiN Hot Carrier Tunneling Injection Layers', *IEEE Trans. Electron. Dev.* **ED-36**, 2895 (1989).

23. I Akasatu, H Amano, M Kito and R Hiramatsu, 'Photoluminescence of Mg-Doped P-type GaN and Electroluminescence of GaN P-N Junction LED', *J. Lumin.* **48–9**, 666 (1991).

24. H Amano, T Asahi, M Kito and I Akasaki, 'Stimulated Emission in MOVPE Grown GaN Film', *J. Lumin.* **48–9**, 889 (1991).

25. O Mishima, K Era, J Tanaka and S Yamaoka, 'Ultraviolet Light Emitting Diode of a Cubic Boron Nitride PN Junction Made at High Pressure', *Appl. Phys. Lett.* **53**, 962 (1988).

26. O Wada, S Yamakoshi, H Hamaguchi, T Sanada, Y Nishitani and T Sakurai, 'Performance and Reliability of High Radiance InGaAsP/InP DH LEDs Operating in the 1.15–1.5 μm Wavelength Region', *IEEE J. Quantum Electron.* **QE-18**, 368 (1982).

27. T Takagi, 'Spectral Half-Width of Spontaneous Emission of GaInAsP Lattice Matched to InP', *Jpn. J. Appl. Phys.* **18**, 2017 (1979).

28. T Fukui and Y Horikoshi, 'Anomalous Injection near the InGaAsP-InP Heterojunction Interface', *Jpn. J. Appl. Phys.* **18**, 961 (1979).

29. W O Groves, A H Herzog and M G Craford, 'The Effect of Nitrogen Doping on GaAsP Electroluminescent Diodes', *Appl. Phys. Lett.* **19**, 184 (1971).

30. D Botez and M Ettenberg, 'Comparison of Surface and Edge Emitting LEDs for use in Fibre-Optical Communications', *IEEE Trans. Electron. Dev.* **ED-26**, 1230 (1978).

31. A A Bergh and P J Dean, 'Light Emitting Diodes', *Proc. IEEE* **60**, 156 (1972).

32. P W Shumate and M DiDomenico, Jr, 'Lightwave Transmitters', in Topics in Applied Physics, vol. 39: *Semiconductor Devices for Optical Communication*, H. Kressel, ed, Springer Verlag, 1980, p. 180.

33. J Gowar, *Optical Communication Systems*, Prentice-Hall International, 1984, p. 226.

34. A Descombes and W Guggenbuhl, 'Large Signal Circuit Model for LEDs Used in Optical Communication', *IEEE Trans. Electron. Dev.* **ED-28**, 395 (1981).

35. J P Wittke, M Ettenberg and H Kressel, 'High Radiance LEDs for Single Fibre Optical Links', *RCA Review* **37**, 159 (1976).

36. L R Dawson, 'High Efficiency Graded Band Gap $Ga_{1-x}Al_xAs$ Light Emitting Diodes', *J. Appl. Phys.* **48**, 2485 (1977).

37. See [8], p. 110.

38. C A Burrus and B I Miller, *Opt. Commun.* **4**, 307 (1971).

39. J Mroczka, 'Temperature Stabilisation of Light Emitting Diode Radiation', *J. Phys. E: Sci. Instrum.* **21**, 306 (1988).

40. K Gen-ei, A Tanioka, H Suhara and K Chinen, 'High Coupled Power 1.3 μm Edge-Emitting Light-Emitting Diode with a Rear Window and an Integrated Absorber', *Appl. Phys. Lett.* **53**, 1138 (1988).

41. D Marcuse, 'LED Fundamentals: Comparison of Front and Edge Emitting Diodes', *IEEE J. Quantum Electron.* **QE-13**, 819 (1977).

42. D Botez and M Ettenberg, 'Comparison of Surface and Edge-Emitting LEDs for Use in Fibre Optical Communications', *IEEE Trans. Electron. Dev.* **ED-26**, 1230 (1979).

43. W N Carr, 'Photometric Figures of Merit for Semiconductor Luminescent Sources Operating in Spontaneous Mode', *Infrared Physics* **6**, 1 (1966).

44. A G Fischer and C J Nuese, 'Highly Refractive Glasses to Improve Electroluminescent Diode Efficiencies', *J. Electrochem. Soc.* **116**, 1718 (1969).

45. T-K Yoo, S H Hahm and Y-S Kwon, 'Surface Emitting AlGaAs/GaAs DH LED with Buried Window Cylindrical Lens', *Jpn. J. Appl. Phys.* **27**, L2357 (1988).

46. D N Christodoulides, L A Reith and M A Saifi, 'Theory of LED Coupling to Single Mode Fibres', *J. Lightwave Technol.* **LT-5**, 1623 (1987).

47. K-L Chen and D Kerps, 'Coupling Efficiency of Surface Emitting LEDs to Single Mode Fibres', *J. Lightwave Technol.* **LT-5**, 1600 (1987).

48. B Hillerich, 'Influence of Lens Imperfections with LD and LED to Single Mode Fibre Coupling', *J. Lightwave Technol.* **LT-7**, 77 (1989).

49. See [8], p. 193.

50. S Yamakoshi, M Abe, O Wada, S Komiya and T Sakurai, 'Reliability of High Radiance InGaAsP/InP LEDs Operating in the 1.2–1.3 μm Wavelength', *IEEE J. Quantum Electron.* **QE-17**, 167 (1981).

51. A A Bergh, 'Bulk Degradation of GaP Red LEDs', *IEEE Trans. Electron Dev.* **ED-18**, 166 (1971).

52. M Ettenberg and C J Nuese, 'Reduced Degradation in $In_xGa_{1-x}As$ Electroluminescent Diodes', *J. Appl. Phys.* **46**, 2137 (1975).

53. S Yamakoshi, O Hosegawa, H Hamaguchi, M Abe and T Yamaoka, 'Degradation of High Radiance $Ga_{1-x}Al_xAs$ LEDs', *Appl. Phys. Lett.* **31**, 626 (1977).

54. See [8], p. 201.

55. Y L Khait, J Salzman and R Beserman, 'Kinetic Model for Gradual Degradation in Semiconductor Lasers and Light Emitting Diodes', *Appl. Phys. Lett.* **53**, 2135 (1988).

56. R J M Zasiers, H J L Bressers, B Ouwehand and D Baumann, 'Development of a New Low Stress Hyperred LED Encapsulant', *IEEE Trans. Components, Hybrids and Manufacturing Technol.* **CHMT-12**, 387 (1989).

57. S Horiuchi, T Tanaka, K Ikeda and W Susaki, 'A Monolithic Linear Array of High Radiance AlGaAs Double Heterostructure LEDs with Self-Aligned Spherical Lenses', *Proc. IEEE* **66**, 261 (1978).

58. T Sugahara, O Wada, T Fujii, S Hiyamizu and T Sakurai, 'Monolithic 1×4 Array of Uniform Radiance AlGaAs–GaAs LEDs Grown by Molecular Beam Epitaxy', *Jpn. J. Appl. Phys.* **21**, L349 (1982).

59. P P Deimel, J Cheng, S R Forrest, P H-S Hu, R B Huntington, R C Miller, J R Potopowicz, D D Roccasecca and C W Seabury, 'Individually Addressable Monolithic 1×12 Light Emitting Diode Array', *J. Lightwave Technol.* **LT-3**, 988 (1985).

60. Y Ota, R C Miller, S R Forrest, D R Kaplan, C W Seabury, R B Huntington, J G Johnson and J R Potopowicz, 'Twelve Channel Individually Addressable InGaAs/InP p-i-n Photodiode and InGaAsP/InP LED Arrays in a Compact Package', *J. Lightwave Technol.* **LT-5**, 1118 (1987).

61. K Hatada, H Fujimoto, T Ochi and Y Ishida, 'LED Array Modules by New Technology Microbump Bonding Method', *IEEE Trans. Components, Hybrids and Manufacturing Technol.* **CHMT-13**, 521 (1990).

62. C H Hong, C-T Kim and Y-S Kwon, 'A Vertical Integration of GaAs/GaAlAs LED and Vertical FET with Embedded Schottky Diodes', *Jpn. J. Appl. Phys.* **29**, L2427 (1990).

63. H K Choi, J P Mattia, G W Turner and B Y Tsaur, 'Monolithic Integration of GaAs/AlGaAs LED and Si Driver Circuit', *IEEE Electron. Dev. Lett.* **EDL-9**, 512 (1988).

4

Lasers

The late 1950s and early 1960s was an intense period for both theoretical work on, and practical realization of, several different types of laser, with the acronym (Light Amplification by Stimulated Emission of Radiation) being introduced at this time. The first semiconductor laser was reported in 1962 [1]; it used a pn junction in GaAs, was operated in the pulse mode at a temperature of 77 K and gave a peak output wavelength of 842 nm with a spectral width of 1.5 nm. The threshold current density was very large by modern standards (8500 A cm^{-2}).

This chapter starts by reviewing the basic laser mechanisms relevant to semiconductor devices. Output characteristics are then described. This leads on to the vast improvement in performance introduced by the heterojunction laser. The concept of stripe geometry is then introduced. All the various specialist types of laser are then discussed, with buried structures, single frequency lasers, quantum well and strained layer structures, large optical cavities, laser arrays, surface emitters and visible lasers all having detailed sections. Control electronics and aspects of reliability and integration conclude this chapter. It will be seen that semiconductor lasers, more than any other optoelectronic device, have helped realize the potential of fiber optic communication.

4.1   Principles of homojunction lasers

In terms of their physical construction an LED and a laser diode (LD) have a lot of similarities. This section starts by reviewing LED emission and points out the important differences that lead to emission from LD devices; an overall comparison is provided at the end.

4.1.1   Stimulated emission

As shown in Figure 3.2, LED based emission occurs under forward bias of a pn junction. For a simple direct gap transition, electrons injected from n to p and holes injected from p to n become excess minority carriers, where they then recombine; the light emitted is characteristic of the transition involved, in this case the band gap. Such a phenomenon was reviewed in more detail in section 3.1.1. Because the carriers recombine with an average lifetime, but with no specific lifetime preattached to any individual carrier, recombination will occur even after the bias voltage has been removed, and each recombination event is independent of any other. For these reasons, LEDs are spontaneous emitters.

When a photon is incident on a semiconductor, how it interacts with the host electrons depends on the latter's excitation state. If we consider only the electrons of importance to semiconductors, then we only need consider the valence and conduction bands. For interaction with a valence band electron, as in Figure 4.1(a), a photon is absorbed and the energy is used to create an electron–hole pair. However, if the interaction is with a conduction band electron, a photon will be created out of the recombination of an electron–hole pair (Figure 4.1(b)). Thus one photon produces a second, and these two can now produce more photons; a single photon has stimulated the emission of subsequent photons. It follows that all the photons have the same wavelength. But because the emission of the second photon is at exactly the same point in time and space as the interaction of the first with the conduction band electron, the stimulated emission has the same phase as the incoming radiation.

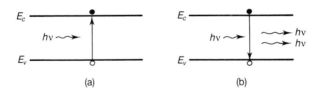

Figure 4.1 An incoming photon interacting with (a) a valence band electron, and (b) a conduction band electron.

4.1.1.1   Boltzmann equation and Einstein coefficients
In section 1.3.1 we described electrons in a solid as behaving via Fermi–Dirac statistics, and derived population distributions for the valence and conduction bands accordingly. Maxwell–Boltzmann statistics are applicable to any number of particles within a given energy level (as opposed to only two for Fermi–Dirac), but are considerably easier to manipulate. Without losing site of our ultimate aim in this section, which is to prove the need for a population inversion, we can talk about a two-level system involving Maxwell–Boltzmann statistics, and apply the final results to the energy structure of a semiconductor (which contains

two important energy bands of many different levels described using Fermi–Dirac statistics).

For a system of energy levels with values given by E_1 and E_2, the number of particles N_1 and N_2 in each level is described by the Boltzmann equation

$$\frac{N_1}{N_2} = \exp\left(\frac{E_2 - E_1}{kT}\right) = \exp\left(\frac{h\nu}{kT}\right) \tag{4.1}$$

where $E_2 - E_1 = h\nu$. If levels 1 and 2 are degenerate, i.e. have sublevels of equal energy, then (4.1) is modified to

$$\frac{N_1}{N_2} = \frac{g_1}{g_2} \exp\left(\frac{h\nu}{kT}\right) \tag{4.2}$$

where g_1 and g_2 are the number of sublevels within levels 1 and 2 respectively. It is clear that $N_2 < N_1$, and this is shown in Figure 4.2(a). If $N_1 = N_2$, then the probabilities of an incoming photon being absorbed (creating an electron–hole pair) or stimulating emission (creating a photon) are equal; it follows that for any given distribution of N_1 and N_2, the probability of either phenomenon happening is proportional to the value of N_1 or N_2. The rate of absorption or stimulated emission will also depend on the energy density of the radiation field ρ_ν at frequency ν. Thus we can write a stimulated emission rate R_{21} from level 2 to level 1 as

$$R_{21} = B_{21} N_2 \rho_\nu \tag{4.3}$$

where B_{21} is a coefficient. Similarly for the absorption rate R_{12} from level 1 to level 2

$$R_{12} = B_{12} N_1 \rho_\nu. \tag{4.4}$$

The third factor occurring in such a system, spontaneous emission, is only dependent on the population of the upper level. Its rate, R_s, can be described as

$$R_s = A_{21} N_2 \tag{4.5}$$

where A_{21} is again a coefficient, which is the reciprocal of the population decay time. For a system in thermal equilibrium, N_1 and N_2 should be constant, and so the rate of upward transitions should equal that of downward ones:

$$R_{12} = R_{21} + R_s, \tag{4.6}$$

$$\text{or} \quad B_{12} n_1 \rho_\nu = B_{21} N_2 \rho_\nu + A_{21} N_2. \tag{4.7}$$

where B_{12}, B_{21} are known as Einstein coefficients. ρ_ν can then be isolated to give

$$\rho_\nu = \frac{A_{21}/B_{21}}{(B_{12} N_1 / B_{21} N_2) - 1} \tag{4.8}$$

which, using (4.2), can be expressed in terms of ν;

$$\rho_\nu = \frac{A_{21}/B_{21}}{(B_{12} g_1 / B_{21} g_2) \exp\left(h\nu/kT\right) - 1}. \tag{4.9}$$

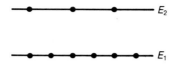

Figure 4.2 Population of two energy levels E_1 and E_2, with $E_1 < E_2$.

Planck's radiation law gives an expression for ρ_ν as a function of ν:

$$\rho_\nu = \frac{8\pi h\nu^3}{c^3 \left[\exp(h\nu/kT) - 1\right]} \, . \tag{4.10}$$

By comparing like terms in (4.9) and (4.10), the Einstein coefficients can be isolated to give

$$B_{12} = \frac{g_2}{g_1} B_{21} \tag{4.11}$$

thereby proving that absorption and stimulated emission are equally probable when $N_1 = N_2$ and the energy levels have the same degree of degeneracy (usually 1). (4.9) and (4.10) also give

$$\frac{A_{21}}{B_{21}} = \frac{8\pi h\nu^3}{c^3} \, . \tag{4.12}$$

From (4.3) and (4.5) we can see that the ratio of stimulated emission to spontaneous emission is given by

$$\frac{R_{21}}{R_s} = \frac{B_{21}\rho_\nu}{A_{21}} \, . \tag{4.13}$$

Using (4.10), (4.12) and (4.13)

$$\frac{R_{21}}{R_s} = \frac{1}{\exp\left(h\nu/kT\right) - 1} \, , \tag{4.14}$$

indicating for the system we have described so far, i.e. one where $N_1 > N_2$ and the system is in thermal equilibrium, spontaneous emission dominates over stimulated emission. We can also see by comparing (4.3) and (4.4), and using the result of (4.11), that

$$\frac{R_{21}}{R_{12}} = \frac{N_2}{N_1} \tag{4.15}$$

and that for stimulated emission to dominate over absorption $N_2 > N_1$. Thus we must have a means of creating population densities such that the upper level contains more electrons than the lower. Equation (4.1) would tend to suggest that this cannot happen for any equilibrium case, as all the terms inside the exponential are positive. This population inversion means that, because h and k are constants and we cannot alter $\nu = (E_2 - E_1)/h$, T must be negative for this condition to occur. As we cannot externally create a negative temperature, the act of population inversion by other methods implies that the concept of negative temperature must be invoked to satisfy (4.1). This does not mean that the system is 'colder' than absolute zero, in the sense that we intuitively understand it. Although many early texts on lasers refer to the 'negative temperature condition', it is really just a mathematical phenomenon that should not be considered too deeply. The term 'population inversion' is far more relevant, and nowadays much more common a term, for describing the prerequisite for stimulated emission.

4.1.1.2   Population inversion in semiconductors

Having considered the pre-condition for lasing in a two-level system, that the population in the upper level must be greater than that in the lower one, it is perhaps intuitively straightforward to transfer this idea to semiconductors; the population of electrons in the lower part of the conduction band must be greater than that in the higher part of the valence band. It should also follow that because the population densities are continually being depleted by the creation of stimulated photons, there must be some 'pumping' mechanism to replenish the electrons and holes lost in this way. Electrical pumping is by far the most convenient method of providing electrons and holes directly into a semiconductor. For a forward biased pn junction, as we saw in section 2.1.4.1, electrons injected into the n-side become excess minority carriers on the p-side, and holes injected into the p-side become excess minority carriers on the n-side. This was used to create spontaneous emission as described in section 3.1.1.1. However, if the excess 'minority' carrier concentration is very high, then the population inversion conditions referred to above would be satisfied. This could be done by heavily doping both the n-side (to create a large electron concentration) and the p-side (to create a large hole concentration, i.e. electron depletion), and then applying a forward bias such that a large current flows across the junction, i.e. the large concentration of electrons and holes diffuse towards each other to create a region of population inversion in the junction region. This is shown in Figure 4.3. The initial band diagrams under zero bias are as in Figure 4.3(a), where because of the heavy doping the Fermi level actually lies inside the valence band on the p-side and the conduction band on the n-side. Under forward bias (Figure 4.3(b)) the Fermi and other associated energy levels move relative to each other, giving rise to a familiar diffusion current as described in section 2.1.4.1. However, if the forward bias is high enough (Figure 4.3(c)), the Fermi level on the n-side E_{fn} rises above the conduction band level on the p-side E_{cp}; similarly E_{fp} is below E_{vn}. So the junction region rapidly fills up with conduction band electrons and valence band holes from the n- and p-sides respectively; the condition for population inversion is satisfied. Carriers will recombine to give spontaneous emission and the photons created will now be able to stimulate further emission. There is a point to be made here referring to the assumption in Figure 4.3(a) that the Fermi levels should be inside either the conduction or valence bands on either side of the junction. Because the population inversion in Figure 4.3(c) only occurs in the junction region for the transition of energy $h\nu \leq E_{fn} - E_{fp}$, and because each stimulated photon must have at least the band gap energy E_g, it follows that

$$E_g \leq h\nu \leq E_{fn} - E_{fp}. \tag{4.16}$$

Clearly $E_{fn} - E_{fp} \geq E_g$, and so the Fermi level must lie outside the band gap on at least one, and preferably both, sides of the junction.

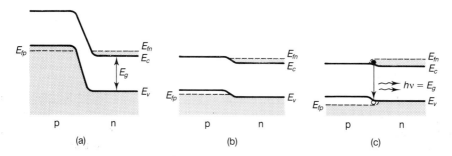

Figure 4.3 A junction formed from degenerate p and n semiconductors; (a) no bias, (b) forward bias, and (c) sufficient forward bias to cause a population inversion in the depletion region.

If the stimulated photons move away into the bulk n- or p-type semiconductor regions, then in these areas they will be quickly absorbed because no population inversion condition exists. If, however, the photons move in the plane of the junction as in Figure 4.4, then more stimulated emission can occur until photons are released to the outside world. Four-directional output seems very wasteful and makes lasing action more difficult, and ideally we would like the emission to be in just one direction. Some method of confinement and feedback is therefore necessary, and this is considered in the next section.

4.1.2 Optical considerations

Besides the condition of population inversion necessary for the creation of stimulated emission, there are other optical conditions that must be satisfied before a semiconductor device can behave as a laser.

4.1.2.1 Confinement
We have seen in the last section that the stimulated emission region (active region) of a semiconductor pn junction is very small compared to the overall size of the device. Any photons that exit this region into the bulk semiconductor are likely to

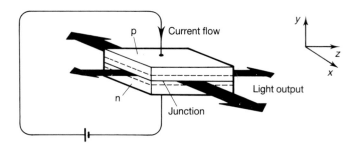

Figure 4.4 Structure and light output from a degenerate pn junction under high forward bias.

be destroyed with the creation of an electron–hole pair, and hence will not take part in any further stimulation of photon production; this mechanism should then be minimized. Fortunately, the extremely high carrier densities at the junction give a change in the refractive index in this region; a waveguide is then formed, confining light by total internal reflection (Figure 4.5). The refractive index difference is small (0.1–1.0%), giving a very high critical angle (82°–87°), and hence the confinement is not ideal; how this is improved on by the use of heterostructures is considered in section 4.2. For all semiconductor lasers there is a confinement factor, Γ, which is the total light confined to the active region of thickness d:

$$\Gamma = \frac{\int_0^d |E(y)|^2 \, dy}{\int_{-\infty}^{\infty} |E(y)|^2 \, dy} \tag{4.17}$$

where E is the magnitude of the electric field vector along the thickness direction y. Γ can be approximated by

$$\Gamma = 1 - \exp(-C\Delta nd) \tag{4.18}$$

where C is a constant and Δn is the difference in the refractive index between the active region and its surroundings.

4.1.2.2 Gain
As mentioned in section 4.1.1.2, photons released by stimulated emission are likely to cause further stimulations as long as there is a population inversion; this is the phenomenon of optical gain. Along any optical path there will always be losses (absorption, α) as well as gain g. Relationships can be found between α, g and the population densities of a two-level system, e.g. [2, 3].

4.1.2.3 Optical cavity and feedback
So far, we have considered two of the conditions necessary to produce laser action: population inversion, which leads to stimulated emission, and gain. The gain obtained in a single travel of an electromagnetic wave down a laser cavity is small,

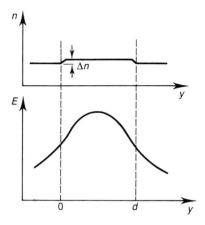

Figure 4.5 The waveguiding effect of the depletion region in a semiconductor laser.

and so in order to increase the overall gain multiple passes of a wave must occur. This is achieved using mirrors placed at either end of the cavity. The details of this varies from laser to laser. For instance, a gas laser has two mirrors, one with a high reflection coefficient at the laser wavelength and placed at the 'back' of the laser, and the other mirror of a lower reflectivity placed at the front (Figure 4.6(a)). The rear mirror acts to reflect nearly all the light back into the cavity, and the front mirror allows partial reflection to increase the gain, and partial transmission to access the laser output. For a semiconductor laser, the cleaved ends of the crystal

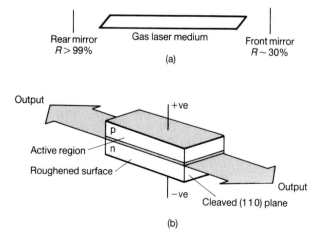

Figure 4.6 An optical cavity for (a) a gas laser, and (b) a semiconductor laser.

forming the device act as the mirrors. For a GaAs device, cleaving along the (110) plane creates two parallel identical mirrors. Light can reflect at both ends, but not at the sides as these are deliberately roughened to prevent feedback (Figure 4.6(b)). Sometimes the back mirror of the device is metallized to increase the reflectivity (otherwise the output is wasted, apart from the small amount needed for the drive circuit's feedback photodiode (see section 4.9)). The reflectivity R at each mirror can be calculated as

$$R = \left(\frac{n-1}{n+1}\right)^2 \qquad (4.19)$$

where $n = 3.6$ for GaAs, giving $R = 0.32$. The electromagnetic waves generated in the cavity must have the form of standing waves, which places a restriction on the number of wavelengths that can resonate, given by

$$L = \frac{m\lambda_0}{2n} \qquad (4.20)$$

where L is the cavity length, and m is an integer. Obviously, many values of λ_0 satisfy this condition, but only those within the spontaneous emission spectrum will be produced (Figure 4.7(a)). Further, optical losses in the path travelled by the wave means that only the strongest lines will survive (Figure 4.7(b)), leading to a set of lasing modes as given in Figure 4.7(c). These modes will be longitudinal, as they occur because of standing waves formed in the direction shown in Figure 4.8(a).

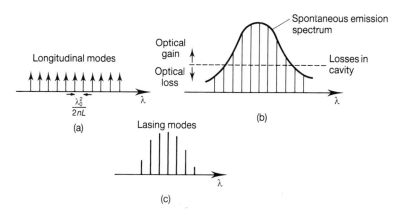

Figure 4.7 (a) Resonant modes of a laser cavity. (b) Spontaneous emission spectrum. (c) Optical gain wavelengths.

Transverse modes, as shown in Figure 4.8(b), can be formed but the laser is usually designed such that only one of these is allowed, otherwise there could be 'hot spots' in the output corresponding to higher order modes.

Lateral modes are usually damped by the side roughening already referred to, although the unrestricted width of the active region does not prevent this happening entirely, leading to subpeaks on the sides of the fundamental modes (Figure 4.8(c)). How this effect is eliminated using a stripe geometry laser is considered in section 4.3.

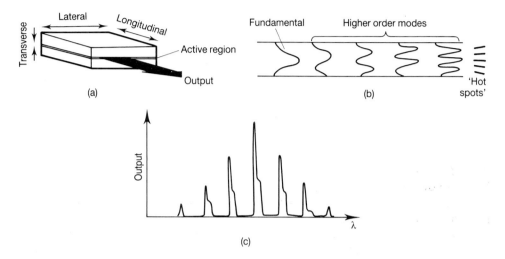

(a)

(b)

(c)

Figure 4.8 (a) Mode orientations in a semiconductor laser. (b) Transverse modes and 'hot spots'. (c) Subpeaks on the sides of fundamental mode oscillation due to unwanted lateral modes.

To find the mode spacing of Figure 4.7(a) with respect to wavelength, (4.20) is differentiated to give

$$\frac{\Delta m}{\Delta \lambda_0} = \frac{-2nL}{\lambda_0^2} + \frac{2L}{\lambda_0}\frac{dn}{d\lambda} . \tag{4.21}$$

This can be rearranged to give, for $\Delta m = 1$ (i.e. adjacent modes),

$$\Delta \lambda = \frac{\lambda_0^2}{2nL\left[(\lambda_0/n)(dn/d\lambda) - 1\right]} . \tag{4.22}$$

Although electromagnetic theory does show that n is a function of λ, over the very small changes in wavelength between adjacent modes $dn/d\lambda$ is very small, and hence to a good approximation the mode spacing $\Delta \lambda$ is given by

$$|\Delta \lambda| = \frac{\lambda_0^2}{2nL} \tag{4.23}$$

where we have ignored the negative sign as it has no special significance.

Example 4.1

Calculate the mode spacing for a typical GaAs laser of $\lambda_0 = 0.94$ μm, $n = 3.6$ and $L = 300$ μm.

Solution: from (4.23)

$$\Delta\lambda = \frac{(0.94 \times 10^{-6})^2}{2 \times 3.6 \times 300 \times 10^{-6}} = 4 \,\text{Å}. \tag{4.24}$$

4.1.2.4   Lasing threshold

We are now in a position to determine the threshold condition for lasing action to occur, given that the three necessary prerequisites have been satisfied, namely population inversion, gain and feedback.

Because there are both absorption and gain along the direction x of the longitudinal modes, the irradiance of the beam $I(x)$ is

$$I(x) = I(0) \, \exp\left(\Gamma g - \alpha\right)x \,. \tag{4.25}$$

The light will be reflected at both ends of the cavity with a reflectivity R, assuming that the cleaved ends of the cavity are not metallized (if they are, replace R^2 in the next equation with $R_1 R_2$, representing the different reflectivities of the individual mirrors). For stability the net gain around the cavity must equal the net losses, and hence

$$R^2 \, \exp\left(\Gamma g - \alpha\right)2L = 1 \,. \tag{4.26}$$

This can be rearranged to give, in terms of g,

$$g_{th} = \frac{1}{\Gamma}\left(\alpha + \frac{1}{L}\log_e \frac{1}{R}\right) \tag{4.27}$$

where g_{th} is the threshold gain coefficient. As α obviously represents the absorption losses and Γ the losses due to lack of ideal confinement, the term $(1/L \log_e 1/R)$ represents the amount of light transmitted out of the cavity.

Early results on semiconductor lasers suggested that there was a power law relationship between current density J and gain coefficient g [4]. This relationship could be written as

$$g = BnJ^n \tag{4.28}$$

where Bn was a constant and n varied in the range 1–1.5. The index n had a temperature dependence, given by

$$n = \left[1 + \left(\frac{kT}{E_t}\right)^2\right]^{1/2} \tag{4.29}$$

where E_t was a measure of the band tail depth. Later results show a variation on this (Figure 4.9) with the gain tending to saturate at high values of current and be higher than expected at low currents [5]. The current density J_e per micron of active layer thickness expected of an ideal device can be related to the current density J and internal quantum efficiency η_i of real devices by

$$J = \frac{J_e d}{\eta_i} \tag{4.30}$$

where d is the active layer thickness. The linear dashed line in Figure 4.9 can be written as

$$g = \frac{g_0}{J_0}(J_e - J_0), \tag{4.31}$$

where g_0 and J_0 are constants. Hence combining (4.30) and (4.31) gives

$$J = \frac{J_0 d}{\eta_i} + \frac{g J_0 d}{g_0 \eta_i}. \tag{4.32}$$

Using (4.27) and (4.32), a threshold current density can be found:

$$J_{th} = \frac{J_0 d}{\eta_i} + \frac{J_0 d}{g_0 \eta_i \Gamma}\left(\alpha + \frac{1}{L}\log_e \frac{1}{R}\right). \tag{4.33}$$

Note that this is slightly different from the commonly seen expression for J_{th}, where the first term on the right hand side of (4.33) is often ignored:

$$J_{th} = \frac{J_0 d}{g_0 \eta_i \Gamma}\left(\alpha + \frac{1}{L}\log_e \frac{1}{R}\right). \tag{4.34}$$

J_0 and g_0 are constants to be interpreted from data taken on individual lasers, η_i is usually in the range 0.6–0.7 but can be close to 1 for some lasers. The term Γ as a function of the difference in refractive index Δn at the edge of the confinement region is shown in Figure 4.10 [6]. $J_0 d/g_0 \eta_i \Gamma$ is often termed $1/\beta$, where β is known as the gain factor.

Example 4.2

Find the threshold current for a laser using the following data: front and rear mirror reflectivities = 0.32 and 0.99 respectively, cavity length and width are 300μm and 30 μm respectively, $\alpha = 10^2$ cm^{-1}, $\beta = 0.11$ cm A^{-1}.

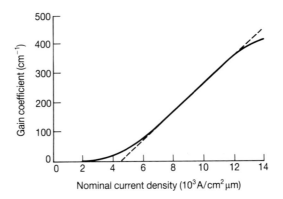

Figure 4.9 The dependence of gain coefficient on nominal current density at 297 K in GaAs with 4×10^{17} net acceptors and 6×10^{17} total charged impurities cm^{-3} (©AIP: reproduced by kind permission).

Solution: in this case (4.34) becomes (working in cm)

$$J_{th} = \frac{1}{\beta}\left(\alpha + \frac{1}{2L}\log_e \frac{1}{R_1 R_2}\right)$$

$$\text{giving } J_{th} = 9.09 \times \left(100 + \frac{1}{2 \times 300 \times 10^{-4}}\log_e \frac{1}{0.32 \times 0.99}\right)$$

$$= 1083 \text{ A cm}^{-2}$$

$$\text{and so } I_{th} = 1083 \times 300 \times 10^{-4} \times 30 \times 10^{-4}$$

$$= 97 \text{ mA}. \tag{4.35}$$

4.1.2.5 *Temperature dependence*
Experimentally it has been found that

$$J_{th} \propto \exp\left(\frac{T}{T_0}\right) \tag{4.36}$$

where T_0 is in the range 40–200 K. This is shown in Figure 4.11(a) [7]. There are many factors behind this temperature dependence. Junction heating is one, the temperature dependence of radiation and carrier confinement are others. Thus the double heterostructure lasers to be discussed later have a weak temperature dependence of J_{th} because of the high heterojunction barriers. The dependence of J_{th} on increasing band gap difference is shown in Figure 4.11(b) [8].

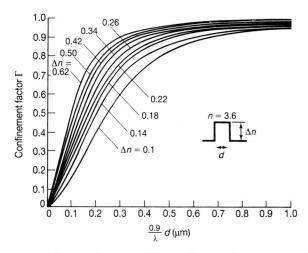

Figure 4.10 The confinement factor Γ as a function of d/λ for various values of the step Δn at the two heterojunctions of a double heterojunction (DH) laser (©Springer Verlag: reproduced by kind permission).

Example 4.3

Calculate the temperature at which the room temperature value of the threshold current doubles for a particular laser of $T_0 = 125$ K.

Solution: using (4.36)

$$\frac{J_{th}}{2J_{th}} = \frac{\exp(293/125)}{\exp(T/125)}$$

$$\text{giving } T = 293 + 125\log_e 2$$

$$= 380\,\text{K, or } 107\,^{\circ}\text{C.} \tag{4.37}$$

4.1.3 Output characteristics

Having determined all the conditions necessary for laser action to occur, and derived an expression for threshold current, we can now see how these produce the output characteristics of a laser, both in terms of power and radiation pattern.

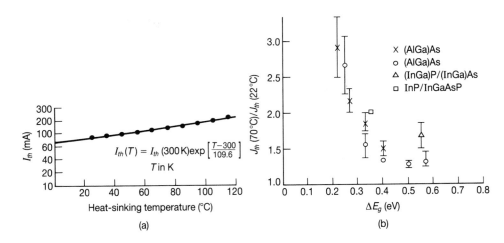

Figure 4.11 (a) The temperature dependence of c.w. current threshold of a laser (©AIP: reproduced by kind permission). (b) The ratio $J_{th}(70°\text{C})/J_{th}(22\,°\text{C})$ as a function of the band gap difference in the active region of DH lasers (©Springer Verlag: reproduced by kind permission).

4.1.3.1   Power and external efficiency

In terms of its operation, an LED works only by spontaneous emission; so does a laser diode, up to the threshold current value, because up to here the stimulated emission gain coefficient is not sufficiently high for the amplification to dominate over spontaneous emission. Therefore, below current values of J_{th} the power output from a laser diode will have a linear dependence on current, as shown in Figure 3.11 for an LED.

Above threshold, stimulated emission becomes the dominant mechanism for photon production, and so a linear increase in forward current, giving as it does a linear increase in carrier concentration, should also give a linear dependence of light output on current above threshold. This indeed does happen to a reasonable degree, but because the stimulated process is so much more efficient than the spontaneous one the slope of the power–current curve is much steeper. An example is shown in Figure 4.12. Region (a) is the region where spontaneous emission dominates, and the laser behaves as an LED. Region (b) is a non-linear transition region, where the spontaneous and stimulated emission regimes are both significant and the brightness of the device increases rapidly. Such a device is called a superradiant LED, and is discussed in section 4.1.3.5. The stimulated emission region, characterized by a steep slope of output power/current density, is shown in region (c). The threshold current density J_{th} can be found experimentally by extrapolation to the current density axis.

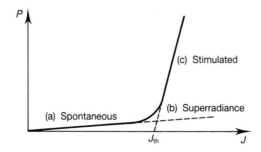

Figure 4.12 Power output vs current input characteristic of a semiconductor laser.

We can define a quantum efficiency term for a laser, which in this case is a differential efficiency for a diode above threshold:

$$\eta_e = \frac{e}{h\nu} \frac{\Delta P}{A \Delta J} \tag{4.38}$$

where $\Delta J = J - J_{th}$, i.e. the additional current density above threshold, and A is the cross-sectional area of the active region. Strictly speaking we should have two quantum efficiencies, η_{sp} and η_{st}, representing the spontaneous and stimulated processes respectively, because the value of P involves both types of radiation. In section 3.3.4, we introduced a transmission factor F_{sp} to take account of how much generated light was coupled to the outside. There is a similar term F_{st} for a laser diode. F_{st} should be much greater than F_{sp} because we do not need to consider a critical angle; most of the power inside the cavity is directed normal to the end faces. The expression for output power then becomes

$$P = \underset{\substack{\text{spontaneous}\\\text{emission}}}{F_{sp}\,\eta_{sp}\,\frac{JAh\nu}{e}} + \underset{\substack{\text{stimulated}\\\text{emission}}}{F_{st}\,\eta_{st}\,\frac{Ah\nu}{e}(J - J_{th})}. \tag{4.39}$$

In practice stimulated dominates over spontaneous emission once threshold has been achieved, and so (4.39) is reduced to

$$P = F_{st}\,\eta_{st}\,\frac{Ah\nu}{e}(J - J_{th}). \tag{4.40}$$

We have already seen in (4.27) an expression giving the relevant terms to determine F_{st}. This is given by

$$
\begin{aligned}
F_{st} &= \frac{\text{total output power}}{\text{total power produced}} \\
&= \frac{(1/L)\,\log_e(1/R)}{\alpha + (1/L)\,\log_e(1/R)} \\
&= \left[1 + \frac{\alpha L}{\log_e(1/R)}\right]^{-1}.
\end{aligned}
\tag{4.41}
$$

Using (4.38), (4.40) and (4.41) the external differential quantum efficiency can then be found:

$$\eta_e = \eta_{st} \left[1 + \frac{\alpha L}{\log_e (1/R)} \right]^{-1} \tag{4.42}$$

where we are still making the assumption that the mirror reflectivities are equal. If not, then $\alpha L / \log_e (1/R)$ is replaced by $2\alpha L / \log_e (1/R_1 R_2)$.

Example 4.4

Use the parameters of the laser in example 4.2 to determine η_e, assuming $\eta_{st} = 0.95$.

Solution: from example 4.2, remembering that we are dealing with a laser of different end reflectivities, (4.42) becomes

$$\begin{aligned}
\eta_e &= \eta_{st} \left[1 + \frac{2\alpha L}{\log_e (1/R_1 R_2)} \right]^{-1} \\
&= 0.95 \left[1 + \frac{2 \times 100 \times 0.03}{\log_e (1/(0.32 \times 0.99))} \right]^{-1} \\
&= 0.15. \tag{4.43}
\end{aligned}$$

In this case the diode is not particularly efficient because of the fairly high value of α.

Thus an efficient diode can be obtained by increasing η_{st} or decreasing α, which are both desirable as they do not introduce other problems. Decreasing L or R also increases η_{st}, but as shown from (4.33) this has the deleterious effect of increasing the threshold current. By rearranging (4.42) to isolate L

$$L = \frac{\log_e (1/R)}{\alpha} \left(\frac{\eta_{st}}{\eta_e} - 1 \right) \tag{4.44}$$

it can be seen that a plot of diode length vs measured external efficiency can give a value for the internal efficiency η_{st}, as all the other terms are known. Using this method, η_{st} has been found to be close to 1, indicating a near total conversion of input electrons to generated photons.

From (4.36) it might be expected that the output power–current curve shown in Figure 4.12 doesn't change in form with temperature, but only in the point where lasing starts. This has been confirmed by many authors, and an example of a temperature dependent family of curves is shown in Figure 4.13.

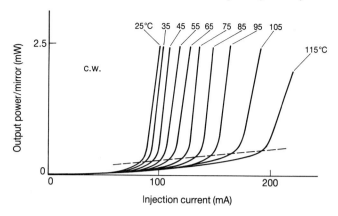

Figure 4.13 Output power vs input current as a function of heat sink temperature (©AIP: reproduced by kind permission).

4.1.3.2 Power conversion efficiency

Because of the very high current densities involved in laser diodes, joule heating becomes significant and the total power conversion efficiency η_p is given by

$$\eta_p = \frac{P}{I^2 R_s + (Ih\nu/e)} \tag{4.45}$$

where R_s is the diode series resistance. Values of η_p are much lower than those of η_e or η_i.

Example 4.5

Calculate the power conversion efficiency of the laser from example 4.2 if the series resistance is 10 Ω and the power output is 10 mW at 0.80 μm.

Solution: from example 4.2 and (4.45)

$$\begin{aligned}
\eta_p &= \frac{10^{-2}}{\left((97 \times 10^{-3})^2 \times 10\right) + (97 \times 10^{-3} \times hc)/(0.80 \times 10^{-6} \times e)} \\
&= 0.04. \tag{4.46}
\end{aligned}$$

4.1.3.3 Spectrum

Besides a large increase in output power, there is another characteristic, mentioned earlier in section 4.1.2.3, that characterizes laser output; its very narrow spectral width containing a family of wavelengths separated by a distance $\lambda_0^2/2nL$ as in (4.23). The transition from spontaneous to stimulated emission, as shown in Figure 4.12, is shown in terms of spectral characteristics in Figure 4.14, where the individual figures (a), (b) and (c) correspond to those equivalently marked areas on Figure 4.12. As can be seen, the broad spectrum of spontaneous emission (Figure 4.14(a)) gives way firstly to a comparatively narrow superradiant region (Figure 4.14(b)) and then to the very narrowly defined lasing region (Figure 4.14(c)). The shift in laser wavelength away from the peak in the spontaneous emission spectrum is because of the narrowing of the band gap due to the high carrier densities.

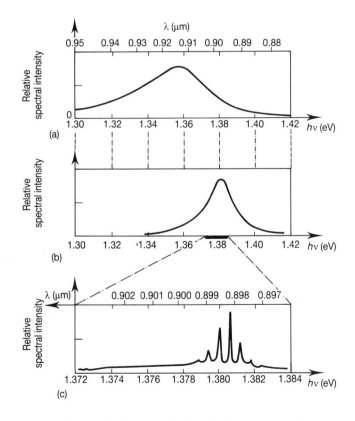

Figure 4.14 Spectral characteristics of the output radiation at different current levels in a semiconductor laser: (a) spontaneous emission, (b) superradiance, and (c) stimulated emission.

4.1.3.4   Radiation pattern

We have already mentioned in section 4.1.2.3, when discussing resonant modes, that the thickness d of the active region is reduced to allow only one mode to propagate, hence minimizing the occurrence of hot spots in the output beam (Figure 4.8(b)). Although the active region is very narrow, this doesn't lead to a narrow slit-like output beam; there is substantial diffraction of the output at the interface with air, leading to the radiation pattern as shown in Figure 4.15. This leads to a very important difference between a semiconductor laser and all other types: the output beam from a laser diode is not a narrowly defined spot or even a stripe. It rapidly becomes a broad beam, and in order for the light not to be wasted a collecting lens should be placed immediately adjacent to the output. Laser design geometries can produce a much more defined beam, as we shall see in section 4.3, but they certainly do not approach the very small divergence angles (typically 1–2 minutes of arc) typical of the best gas lasers; angles of the order of several degrees are far more typical.

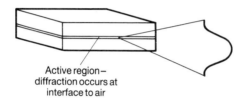

Active region –
diffraction occurs at
interface to air

Figure 4.15 Diffraction at the output from a semiconductor laser.

4.1.3.5   Superradiance

There is a mode of operation given by region (b) of both Figures 4.12 and 4.14, which corresponds to a non-linear transition between the two linear dependencies of spontaneous (a) and stimulated (c) power–current regimes. Because a device operated here does not form part of the pure stimulated regime given by (c), it is strictly speaking an LED, but the non-linear dependence of output power on current leads to the term superradiance or superluminescence. It is also known as amplified spontaneous emission. Although the device operates as an LED, structurally it is very similar to a laser, but one end of the optical cavity is made lossy to prevent reflections (and hence feedback) to produce significant oscillation. The output is thus only from the opposite end.

In this mode there is gain due to a single pass amplification mechanism and the output therefore increases rapidly with drive current. At the same time the spectral width decreases to about 10–20 nm, as shown in Figure 4.14(b). Because the efficiency of spontaneous emission is lower than that due to stimulation, for a given output, the length of the cavity L in a superluminescent LED must be greater than that in a laser diode. Also, again for a comparable power output, the required current density is about three times higher for the LED compared to the laser. This can lead to problems of long term reliability. However, the superluminescent LED has advantages over the conventional LED, not the least of which is that the increased light output coupled with a limited degree of beam convergence gives a large (~ 50) gain in the amount of power that can usefully be transmitted into a fiber.

4.1.4   Comparison with an LED

We are now in a position to note the basic differences between the output characteristics of an LED and a laser. These are:

  (i) an LED emits spontaneous radiation, which is broad in its spectral nature and incoherent. A laser emits stimulated radiation, which has a narrower linewidth and is coherent.
 (ii) LEDs can give an output power as high as a semiconductor laser, although an individual laser shows more output in stimulated mode than when operating as an LED.
(iii) A laser is a threshold device, an LED isn't.
 (iv) A laser has a strong dependence of threshold current, and hence output power, on temperature, whilst an LED has a weak temperature dependence.
  (v) Although the two devices can generate similar amounts of optical power, the better directed laser beam means that more light from this source can be coupled to a fiber.

4.2   Heterojunction lasers

Early semiconductor lasers based on homojunctions were little more than laboratory curiosities, used largely to look at the basic physics of stimulated emission and gain, rather than with any technological application in mind. They were inferior to other lasers in many respects, namely:

  (i) they could only operate at low temperature, usually in pulsed mode with high drive currents ($\sim 10^4$ A cm^{-2}) – room temperature generation demanding even higher current operation ($\sim 10^5$ A cm^{-2}),
 (ii) the output had a large spectral width compared to other lasers sources, especially gas lasers,
(iii) the output was not spatially coherent, because of diffraction at the output aperture,
 (iv) output power was very low in comparison with other lasers,
  (v) reliability was poor, with devices showing a rapid decay in performance and premature failure.

Devices were made in most III–V materials as well as many other compound semiconductors, and given in [9] is a complete list of homojunction materials that exhibit laser action, including the excitation mechanism (there is a similar table in [10]).

The proposal for using optical fibers as media for lightwave communications revived the interest in semiconductor lasers from a technology point of view. Here was a real use for such a laser, where the small size of the device and its power supply were its major advantages over other lasers. The timing of this proposal coincided with the maturing of both crystal growth and several of the epitaxial technologies (see Chapter 8) needed for heterostructure devices. There was suddenly a demand to solve the problem of reliability, room temperature operation and threshold current, along with the technologies potentially able to solve these problems. It wasn't long before heterostructure lasers were being made, and then double heterostructure devices, and soon an initially bewildering range of device designs to overcome different aspects of laser operation were being published; new structures are being proposed and made even now, showing that the scope for innovation is far from limited.

This section reviews the basic heterostructure device, and how its performance is an improvement over a homojunction system. Double heterostructures are then introduced, a review of the semiconductor materials used is presented, and then a selection of the significant designs are discussed.

4.2.1   Single heterostructure

The problems with a homojunction device which can be overcome with a heterostructure are:

(i) poor optical confinement,
(ii) marginal population inversion,
(iii) poor carrier confinement,

all three of which lead to a high operating current, which is a major factor in device degradation and hence long term reliability (see section 4.10). In addition, factor (ii) often limited operation to 77 K to reduce the density of intrinsic carriers. Although heterostructures were discussed in section 3.5.3 on advanced LEDs, their uses in semiconductor lasers have been where they have represented the greatest advance in technological achievement. It is then worthwhile to briefly review here the working of the two types of heterostructure, isotype (N–n or P–p) and anisotype (N–p or P–n), where the capital letter signifies the material of higher bandgap.

4.2.1.1   Isotype
Examples of both N–n and P–p isotype heterojunctions are shown in Figures 4.16(b) and (d) respectively. In Figure 4.16(b) the conduction band on the N side

bends upwards, whilst on the n-side it bends downwards. At first this behaviour might seem confusing, especially as the valence band only has a small discontinuity. But if we remember that for any junction in equilibrium (i) the Fermi levels must be equal, and (ii) the band gap in any semiconductor must be constant within that material (for a given doping) then the situation becomes clearer. For N and n separated, as in Figure 4.16(a), there will be a difference in conduction band and valence band energies, relative to a constant Fermi level, of ΔE_c and ΔE_v respectively. Thus bringing N and n together results in E_v bending up on the N-side and down on the n-side, with E_c correspondingly moving up or down on the N- or n-side respectively to maintain the band gap. At the junction there will be discontinuities in both E_v and E_c. As seen from Figure 4.16(a), in going from N to n, ΔE_v is positive. So there will be a positive discontinuity in E_v after junction formation given by ΔE_v. Similarly, the negative value of ΔE_c in Figure 4.16(a) gives a negative discontinuity in E_c after junction formation; however, here the two conduction bands are moving in opposite directions, and hence ΔE_c appears as a spike. Hence, as shown in Figure 4.16(b), the rise in E_c on the N-side acts to deplete this region of electrons, whilst the fall in E_c on the n-side acts as an accumulation, or electron confinement, region.

At first, a plausible alternative to the diagram of Figure 4.16(b) might seem possible. Why is the spike in E_c, and not E_v – in other words, isn't the band diagram of Figure 4.16(c) equally possible? A further consideration of junction formation will see why this is not so. In forming the junction, the electrons flow from a high potential region to a low potential region until the Fermi levels have equalized, in our case from N to n. This leads to depletion on the N-side and accumulation on the n-side, giving the corresponding band bending as in Figure 4.16(b). The formation of a potential barrier ΔE_c at equilibrium prevents further electron movement. In Figure 4.16(c), there is no barrier in E_c to charge movement, implying that electrons are free to move indefinitely. Clearly this is untrue, and so Figure 4.16(c) cannot represent an energy model of carrier movement; Figure 4.16(b) is then the correct interpretation.

A band structure for a P–p contact is shown in Figure 4.16(d). Similarly to the N–n contact, hole transfer from P to p cause a hole potential barrier at the interface, and hence corresponding depletion and accumulation layers. ΔE_c and ΔE_v also appear, and are similarly defined as for the N–n structure.

4.2.1.2 Anisotype

Equilibrium band diagrams for N–p and P–n contacts are shown in Figure 4.17. A spike appears both in the conduction band on the N–p system (Figure 4.17(b)) and in the valence band of the P–n system (Figure 4.17(d)). Majority carriers are thus held back from moving from the wide gap material to the narrow gap. Similarly majority carriers are held in the narrow gap material by the large difference in either E_v (N–p junction) or E_c (P–n junction).

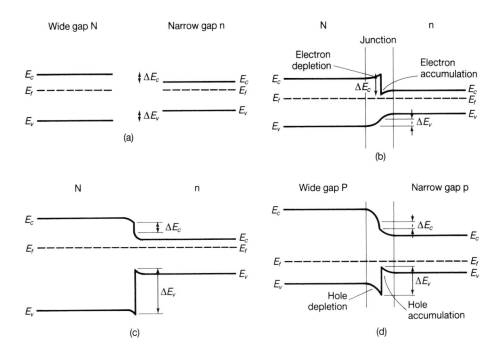

Figure 4.16 Isotype heterojunctions: (a) N and n separated, (b) band diagram through an N–n junction, (c) impossible alternative to (b), and (d) band diagram through a P–p junction.

Single heterostructure (SH) lasers did alleviate the problems mentioned at the beginning of this section, but their practical use was short lived as it became clear that double heterostructure (DH) lasers were needed, and these were produced within a year of the first SH laser.

4.2.2 Double heterostructure

The advantages of a DH laser over both a single heterostructure and especially a homojunction system will be apparent from a discussion of Figure 4.18. This shows a double heterostructure system consisting of one isotype (p-GaAs to P-AlGaAs) and one anisotype (p-GaAs to N-AlGaAs) junction (Figure 4.18(a)). Extracting the relevant combinations from Figures 4.16 and 4.17 the equilibrium band diagram through the structure looks as in Figure 4.18(b). There is a potential barrier to electron movement from N to p given by the spike in E_c, and from p to P given by the large potential barrier at this interface. There are similar restrictions on hole movement at the two interfaces. With the application of sufficient forward bias

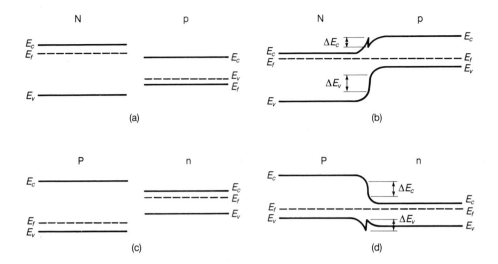

Figure 4.17 Band diagrams of anisotype heterojunctions: N–p (a) separated, and (b) joined; P–n (c) separated, and (d) joined.

(Figure 4.18(c)) some electrons have enough energy to overcome the N–p spike in E_c and enter the p-doped central region. However, they are still prevented from leaving at the p–P junction because the barrier height there is still large. Thus a large number of injected carriers are confined more readily, obtaining a population inversion with a lower threshold current. A similar diagram can be drawn for a PnN system under both equlibrium and forward bias conditions (Figures 4.18(d) and (e)). Here we have a degenerate n-type region as the central layer, and the injection of holes from P to n in forward bias creates the population inversion.

For both NpP or PnN structures there are two further advantages of DH systems: the sandwich formed by two wide gap materials either side of a narrow gap material leads to a large refractive index difference. As noted in section 4.1.2.1, the refractive index difference between the population inversion region and the surrounding semiconductor is brought about by the high carrier densities, and it is of the order of 0.1–1.0%. For heterostructure systems, wide gap materials have a smaller refractive index n than those with a narrow gap because of the dependence of n of λ. In the GaAs–Al$_x$Ga$_{1-x}$As system for instance, n varies as $\Delta n = 0.62\Delta x$ [11], leading to Δn values of the order of a few percent (Figure 4.18(f)). This significant increase in optical confinement over homojunction systems means that losses outside the population inversion region are much reduced, leading to an increase in the confinement factor Γ from (4.18), and hence a decrease in the threshold current from (4.33). As shown in Figure 4.19, the years following the invention of the double heterostructure laser saw a rapid fall in the room temperature threshold current from $\sim 10^5$ A cm^{-2} for the first homojunctions, to $\sim 4 \times 10^3$ A cm^{-2} for the

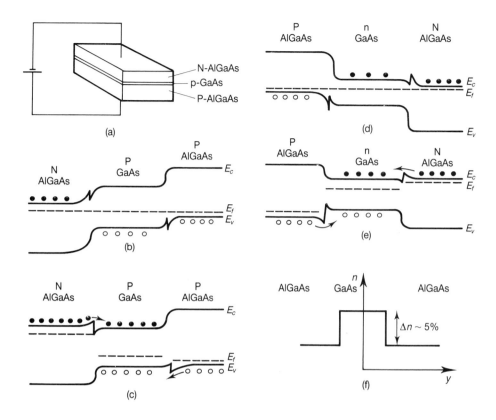

Figure 4.18 A double heterojunction system: (a) structure of NpP, band diagram with (b) no bias, and (c) forward bias, (d) PnN system with no bias, (e) with bias, and (f) refractive index variation through the junction.

first DH structures and 500 A cm^{-2} within a few years [12]. In addition, because the high potential barriers are designed to cause carrier confinement, the threshold current is not as temperature sensitive, as shown in Figure 4.20 [13].

4.2.3 Energy band parameters

The discussion so far has centred around a phenomenological description of band bending with regard to difference in Fermi levels and carrier injection and confinement. We can now readily calculate the differences in E_c and E_v for any system, and as an example we will use the N–p structure as shown in Figure 4.21. Electron affinities χ (the energy required to remove an electron to the vacuum level from the bottom of the conduction band) and work functions φ (similarly defined from the

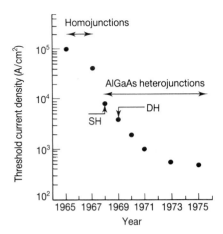

Figure 4.19 Historical trend in threshold current density of early GaAs-based laser diodes (©Springer Verlag: reproduced by kind permission).

Fermi level) are shown for the two separate systems in Figure 4.21(a). Note that low band gap materials generally, but not always, have a higher affinity as shown in Table 4.1 [14], although it must be said that different sources give variable values for χ, largely due to taking the direct or indirect nature of the band gap without explicitly mentioning it. For instance, AlAs is quoted with two band gaps: 2.95 eV (direct) and 2.16 eV (indirect), but with 3.5 eV quoted for χ. This is the indirect gap value. To find the direct gap value, the difference in band gaps is subtracted from this, i.e. direct gap $\chi = (3.5 - (2.95 - 2.16)) = 2.71$ eV.

From Figure 4.21(b), the amount of band bending is given by the difference in the work functions, $\varphi_p - \varphi_N$. Thus the built-in potential of the junction V_{bi} can be given by

$$
\begin{aligned}
eV_{bi} &= \varphi_p - \varphi_N \\
&= (E_{gp} + \chi_p - V_p) - (\chi_N + V_N)
\end{aligned}
\tag{4.47}
$$

where V_p and V_N are the differences between the Fermi levels and the top of the valence band for the p-material (V_p) or the bottom of the conduction band for the N-material (V_N). Equation (4.47) can be reduced to

$$
eV_{bi} = E_{gp} + \Delta\chi - (V_p + V_N).
\tag{4.48}
$$

The conduction band spike ΔE_c has a value given by the electron affinity difference, from Figure 4.21(a):

$$
\Delta E_c = \chi_N - \chi_p = \Delta\chi.
\tag{4.49}
$$

Also from Figure 4.21(a), the valence band has a discontinuity ΔE_v given by

$$
\begin{aligned}
\Delta E_v &= (E_{gN} + \chi_N) - (E_{gp} + \chi_p) \\
&= \Delta E_g - \Delta\chi.
\end{aligned}
\tag{4.50}
$$

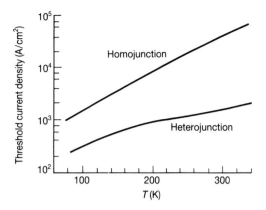

Figure 4.20 A comparison of the threshold current density dependence on temperature for homojunction and heterojunction lasers (©AIP: reproduced by kind permission).

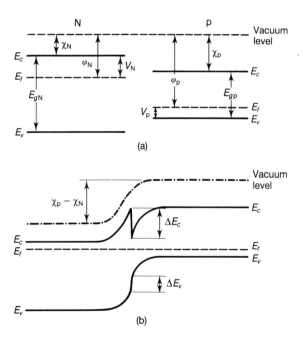

Figure 4.21 Parameters used in the calculation of ΔE_c and ΔE_v in a heterojunction.

Combining (4.49) and (4.50) gives

$$\Delta E_c + \Delta E_v = \Delta E_g \,. \tag{4.51}$$

Material	E_g (eV)	χ (eV)
InSb	0.17	4.59
InAs	0.36	4.90
Ge	0.66	4.13
GaSb	0.73	4.06
Si	1.11	4.01
InP	1.35	4.35
GaAs	1.42	4.07
AlSb	1.60	3.65
AlAs	2.16	2.71
GaP	2.25	4.30

Table 4.1 Values of band gap E_g and electron affinity χ for various semi-conductors.

4.2.4 Band gap against stoichiometry

Various formulae have been put forward to calculate the band gap as a function of x. To a first approximation, the variation for a compound $A_{1-x}B_xC$ is linear and is given by

$$E_g(A_{1-x}B_xC) = E_g(AC) + [E_g(BC) - E_g(AC)]x. \qquad (4.52)$$

This relationship would be true for any transition which remained fixed at a given point in k–space. However a second-order perturbation of the Schrödinger potential will give a change in E_g proportional to $x(1-x)$. Equation (4.52) then becomes

$$E_g(A_{1-x}B_xC) = E_g(AC) + [E_g(BC) - E_g(AC)]x - cx(1-x). \qquad (4.53)$$

In its final form

$$E_g(A_{1-x}B_xC) = E_g(AC) + [E_g(BC) - E_g(AC) - c]x + cx^2 \qquad (4.54)$$

where c is positive because of the superlinear dependence of E_g on x. Equation (4.54) was first proposed in [15], where various values of c were calculated – these are reproduced in Table 4.2. Note that there will be two versions of (4.54) for materials that change from direct to indirect gap: AlGaAs is an example. The values of binary band gaps and c used in calculating the value of the ternary band gap should always be consistent, i.e. be direct band gap values to calculate E_g for $0 < x < 0.44$.

Material	c
$Al_xGa_{1-x}As$	0.27
$GaAs_{1-x}P_x$	0.21
$InAs_{1-x}P_x$	0.27
$InAs_xSb_{1-x}$	0.58
$In_{1-x}Ga_xAs$	0.32
$In_{1-x}Ga_xSb$	0.43

Table 4.2 Values of the c parameter for various semiconductors.

4.2.5 Lattice matching

Although we will show later in this chapter (section 4.5.5) that lattice mismatching can be used to an advantage under certain circumstances, we will assume for the minute that the materials that make up the material of a double heterostructure have to have the same lattice constant and are grown epitaxially. In other words we are dealing with a single crystal structure of fixed atomic spacing, despite the structure consisting of different semiconductors. In any detailed assessment of lattice matching, the best place to start is the lattice constant a vs bandgap E_g diagram for III–V compound materials, shown in Figure 4.22, and the table of values for important binary semiconductors taken from this graph, shown in Table 4.3.

The successful growth of heterostructures requires consideration of both band gap (hence operating wavelength) and lattice constant. As an example, take the growth of $Al_xGa_{1-x}As$ on GaAs. It can be seen that AlAs and GaAs have nearly the same lattice constant, but quite different band gaps. This relationship is shown in more detail in Figure 4.23 [16], where the separation dependence of E_g on x can clearly be seen. Thus $Al_xGa_{1-x}As$ can be grown on GaAs, for any value of x, without undue fear of a lattice mismatch introducing defects (usually in the form of dislocations), giving a band gap variation from 580 to 870 nm. This tremendous flexibility is the prime reason why the AlGaAs/GaAs system remained so popular for so long; it was straightforward to make good quality epitaxial material using the very earliest techniques. As might be expected, the AlGaAs/GaAs system is the exception rather than the rule; most heterostructure systems have a change in lattice constant as well as band gap. A good example of this is $GaAs_{1-y}P_y$/GaAs, which again can be seen in Figure 4.22 and Table 4.3: the band gap and lattice constant variation as a function of y are plotted in Figure 4.24. There is a mismatch of ∼3.5% between GaAs ($a = 5.65$ Å) and GaP ($a = 5.45$ Å). Clearly if y is well

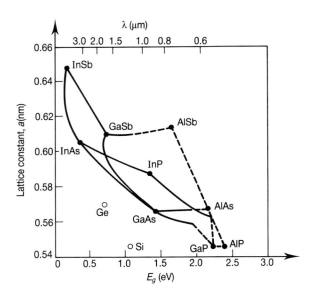

Figure 4.22 The variation of lattice constant as a function of band gap for the III–V ternary alloys. The solid line indicates direct gap material, the dashed line indirect gap.

	N	P	As	Sb
Al	~ 6.0	2.45	2.15	1.65
	4.40	*5.46*	*5.66*	*6.14*
Ga	3.4	2.26	1.42	0.73
	4.51	*5.45*	*5.65*	*6.10*
In	1.95	1.34	0.36	0.18
	5.01	*5.87*	*6.06*	*6.48*

Table 4.3 Band gap energy (in eV – shown in Roman) and lattice constant (in Å – shown in italic) of binary III–V compounds.

away from 0 or 1, growth of $GaAs_{1-y}P_y$ on a substrate of either GaAs or GaP will be full of defects. It is therefore standard practice for a system like this to provide a grading layer between the substrate and the desired compound; an example was shown earlier in Figure 3.22.

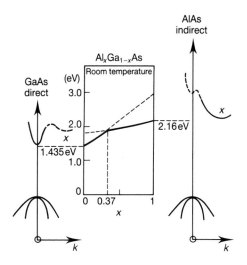

Figure 4.23 The change from a direct gap to an indirect gap material in $Al_xGa_{1-x}As$ as a function of x (©John Wiley & Sons: reproduced by kind permission).

Example 4.6

Calculate the values of ΔE_v and ΔE_c for $x = 0.3$ at a GaAs–$Al_xGa_{1-x}As$ interface.

Solution: if we assume a linear relationship between χ and x for the GaAs–$Al_xGa_{1-x}As$ system, then Table 4.1 shows us that $\Delta\chi = 1.36\,\Delta x$. For $x = 0.3$ the band gap difference can be estimated from Figure 4.23 as 0.36 eV. From (4.49), $\Delta E_c = 0.408$ eV. Then from (4.51) $\Delta E_v = -0.048$ eV. The positive value of ΔE_c and the negative value of ΔE_v are confirmed in the band diagram in Figure 4.21(b), where it is clear that, in moving from one side of the barrier to the other, E_c and E_v suddenly jump in opposite directions.

In the infra-red part of the spectrum where optical fibers are of greatest interest because of low absorption and dispersion characteristics, ternary compounds

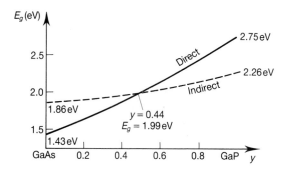

Figure 4.24 The change from a direct gap to an indirect gap material in $GaAs_{1-y}P_y$ as a function of y.

cannot be found of the correct wavelength with good lattice matching to available substrates. Either grading layers are needed, or lattice matched quaternary $(A_{1-x}B_xC_{1-y}D_y)$ compounds must be made. As with III–V ternary compounds, not all quaternaries can be ideally matched to a substrate. However, the significant exception to this is the $In_{1-x}Ga_xAs_{1-y}P_y$ system. This is shown in a rather different diagram to the ternaries in Figure 4.25. Each corner of this diagram represents one of the four binary compounds, and each axis one of the four ternary compounds, that make up this system. For instance, the bottom left hand corner is InAs, and rising vertically from there is $In_{1-x}Ga_xAs$ until the top left hand corner is reached for GaAs. Every compound inside the boundary is $In_{1-x}Ga_xAs_{1-y}P_y$. The solid lines represent iso-band gap lines; every band gap from 0.36 eV (InAs) to 2.2 eV ($In_{0.73}Ga_{0.27}P$ – right hand vertical axis) can be made in a direct gap semiconductor. The top right hand corner represents indirect band gaps of even higher energy, but these are of no interest in this discussion. The important feature of this diagram is the interaction between the iso-band gap lines and the iso-lattice constant (of InP) line – every compound that satisfies x and y on this line can be lattice matched to InP. On the InAs/GaAs axis the compound has $x = 0.47$ and $y = 0$ for $E_g = 0.7$ eV – hence $In_{0.53}Ga_{0.47}As$. At the other end, of course, is just InP (E_g=1.35 eV, $x = 0, y = 1$). Compounds along this line can be determined by reading off values of x and y.

Example 4.7

Estimate the stoichiometry of the compound $In_{1-x}Ga_xAs_{1-y}P_y$ that will give emission at 1.3 μm.

Solution: for emission at 1.3 μm, $E_g = 0.954$ eV. As closely as can be estimated from Figure 4.25, the values of x and y are 0.25 and 0.45 respectively, giving $In_{0.75}Ga_{0.25}As_{0.55}P_{0.45}$. Similarly for $\lambda = 1.55$ μm, the active region will have the composition $In_{0.63}Ga_{0.37}As_{0.80}P_{0.20}$.

If the compounds estimated in example 4.7 are the active layers of a laser, then either side of this can be InP, which has a higher band gap, and hence lower refractive index than the compound. As shown in Figure 4.26, a relatively simple NnP or NpP heterostructure can cover a wide range of wavelengths from 920 to 1770 nm. Similar diagrams to that of Figure 4.25 have been computed for other III–V quaternaries, but none provide lattice matching to a common substrate. Grading layers are then needed [17].

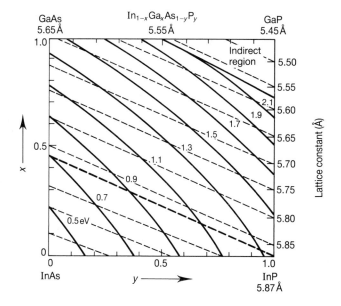

Figure 4.25 Iso-band gap and iso-lattice constant lines of the $In_{1-x}Ga_xAs_{1-y}P_y$ system at 300 K.

4.2.6 Multiheterostructures

The idea behind introducing three [18] or four [19] heterojunctions is to make the optical cavity and active layer thickness unequal. This reduces the optical flux

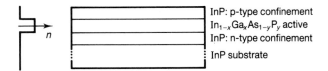

Figure 4.26 Cross-section through an InGaAsP laser.

density in the cavity and hence reduces mirror damage at either end of the crystal. Three and four junction systems are shown in Figures 4.27(a) and (b) respectively. For the three junction (four layer) system, the thin active region 3 cannot confine the transverse modes which spread into region 3, with some leaking into 1 and 4 – good design should minimize this. This is the large optical cavity (LOC) design, which we shall return to later in section 4.6.2. The use of four junctions (five layers) with symmetry produces a greater waveguiding effect than the three junction system. Typical details of the structure in Figure 4.27(b) will show all regions to be $Al_xGa_{1-x}As$ except for 3, which is GaAs. $x = 0.4$ for regions 1 and 5, and $x = 0.1$ for regions 2 and 3. Doping density increases from the central region outwards. The active layer is usually 0.1 to 0.2 μm thick, with the immediately adjacent guiding layers ten times thicker.

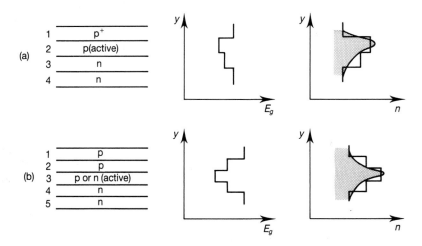

Figure 4.27 (a) A three junction, and (b) a four junction heterostructure.

Even more efficient optical confinement is provided in the structure shown in Figure 4.28. However, it is not the waveguiding effect of refractive index that confines the laser emission to regions 2–4; rather it is the highly absorbing GaAs contact layers that do not allow any mode propagation in regions 1 and 5. If regions 2 and 4 are too thin, then too much of the emission intensity will leak into the cap regions and be absorbed. This will in turn lead to a necessary increase in current to restore the lasing action. Thus the gain of such a device can be expected to be a function of the active region width, the relative refractive index Δn between it and the surrounding layer, and the width of the layers. Figure 4.29 shows this dependency, with Figure 4.29(a) showing that a narrower active region has a higher gain, and a smaller value of the width of region 2 has the same effect (Figure 4.29(b)). Because J_{th} is proportional to g_{th}, narrow active regions and small spacings increase the threshold current density [20].

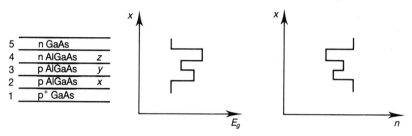

Figure 4.28 Four junction system with highly efficient optical confinement.

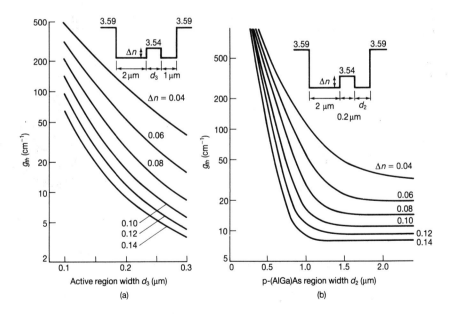

Figure 4.29 (a) The gain coefficient at threshold as a function of Δn and (a) active region width, and (b) width of the p-AlGaAs region 2 (©Academic Press, Inc.: reproduced by kind permission).

4.3   Stripe geometry

Having discussed in some detail the optimization of band structure in a semiconductor laser, we now turn our attention to the physical structure. We will note that in just the same way as a double heterostructure system is how almost all lasers have their band diagrams engineered, then likewise the formation of an active stripe is almost universal.

The stripe laser was first reported in 1967 [21], and a typical stripe system is shown in Figure 4.30(a), in comparison with a broad area laser in Figure 4.30(b). The current is fed into the device through a narrow contact stripe, which extends the whole length of the device. The aspect ratio of the contact (length/width) is high, in contrast to the broad area device discussed up until now where, as shown in Figure 4.30(b), the whole of the semiconductor width accesses a uniform current density. The broad area laser then emits a fan shaped beam along the z direction of its output (see Figure 4.15), with the envelope of the beam represented by a radial section of a cylinder.

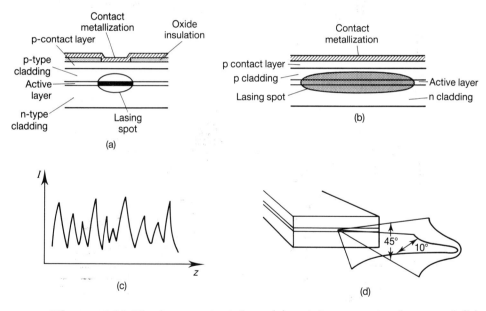

Figure 4.30 The beam output from (a) a stripe geometry laser, and (b) a broad area laser. (c) 'Hot spots' in a broad area output. (d) Two-dimensional profile of a stripe geometry laser output (Peter K Cheo, *Fiber Optics and Optoelectronics*, 2nd ed., ©1990, p. 244. Reprinted by permission of Prentice-Hall, Englewood Cliffs, New Jersey).

The main problem with broad area lasers is the formation of lateral modes (see Figure 4.8(a)). This can happen despite roughening of the lateral end faces, and leads to inhomogeneities along the z-axis of the output beam. A typical 'hot spot' pattern is shown in Figure 4.30(c). The most effective way to suppress all but one (the fundamental) of the lateral modes is to remove any gain mechanism across the z-direction, i.e. constrict the gain to the central part of the device – hence the need for a stripe. There are similarities here between suppression of lateral and transverse modes, where we noted that if the active layer thickness d was small enough, again only one fundamental transverse mode could propagate (section 4.1.2.3). As we shall see in later sections, mode propagation is also affected as much by refractive index variations as by geometry.

The output beam from a stripe geometry laser is then fan shaped in two dimensions (Figure 4.30(d)), with a divergence angle parallel to the junction ($\sim 10°$) much less than the perpendicular divergence due to aperture diffraction ($\sim 45°$). In terms of intensity vs wavelength, stripe geometry has the advantage of removing side peaks from the main modes; these peaks are otherwise due to non-fundamental lateral modes (Figure 4.8(c)). Other advantages of this type of design include a reduced operating current (hence reduced heating effects on output and reliability), less stringent demands on fabrication because of the smaller active volume and the greater protection offered by isolating the active region from an open surface along two sides.

Later discussion in this section concentrates on the various types of stripe geometry, but we first look at the mathematical concepts behind the device. The following analysis has been confirmed by experimental results [22] of spontaneous emission as a function of distance z across the device.

4.3.1 Carrier and gain profiles

The rigorous solution of the carrier concentration profiles, which obviously affect the gain, in three dimensions is very complex. However, we can make several simplifying assumptions which have been shown experimentally to be valid [22]:

(i) The device has a constant physical structure, and a constant injected current density, along the length of the stripe, i.e. the x-direction. Subsequent calculations are then valid for any value of x.

(ii) The amount of injected current leaking away at the edge of the electrode is negligible, and so a constant current density reaches the active layer.

(iii) The active layer thickness d is much smaller than the carrier diffusion length (L_n for electrons) and the stripe width w. There is thus a constant carrier concentration in this layer as a function of distance y, and the problem of carrier profiles is then reduced to a one-dimensional diffusion problem.

(iv) The nature of the current density J outside the stripe width w is of no consequence, providing that it is less than threshold. Some treatments, e.g. [22], assume a proton-bombardment fabricated laser, with J being represented as a step function. For oxide stripe lasers, however, J is more likely to follow an exponential decay away from the stripe region [23] as the adjoining areas have a finite conductivity. Thus the current density can have either of the two forms shown in Figure 4.31(b).

(v) All carriers in the active region ($|z| < w/2$) recombine radiatively. The rate of change in concentration of n is then given by a recombination rate r

$$r = \frac{J}{ed}.$$

(4.55)

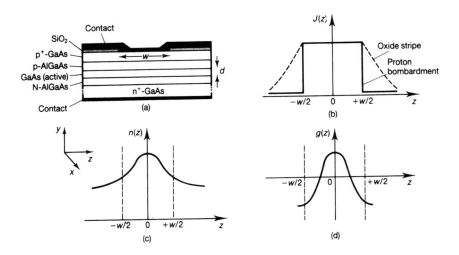

Figure 4.31 The stripe geometry laser: (a) cross-section, (b) current density profile, (c) carrier density profile, and (d) gain profile.

4.3.1.1 Carrier profile

For a steady state situation, the one-dimensional continuity equation (1.63) becomes

$$D_n\frac{\mathrm{d}^2 n}{\mathrm{d}z^2} + r - \frac{n}{\tau_n} = 0$$

(4.56)

$$\text{and hence}\quad \frac{\mathrm{d}^2 n}{\mathrm{d}z^2} = \frac{n}{L_n^2} - \frac{r}{D_n}.$$

(4.57)

where $L_n = \sqrt{D_n\tau_n}$ (from (1.64)). In (4.57) carrier concentration is defined by the diffusion length; but D_n depends on n from (1.55) and Figure 1.21. A solution is then non-linear, but over the limited region underneath the stripe the variation in n is small ($\sim$30–50%) and so D can be approximated as constant. A linear solution to (4.57) can then be found which is symmetric about $z = 0$, assuming a symmetrical diffusion of carriers:

$$n(z) = \frac{rL_n^2}{D_n} + \left[n(0) - \frac{rL_n^2}{D_n}\right] \cosh\left(\frac{z}{L_n}\right) \tag{4.58}$$

where $n(0) = n$ at $z = 0$. Outside the stripe region, the term in r is removed from (4.57) (assuming no recombination), and different values of diffusion constant D_n' and diffusion length L_n' must be used. Thus for $|z| > w/2$

$$\frac{\mathrm{d}^2 n}{\mathrm{d}z^2} = \frac{n}{L_n'^2} \tag{4.59}$$

which has a solution

$$n(z) = n\left(\frac{w}{2}\right) \exp\left(\frac{-z}{L_n'}\right) \tag{4.60}$$

Carrier concentration $n(z)$ and diffusion current (proportional to $\mathrm{d}n/\mathrm{d}z$) must be continuous at $z = \pm w/2$, and solving (4.58) and (4.60) in terms of these constraints gives

$$n(0) = \frac{rL_n^2}{D_n}\left[1 - \frac{1}{\cosh\left(w/2L_n\right) + \gamma \sinh\left(w/2L_n\right)}\right] \tag{4.61}$$

$$\text{where} \quad \gamma = \frac{D_n L_n'}{D_n' L_n}. \tag{4.62}$$

Substituting (4.61) into (4.58) gives the carrier profile within the stripe defined region ($|z| < w/2$):

$$n(z) = \frac{rL_n^2}{D_n}\left[1 - \frac{\cosh\left(z/L_n\right)}{\cosh\left(w/2L_n\right) + \gamma \sinh\left(w/2L_n\right)}\right]. \tag{4.63}$$

By substituting $z = w/2$ in (4.63) an expression for $n(w/2)$ can be found:

$$n(w/2) = \frac{rL_n^2}{D_n}\left[\frac{\gamma \sinh\left(w/2L_n'\right) \exp\left(w/2L_n\right)}{\cosh\left(w/2L_n\right) + \gamma \sinh\left(w/2L_n\right)}\right]. \tag{4.64}$$

For $|z| > w/2$, $n(z)$ is defined by (4.60), and so using (4.60), (4.63) and (4.64) a plot of $n(z)$ vs z can be obtained as in Figure 4.31(c). The ratio $n(w/2) : n(0)$ is useful for determining the diffusion length, and (4.61) and (4.64) give

$$\frac{n(w/2)}{n(0)} = \gamma \sinh\left(\frac{w}{2L_n}\right)\left[\frac{1}{\cosh\left(w/2L_n\right) + \gamma \sinh\left(w/2L_n\right) - 1}\right]. \tag{4.65}$$

4.3.1.2   Gain profile

It can be shown [22] that the gain g has a direct dependence on carrier concentration. This is a local gain, and the dependency on $n(z)$ can be expressed as

$$g(z) = an(z) - b \tag{4.66}$$

for $|z| < w/2$, where a and b are constants. The mode gain G_m of any mode m, i.e. the sum of the local gain in a particular direction, is given by

$$G_m = \frac{\int_{-\infty}^{\infty} g(z)\, E_m^2(z)\, dz}{\int_{-\infty}^{\infty} E_m^2(z)\, dz}, \tag{4.67}$$

where $E_m(z)$ is the field distribution of any mode m. The exact form of these is best described by Hermite–Gaussian functions [21], but a trigonometric approximation will be used here. If we also assume that the mode is confined within $\pm w/2$, then the fundamental can be described by

$$G_0 = \frac{2}{w} \int_{-w/2}^{w/2} g(z)\, \cos^2(k_0 z)\, dz \tag{4.68}$$

where $\quad k_0 = \dfrac{\pi}{w}. \tag{4.69}$

Substitution of (4.63) and (4.66) in (4.68) gives, on integration,

$$G_0 = \frac{arL_n^2}{D}\left[1 - \frac{2L_n/w}{(w/2\pi L_n)^2 + 1} \frac{\tanh(w/2L_n)}{1 + \gamma \tanh(w/2L_n)}\right] - b. \tag{4.70}$$

The gain for higher order modes has a similar form:

$$G_0 = \frac{arL_n^2}{D}\left[1 - \frac{(m+1)^2\, 2L_n/w}{(w/2\pi L_n)^2 + (m+1)^2} \frac{\tanh(w/2L_n)}{1 + \gamma \tanh(w/2L_n)}\right] - b. \tag{4.71}$$

The parameters a and b have to be determined experimentally for a given structure [22], and the gain profile can then be determined as a function of z. A typical example is shown in Figure 4.31(d), where

$$|z| < w/2 \quad g_{th}(z) = 146\left[1 - 0.72\cosh\frac{z}{L_n}\right] \mathrm{cm}^{-1} \tag{4.72}$$

$$\text{and } |z| > w/2 \quad g_{th}(z) = 322\exp\left[\frac{-z}{L_n'}\right] - 146\,\mathrm{cm}^{-1}. \tag{4.73}$$

By rearranging (4.70) in terms of r, and substituting in a value of $w = \infty$, a ratio of the threshold recombination rates $r_{th}(w)$ and $r_{th}(\infty)$ can be obtained for a stripe contact of width w and a broad area laser ($w = \infty$):

$$\frac{r_{th}(w)}{r_{th}(\infty)} = \left(1 - \frac{2L_n/w}{(w/2\pi L_n)^2 + 1} \frac{\tanh(w/2L_n)}{1 + \gamma \tanh(w/2L_n)}\right)^{-1}. \tag{4.74}$$

This function is plotted against normalized (to diffusion length L_n) stripe width in Figure 4.32. As w narrows, out-diffusion of carriers increases and there is also a reduction in mode coupling to the gain profile; both result in an increase in threshold with the former being the most significant. Further, the proton bombardment ($\gamma = 0.25$) enhances both of these factors. Experimental results [22] have confirmed the validity of this plot.

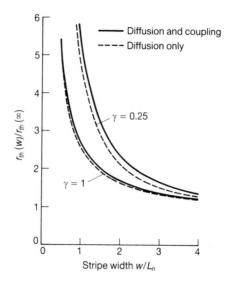

Figure 4.32 The increase in lasing threshold current density for a stripe geometry laser as the stripe width decreases relative to a diffusion length. The data is normalized to a diffusion length of 6.2 μm (©John Wiley & Sons: reproduced by kind permission).

4.3.1.3 Lateral current confinement

The analysis in the last two sections, although complicated enough, explicitly (condition (ii) under 4.3.1) ignored any current leaking laterally from the stripe contact edge. This will be a valid approximation for large stripe widths, but as w becomes smaller the relative effect of this phenomenon will increase. The problem is illustrated in Figure 4.33 [24]. For the z-direction, the potential variation is given by

$$\frac{\mathrm{d}V}{\mathrm{d}z} = -R_s I \tag{4.75}$$

where R_s is the sheet resistance and I the lateral current. If we assume the laser has unit length, then

$$\frac{\mathrm{d}I}{\mathrm{d}z} = -J(z) = -J_{th}(\infty) \exp\left(\frac{eV}{nkT}\right) \tag{4.76}$$

where $J_{th}(\infty)$ is the threshold current density for a broad area device and n is the laser diode's ideality factor. Note that because $J(z = 0) = J_{th}(\infty)$, we are assuming that for $z > 0$ there is no lasing action. For current considerably higher than $J_{th}(\infty)$ this will not be true. Differentiating (4.75) and substituting I from (4.76) gives

$$\frac{\mathrm{d}^2 V}{\mathrm{d}z^2} = J_{th}(\infty) R_s \exp\left(\frac{eV}{nkT}\right). \tag{4.77}$$

Solving (4.77) and substituting from (4.75) gives

$$2(I)_{x=0} = 2^{3/2} J_{th}(\infty)\left(\frac{nkT}{R_s e J_{th}(\infty)}\right)^{1/2} \tag{4.78}$$

where $2(I)_{x=0}$ obviously represents the fact that the contact has two edges. Equation (4.78) is equivalent to saying that there is an increase in current density equivalent to an effective increase in stripe width Δw where

$$\Delta w = \left(\frac{8nkT}{R_s e J_{th}(\infty)}\right)^{1/2}. \tag{4.79}$$

Thus the threshold current density obeys the following equation:

$$J_{th} = J_{th}(\infty)\left(1 + \frac{\Delta w}{w}\right) \tag{4.80}$$

which clearly becomes increasingly important as the stripe width w is narrowed – this is shown in Figure 4.33(b). Although it appears from (4.79) that the threshold current can be minimized by increasing the top layer sheet resistance, this is not the case as the overall device resistance will also increase. Additional consideration of factors such as series resistance (in the other layers and the substrate) have been neglected in this analysis, but fortunately for most practical devices they have a negligible effect [24].

Example 4.8

Calculate the room temperature threshold current density of a laser of stripe width 20 μm, series resistance 18 Ω and diode ideality factor 1.2, if an otherwise identical laser of stripe width 100 μm has $J_{th} = 1000$ A cm^{-2}.

Solution: from Figure 4.33 we can assume the wide laser represents $J_{th} = \infty$. From (4.79)

$$\begin{aligned}
\Delta w &= \left(\frac{8 \times 1.2 \times k \times 293}{18 \times e \times 1000}\right)^{1/2} \\
&= 3.7 \times 10^{-3} \text{ cm.}
\end{aligned} \tag{4.81}$$

From this result and (4.80)

$$\begin{aligned}
J_{th} &= 1000\left(1 + \frac{3.7 \times 10^{-3}}{20 \times 10^{-4}}\right) \\
&\simeq 2800 \text{ A cm}^{-2}.
\end{aligned} \tag{4.82}$$

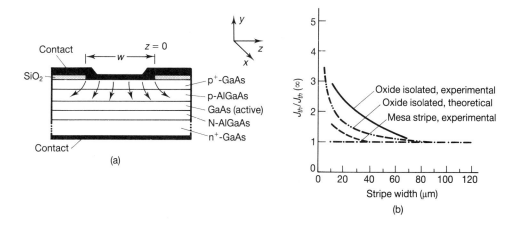

Figure 4.33 (a) Current leakage under the isolation of a narrow stripe laser. (b) The ratio of J_{th}/J_∞ as a function of stripe width, where J_∞ is the threshold value measured on a broad area device (©Academic Press, Inc.: reproduced by kind permission).

4.3.2 Fundamental mode operation

We have seen how a stripe geometry laser confines the carriers, and hence the gain in the lateral dimension. Some method of suppressing unwanted lateral modes is now needed, and this is an important factor in stripe laser design. For the oxide stripe laser discussed so far, there will be a weak change in refractive index in the central region as a result of the increased density there. This phenomenon was discussed in section 4.1.2.1. If we consider the active area under the stripe as a box surrounded by media of different refractive index, hence providing confinement, fundamental mode operation [25] will give

$$\frac{\Delta n}{n} \leq \frac{1}{8}\left(\frac{\lambda}{nw}\right)^2 \tag{4.83}$$

and this is shown in Figure 4.34 [26]. Because of the very small value of Δn due to the carrier concentration increase (about 0.1%) fundamental mode operation is valid for all stripe widths below 10–15 μm. Above this, as shown in Figure 4.35(a) [27], the number of modes m able to propagate increases rapidly with w, and is given by [25]

$$m = \text{Integer}\left[1 + \frac{2nw}{\lambda}\left(\frac{2\Delta n}{n}\right)^{1/2}\right]. \tag{4.84}$$

This is shown in Figure 4.35(b).

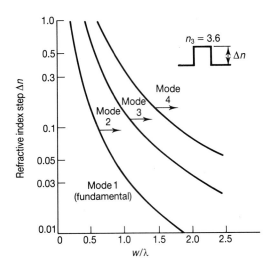

Figure 4.34 The modal cut-off characteristics for symmetrical DH lasers (©Academic Press, Inc.: reproduced by kind permission).

4.3.3   Beam astigmatism

The wavefront associated with the output beam of a stripe geometry laser is cylindrically concave [28], as shown in Figure 4.36(a). This is a direct result of the gain distribution shown in Figure 4.31(d). Thus the output looks the same in the y-direction, normal to the junction (as in Figure 4.30(d)), but in the z-direction parallel to the junction and perpendicular to the propagation direction, the beam has a virtual waist located in the active region. This is shown in Figures 4.36(b) and (c). The importance of astigmatism has been shown [29] to have an influence on the spontaneous emission, such that narrowing the stripe width leads to a much broader output spectrum with planar stripe lasers than with index guided (section 4.3.4) devices.

4.3.4   Structures

Presented in sections 4.3.1–4.3.3 were some of the characteristics of stripe geometry lasers, where just one type of laser, the oxide stripe, was considered. We will see in this section how different techniques can be used to make stripe contact lasers, each of which has its own advantages in exploiting particular phenomena. To recap the salient points of the stripe design, these are:

(i) minimization of lateral current spreading,

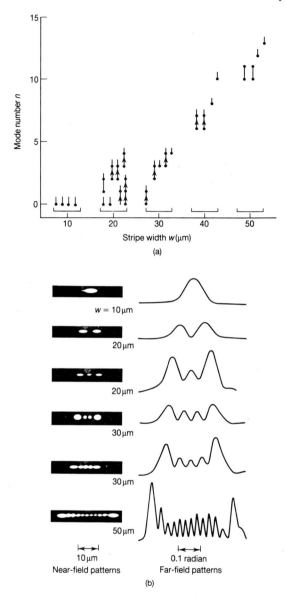

Figure 4.35 (a) Lasing mode number n as a function of the stripe width w near threshold. Arrows and lines mean mode transition and mode degradation respectively with increase of injected current. (b) Near and far field patterns for various stripe widths near threshold (©Physical Society of Japan: reproduced by kind permission).

(ii) optical confinement in the z-direction, perpendicular to the propagation direction,

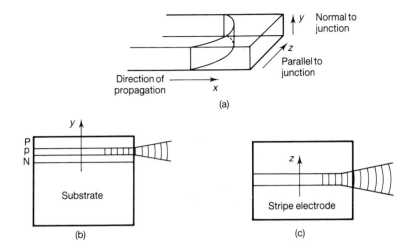

Figure 4.36 (a) Cylindrical phase front of a wave propagating in a medium in which confinement parallel and perpendicular to the junction are provided by the imaginary and real parts respectively of the dielectric constant. (b) Side view, and (c) top view of astigmatic wavefronts from a stripe geometry laser ((b) and (c) from Peter K Cheo, *Fiber Optics and Optoelectronics*, 2nd ed., ©1990, p. 249. Reprinted by permission of Prentice-Hall, Englewood Cliffs, New Jersey).

(iii) consideration of stripe width w and refractive index difference Δn in the z-direction to restrict lateral modes,

(iv) reduction of astigmatism,

(v) ease of fabrication and reliability.

There are other considerations of output parameters, such as self-focusing in the waveguide [30], which results in a dip in the output power in the z-direction (Figure 4.37). Slight changes in local carrier density have a knock-on effect on refractive index, which in turn creates a weak local antiwaveguiding effect within the active region.

4.3.4.1   Oxide stripe

This was one of the earliest types of stripe geometry laser to be made, and also one of the simplest. A cross-section of a typical structure is shown in Figure 4.38(a) [21]. After the semiconductor structure has been fabricated, a coating of insulating material (usually silicon dioxide) is deposited over the top of the p-layer. This is then selectively etched and metallized to form the stripe contact. Although simple to fabricate, this structure suffers from an inability to provide effective lateral confinement to the current through the device, as previously shown in Figure 4.31(b). A variation on this theme is to replace the oxide with an n-region

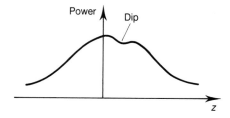

Figure 4.37 Lateral dip in the output power from a stripe geometry laser.

of AlGaAs [31]. This results in fewer crystal imperfections because of lower strain, and improved thermal resistance.

4.3.4.2 Implantation
In this structure, shown in Figure 4.38(b), the metallization is defined lithographically and used as a mask against proton bombardment (see section 8.7.4.6). This treatment breaks up the crystal structure and creates a polycrystalline material of a high defect density and resistivity. Lateral current confinement is improved, leading to lower threshold currents and increased mode stability [32]. A similar effect can be obtained by oxygen implantation through a mask and then metallizing, as in Figure 4.38(c) [33]. Here a high resistivity region is created by chemical doping, not crystal damage, as each oxygen ion can remove two carriers from the semiconductor.

4.3.4.3 Selective diffusion
In this structure, shown in Figure 4.38(d), a layer of SiO_2 has been used as a mask to selectively diffuse a p-dopant, such as zinc, through an n-region to the underlying p-contact layer [27]. After removal of the oxide and subsequent metallization, effective confinement of the current is made by the 'spike' of dopant reaching from the metal through the n-region. Lateral mode confinement is good and threshold currents are comparable to those of a proton bombardment structure.

A variation on this theme is provided for in the V-groove structure shown in Figure 4.38(e). Here a groove is etched into the top of the semiconductor structure, giving an even narrower current path than in the case of Figure 4.38(d).

4.3.4.4 Mesa stripe
All the lasers described in sections 4.3.4.1–4.3.4.3 are made using planar stripe geometry, and all look to current confinement as their main design criterion. All suffer from lateral current loss, however, which becomes an ever increasing problem as stripe widths narrow. There is also the problem of a low refractive index difference Δn at the sides of the active region. Δn is caused by the increase in carrier concentration and is very small ($\sim 0.1\%$). This presents a similar problem in the lateral (z-direction) to that in the transverse (y-direction) of a homojunction

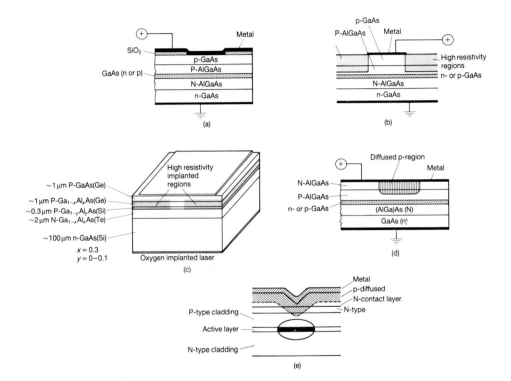

Figure 4.38 Various methods of implementing stripe geometry: (a) oxide isolation, (b) proton bombardment, (c) oxygen implantation, (d) selective diffusion, and (e) V-groove ((a), (b) and (d) ©Academic Press, Inc.: reproduced by kind permission; (e) Peter K Cheo, *Fiber Optics and Optoelectronics*, 2nd ed., ©1990, p. 244. Reprinted by permission of Prentice-Hall, Englewood Cliffs, New Jersey).

laser. In that case, a bigger refractive index difference was made by introducing heterostructures; for a mesa stripe laser, various techniques have been tried to obtain a large Δn. This and subsequent sections outline the main developments in this area.

The simplest type of mesa is formed by simply etching away the undesired regions of the semiconductor and coating with oxide and metal in the standard way (Figure

4.39(a) [34]). The effectiveness of a mesa stripe is shown in Figure 4.40 [35]. For large stripe widths, oxide isolated, proton bombardment and mesa stripe provide comparable values of threshold current. However, as the stripe width is reduced to less than ~ 12 μm the two planar devices begin to lose their effectiveness compared to the mesa stripe.

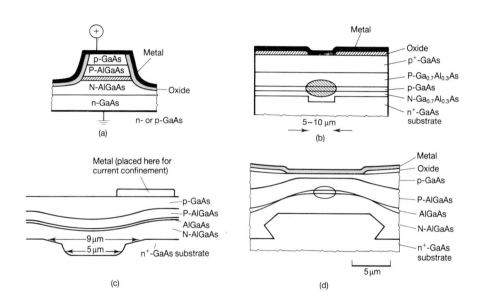

Figure 4.39 Other methods of implementing stripe geometry: (a) Mesa etching (©1975 IEEE: reproduced by kind permission), (b) channelled substrate, (c) constricted heterostructure over an etched channel, and (d) constricted heterostructure over a mesa ((b) and (d) ©John Wiley & Sons: reproduced by kind permission).

4.3.4.5 Buried heterostructure – basic

The etched mesa structure is undesirable from a long term reliability point of view, because of the large area of exposed surface. The regrowth of AlGaAs in the space etched by the mesa results in good current and optical confinement, as well as environmental protection of the active region [36]. This buried heterostructure (BH) device can be made with very narrow stripe widths with correspondingly low threshold currents. Of course, this leads to low output powers, but mode confinement is extremely good and superior to a planar stripe laser of similar geometry.

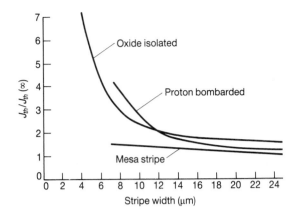

Figure 4.40 The ratio J_{th}/J_∞ as a function of stripe width of oxide isolated, proton bombarded and mesa etched AlGaAs lasers (©Springer Verlag: reproduced by kind permission).

4.3.4.6   Buried heterostructure – variations

There have been many variations on the buried heterostructure theme. An example is the channelled substrate planar (CSP) device [37] shown in Figure 4.39(b). In this structure the lateral modes are stabilized along the junction plane, leading to a reduction or even elimination of 'kinks' in the power–current curve using this type of laser. The structure is formed by a set of planar DH layers grown over an etched groove in the substrate. In operation, transverse waveguiding results because of the geometry of the channel. Fundamental mode operation occurs as long as the channel width is less than 8–10 μm.

The active region can also be made small enough to sustain only one lateral mode by growth on a non-planar substrate. Two examples of this are shown in Figure 4.39(c), where growth is over an etched channel, and Figure 4.39(d), where growth is on a crystallographically etched mesa. These structures are known as constricted double heterostructure (CDH) lasers. In Figure 4.39(c) a single channel is etched to form a dovetail shape, and subsequent growth provides an AlGaAs confinement layer that is thickest over the channel [38]. Similarly the active region has a thickness variation along the lateral direction, and is designed to be so thin away from the centre that it is effectively cut-off. Figure 4.39(d) shows two etched channels, but the active region is grown on top of the mesa instead of in the channel. Otherwise, the operating principle is similar, but it is easier to make this device than the previous one because the visibility of the mesa and channel patterns makes alignment of the contact stripe much easier.

The buried crescent (BC) heterostructure is an extension of the above theme [39]. A cross-section of the structure is shown in Figure 4.41(a). The crescent shaped active region, in this case InGaAsP, is completely embedded in InP on a dovetail channelled structure. In addition, two reverse biased pn junctions on either side of the active layer act to give current confinement, unlike the simpler structure of Figure 4.39(c). The use of InP as the junction at the edge of the crescent exploits the fact that this semiconductor is transparent to the emission wavelength of any InGaAsP structure, and so no absorption occurs in the InP. The result is a very low threshold current laser working in the fundamental mode.

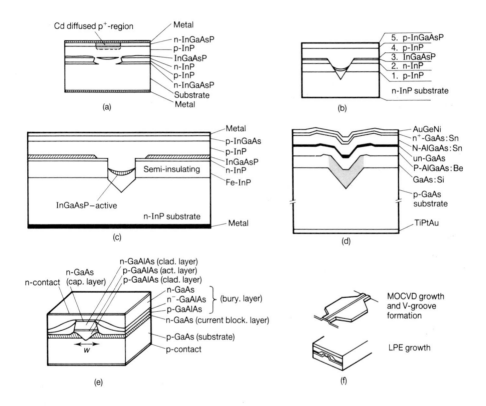

Figure 4.41 Buried heterostructure lasers: (a) InGaAsP buried crescent (BC), (b) InGaAsP VSB, (c) InGaAsP BC with semi-insulating current confinement layers, (d) AlGaAs V-groove with crystallographically controlled doping, (e) AlGaAs B-VSIS, and (f) AlGaAs T³ structure ((a), (b) and (f) ©1981, 1982, 1987 IEEE, (c) and (e) ©AIP, (d) ©IEE: reproduced by kind permission).

Buried crescent structures have also been embedded into V-grooved substrates, as shown in Figure 4.41(b) [40]. Here the basic epitaxial structure is grown in InP, which is then crystallographically etched to form a V-groove. Growth of the material in the groove then takes place, followed by contact region formation. Once the etching has been characterized, this V-grooved substrate buried heterostructure (VSB) laser is simpler to fabricate than the previous types, has a channel width that is easily controllable by the growth of the first material within the groove and results in low threshold currents – again it has two reverse biased pn junctions at either side of the active region. The VSB laser has proved to be quite popular because of its growth simplicity; a variation on the structure is given in Figure 4.41(c) [41], where a semi-insulating layer provides the current confinement. Thus the parasitic capacitances of reverse biased junctions are overcome with this structure, leading to operation at higher frequencies. 1.3 μm and 1.55 μm lasers have been made using VSB structures.

V-grooves have also been used as the basis for a laser whose doping is controlled by the crystallographic nature of GaAs:Si [42]. The structure is shown in Figure 4.41(d), and the layer of interest is the GaAs:Si grown on the top of the p-GaAs substrate. Outside the groove, this layer is n-type, as it is grown on a (100) surface. However, in the (111) faced groove the conductivity changes to p-type. Current confinement is thus provided to the shaded region.

A V-groove in conjunction with a planar, as opposed to crescent-shaped, active region is shown in Figure 4.41(e). This buried V-channelled substrate inner stripe (B-VSIS) structure provides good current confinement leading to low thresholds as before, and also offers fundamental mode operation even at fairly large stripe widths of 5–6 μm [43].

Up to now all the heterostructures described have been concerned with the lateral and transverse directions. We shall return to the longitudinal structures in more detail in section 4.4 on single frequency lasers, but introduced here to complete this section is the thin tapered thickness (T^3) laser. This is shown in Figure 4.41(f), and has an active layer thinner near the mirrors than in the central region [44]. This gives a very narrow beam output, with typical divergence angles of 10° perpendicular to the junction.

4.3.4.7 Ridge structures

These lasers rely on large physical discontinuities in cross-section for their individual properties. A simple ridge structure is shown in Figure 4.42(a). The fabrication is straightforward compared to the structures met in the previous section, and only standard patterning/etching techniques are required with no growth over non-planar structures needed. The cladded ridge structure in Figure 4.42(b) is slightly more involved, and the buffer layer provides environmental protection for the active layer. The active region is fairly wide, and so there should be a better match of optical output to a fiber, although threshold currents will be generally higher than for BH lasers [45].

As might have been expected, ridges have also been used in buried structures to form the RBH (ridge buried heterostructure) laser shown in Figure 4.42(c) [46]. In fabricating this device, a ridge is formed in the substrate as the initial structure.

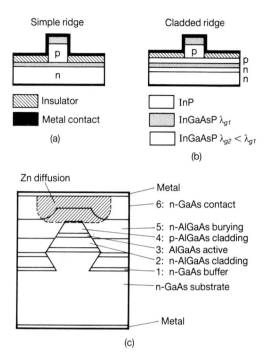

Figure 4.42 Ridge lasers: (a) simple ridge, (b) cladded ridge, and (c) ridge-buried heterostructure (RBH) (©1983, 1987 IEEE: reproduced by kind permission).

Subsequent growth of the various layers then occurs separately on both ridge and substrate. The active region is self-aligned to the ridge, and continuing the growth process to layer 5 ensures this region is buried.

4.4 Single frequency lasers

In previous sections we have looked at how single mode operation of a laser could be obtained in both the lateral and transverse sense, and (4.20) showed how the number of longitudinal modes could be calculated from a knowledge of cavity length, operating wavelength and refractive index. The spacing between these modes could be calculated via the same parameters using (4.23). For a typical GaAs laser, example 4.1 showed that the mode spacing was $\sim 4\,\text{Å}$. A single frequency laser operates in only one longitudinal mode. This is an important characteristic which should not be confused with single mode lasers, which operate in the fundamental transverse and lateral modes but with several longitudinal modes. The demand for single frequency lasers has come from the telecommunications industry in a desire to increase the bandwidth of an optical signal. The reasons for using single frequency to increase bandwidth can all be related to the various forms of dispersion in an optical fiber. A full review of dispersion is given in many books on fiber based communications, e.g. [47], but briefly the process involves two signals launched at different times merging together as shown in Figure 4.43(a). This can happen by three different phenomena for a step-index fiber: intermodal dispersion, waveguide dispersion and material dispersion. The first term is shown in Figure 4.43(b) where two modes A and B are propagated down a fiber. (Although a ray model is shown here, this is an oversimplified description of mode propagation. It is shown because this way is the easiest to represent.) A travels down the centre and B undergoes total internal reflection. Obviously B takes longer to reach the end of the fiber than A; if these are part of the same input signal the output signal will be smeared out. The single mode fiber, which only supports a mode passing down the fiber axis, has been developed to overcome this problem. Unlike a multimode step-index fiber, the single mode has a very narrow core diameter ($\sim 10\,\mu$m as opposed to $\sim 100\,\mu$m) and a smaller difference in core and cladding refractive index ($\sim 0.5\%$ as opposed to ~ 1–2%).

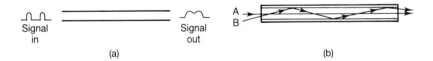

Signal in   Signal out

(a)

A
B

(b)

Figure 4.43 (a) The effect of time dispersion down an optical fiber. (b) Mechanism of intermodal time dispersion.

The waveguide dispersion mechanism involves a change in velocity of a pulse of light due to the spectral width of the source. Because the refractive index of all materials, including fibers, changes with wavelength, light at two ends of the spectral range will travel at two different speeds and hence arrive at different times; this is a similar effect to the intermodal dispersion which introduces a path difference to achieve the same effect. Thus sources of a very narrow spectral width will minimize this problem.

The last dispersion mechanism, material dispersion, affects both lasers and LEDs equally and is due to the operating wavelength and spectral width of the light source. It has a zero effect at a wavelength of $\sim 1.3\,\mu$m, increases with increasing wavelength after that, but at wavelengths $< 1.3\,\mu$m it increases dramatically. This and the attenuation characteristics of fibers have been the principle reasons behind developing long wavelength devices.

So dispersion effects can be minimized by using long wavelength sources of narrow spectral width in conjunction with single mode fibers. The narrow spectral width is achieved by a single frequency laser. At first sight it might seem possible to merely insert a narrow bandpass filter in front of the laser output, but there are two problems with this approach. The first is that it is technically near impossible to make such a narrow gap (of only a few Å or less) filter that would be effective. The second is related to the laser itself. When oscillating in several longitudinal modes the device can be thought of as a coupled oscillator, as shown in Figure 4.44. At any point in time the energy of the system can be in any one of the resonant modes, and with the passage of time there is coupling and transfer of energy between modes, although the total energy of the system remains constant. There will be two natural oscillating frequencies of the system in Figure 4.44 which are analagous to the longitudinal modes in a laser cavity. This would introduce an undesirable noise factor in the output, called partition noise. The only practical solution to the single frequency problem is to design the laser to resonate in only one stable longitudinal mode. There have been ingenious attempts to do this, most of which work to one extent or another. Narrow stripe lasers can show single longitudinal mode operation under d.c. conditions, but often rapid modulation broadens the output spectrum by as much as 100%. This dynamic mode of operation is obviously how semiconductor lasers are used in telecommunications systems, and a laser design is needed to ensure single mode operation under high frequency conditions. These are often called dynamic single mode (DSM) lasers which is a more complete description than single frequency, as it implies d.c. and modulation conditions. There are 11 major designs of single frequency laser, which can be broken down into four families of devices and associated hybrids [48]. We will take a similar approach here, starting with historically the earliest and most popular mechanism, the frequency selective device.

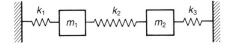

Figure 4.44 A coupled oscillator.

4.4.1 Frequency selective feedback

The fundamental philosophy behind the three types of laser using this approach is to take a single laser cavity and only allow one mode to resonate by providing a feedback mechanism that only picks out one frequency. The three approaches of external grating, distributed feedback (DFB) and distributed Bragg reflector (DBR) are shown in Figure 4.45 [48], and are now discussed in more detail.

4.4.1.1 External grating
As shown in Figure 4.45(a), this is quite a simple technique for providing frequency selective feedback. A diffraction grating is rather like a frequency selective mirror, and is often used in place of a standard mirror when single mode operation of

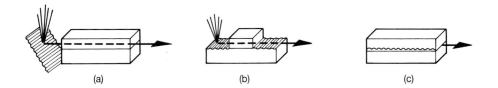

Figure 4.45 Three different methods of obtaining a single frequency laser: (a) external grating, (b) distributed Bragg reflection (DBR), and (c) distributed feedback (DFB) (©1983 IEEE: reproduced by kind permission).

argon and krypton ion gas lasers is required. Spectral lines as narrow as $\sim 10^{-6}\,\text{Å}$ can be achieved – equivalent to $\sim 10^4$ Hz at a wavelength of 1.55 μm [49]. This external technique is difficult to make for mass production, and a more integrated approach is required. This is provided by the next two designs.

4.4.1.2   Distributed feedback (DFB)

In this device a wavelength selective grating forms part of the cavity structure, as shown in Figure 4.46. The grating is formed, in the case of this device, by depositing all the epitaxial layers up to the p-$Ga_{0.88}Al_{0.12}As$ layer at one go, and then stopping the growth. Electron beam lithography is used to define the grating area, which is then formed using either wet or, more recently, reactive ion etching. A photograph of a fabricated grating is shown in Figure 9.20(b), and electron beam lithography and reactive ion etching are described in sections 9.1.9 and 9.4.2 respectively. Further epitaxial growth and metal deposition complete the structure. The period d of the grating is given by

$$d = \frac{l\lambda_B}{2n} \tag{4.85}$$

where λ_B is the Bragg wavelength given by

$$\lambda_0 = \lambda_B \pm \frac{(m+1/2)\lambda_B^2}{2nL} \tag{4.86}$$

and λ_0 is the oscillating wavelength, and l and m are integers. Thus many longitudinal modes exist, but only those closest to the Bragg wavelength (i.e. $m = 0$) have the lowest threshold. Single mode operation can be obtained at one of these modes because the end facet reflections make their individual gains different, although quarter wave shifting (see end of this section) is more effective.

Example 4.9

Calculate the Bragg wavelength and grating periodicity for a DFB laser of cavity length 300 μm, a material refractive index of 3.4 and an oscillating wavelength of 1.5500 μm.

Solution: isolating λ_B from (4.86) gives

$$\lambda_B^2 \pm 4nL\lambda_B \mp 4nL\lambda_0 = 0 \tag{4.87}$$

which can be solved as a quadratic, e.g.

$$\lambda_0 = \pm \left(\frac{-4nL \pm \sqrt{16n^2L^2 + 16nL\lambda_0}}{2} \right). \tag{4.88}$$

There are several variations of $\pm$ in this solution. Taking the solution which is the only 'sensible' one, i.e. $\lambda_B \simeq \lambda_0$, gives $\lambda_B = 1.5494$ or 1.5506 μm. From equation (4.85)

$$d = \frac{1.55}{2 \times 3.4} = 0.23\,\mu\text{m}. \tag{4.89}$$

The high definition provided by e-beam lithography and reactive ion etching is usually necessary to achieve this periodicity. An alternative approach is to use holographic lithography.

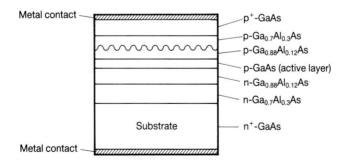

Figure 4.46 Corrugated structure along the length of a DFB laser (©John Wiley & Sons: reproduced by kind permission).

The term 'distributed feedback' in the context of a semiconductor laser was first used in 1971 [50], and soon after a physical model was developed by assuming a coupling between two counter-running waves via Bragg scattering [51]. The analysis provides for the formula quoted in (4.86). There then followed a quick progression through the fabrication of a single heterostructure DFB laser [52], a double heterostructure device [53], both operating at 77 K, and finally room temperature operation in 1975 [54]. All these devices were based on GaAs/AlGaAs. InGaAsP/InP DFB structures were first made in 1979 [55], with room temperature operation a couple of years later [56].

A problem with DFB lasers has been something that up to now has been considered to be an integral feature of any laser: the Fabry–Perot cavity. The reflective feedback from the end facets of the laser can have serious effects on the threshold current and oscillating wavelength of the DFB laser. It has been shown that to minimize this, oscillation in the DFB mode should occur at a much lower value of threshold current than for the Fabry–Perot mode [57]. Hence DFB lasers have been made with sawed end facets or with antireflection coatings, and even with windows in the structure that essentially bury one facet, as in Figure 4.47 [58]. All have been successful in suppressing the Fabry–Perot modes.

It should be noted that, from (4.86), DFB lasers have an inherent two mode property. Although their individual gains are different, it is desirable to eliminate one of these in order to obtain single mode operation. The first analysis of DFB lasers [51] produced two fundamental equations to describe the two counter-running waves R and S in a DFB laser:

$$\frac{-\mathrm{d}R}{\mathrm{d}z} + (g - \jmath\delta)R = \jmath\kappa S \tag{4.90}$$

$$\text{and} \quad \frac{\mathrm{d}S}{\mathrm{d}z} + (g - \jmath\delta)S = \jmath\kappa^* S \tag{4.91}$$

where g is the gain constant, κ a feedback parameter and δ a Bragg parameter indicating deviation of the oscillation frequency from the Bragg frequency. Further analysis [59] produced a determinantal equation

$$\left|\kappa\left(\frac{L}{2}\right)\right|^2 \left|r\left(\frac{-L}{2}\right)\right|^2 - \left|-\frac{\mathrm{d}r}{\mathrm{d}z}\left(\frac{L}{2}\right) + \left[g - \jmath\delta\left(\frac{L}{2}\right)\right]r\left(\frac{L}{2}\right)\right|^2 = 0 \tag{4.92}$$

where $r(z)$ is a solution of the differential of (4.90). Equation (4.92) is real and hence for a given value of cavity length L can be satisfied by an appropriate choice for g. A mode that can then exist for one frequency in the left hand side of the above equation crosses zero as g is raised from 0. This is done by producing an antisymmetric step in κ. A uniform DFB structure is effectively cut in the middle, one half period removed and the two sections recombined, as shown in Figure 4.48. κ is then phase shifted by π in passing from one side to the other. Because half a period is removed from the grating and, from (4.85), each period corresponds to half a wavelength of the oscillation, this results in a $\lambda/4$ shifted DFB laser, which is the most effective DFB device in terms of single mode linewidth. An alternative approach is to introduce a $\pi/2$ phase shift in each of the forward and backward travelling waves by changing the thickness of the optical guide over a short length

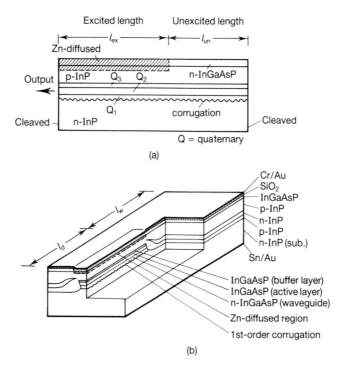

Figure 4.47 Suppression of F–P resonances in the DFB laser: (a) by keeping part of the laser unexcited, and (b) by forming a window region between the end of the DFB region and the facet (©1983 IEEE: reproduced by kind permission).

of the structure. Besides the analysis of $\lambda/4$ shifted DFB lasers quoted in [51] and [59], [60] also contains calculations of thresholds and efficiencies in such devices.

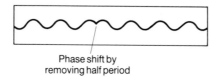

Phase shift by
removing half period

Figure 4.48 The $\lambda/4$ DFB laser, with a phase shift region in the corrugated structure.

Fabrication of DFB lasers is a tricky operation, requiring a lot of skill and experience. $\lambda/4$ shifted DFB lasers are even harder, requiring a tri-level process (see section 9.1.7) using positive and negative photoresists and a holographic exposure. Because of the different resist characteristics, the holographic interference pattern is inverted in the two regions. A π phase shift in the region under the positive photoresist is then produced [61].

DFB lasers exhibit very narrow linewidths, and very good temperature stability. Linewidths of the order of a few MHz are possible (10^{-3}–10^{-4} Å), but are very dependent on cavity length [62]. The operating temperature advantages of the DFB laser stem from the mechanism that is driving the change in wavelength. For a typical DH laser, using a Fabry–Perot cavity, this is the temperature dependence of the band gap, and leads to a wavelength shift of 2 Å K^{-1}. However, for a DFB laser, which follows the much more stable temperature dependence of refractive index, the wavelength shift is much smaller at 0.6 Å K^{-1} [63]. High powers can be obtained from single mode DFB lasers, with outputs greater than 50 mW readily achieved [64].

4.4.1.3   *Distributed Bragg reflector (DBR)*

An essential feature of a DFB laser is the presence of a corrugated structure within the active region: a distributed Bragg reflector (DBR) laser uses the same kind of structure outside the active region, as shown in Figure 4.49. An essential feature of the DBR laser is efficient coupling between the active lasing region and the passive waveguide structures. Another difference from DFB lasers is that for the DBR devices the resonant mode characteristics are usually asymmetric about the Bragg wavelength λ_B, with the deviation of the lasing wavelength from λ_B being determined by the length of the active region. The relationship between coupling the modes into and out of the active region for both DFB and DBR lasers is shown in Figure 4.50 [65]. Calculations have been performed on the derivation and performance of the coupling efficiency C_0, and a typical example for a DBR laser is shown in Figure 4.51(a) [66], where C_0 is measured as a function of the widths of the active and passive regions, w_A and w_E respectively. A similar diagram is shown in Figure 4.51(b) with passive waveguide thickness t_e and epitaxial layer displacement s as the parameters [65]. It can be seen that with careful design of the structure efficiencies close to 100% can be achieved. A DBR laser has a greater shift in output wavelength with temperature (~ 1.1 Å K^{-1} [66]) than a DFB laser, though both can operate over large temperature ranges without modal jumps.

4.4.2   Short cavity laser

Seemingly a very simple way of obtaining single frequency operation is to shorten the cavity length. It can be seen from (4.20) that the number of modes will reduce, and from (4.23) the wavelength spacing between adjacent modes can be calculated. However, this simple approach doesn't explain how single mode operation can be achieved from cavities of a fairly long length (200–300 μm). This phenomenon only occurs at currents well above threshold, and is because the secondary modes saturate at high injection currents. All subsequent lasing action occurs in the

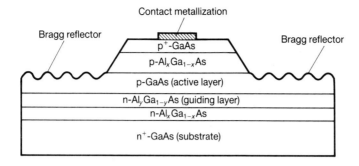

Figure 4.49 The distributed Bragg reflector (DBR) laser.

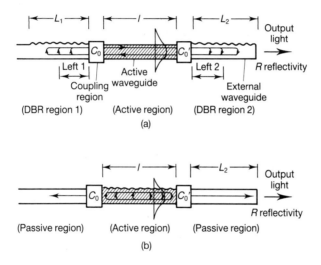

Figure 4.50 Conceptual diagrams of (a) a DBR integrated laser, and (b) a DFB integrated laser. Parameter C_0 or C_0' denotes a coupling efficiency between an active and passive region with a certain coupling scheme (©1983 IEEE: reproduced by kind permission).

primary mode, making this one dominant and giving single mode operation. The difference in gain between primary and secondary modes depends on the mode spacing, and so it is reasonable to assume that the minimum primary mode power required for single frequency output will also depend on mode spacing and hence, from (4.20) and (4.23), the cavity length.

Calculations have been performed relating laser parameters to single mode operation, and short ($\sim 50\,\mu$m) cavity length lasers have been fabricated and demon-

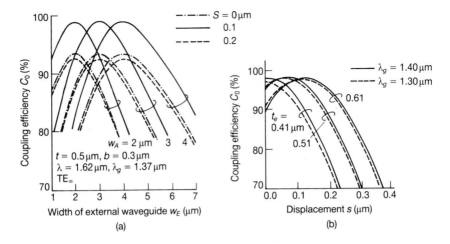

Figure 4.51 Calculated coupling efficiency of a butt-jointed built-in external waveguide DBR laser, as a function of (a) width w_E, thickness of core t and cladding b of external waveguide, band gap wavelength λ and λ_g of laser and waveguide respectively, width w_A of the active region of the laser and displacement s of the waveguide/laser edge, and (b) as a function of s, t_e and λ_g (©1983, 1984 IEEE: reproduced by kind permission).

strated [67]. (Shorter cavities will have longitudinal modes spaced further apart than standard length cavities, and this will exaggerate the difference effect.)

Because the cross-sectional area of the device is small, output powers are low, and the operation of these devices requires care to stay away from high current densities. This can lead to a lot of power in the single mode and a depletion rate of electrons by stimulated emission greater than the supply rate by diffusion of injected carriers. Suppression of the primary mode will then result, a phenomenon known as spatial hole burning.

The main problem with short cavity lasers is the reproducibility of fabrication, as small area devices place much greater demands on growth uniformity than large area structures. Short cavities can also be used in vertical surface emitting lasers, as we shall see in section 4.7.1.

4.4.3   Injection locked laser

The use of one semiconductor laser to cause lasing action in another is the basis of this type of system. It is then an external means of producing single mode, as opposed to the frequency selective and short cavity approaches which have the single mode mechanism 'built-in'. The principle was first demonstrated in 1976 [68] using AlGaAs lasers, and later using InGaAsP devices [69].

4.4.4   Coupled cavity designs

The last family of single frequency devices all have one thing in common; the light coming out of the laser cavity has to pass through an additional cavity. In this way the only modes that interfere constructively are those that resonate in both cavities. Consider Figure 4.52. It can be seen that the axial mode spacing of the coupled cavities $\Delta\lambda_c$ is much greater than for either one alone. The result is that only one mode within the gain spectrum of the laser will resonate in both cavities, giving a single mode output.

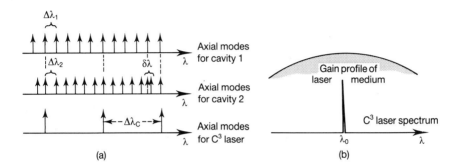

Figure 4.52 Spectral characteristics of cleaved coupled cavity (C^3) lasers: (a) allowed Fabry–Perot modes for both diodes, and for the coupled cavity, and (b) the narrow output spectrum.

Several second cavity designs have been used. An approach using a frequency selective mirror is shown in Figure 4.53 [70]. The mirror is a metal–dielectric–metal design with a mode spacing of 70 Å, compared to that of the laser of 10 Å. Single mode discrimination was good although the power output was quite low ($\sim$10 mW).

Another technique involves simply grooving the laser to produce a structure as in Figure 4.54 [71]. The groove provides electrical isolation but the physical closeness of the (now) two lasers ($\sim 1\,\mu$m) ensures good optical coupling, although the mirrors formed by the etching of the groove are obviously not as good as those produced by cleaving. They are also unlikely to be perfectly parallel to the end facets due to slight errors in lithography and the nature of the etch process.

4.4.4.1   Cleaved coupled cavity (C^3) laser

The third major type of coupled cavity design, the cleaved coupled cavity (C^3) laser, has proved to be more popular than the other two. As the name implies, the cavities to be coupled together in this structure are formed by cleaving along crystallographic planes. Thus unlike groove etching techniques, the end mirrors are perfectly flat and theoretically parallel to each other for each cavity. The basic laser material can be any of the stripe contact types described in section 4.3, and

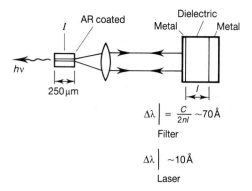

Figure 4.53 Experimental set-up to obtain single frequency using a metal film reflection filter (©1985 IEEE: reproduced by kind permission).

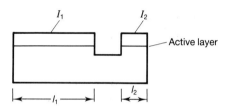

Figure 4.54 Grooved coupled cavity structure.

a schematic of the final structure is shown in Figure 4.55 [72]. The two cavities can have their currents controlled independently and this is the main advantage of the C^3 system over other single frequency techniques. Unlike the popular DFB and DBR lasers, the single frequency nature is brought out in the operation rather than the fabrication of the device. It can be tuned in its operation to any one of several wavelengths over a fairly wide range. If one diode is always operated above threshold, then this obviously acts as the laser source. If the other is always provided with a below threshold current, then the modulation of this current can be used to alter its carrier density and hence refractive index. This has the subsequent effect of altering the resonant modes.

Cleaved coupled cavity lasers, as with most other types, have also been analysed theoretically [73]. As might have been expected, the gap length between the two cavities has a strong influence on device performance, with λ_0, $\Delta\lambda$ and threshold current all showing variations over a comparatively small gap range of 2.1–2.4 μm, presenting a major constraint on maintaining precise gap lengths in this region.

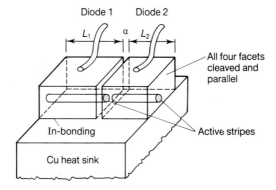

Figure 4.55 Schematic detail of the C^3 laser.

4.5 Quantum well lasers

Although the pursuit of single frequency lasers, using the variety of techniques outlined in section 4.4, dominated the demand-driven research in the 1980s, paralleling that effort was a comparatively small one on quantum well (QW) and multiple quantum well (MQW) lasers. By the late 1980s it could be said that research in the latter was equal to that of single frequency lasers, at least in academic establishments, as the quality of epitaxial growth techniques improved dramatically. This section reviews the history of quantum well lasers, and also shows that they are not just of academic interest. The quantum size effects (QSEs) prevalent in these devices, which are not seen in bulk lasers, can lead to interesting new observations and properties.

4.5.1 Principles

The structure of a QW laser is similar to that of a DH laser, except that in the former case the thickness of the active GaAs region is kept deliberately small. How small is what we will now discuss in relation to Figure 4.56.

From Figure 4.56(a) it is clear that electrons and holes are confined to the central GaAs region by the band structure at the GaAs/AlGaAs interfaces. If the length L_y of this region is made small enough (determined by the de Broglie equation $\lambda = h/p \sim L_y < 500$ Å, depending on the material) then the carriers are now confined in a finite potential well. The band structure within this well has to be modified to take account of this. The energy of an unconfined electron has to be separated into a confinement component in the y-direction and the two unconfined components in the plane of the quantum well layer, x–z, giving

$$E(n, k_x, k_z) = E_n + \frac{\hbar^2}{2m^*}(k_x^2 + k_z^2), \tag{4.93}$$

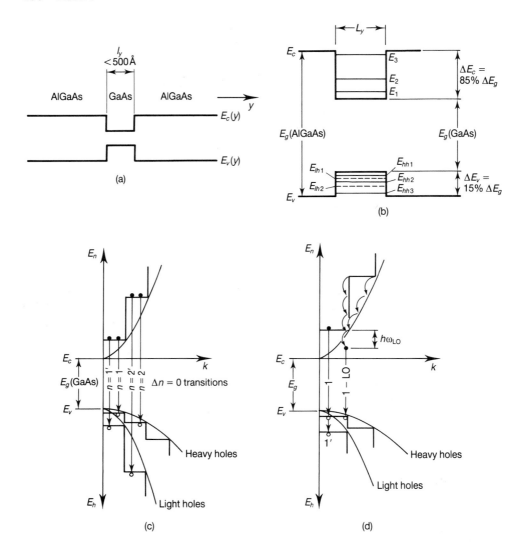

Figure 4.56 The quantum well (QW) laser: (a) single GaAs QW surrounded by AlGaAs (©Holt, Rinehart & Winston, Inc.: reproduced by kind permission), (b) Discrete energy levels within the well, (c) density of states for electrons and holes within the well, and (d) comparison of the downward scattering of electrons in a QW compared to a bulk semiconductor ((b), (c) and (d) ©1980 IEEE: reproduced by kind permission).

where E_n is the nth eigenvalue of the confined particle. Figure 4.56(a) then becomes, in more detail, Figure 4.56(b) where the values of E_n are shown as E_1, E_2,

E_3 for electrons, E_{hh1}, E_{hh2}, E_{hh3} for heavy holes and E_{lh1}, E_{lh2} for light holes [74]. (The concept of light and heavy holes has not been introduced before now as it has not been needed. Basically the terms occur because the valence bands in most semiconductors are degenerate about their upper maxima. This manifests itself as two or more separate valence bands, having the same maxima but different curvatures. For GaAs, there are two main bands only. One has a large density of states, i.e. a large effective mass, and is called the heavy hole band, and the other, for opposite reasons, is called the light hole band. More details on the nature of light and heavy holes can be found in many solid state textbooks, e.g. [75]). The usual parabolic forms of the conduction and valence band density of states functions now have to be replaced by a 'staircase' representation of discrete levels, each corresponding to a constant density of states per unit area given by

$$g(E)\mathrm{d}E = \frac{m}{\pi\hbar^2}\,\mathrm{d}E . \tag{4.94}$$

There are then no allowed electron states below E_1. This is shown in Figure 4.56(c). This diagram also shows the selection rules for recombination. When an electron and hole recombine $\Delta n = 0$; an example is $n = 1$ electrons can only recombine with $n = 1$ holes. This illustrates the first important point about quantum well lasers; a large number of electrons all of the same energy (at E_1 for example) can recombine with a similar block of holes. Contrast this with the bulk effect, where recombining carriers are distributed in energy over a parabolically varying density of states – a QW laser should give a much narrower output wavelength.

Figure 4.56(d) shows what happens when carriers are injected into a QW laser at high energies. They are scattered, with the emission of phonons, to a lower energy level, a process known as thermalization. This phonon interaction in QW laser operation is a major effect, whereas in bulk samples it is weak. This process is very dependent on the width L_y of the active region, which we shall now look at in more detail.

4.5.2   Active region width

We have so far considered what happens in a QW laser when the active region thickness is small – small being defined as the region where significant QSE occurs, of the order of a few hundred angstroms. A typical luminescence spectrum is then as in Figure 4.57(a), for a thickness of 200 Å. After injection, carriers can diffuse to the quantum well, be collected and recombine there with the emission characteristic of (in this case) GaAs confined particle transitions rather than the much larger band gap AlGaAs (7000–8500 Å rather than 6200–6400 Å). However, if L_y is reduced to 80 Å the confined particle radiation is much smaller than that of the direct band gap AlGaAs confining layer radiation (Figure 4.57(b)). It is then clear that for small L_y, defined as approaching the same size as the electron scattering path length l_p, electrons are not scattered in sufficient numbers to thermalize to the lower states of the quantum well. l_p has been measured and shown to have a temperature dependence, its value being 63 Å at 77 K and 35 Å at room temperature in GaAs [76]. As expected, electrons are scattered more efficiently at higher temperatures (= more vibrational energy = more phonons) and so active region widths have to be narrower. The hole scattering length is not well known, but is estimated to be smaller than that for electrons because holes have a greater effective mass. This leads to a simple way of measuring the valence and conduction band discontinuities ΔE_v and ΔE_c as shown in Figure 4.56(b). The recombination radiation of the AlGaAs confining layer is compared with that of 'hot' (i.e. those injected into narrow gap quantum wells) electrons recombining with bound holes in the quantum well as shown in Figure 4.58 (processes 1 and 2 respectively). The former is simply the band gap of AlGaAs. For the hot electrons, they do not have sufficient space to thermalize and hence essentially recombine from their injected level, i.e. the conduction band minimum of AlGaAs. The recombination wavelength is then $\Delta E_c + E_g(GaAs)$, leading directly to a calculation of ΔE_c and, by comparing the two emission wavelengths, ΔE_v.

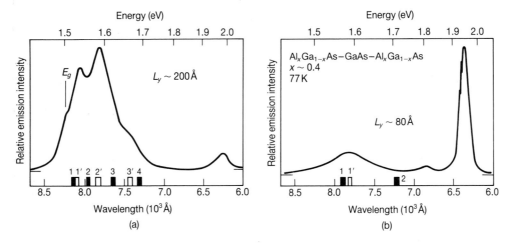

Figure 4.57 Photoluminescence spectra from (a) a 200 Å, and (b) an 80 Å GaAs QW laser (©1980 IEEE: reproduced by kind permission).

4.5.2.1   MQW laser

It is then apparent that there is a minimum thickness needed to the active region to make it efficient in laser operation. Some results, e.g. [77], suggest that stimulated emission can be obtained even from active regions as thin as 6 Å. The single quantum well approach can be extended to coupled quantum wells or, as this type of laser has come to be known as, the multiple quantum well (MQW). In this device one GaAs quantum well is coupled to another via a thin (100–200 Å) AlGaAs barrier layer (Figure 4.59). Several GaAs/AlGaAs layers are joined together in this

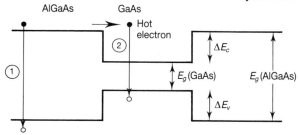

Figure 4.58 'Hot' electron recombination within a quantum well.

way, giving the MQW structure. The overall active region is considerably greater than l_p and carriers not captured by the first well can be captured by a subsequent one. Laser operation then occurs on the lower confined particle states, which are not broadened much because even for thin barrier layers there is only one loose coupling between lower energy levels of adjacent wells. As a result, the energy levels and hence emission wavelengths are similar comparing QW and MQW structures.

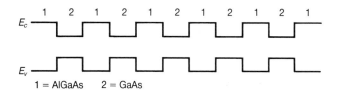

Figure 4.59 A multiquantum well (MQW).

An MQW laser was in fact the first quantum well laser to be made [78]. The device was made using GaAs/AlGaAs layers using MBE, and importantly was a photopumped laser. Perhaps surprisingly the first injection MQW laser was made using LPE [79], a technique not thought to be capable of such fine growth control. As mentioned earlier though, most research on MQW devices has been based around MBE or MOVPE systems.

An MQW is the active region of a laser that can emit a single frequency at several different wavelengths, known as a multiple array grating integrated cavity (MAGIC) laser. A central stripe pumped above threshold acts as the output coupler, whereas any of the other stripes can be simultaneously and independently pumped. The stripes are of different lengths, giving different output wavelengths. These are optically coupled to the central stripe by an external grating [80].

4.5.3   Injection current

One of the advantages of a narrow active region is the expectation of low threshold current densities. A consideration of charge movement will show that the carrier density in a quantum well structure is given by

$$n = \frac{J}{e}\frac{\tau}{L_y} \tag{4.95}$$

where τ is the carrier lifetime. As has been seen earlier in section 4.1.2.4, there is a minimum value of J needed to overcome the losses produced around a cavity and hence cause gain. This has a dependency on n as shown in Figure 4.60 [81]. At the onset of lasing, n has to be ~ 1–3×10^{18} cm^{-3} depending on emission wavelength. If L_y is made smaller, J can be made correspondingly smaller to maintain n. There are many examples of using this to make very low threshold diodes, with J_{th} of the order of 200–300 A/cm^2. Of course, the reader may well be aware that a thin active region leads to substantial losses and so increases J_{th} – new methods of optical confinement are treated in the next section, which produce J_{th} values even lower than those quoted above.

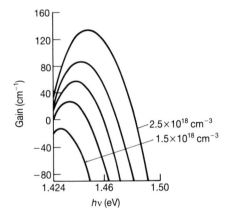

Figure 4.60 Gain spectra at several carrier concentrations of an MQW laser (©AIP: reproduced by kind permission).

Another useful characteristic of MQW lasers is their temperature dependence. Equation (4.36) has suggested an empirical relationship, with the constant T_0 being an important parameter: the higher the value of T_0 the less temperature dependent is the threshold current. Most MQW GaAs lasers have $T_0 \sim 500$ K, which is much greater than the standard values of DH lasers (~ 100–200 K). This significantly reduced temperature sensitivity of MQW lasers has been related to the 'staircase' density of states distribution and the disturbed electron and phonon distributions of the active region [82].

4.5.4 Optical confinement

Section 4.2 on heterojunction lasers showed some of the advantages of double heterostructure lasers over homojunction or single heterostructure types, namely the better carrier and optical confinement leading to lower threshold currents. The step function in band gap introduced in the DH laser can also be used to confine MQW laser output, as shown for example in Figure 4.61. Here different mole fractions of AlGaAs provide barrier layers in the MQW and optical confinement regions outside it [83]. This confinement helps to contain the otherwise large losses from a narrow active region, leading to low threshold currents.

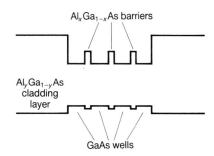

Figure 4.61 An MQW structure also acting to give greater optical confinement (©AIP: reproduced by kind permission).

A popular alternative that also provides confinement is using graded index profiles to the outer layers, and was first proposed without quantum wells in mind [84, 85]. The structure is shown in cross-section in Figure 4.62. There are three distinct regions to the structure in terms of optical confinement. The centre active region can be either a single or multiple quantum well structure. This is confined on both sides by a medium of wider band gap, and lower refractive index n, and where the composition is graded to give a parabolic profile to n. Outside this region the composition, and hence E_g and n, are uniform. The refractive index through this graded region is shown in Figure 4.62(c), and varies as

$$n(r) = n_y \left[1 - 2 \left(\frac{2r}{w} \right)^g \Delta \right]^{1/2} \tag{4.96}$$

within the parabolic profile. g is an exponent, $\Delta = (n_y - n_z)/n_y$ (known as the relative refractive index), and w is the total width of the graded region. This is known as a GRINSCH laser (GRaded INdex Separate Confinement Heterostructure), and if used with a multiquantum well device becomes a GRINSCH-MQW laser.

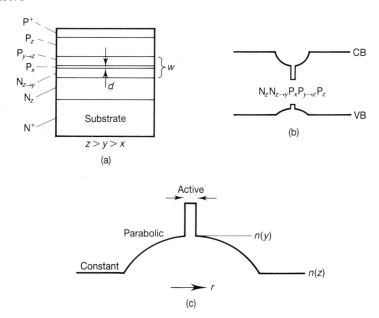

Figure 4.62 A graded index separate confinement heterostructure (GRIN-SCH) laser: (a) structure, (b) energy bands, and (c) refractive index profile ((a) and (b) ©AIP: reproduced by kind permission).

This structure leads to some very important properties related to the threshold current density J_{th}. An expression for J_{th} was derived in some detail in section 4.1.2.4, resulting in (4.33). We reproduce this here in a slightly modified form:

$$J_{th} = \frac{J_0 d}{\eta_i} + \frac{J_0 d}{g_0 \eta_i \Gamma} \alpha + \frac{J_0 d}{g_0 \eta_i \Gamma L} \log_e \frac{1}{R}. \tag{4.97}$$

All the symbol terminologies have been explained earlier, but as a timely reminder, the three terms on the right hand side of (4.97) represent intrinsic gain (I), internal absorption losses (A) and end mirror losses (M) respectively. The relative values of the three terms are plotted in Figure 4.63 [85]. For a standard DH laser, both mirror and absorption losses increase rapidly for thin active regions, leading to very high threshold currents; we have seen this before in Figure 4.32. However, for the GRINSCH structures the M and A terms remain constant and reducing the active layer thickness reduces J_{th} – Figure 4.64 [84]. The mirror reflectivity then becomes the dominant loss term. Using metallization coatings to produce one high reflectivity end facet can then reduce this term further, and the absorption term can be reduced by using short cavities. It would then appear that arbitrarily low threshold currents could be produced, but the lower limit is set by the amount of output power needed. An idea of this can be obtained by rearranging (4.38) in terms of current:

$$I - I_{th} = \frac{\Delta P e}{\eta_e h \nu}.$$ (4.98)

Example 4.10

A particular laser has $\eta_e = 0.8$, $\lambda = 1.55$ μm and a minimum output power requirement of 100 μW. Calculate the value of threshold current below which further reductions in I_{th} are not really justified, i.e. the dominant current changes are in the operational mode, rather than in the threshold.

Solution: from (4.98)

$$I - I_{th} = \frac{100 \times e \times 1.55 \times 10^{-6}}{0.8 \times hc} = 156 \, \mu\text{A}.$$ (4.99)

If the threshold current is much lower than this value then the criterion of the dominant current change being operational is justified.

The factor T_0 in the temperature dependence of threshold current increases in GRINSCH-SQW lasers with cavity length. This is shown in Figure 4.65, and is related to the decrease in both loss and gain coefficients with temperature [86]. As temperature increases, changes in gain tend to increase threshold whereas changes in α tend to decrease it. The relative importance of these two terms, which are related to cavity length, explain the geometric dependence of T_0 in these devices.

4.5.5 Strained layer superlattices

A strained layer superlattice (SLS), or pseudomorphic, structure is essentially a multiquantum well taken to the extreme of each well/barrier being only a few atoms thick, and grown to be deliberately non-lattice matched. This doesn't lead to dislocations and defects, as it would if the layers were many atoms thick, but instead the thin layers are strained to match up the lattice constants. This is not just an academic point. The capability to grow strained layer superlattices, and to make SLS devices, that are essentially defect free means that the constraint of high quality interfaces is no longer strictly limited to lattice matched crystal systems. The strain involved in these devices is of the order of 0.1–5%, and can be calculated from the materials' parameters [87].

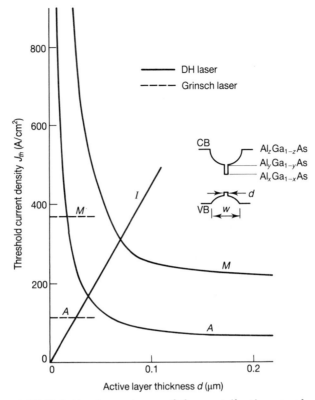

Figure 4.63 Relative importance of the contributions to threshold current density by the intrinsic, internal loss and the mirror loss terms (©AIP: reproduced by kind permission).

Although SLS structures had been made throughout the 1970s it wasn't until the early 1980s that devices were made, with the first injection laser published in 1984 [88]. This used a 40 Å $In_xGa_{1-x}As$/30 Å GaAs superlattice, which exhibited a strain of $\sim 2.5\%$, to produce an output power of 5 mW at 1 μm. GRINSCH-SLS devices were made soon after – the cross-section of a typical device involving AlGaAs/GaAs and InGaAs is shown in Figure 4.66 [89]. Very low threshold current densities of less than 200 A/cm^2 were observed with these devices. The first SLS structures to run in continuous mode at room temperature were made in 1987, with typical output powers of 20 mW [90] at 1 μm. These were also made using a GRINSCH arrangement. At about the same time visible laser operation was announced using SLS devices [91]. This is quite a difficult problem because, for GaAs quantum wells, visible light emission requires a narrow well width to ensure transitions from energy states other than the minimum. This unfortunately leads to a broadening of the spectral output. Energetically, AlGaAs is more suited to visible emission than GaAs, but there is still a problem of line broadening which increases

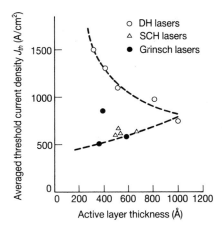

Figure 4.64 A comparison of the averaged threshold current density of GRINSCH lasers and symmetric SCH lasers with regular DH lasers in the very thin active layer range (©AIP: reproduced by kind permission).

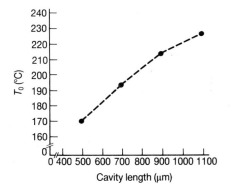

Figure 4.65 Temperature parameter T_0 measured at four cavity lengths for GRINSCH-SQW lasers (©AIP: reproduced by kind permission).

with an increasing fraction of Al in the material. To get around these problems, a single quantum well of AlGaAs/GaAs was proposed within an AlGaAs confining GRINSCH structure. Lasers operating in the all important 1.55 μm region have also been made using the SLS approach, with a structure based on InGaAs/InP [92].

Threshold current densities for these devices continue to tumble rapidly. From only breaking the 100 A/cm^2 barrier in 1990, values the following year were as low as 45 A/cm^2. This was for an InGaAs/GaAs SLS system emitting at ~ 1 μm [93]. The other advantage to this popular InGaAs/GaAs/AlGaAs system can be seen by considering Figure 4.67. The transparency of a GaAs substrate to the emitted

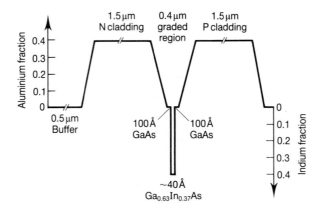

Figure 4.66 A typical layer structure and composition of a GRINSCH strain layer SQW laser (©AIP: reproduced by kind permission).

radiation allows input and output through the substrate, and in addition reduces optical coupling between the lasers and any adjacent circuitry. The use of these types of lasers in optoelectronic integrated circuits could be promising.

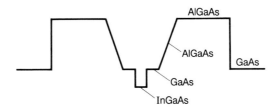

Figure 4.67 The InGaAs/GaAs/AlGaAs strained layer superlattice (SLS) system.

4.5.6   Quantum wires and dots

In a quantum wire (QWR) the electrons are now confined in two directions, leading to a different energy level structure to that of a quantum well. As might be guessed, a quantum dot represents confinement in three dimensions.

Quantum wire lasers were first made in 1982 [94], and the fabrication process is shown in Figure 4.68. Figure 4.68(a) shows a standard MQW superlattice. This is then coated with a layer of photoresist which is exposed to reveal windows (Figure 4.68(b)). A mesa etch will produce a structure as in Figure 4.68(c). Photoresist removal and the deposition of an AlGaAs cap layer complete the structure. Several analyses have been done on the operation of quantum wire lasers, with the most significant result being the prediction of much lower threshold currents even than quantum well devices [95]. This has been experimentally verified using a different type of QWR laser to that described above, a V-groove laser [96].

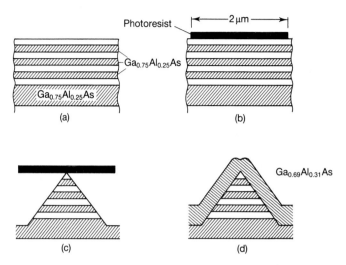

Figure 4.68 Processing of a quantum wire laser: (a) MQW superlattice, (b) resist definition, (c) mesa etch, and (d) resist removal and capping (©AIP: reproduced by kind permission).

The potential advantage of a quantum dot laser is that its output spectrum would result wholly from discrete states, and thus a narrow linewidth should be obtained. In this respect the active region is behaving much like a gas laser, such as an argon ion type. A quantum dot laser has been simulated by the application of a high magnetic field to an MQW device, and an output spectrum characteristic of a series of discrete states was obtained [97].

4.6 High power lasers

Although the development of single frequency lasers has been the dominant technology driver because of its impact on information capacity of an optical communication system, the actual power output of lasers has also been a focus of much activity. For communications, the obvious advantages of a high power output are an increased distance of optical fiber between repeater stations and/or an increased signal to noise ratio at the receiver. High power semiconductor lasers also find uses in other fields, such as bar code scanning, laser printers or as optical pump sources for lasers such as Nd^+:YAG. A lot of the techniques used to produce high power devices have already been covered in section 4.3, and particularly sections 4.3.4.5 and 4.3.4.6. The channelled substrate planar (CSP – Figure 4.39(b)), constricted double heterostructure (CDH – Figures 4.39(c) and (d)) and buried V-channelled substrate inner stripe (B-VSIS – Figure 4.41(e)) laser are all examples of high power devices. To some extent, the devices presented in this section overlap with the examples given above, but the high power criterion is extended to include a larger range and, for the ultimate in output power, multiple laser arrays.

4.6.1   Limits on laser power

A fundamental problem was alluded to in section 4.3.4. For a high power device, the strong stimulated emission near the centre of a stripe laser begins to produce a localized depletion of the gain profile, and hence the output power, as shown in Figure 4.37. This spatial hole burning, and the non-uniform gain profile across the stripe will, because of its effect on refractive index, give a spread of peak gain g_{max} with respect to wavelength. The spectral broadening of the output wavelength λ can be quantified as

$$\frac{\Delta\lambda}{\lambda} = k\frac{\Delta g}{g_{max}} \tag{4.100}$$

where k is a constant dependent on the material (examples are $k = 5 \times 10^{-3}$ for GaAs and 4×10^{-2} for InGaAsP [98]). Equation (4.100) provides a useful design constraint on a high power laser operating in single longitudinal mode.

Example 4.11

Calculate the spectral broadening of a 1.55 μm InGaAsP laser with $\Delta g/g_{max} = 0.1$ and $k = 0.04$.

Solution: from (4.100)

$$\Delta\lambda = 1.55 \times 10^{-6} \times 0.04 \times 0.1 = 6\,\text{nm}, \tag{4.101}$$

enough to support several extra modes.

Negative index waveguides, where the structure is designed to provide a built-in refractive index difference in the plane of the stripe, with a minimum at the stripe's centre, have been designed to overcome this. There are other methods, such as increasing the rate of carrier diffusion or absorption losses at the stripe edge – the channelled substrate planar (CSP) laser mentioned above and in more detail in section 4.3.4.6 is an example of the latter approach. Other three-dimensional waveguide designs were given in the same or associated sections.

One aspect not considered so far in output power design is the effect on the end mirrors. If the power level is high enough, localized melting of these mirrors occurs. This can be reduced by coating the ends with a dielectric of thickness $\lambda/2n_d$ and refractive index n_d, and hence the 'reflection' occurs by constructive interference between waves reflected at the dielectric–air boundary and those at the semiconductor–dielectric boundary. A material of high thermal conductivity and having a thermal expansion coefficient close to that of the semiconductor is used; an example is Al_2O_3 on GaAs.

Another way of reducing the power level at a mirror facet is by introducing non-absorbing mirrors (NAMs) into the structure. This is done by selective diffusion of Zn along the length of the stripe but away from the facet ends. The band gap difference between the bulk and the end of the active region created by this process results in a mirror effect, giving an increase in optical power allowed in the cavity before facet damage occurs. The following two sections give a brief history of laser designs and the output power obtained. However, it must be borne in mind that there is a strong interdependency between power and laser lifetime, and so comparisons between different techniques are fairly meaningless without this. One laser may give a very high power, and fail after a few hours; another may be stable for thousands of hours but at a lower power level. Unfortunately there is no quality standard on reliability to compare different power levels.

4.6.2 Large optical cavity (LOC) laser

Perhaps the most obvious way to obtain a high power is to increase the volume of the cavity in which gain takes place or, as with the large optical cavity (LOC) device, increase the effective waveguiding volume. The concept has been known for a long time [18], and is based around a 'standard' three-layer double heterostructure device alluded to previously in section 4.2.6, and shown in Figure 4.27(a). The structure is repeated in Figure 4.69 and is now discussed in more detail. Two types are shown: a symmetric structure in Figure 4.69(a), and an asymmetric one in Figure 4.69(b). The key feature is a region of one or two layers of material with a refractive index intermediate between those of the active and cladding layers. It is clear that, in either case, the recombination and optical cavity region are separated; the former is in p-type material, the latter in n-type. The fact that the optical modes propagate in n-type leads to low losses in this type of device. Making an optical cavity much larger than the recombination region gives a large spot size and hence reduced power densities at the end facets – this results in a decreased probability of mirror damage. Details of mode propagation in LOC lasers have been published in the literature [99] and it has been shown that the asymmetric structure of Figure 4.69(b) more easily leads to single (transverse) mode operation.

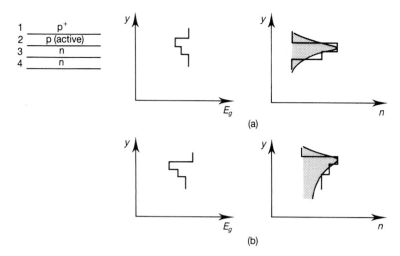

Figure 4.69 (a) Symmetric, and (b) asymmetric LOC laser.

LOC lasers have been made using several techniques previously mentioned, including buried heterostructure (BH – section 4.3.4.5 and [100]) and constricted double heterostructure (CDH – section 4.3.4.6 and [101]). The latter appears to give higher power, with c.w. outputs up to around 100 mW. Pulsed operation can give much higher output powers, of course, with thermal dissipation problems being considerably reduced. Outputs up to 2 W per end facet have been reported [102].

Two other features of LOC lasers need to be mentioned here. First, in having the structure that they do there will be inevitable leakage of carriers between the active and the guide layer, much more so than for a standard heterostructure device. This will result in an increase in threshold current temperature sensitivity. Second, alluding to a point mentioned earlier in section 4.6.2, the refractive index depressions in the recombination region caused by the high carrier concentration will make the optical mode spot size sensitive, as the refractive index difference between active and guide layers is very small [103].

4.6.3   Other designs

These fall into two different categories; quantum well and non-quantum well. The former are considered later in this section. Examples of the latter include the buried twin-ridge substrate (BTRS) laser as shown in Figure 4.70(a) [104]. The twin ridge structure allows an extremely thin active region to be formed which enlarges the near field spot size. The buried stripe structure confines the injection current, as discussed in section 4.3.4.5. The square channel formed at the corner of the ridges confines the lateral mode by providing an abrupt change in refractive index.

Multiple coating of the end facets completes the structure, which has obtained c.w. outputs as high as 200 mW. The structure can be further improved upon by considering Figure 4.70(b) [105]. This is a cross-section *parallel* to the power output, and shows that the current injection regions are thin at the facet ends, where heating effects are greatest, and thick in the centre. Facet damage due to heating is minimized and a greater power output can result. A simplified device diagram is shown in Figure 4.70(c), which shows how the width of the ridge in the inner region is greater than that at the facets, realizing the active layer thickness variations shown in Figures 4.70(a) and (b).

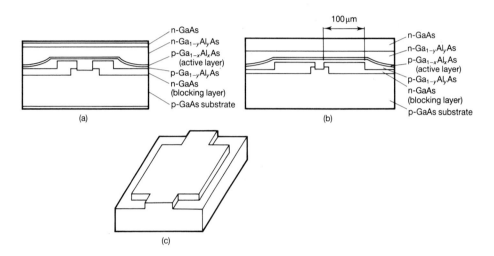

Figure 4.70 The buried twin-ridge substrate (BTRS) laser: (a) basic structure, (b) cross-section parallel to the power output of an improved design, and (c) 3-D representation of the inner ridge being wider than near the cavity facets (©1985, 1987 IEEE: reproduced by kind permission).

Another buried structure is shown in Figure 4.71, but this device uses flared waveguides to increase the output power [106]. If the guides are designed correctly, the spot will always be confined by the guide yet will expand rapidly enough over a short distance to produce a large spot without excitation of higher order lateral modes. Output powers up to 120 mW have been obtained.

For quantum well devices, almost all the high power output results have been with the GaAs–AlGaAs system. Long wavelength diodes have produced up to ~ 100 mW, but the near infra-red devices now have multiple watt performance. Using the excellent confinement properties of single quantum well (SQW) devices, c.w. outputs of 2.6 W for an AlGaAs-SQW and 2.9 W for a GaAs-SQW have been observed [107]. Pulsed output up to 10.7 W has been obtained for the same material [108]. C.w. output for the InGaAsP–GaAs SCH-SQW structure whose

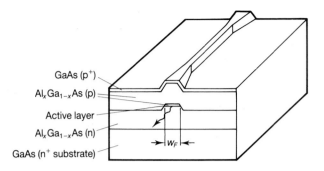

Figure 4.71 A flared waveguide BH laser (©AIP: reproduced by kind permission).

band diagram is shown in Figure 4.72 has been measured at 5.3 W at 0.8 μm [109].

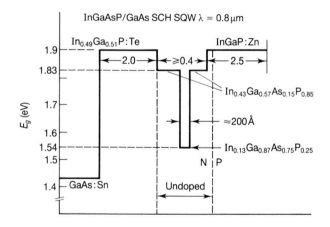

Figure 4.72 Band diagram of a InGaAsP–GaAs SCH-SQW laser (©1991 IEEE: reproduced by kind permission).

4.6.4   Laser arrays

Paralleling the output of several semiconductor lasers to increase the power level has been a technique used for many years. The first such array was reported in 1978 [110], although combinations of individual lasers had been made previously. The fine stripe elements of the array form a set of parallel waveguides; coupling between adjacent guides could then be expected. The relative phase relationship between the coupled modes has a crucial effect on output power; the theory of coupled modes is covered in many textbooks on optics, and forms the basis of an important device in optical communication, the evanescent coupler, which can be used as a full power coupler (i.e. an optical switch) or a half power (3 dB) coupler.

The normalised amplitudes for all the allowed modes of a 10-element array ($L = 1$ to $L = 10$) have been calculated by coupled mode analysis [111] and are shown in Figure 4.73(a). At $L = 1$ all modes are in phase; at $L = 10$ all modes are 180° out of phase. In between these two extremes are a range of phase relationships between adjacent modes. Lateral far field patterns, as shown in Figure 4.73(b), confirm these phase relationships. A more detailed analysis, which involves modelling a laser with gain and refractive index distributions, has also been reported [112].

Many different means have been proposed to fabricate and operate laser diode arrays, all with the aim of maximizing the power output. Perhaps one of the simplest means is to address each element independently, allowing for operational tuning out of device and coupling non-uniformities [113]. The overall device is considerably bigger, as several contact pads are needed, and a more complex metallization than the standard one is required.

An approach using integrated phase shifters is shown in Figure 4.74. The structure is shown prior to active layer deposition, where the non-etched regions form phase shifting sections to control the phase difference between adjacent elements, in this case for a CSP-LOC laser [114]. Alternatively, phase shifting facet coatings can be deposited. By either of these methods, the desired operating mode can be combined with a 0° phase shift between adjacent elements, giving maximum output in one far field lobe, as in Figure 4.73(b).

Another technique is to vary the lateral spacing between each element of an array. The coupling coefficient between adjacent elements can then be adjusted, again leading to a single field lobe with all elements in phase [115]. The fundamental mode of this variable spacing array (VSA) can be readily matched to a uniform gain distribution across the entire aperture. A not dissimilar idea is to vary the stripe width across the array [116]. This is called a 'chirped' array, and is an effective means of mode control.

It can be guessed from the methodology behind these devices that maintaining the in phase nature of the output beam is a real problem. Often the far field pattern consists of more than one mode, which is obviously undesirable for most applications. The Y-junction coupled array was proposed to overcome this problem [117]. Such an array is shown in Figure 4.75(a). It consists of parallel waveguide lasers interconnected as a series of Y-junctions. The principle of operation, shown in Figure 4.75(b), is that modes incident from the 'branches' to the 'stem' of the 'Y' will add according to their phase relationship: in phase components add to produce one mode of high power, out of phase components destructively interfere to lose power. Laser diodes incorporating Y-junctions have been made in both BH

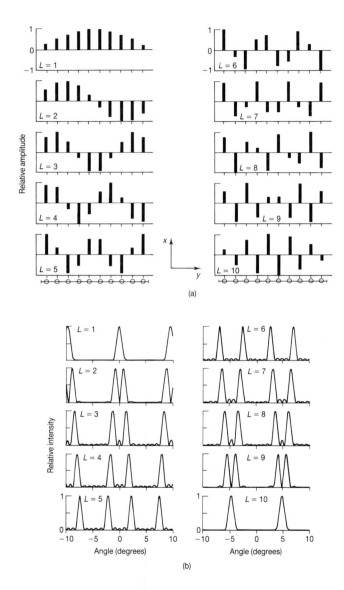

Figure 4.73 A ten-element laser array: (a) normalized amplitudes of the allowed modes (the open circles show the position of the emitters), and (b) normalized far field intensity distribution for the allowed modes with the emitters on 5 μm centres (©AIP: reproduced by kind permission).

and CSP designs, and also with flared output waveguides to enhance the near field spot size [118].

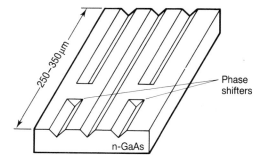

Figure 4.74 Etched substrate prior to growth for a CSP-LOC phase locked array with internal phase shifters (©1983 RCA: reproduced by kind permission of General Electric).

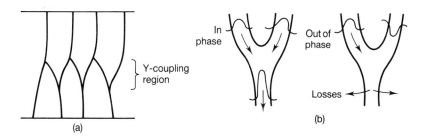

Figure 4.75 (a) A Y-coupled junction array, and (b) principle of operation.

Extremely high power outputs can be obtained from diode arrays: up to 76 W c.w. has been reported [119], although long lifetimes were only available at lower power levels. It is expected that a source consisting of several banks of high power diode arrays could take over from flashlamps as the dominant mechanism for the pumping of Nd$^+$:YAG lasers.

4.7 Surface emitting lasers

Before describing the techniques used for making surface emitting lasers, it should first be mentioned why such devices are useful. There are basically two reasons:

(i) it should be easier both to fabricate and to access the light from an array of devices if they are surface emitters, in particular two-dimensional arrays.

(ii) Due to diffraction from a narrow aperture the output beam from an edge emitting laser (i.e. all types we have met up until now) is highly divergent.

This has already been described in section 4.1.3.4, and various means have been proposed to limit the problem. However, a surface emitter similar to a standard LED would not have its output diffraction limited.

There have been three main ways of making surface emitting lasers. Two involve light being taken out at an orthogonal angle to the plane of laser oscillation, either by reflective (section 4.7.2) or refractive (section 4.7.3) means, and the other, in the next section, involves causing the laser to oscillate in a different direction.

4.7.1   Vertical cavity laser

The vertical cavity surface emitting laser (VCSEL), which on first appearance looks very much like a standard heterojunction LED, was first made in 1979, and is shown in Figure 4.76(a) [120]. Current is passed through the device from the centrally placed electrode on the p-side to the circular electrode on the n-side. The p-electrode doubles as a mirror whilst the n-side has its own centrally placed reflector. The InP substrate is fairly transparent to the lasing wavelength of 1.18 μm, although the threshold current even at 77 K operation remained fairly high ($\sim$11 kA/cm^2). This was largely due to the poor carrier confinement caused by the design of the laser. Advantages of this technique of surface emission include the possibility of single frequency operation due to the short cavity length, and the removal of the fragile cleavage process that creates the end mirrors in a standard laser. A way to create current confinement is shown in Figure 4.76(b), where a hole has been etched in the substrate to allow more light to get out of the device and also provide for more current confinement, as the n-electrode is better defined around the output mirror [121]. This design has also been used for GaAs–AlGaAs structures. Multiple Bragg reflectors have been incorporated in these structures to reach room temperature c.w. operation under low threshold conditions [122].

The incorporation of multiple reflectors and multiple quantum well structures in vertical cavity lasers has resulted in large scale integration of two-dimensional arrays. These can be made to have individually addressable matrix elements, with array sizes up to 32×32 devices [123]. Figures 4.77(a) and (b) are impressive SEM images of arrays of different sized vertical cavity lasers.

4.7.2   Angled reflectors

An output mirror angled at 45° to the oscillation direction of a standard laser would seem to be the obvious way of turning the output beam through 90°. This is not as easily realized as it sounds, as normal perpendicular output mirrors are formed by cleavage of the laser diode along crystal planes. Also, it has to be ensured that enough light is reflected back into the cavity for laser oscillation to continue. The first realization of such a structure is shown in Figure 4.78(a) [124].

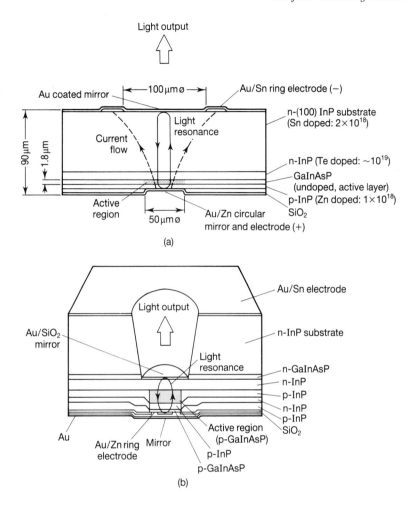

Figure 4.76 Two examples of surface emitting lasers: (a) the first reported device (©Physical Society of Japan: reproduced by kind permission), and (b) with a hole etched in the substrate (©IEE: reproduced by kind permission).

The optical cavity consists of a natural (110) cleavage plane at the left hand end, a chemically etched 45° mirror to cause beam steering and the air–AlGaAs interface at the output. The n-AlGaAs region is highly absorbing; however, because it is thin, actual losses will be small. Also, because this region doesn't form part of the guided volume, the beam will be highly divergent and care has to be taken to ensure sufficient reflection at the air–AlGaAs interface. Because of this early threshold currents were quite high.

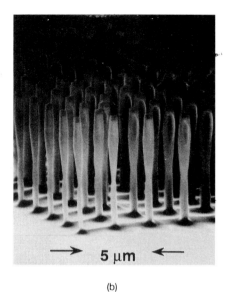

(a)   (b)

Figure 4.77 Arrays of surface emitting lasers: (a) lasers varying in diameter from 1 to 5 μm, and (b) ultrasmall microlasers with diameters down to 0.4 μm (©1991 IEEE: photos courtesy of Photonics Research Incorporated).

A laser using a parabolic output mirror is shown in Figure 4.78(b) [125]. The parabolic shape is formed by a selective etching and mass transport technique, and is used to limit the output beam divergence. Notice also that this laser has the mirror integrated into the structure but external to the optical cavity. Large two-dimensional arrays have been made using these lasers, which work readily under c.w. conditions at room temperature [126].

To make AlGaAs lasers with integrated steering mirrors the mass transport technique noted in [125] cannot be used, as no such mechanism exists for the GaAs/AlGaAs system. 45° reflectors must then be made by more conventional etching techniques such as ion beam assisted etching (section 9.4.4). Individual lasers [127] and arrays [128] have been made using this or similar techniques.

4.7.3   Refractive beam steering

The two methods of beam steering reported in the last two sections have produced individual lasers and arrays that work well at room temperature when compared to standard edge emitting lasers. The ease with which these devices can be integrated to form a two-dimensional array is an additional benefit. Output beam divergence is still of the order of several degrees, however, more commonly in the 10–15°

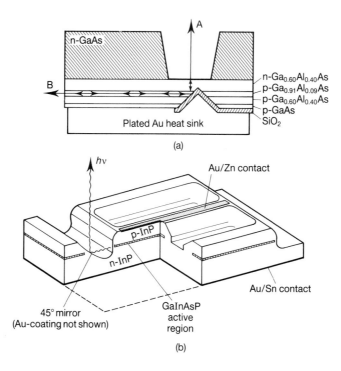

Figure 4.78 Two examples of reflective beam steering: (a) using an end of cavity mirror made with a via hole, and (b) using a parabolic mirror external to the cavity (©AIP: reproduced by kind permission).

range. Refractive beam steering virtually eliminates this problem by reducing the divergence angle to between 0.01°–0.5°. The principle is shown in Figure 4.79(a), and the first laser to demonstrate the method used a distributed feedback (DFB – section 4.4.1.2) structure in the optical cavity [129]. We noted that in the DFB laser it was necessary for a wavefront incident on a corrugation within the structure to be totally reflected back in phase with other reflections. The periodicity of the grating necessary to achieve this is given by (4.85) and (4.86). For the same structure to act as an orthogonal reflector the design constraints on periodicity are a little different. Consider the general case as shown in Figure 4.79. For each reflected ray to be in phase across the wavefront, the additional distance travelled by each ray compared to its predecessor must be an integral multiple of wavelength λ_0, i.e.

$$d + b = \frac{l\lambda_0}{n} \tag{4.102}$$

where l is an integer. Simple geometrical arguments can be used to isolate θ from Figure 4.79, to give

$$\sin \theta = \frac{l\lambda_0}{nd} - 1. \tag{4.103}$$

Unity values of λ_0/nd gives readily accessible solutions. For $l = 0, \theta = 270°$, which corresponds to forward scattered light (Figure 4.79(b)). For $l = 1, \theta = 0$ and the light is turned through 90°, and for $l = 2, \theta = 90°$, corresponding to the case of a DFB laser. Thus for the case of 90° reflection, the constraint on periodicity for general values of λ_0/nd are

$$d = \frac{l\lambda_0}{n}, \tag{4.104}$$

compared to $d = l\lambda_0/2n$ as given by (4.85) (here we have ignored the small difference between λ_0 and λ_B for simplicity). As shown in section 4.4.1.2, the first solution ($l = 1$) of (4.85) gave $d = 0.23$ μm, but for the device to act as a surface emitter (and, incidently, as a DFB laser providing the longitudinal oscillation) both (4.85) and (4.104) must be satisfied. This gives $d = 0.47$ μm. Early device thresholds were fairly high (~ 1.2 kA/cm^2) but output divergences were extremely low – only about 0.35°.

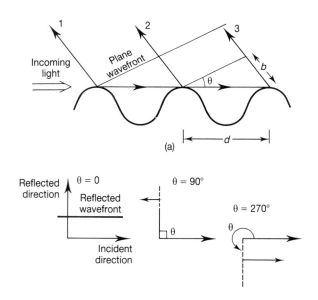

Figure 4.79 (a) The principle of refractive beam steering. (b) Specific examples.

DFB structures are not the only type to provide this kind of beam steering mechanism. Distributed Bragg reflector (DBR) lasers, where the corrugated structure is external to the active region, have also been used. Beam divergence angles as low as 0.17° have been obtained [130]. DBR surface emitters have also been made into large scale arrays. Such a structure is shown in Figure 4.80 [131]. Coupling between the arrays can be either by evanescent fields (Figure 4.80(a)) or by Y-branches (Figure 4.80(b)) – both types were discussed in section 4.6.4. These grating surface emitting (GSE) arrays have a coherent and well collimated output, with beam divergences as low as 0.01°×1°. Threshold current densities are low ($\sim$140 A/cm^2) and output powers of several watts c.w. are obtainable [132].

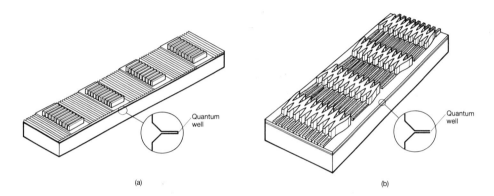

(a)   (b)

Figure 4.80 A 10 × 10 array of lasers with four gain sections and (a) evanescent, (b) Y modes of coupling (©1989 IEEE: reproduced by kind permission).

4.8 Visible lasers

There are three separate commercial driving forces behind the need for visible laser diodes:

(i) as light sources in optical storage. At present, compact disc (CD) players use $Al_xGa_{1-x}As$ lasers operating in the near infra-red. The limiting factor on pit spacing on a CD is diffraction of the laser beam at its output aperture, which is proportional to the wavelength. From this it is obvious that a shorter wavelength would increase the amount of information able to be stored on a compact disc.

(ii) Light sources for general laboratory use. Many applications which currently use bulky, power hungry and physically fragile helium–neon lasers could be taken over by laser diodes. Output diffraction would have to be limited and the fairly large linewidth would have to be tolerated by the user.

(iii) Optical scanners in information reading, such as bar codes systems at, for example, supermarket checkouts.

4.8.1 Red lasers

The favoured structure for a semiconductor laser in the red (600–700 nm) part of the spectrum is based on InGaP/InGaAlP. DH lasers have been made, and were the first to be reported to operate under room temperature c.w. conditions [133]. More recently single or multiple quantum well structures have enabled higher temperature operation and significant reductions in threshold current. A typical cross-section through a device is shown in Figure 4.81 [134]. It consists of a strained layer, single quantum well region of InGaP with InGaAlP as the boundary layers. Graded InGaAlP layers complete the main region with the GRINSCH structure referred to previously in section 4.5.3. Threshold currents are as low as 425 A/cm^2 with output powers of over 1 W.

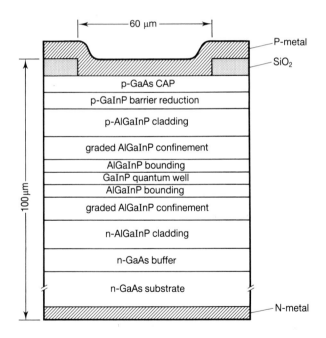

Figure 4.81 An oxide stripe, strained layer SQW-GRINSCH visible light laser (©AIP: reproduced by kind permission).

4.8.2   Blue lasers

The materials mentioned in section 3.2.1.5 on blue LEDs have so far not produced stimulated emission under electrical pumping methods: this is an essential feature if blue lasers are to find applications in information systems such as CD players. Optical pumping has been successful, and it is expected that electrical methods will follow. Instead, II–VI based heterostructures have been used based on ZnSe/ZnCdSe multiquantum wells [135].

An alternative method of obtaining blue coherent light is by using an AlGaAs laser to photopump second harmonic generation in a $KNBO_3$ crystal, giving a frequency doubled (wavelength = 430 nm) output [136]. Whilst not in itself a blue semiconductor laser, the overall device has the same size, and hence can be used in the same type of applications, as a semiconductor device. Initial output powers are quite low (1 mW) but advances are expected to be made with more efficient designs.

4.9   Drive circuitry

In Chapter 3 on light emitting diodes, section 3.4 was devoted to all the different aspects of driving an LED from the basic circuitry to analog and digital waveforms. The same approach is taken in this section for a laser diode. There are many similarities between an LED and LD in terms of the device as a circuit element, and equally there are many important differences. These are highlighted through this section.

4.9.1   Basic operation

The most obvious difference to mention between an LED and an LD at this stage is that the former gives a (nearly) linear light output with drive current, whereas the latter is a threshold device, as shown in Figure 4.82(a). As such, the light output from the laser is only proportional to the current above threshold. Whilst a bias current is usually applied to an LED to make sure that any subsequent analog signal does not take the total diode voltage below zero (and hence no light output), for a laser diode a bias is applied to make sure that, for digital signals, the current is just below threshold and, for analog signals, the total diode current never falls below threshold. This is shown in Figures 4.82(b) and (c), where I_{bd} and I_{ba} represent digital and analog bias levels respectively. Unfortunately, the application of an instantaneous current pulse doesn't immediately result in light output; there is a delay and some serious after effects, as we shall now see.

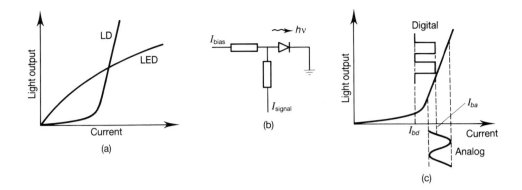

Figure 4.82 (a) Output vs current characteristics of an LED and an LD. (b) Current bias arrangement for driving a laser. (c) Digital and analog manifestations of (b).

4.9.1.1   Turn-on delay
When a semiconductor laser receives a current pulse, either from zero current or just below threshold, there is a delay in the build up of photon density necessary to cause stimulated emission. Below threshold, a laser behaves as an LED, and hence can be described by a rate equation given by

$$\frac{\mathrm{d}n}{\mathrm{d}t} = \frac{J}{ed} - \frac{n}{\tau_s} \tag{4.105}$$

where τ_s is the lifetime of a carrier that recombines spontaneously and d is the active region thickness as used previously. This differential equation has to be solved given the following boundary conditions relating n and t:

$$t = 0 \quad n(0) \;=\; \frac{J_a \tau_s}{ed}$$
$$t = t_D \quad n(t_D) \;=\; \frac{J_{th} \tau_s}{ed} \tag{4.106}$$

where J_a is the value of current density at $t = 0$, and t_D is the time taken for the current to reach threshold. The solution to (4.105) is then

$$n(t)\,\frac{ed}{\tau_s} = J + (J_a - J)\,\exp(-t/\tau_s). \tag{4.107}$$

Hence from (4.106) and (4.107)

$$J_{th} \;=\; J + (J_a - J)\,\exp(-t_D/\tau_s) \tag{4.108}$$

$$\text{and so} \quad t_D \;=\; \tau_s \log_e\!\left(\frac{J - J_a}{J - J_{th}}\right). \tag{4.109}$$

It is clear that t_D is then the delay between the current pulse and the start of the laser action, and that as $J_a \to J_{th}$ then $t_D \to 0$. Thus biasing the device near threshold will result in a significant shortening of the turn-on delay compared to starting from zero.

Example 4.12

A particular laser has a threshold current of 50 mA and a drive current of 70 mA. Calculate the improvement in response time t_D when biasing with a current of 45mA compared to no bias current.

Solution: from (4.109)

$$\frac{t_D(bias)}{t_D(no\ bias)} = \frac{\log_e\left[(70-45)/(70-50)\right]}{\log_e\left[(70-0)/(70-50)\right]} = 0.18. \qquad (4.110)$$

Biasing the diode reduces the response time by a factor of 5.6.

This calculation is fairly simplified, and takes no account of any delay caused by charging the depletion region capacitance or the diffusion capacitance of the device. From basic electrostatics this leads to an accumulation of charges in the active region, whose growth is exponential with time characterized by an effective time constant t_c. t_c could be reduced by driving with a very high current, or an alternative is to preshape the current pulse, as shown in Figure 4.83(a) [137]. This is an exponentially decaying waveform, characterized by $J = J_b \exp(-t/\tau_b) + J_a$. The laser turn-on delay is then derived as

$$\frac{J_b}{J_{th}}\frac{\exp(-t_D/\tau_b)}{1-(t_D/\tau_b)} - \left(\frac{J_b}{J_{th}}\frac{\tau_b}{\tau_b-t_c}+\frac{J_a}{J_{th}}\right)\exp\left(\frac{-t_D}{t_c}\right) + \frac{J_a}{J_{th}} = 1. \qquad (4.111)$$

Figures 4.83(b) and (c) show the effect of varying the independent parameters J_b and τ_b in the current pulse. The results in Figure 4.83(b) set $\tau_b = t_c$ and show how t_D decreases with J_b, reaching a value of $\sim 0.1t_c$ at $J_b = 8J_{th}$, confirming what was mentioned earlier about a high current helping to reduce the delay; here the sharp spike in the current pulse achieves the same thing. Figure 4.83(c) shows the result of setting $J_b = J_a$ and plots the fall in t_D with τ_b. For small values of τ_b/t_c, the exponential portion of the current is too fast for the charge to respond, and the reduction in t_D is small. However, as τ_b becomes greater, t_D asymptotically approaches $0.287t_c$ at $I_b = I_a = 2I_{th}$. This gives a factor > 3 decrease in turn-on delay.

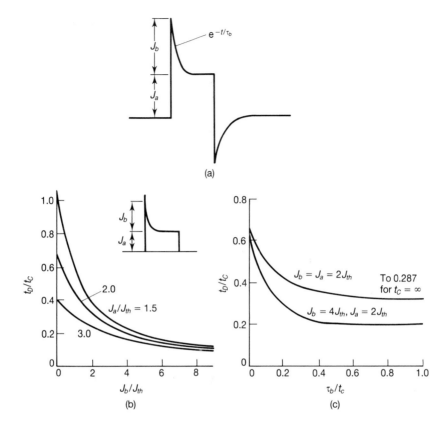

Figure 4.83 Time delay characteristics of laser diodes: (a) current waveform for delay reduction, and reduction of delay time as a function of (b) peak pulse amplitude and (c) pulse decaying time constant.

4.9.1.2   Relaxation oscillations

Besides the turn-on delay described in the last section, operation of a laser diode will give another post-threshold characteristic as shown in Figure 4.84. Details of this phenomenon are given in [138], but a brief qualitative description is given here. As already mentioned, an increase in current density causes an increase in carrier concentrations which, after a time delay characterized by t_D, stimulates recombination and hence coherent light output. The carrier concentrations then fall and overshoot the equilibrium values, leading to a fall in light output. The carrier concentrations then start to recover, etc.; the light output has an oscillation characteristic similar to a damped sine wave. The natural frequency for the system is a function of both the spontaneous and the stimulated recombination lifetimes

τ_s and τ_{ph} respectively. It has been shown [139] that the relationship between these parameters and the current densities of the system can be given by

$$f_r = \frac{1}{2\pi}\left[\frac{1}{\tau_s\tau_{ph}}\frac{I_F - I_{th}}{I_{th}}\right]^{1/2}$$ (4.112)

where I_F is the bias or threshold current. Both lifetime terms τ_s and τ_{ph} should then be minimized, as this 'ringing' in the laser output is highly undesirable, causing as it does a distortion of the input signal. As we have already seen the spontaneous lifetime is inversely proportional to the doping concentration, and so the latter should be high. The stimulated lifetime can be reduced by increasing the cavity loss (not always a good idea for other obvious reasons) or by increasing the transmission factor of the end mirrors.

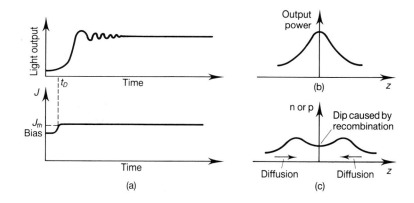

Figure 4.84 (a) 'Ringing' in the laser output due to relaxation oscillations. (b) Output from a narrow stripe laser. (c) Carrier diffusion in a narrow stripe laser.

In practice it has also been found that narrow stripe lasers operating in a single lateral mode do not suffer from ringing. The explanation for this is contained within the working of this type of laser. Stimulated emission occurs most rapidly along the centre of the laser axis, leading to a maximum in the intensity of the fundamental mode. Because the laser is electrically pumped over a width exceeding the half power width of the optical field, there is a ready supply of carriers able to diffuse to the central region to replace those lost by recombination. If the width of the active region is narrow enough, and the carrier diffusivity fast enough, lost carriers will be replaced quicker than the laser output can fall. This is shown in Figures 4.84(b) and (c). As it is the minority carriers that determine the recombination rate, it is advantageous to have the active region doped such that its minority carriers have the greater diffusivity; for GaAs based devices this means electrons as minority carriers, making the active region p-type.

The combination of all the above characteristics means that ringing will not be a problem if the laser is a narrow stripe design operating in single lateral mode, has a p-type active region, is short and has high transmission facets. It can also be seen from (4.112) that by biasing the device near threshold the result will be a low oscillation frequency, giving the laser the ability to handle high frequency signals with minimum distortion.

4.9.1.3   Temperature and ageing effects

Concern with temperature effects in an LED (section 3.4.2) led to a circuit design (Figure 3.14) to compensate for this. For an LED temperature is not such a problem, as it leads to a predictable and steady fall in output as the device gets hotter. However, with a laser being a threshold device, and one which generates considerably more heat, this temperature phenomenon could have a catastrophic effect on the transmission of digital signals. Moreover the problem of device ageing, where J_{th} increases with time, is a similar problem that has to be accounted for. The dependence of J_{th} on T is given by (4.36) and shown in Figure 4.11(a), and the problems of device related ageing were discussed for an LED in section 3.6: the effects for a laser diode are similar.

As mentioned in the last two sections, a bias current just below threshold is advantageous in minimizing both the turn-on delay and the extent of ringing. A subthreshold bias has a further advantage in that it can be readily controlled to compensate for changes in device operation due to temperature and ageing. And by having an operating current J that is close to the bias current J_a the effect of data pattern dependent heating of the laser is minimized, as the laser is always receiving a near constant current.

A simple type of driver circuit is shown in Figure 4.85(a) [140]. R_1 and C_1 are chosen to bias the transistor Q_1 well into its active region. So for a specific input voltage V_{in}, a specific current will flow through the laser. If $V_{in} = 0$ the careful choosing of R_1, R_2 and Q_1 will ensure a bias current flowing through the laser. It can be seen that this circuit has no temperature compensation, which is important as the lasing threshold J_{th} changes by about $+1\%/^\circ$C. Forced cooling of the device could be undertaken, using the laser output in a feedback control system. This could also take account of ageing, but would become impractical if large amounts of cooling were required.

Instead the problem is solved by controlling the laser bias using a circuit such as shown in Figure 4.85(b) [141]. It can clearly be seen that the laser drive current is the sum of the collector currents of transistors Q_2 and Q_3. Q_1 and Q_2 are a conventional emitter coupled pair, which work to switch the laser current. When the base of Q_1 (coupled to the input) is made more positive than the base of Q_2 (coupled to a reference) all the current from the constant source is passed through Q_1, and hence the laser is effectively off; only the bias current passing through Q_3 also passes through the laser. If the base of Q_1 is then made more negative than the base of Q_2, the laser is then on. With this emitter coupled circuit, and the correct

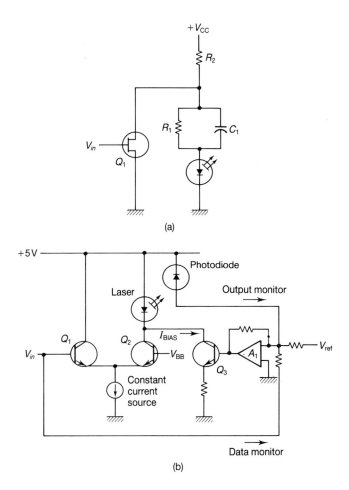

Figure 4.85 Two examples of laser drive circuits: (a) a shunt-driver, and (b) a feedback stabilized driver (©Springer Verlag: reproduced by kind permission).

choice of input levels, none of the transistors can ever be driven into saturation. This results in fast switching since no stored charge needs to be removed from a saturated transistor. The constant current nature of the circuit also ensures the minimum of noise generation due to switching transients. The feedback loop containing Q_3, amplifier A_1, and the photodiode is used to adjust the laser output to a constant value. Comparison with the data pattern gives control of both the on and off states independent of the pattern statistics.

In this circuit, as in many others, the light exiting from the 'front' mirror of the laser is the output, and that from the 'back' mirror is monitored by a photodiode;

implicit in this set up is the assumption that the two outputs have the same relationship independent of any other factors. In practice this has been found not to be the case, and temperature and age related changes can bring about non-linearities in the output even though the back mirror is itself stabilized. Instead of using the calibration system of the back mirror, it is better to monitor the output beam directly, without taking too much of the output power to do so. One such system is shown in Figures 4.86(a) and (b) [142]. After coupling into an optical fiber, some of the output is tapped perpendicularly into a photodiode. Because of reflections at the glass–air interfaces of the fibers about 8% of the light is used as a monitor.

If the output laser's efficiency is changing with time, it is important to be able to alter the bias and drive currents independently. Additional processing of the photodiode output is then required, and details are given in [141]. An additional advantage of this type of circuit is that it can readily adapt to the need to drive different lasers, and is not constrained by the characteristics of just one type.

4.9.2 Modulation effects

As discussed in section 3.4.4, modulation effects are important in describing light-wave transmitters as these are often the limitation on the maximum signal frequency, or bit rate, that can be sent along an optical communication system. When describing LEDs we started off with the current continuity equation (3.38) and ended with (3.58) which related output power $P(x,t)$ to the driving frequency of an analog signal. To do a similar calculation for a semiconductor laser, the starting point is a pair of coupled rate equations. These are similar to (4.105), except that now we have to include terms involving photons and their lifetime:

$$\frac{dn}{dt} = \frac{J}{ed} - A(n - n_0)\xi - \frac{n}{\tau_s} \tag{4.113}$$

$$\frac{d\xi}{dt} = A(n - n_0)\xi - \frac{\xi}{\tau_{th}} + \gamma\frac{n}{\tau_s} \tag{4.114}$$

where A is a proportionality constant, n is the injected carrier density, n_0 the equilibrium density, ξ the stimulated photon density, γ the probability that a photon is emitted spontaneously and τ_s and τ_{ph} are the spontaneous and stimulated lifetimes respectively. These equations can be explained as follows. For (4.113), the first term on the right hand side is the injected carrier density per unit time, the second term gives the number of carriers that undergo stimulated recombination and the third term represents a spontaneous recombination rate as in (4.105). In (4.114) the second term on the right hand side represents a similar stimulated emission rate, and the last term represents the fraction of spontaneous recombinations that radiate into the output mode. Simplifying assumptions used to make these equations and descriptions valid include single mode output and a gain coefficient linearly dependent on n, if $n > n_0$.

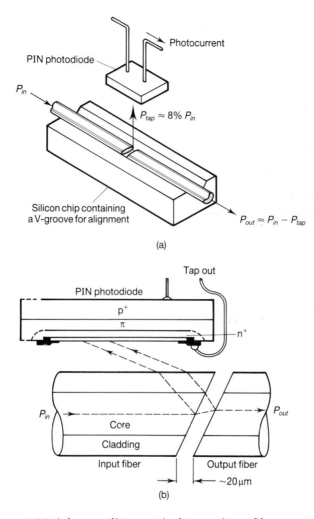

Figure 4.86 A beamsplitter optical tap using a V-groove to align two angle polished fibers: (a) overall schematic, and (b) details of the reflections taking place at the tap (©Springer Verlag: reproduced by kind permission).

4.9.2.1 Stimulated emission lifetime

In section 3.3.3 we noted that the spontaneous recombination lifetime had two components, radiative and non-radiative, and we saw how these affected device performance, particularly emission efficiency and frequency response. The stimulated lifetime, τ_{ph}, has a similarly important role in laser diodes.

Consider Figure 4.87, which shows the path taken by a photon generated in the middle of the laser cavity and undergoing a single round trip to arrive back at its starting point. The total distance travelled $2L$ can be expressed in terms of t, the time taken, by the single expression

$$t = \frac{2Ln}{c}. \tag{4.115}$$

If there are many photons starting at the same point, constituting a power P_0, then the power level at the end of one round trip will be, assuming no further gain,

$$P = P_0 R^2 \exp(-2\alpha L) \tag{4.116}$$

where R is the end mirror reflectivity and α is the absorption coefficient. Although expressed as a function of distance, the exponential drop off in power can also be given as a function of time:

$$P = P_0 \exp\left(\frac{-t}{\tau_{ph}}\right). \tag{4.117}$$

Combining (4.116) and (4.117) gives

$$\exp\left(\frac{-t}{\tau_{ph}}\right) = R^2 \exp(-2\alpha L) \tag{4.118}$$

and hence, from (4.115)

$$\tau_{ph} = \frac{n}{c} \frac{1}{\alpha + (1/L)\log_e(1/R)}. \tag{4.119}$$

Example 4.13

Calculate the stimulated emission lifetime of the laser from example 4.2, using a material refractive index of 3.4.

Solution: from (4.119)

$$\begin{aligned}
\tau_{ph} &= \frac{3.4}{c} \frac{1}{10^4 + (1/(2 \times 300 \times 10^{-6}))\log_e(1/(0.32 \times 0.99))} \\
&= 9.5 \times 10^{-13} \text{ s}. \tag{4.120}
\end{aligned}$$

τ_{ph} is of the order of picoseconds; this is in sharp contrast to the nanoseconds (short) or microseconds (long) nature of the spontaneous emission lifetime.

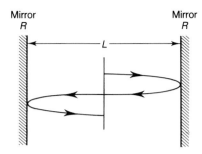

Figure 4.87 The path taken by a photon generated within the optical cavity.

4.9.2.2   Laser performance

Analysis of the rate equations (4.113) and (4.114) under small signal conditions has been treated in several texts, e.g. [143] and [144], and the end result is an important equation given below, which is the equivalent equation to (3.58) for an LED:

$$P(f) = \frac{P_0 \omega_0^2}{(\omega_0^2 - \omega^2) + \jmath\beta\omega} \tag{4.121}$$

where $\omega = 2\pi f$, $\omega_0 = (I_a - I_{th})/\tau_s \tau_{ph} I_{th}$ and $\beta = I_a/\tau_s I_{th}$, and I_a is the bias current. An important result that comes out of this is that the frequency response curves for an LED and a laser are quite different. For the former, the response is essentially flat up to a given frequency and then has a logarithmic roll-off, typically starting in the 10–100 MHz region (Figure 3.17). For the latter, as shown in Figure 4.88(a), there is a dip and then a peak in the response, which occurs at higher frequencies, with a strong dependence of output characteristic on drive current. The resonant frequency depends on the bias level, and there are similarities between this and its equivalent electrical resonant circuit as shown in Figure 4.88(b). The resonant effects are not as marked as (4.121) would predict because of a first order, low pass filtering effect caused by the parasitic and diffusion capacitances of the laser.

4.10   Reliability

The issue of reliability has been of central concern in laser diode development ever since the first devices were made; like many other types of semiconductor device, lasers had a very short lifetime, made worse by pushing them to the limits of their performance. Because lasers are similar in their construction to LEDs, similar degradation mechanisms are expected. This is partially true, but other mechanisms such as high power facet damage do not effect an LED. The reliability

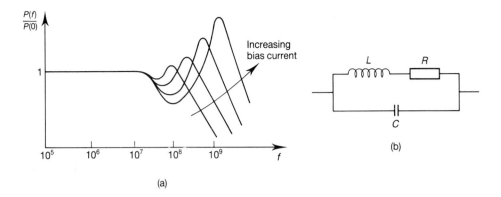

Figure 4.88 (a) Laser output power as a function of bias current and signal frequency. (b) Equivalent high frequency circuit of an a.c. driven laser.

of lasers has been regularly reviewed (e.g. [145]–[147]); this section is given over to a 'review of reviews'.

4.10.1   Catastrophic facet damage

It has been a feature of lasers, ever since they were first made, that increasing the operating current to produce more output power leads to mechanical damage of the end mirrors. This phenomenon is a function of optical density, however, and not the current itself. Important factors are the initial presence of any flaws in the mirror, the width of the emitting region and the pulse length. Damage initiated at flaws will spread to other regions of the facet; the inhibition of damage at the sawn edge of a broad area laser can spread to the cleaved end regions. For this reason, planar stripe contact lasers are much more reliable. Wide area emitting lasers have a higher threshold power for damage than narrow stripe devices. The critical damage level decreases in proportion to $t^{-1/2}$, where t is the pulse length. The safe operating level can be increased by the use of an antireflection coating on the laser facet; this acts to lower the ratio between the optical flux density inside and outside the crystal. Figure 4.89 [148] shows the effect on damage threshold P'_c of varying reflectivity R, where P_c is the damage threshold of an uncoated laser. Although the fit is empirical with a lot of scatter, the trend of reduced damage with increasing facet reflectivity is clear enough. The best fit curve through this data has been calculated as [149]

$$\frac{P'_c}{P_c} = \frac{n(1 - R)}{(1 + R^{1/2})^2} \ . \tag{4.122}$$

The use of dielectric coatings also reduces the effect of erosion, or gradual degradation of the facets. This is a moisture induced phenomenon which reduces the mirror reflectivity and hence leads to a necessary increase in the operating current.

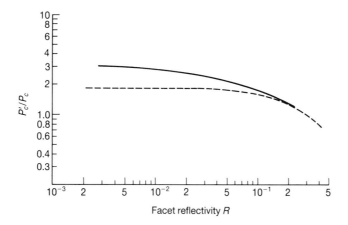

Figure 4.89 The normalized damage threshold as a function of reflectivity of a coated facet, with the other facet uncoated. The dashed line is the predicted threshold for a simple model of damage by heating due to optical absorption at an imperfection (©AIP: reproduced by kind permission).

Catastrophic physical defects appear as dark patches when observed in an SEM. A model has been proposed [150] to explain these phenomena. First, local melting occurs as a result of intense non-radiative recombination at the defect. The dark line is then produced by propagation of a molten zone confined to the active layer, and it is an epitaxially recrystallized region made non-radiative by the high density of point defects formed during rapid cooling. It has been shown [151] that lasers made from InGaAsP/InP have a much better resistance to this form of damage than AlGaAs/GaAs devices, with damage thresholds being of the order of 20 MW cm^{-2} as opposed to 2–4 MW cm^{-2}. InGaAsP/InP lasers also showed no sign of gradual facet degradation, unlike AlGaAs/GaAs devices.

4.10.2 Gradual degradation in active region

Even on lasers that exhibit no facet damage, it has been observed that under certain conditions there is an age related increase in threshold current and decrease in efficiency. This is a result of permanent changes within the recombination region, characterized by an increased 'spottiness' of the output beam and a decrease in the spontaneous carrier lifetime. This latter effect suggests a decrease in the average non-radiative lifetime, characteristic of an increased density of non-radiative centres. Other observations include a superlinear dependence of degradation rate on operating current density, and similar effects in optically pumped structures, suggesting that it is the presence of excess electron–hole pairs that causes the degradation to occur.

There are several stages to the degradation process. Initially, the spontaneous efficiency decreases with only minor effects on the lasing properties. At a later stage dark spot defects (DSDs) or dark line defects (DLDs) appear – the latter are a linear dark feature crossing the luminescent stripe at 45°; as the active stripe is oriented along the $\langle 110 \rangle$ direction, it follows that the DLDs have a $\langle 100 \rangle$ orientation.

Many factors have been found to affect the degradation rate. Perhaps an obvious first one is that a high dislocation density leads to erratic device performance; obvious because existing dislocations provide the nucleus for expanding networks. Doping is important, as Be-doped diodes degrade much more rapidly than equivalent Zn-doped structures. The control and elimination of copper as a contaminant is also important. The stoichiometry of the active region is an additional factor, as is shown in Figure 4.90 [152]. In this test of diode reliability operating wavelength was altered by varying x in an $Al_xGa_{1-x}As$ active region structure; the general trend of improved lifetime with increasing aluminium content, i.e. decreasing wavelength, is very clear. (Although Figure 4.90 is for LED operation the effects are similar in the stimulated emission mode.)

Work damaged diode sidewalls also affect device performance. In one experiment two lasers, one with sides formed by sawing and the other with sides embedded in GaAs, were given identical operating conditions. The broad area laser degraded in a few hours, whilst the stripe contact device operated for thousands of hours [153]. In the same work results were presented on the role of zinc diffusion. The reliability of two stripe contact lasers was assessed, one with a deep zinc diffusion and the other where zinc had been eliminated from the active region. The reported early failure of the devices containing zinc made it obvious that this element is a nucleus for defect formation in the laser.

All the various epitaxial techniques used to form structures have their own characteristics in terms of defect formation and impurity concentrations, which can explain different degradation rates of otherwise identical lasers.

It was initially thought that if one degradation mechanism could be identified as a problem, its time and temperature dependent characteristics could be determined by (3.76) and (3.77) as for a light emitting diode, i.e. an exponential dependency. However, the degradation mechanisms in lasers are a complex interaction between many factors and what may be true for one device structure is not necessarily valid for another. In one type of InGaAsP/InP device, for instance, the presence of DSDs was correlated more with operating current than any other parameter, with the time t taken for the first DSD to appear given by

$$t \propto \exp\left(-AJ^2\right) \tag{4.123}$$

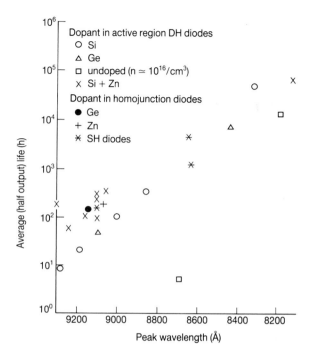

Figure 4.90 Average (half-output) life of incoherent emitters stressed at 1000 A cm^{-2} as a function of emission wavelength.

where A is a constant [154]. There was only a weak dependence on temperature, and the defect density tended to saturate after about 50 hours operation. This showed the possibility of a saturable mode of degradation, and that accelerated life tests could then easily pick out unsuitable diodes. However, when using In-GaAsP/InP lasers in transmitter systems, the opposite conclusion was reached: accelerated ageing is not valid, as the functional lifetime of transmitters is very system specific and dependent on the circuit strategy adopted. The laser degradation mechanisms limiting system lifetime are different from those limiting the coherent light output characteristics [147].

4.10.3 Leakage current

One of the problems in assessing reliability of modern laser diodes is associated with their constructional complexity; the index guided lasers mentioned in earlier sections of this chapter all utilize current restriction layers so that most of the injected current flows through the active region. There is then a leakage current flowing around and outside the active region, i.e. through the buried regions. If this leakage current increases, then so does the threshold current; additionally the efficiency decreases. Again accelerated ageing techniques have been used, this time to stabilize leakage current and hence device output power [155].

4.11   Fabrication and integration

This is a comparatively brief section to conclude the chapter on laser diodes. All the techniques of fabrication are covered in detail in Chapters 8–10, and the different device structures used have been reviewed in the various sections of this chapter. Integration has largely been used for making high power laser arrays but a look at other uses of the technique are given here.

4.11.1   Fabrication

The major steps involved in laser diode fabrication are:

   (i) preparation of a suitable substrate for epitaxial growth, usually by chemical etching/cleaning,
  (ii) growth and delineation of the many epitaxial layers needed to form the main structure. As we have seen, for some diodes this stage is very lengthy, demanding and stretching growth techniques to their limit,
 (iii) substrate thinning to $\sim 100\,\mu$m,
  (iv) junction delineation by oxide stripes or a similar technique,
   (v) metallization to both sides,
  (vi) cleaving to form the laser cavity, determined by the length of the system,
 (vii) cleaving in a perpendicular direction to form the sidewalls, and hence forming laser 'chips',
(viii) mounting of individual diodes on a header and attaching contacts. The header will also act as a heatsink for the device.

4.11.2   Transmitter packaging

Because many semiconductor lasers are used in communications, it is worthwhile here reviewing a few of the techniques used for optically coupling the laser to a fiber in the form of a transmitter package. The package should provide a sealed environment, a low thermal impedance attachment for the laser and stable power monitoring. Additionally, thermoelectric cooling, high speed electrical connections, provision of external laser cavities and other optical devices may be required [156].

Numerous lensing systems have been used to couple the laser output to the fiber, the most critical part of the system, with a lens formed on the fiber end or placed

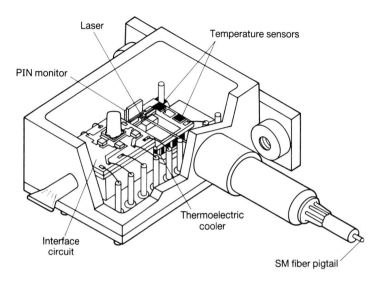

PIN monitor

Laser

Temperature sensors

Thermoelectric
cooler

Interface
circuit

SM fiber pigtail

Figure 4.91 A single mode laser package with an internal thermoelectric cooler (©Van Nostrand Reinhold, Inc.: reproduced by kind permission).

between the laser and fiber. Alignment of both laser and fiber is very critical, as is locking that alignment once it has been determined. An alignment fixture is usually required to ensure that thermal expansion, shrinking of either epoxy or solder, or reflection induced changes in laser output do not have a long term effect on the transmitter. An example of a package is shown in Figure 4.91 [156]. It contains a laser, power monitor, an interface circuit, an integral thermoelectric cooler and a temperature sensor. The fiber has an integral lens, and it is aligned and attached within 30 μm of the laser facet. The fiber exits the microwave-HIC package via a hermetic feedthrough. Further details of fiber alignment and packaging are given in Chapter 10.

4.11.3   Integration

As mentioned earlier, most of the work on laser integration has concentrated on high power devices. Other work has looked at how to form optoelectronic integrated circuits (OEICs) on one chip incorporating laser diode transmitters. By monolithically integrating optical and electronic components to form a complete transmitter, increased system performance can be expected in terms of a reduction in parasitic elements, and hence an increase in operating speed. Additional advantages are the greatly reduced size and cost of an integrated component.

The first reported device was a T-shaped laser structure and a MESFET (MEtal Semiconductor Field Effect Transistor) integrated onto one GaAs substrate. This

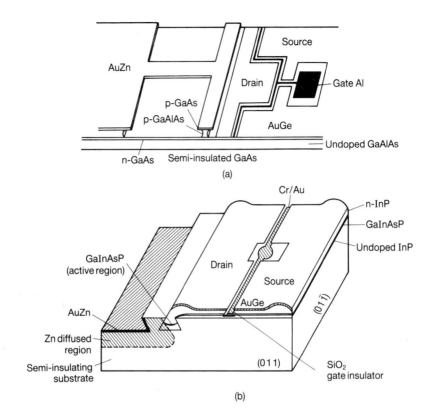

Figure 4.92 A laser integrated with (a) a GaAs MESFET, and (b) an InP MISFET (©AIP: reproduced by kind permission).

is shown in Figure 4.92(a) [157]. The active region of the laser is that part of the n-GaAs which lies underneath the p-AlGaAs region. Under forward bias, holes are injected into the the active region from the p-AlGaAs. Electrons are injected into the active region from the drain contact of the FET, where they recombine with the holes in the familiar lasing action. The bottom, undoped, AlGaAs layer acts to confine the injected carriers and, because of the refractive index difference between GaAs and AlGaAs, the optical mode of the laser is confined to the active region of the device. Several subsequent GaAs based integrations have been reported, and the first InGaAsP laser integrated with a FET followed three years later [158]. The added difficulties here include a more complicated laser structure, a more difficult to handle material and the need for a transistor other than a MESFET (because of the low barrier height of metals on InP) – in this case a MISFET (Metal Insulator Semiconductor Field Effect Transistor) was used. The completed structure is shown in Figure 4.92(b). Transistors other than FETs have been used as device drivers, with high speed performance obtained by using a heterojunction bipolar transistor [159].

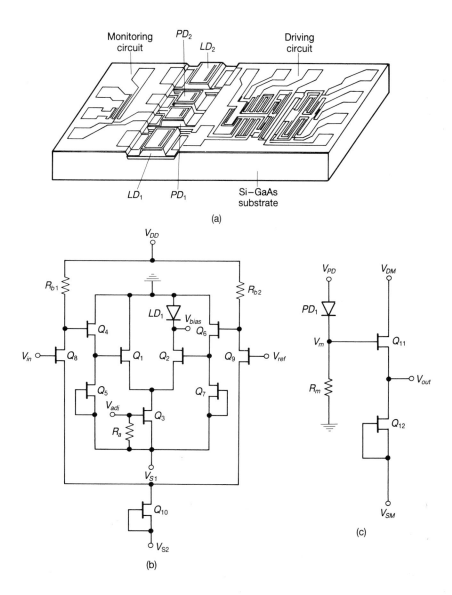

Figure 4.93 An optoelectronic integrated circuit incorporating laser diodes: (a) chip schematic, (b) laser drive circuit, and (c) monitoring circuit (©1986 IEEE: reproduced by kind permission).

Subsequent development then looked to increasing the complexity of OEIC chips. The integration of a laser, four FETs and a resistor was reported in 1985 [160]. It was soon after when the first integration of two laser diodes, two power monitors, and all driving and monitoring circuits was reported. The chip is shown in Figure 4.93 [161], and represented a significant development in integration complexity. The drive circuit is a conventional current switch, a little more complicated than those described earlier, but basically of the same type as Figure 4.85. The other transistors are used to provide input pulse shaping and buffering. The driver and laser (LD) were operated at 2 Gbit/s, with the integral monitor (PD) and amplifier/active load (Q_{11} and Q_{12}) providing negative feedback control of the laser bias when V_{out} is connected to the laser bias node. The second laser/monitor pair was included only as a test structure.

Finally, semiconductor lasers have been integrated with other optical components. A DFB laser has been monolithically integrated with an MQW optical monitor. The advantage of this type of integration is that it can reduce wavelength chirping under high speed modulation [162]. A photonic integrated circuit (PIC), comprising a laser, waveguides and mirrors has also been made [163]. Although PICs had been demonstrated earlier, their fabrication was complex and hence they were very costly. The devices reported in [163] were all made by one planar epitaxial growth step and one etch step. This initially early demonstration opens up the possibility of complex integrated circuits that are communicating with each other purely by photonic means.

4.12   Problems

1. Why is a population inversion necessary for lasing action to occur?
2. Why must the Fermi level on at least one side of a pn junction laser diode be outside the band gap? Is this true for a double heterostructure (DH) laser?
3. What are the minimum doping levels necessary to cause lasing action at a pn junction in GaAs?
4. Why is the spectral width of an LED much greater than that of a semiconductor laser? Subsequently explain why the latter has a greater spectral width than a gas laser.
5. For an InGaAsP laser operating at 1.3 μm, calculate the mode spacing for a cavity length of 400 μm, assuming the InGaAsP refractive index is 3.4.
6. Calculate the number of longitudinal modes present in the device of problem 5 if the spectral width is 600 Å.
7. Why don't all the allowed longitudinal modes of a laser cavity resonate?
8. Calculate the mode spacing of the device in problem 5, both as a wavelength and a frequency. If the spectral width of each mode is 1 Å, compare the bandwidth in a single mode with that needed to carry one telephone conversation down an optical fiber ($\sim$ 6.5 kHz).

9. Calculate the value of the gain coefficient g in a semiconductor laser of cavity length 300 μm, where a single round trip produces an optical gain of 3. The laser has cleaved end mirrors, a refractive index of 3.5 and an absorption coefficient α of 10^4 m^{-1}.

10. For the same laser as problem 9, calculate the external differential efficiency if the internal efficiency is 0.85. Hence calculate the current needed to produce 5 mW at 1.3 μm if the threshold current is 150 mA. What is the power conversion efficiency of the device?

11. Redo the calculations of problems 9 and 10 if one end of the laser is metallized to produce a reflectivity of 0.99, and assuming for this case (although not true in practice) that the threshold current remains unchanged.

12. Calculate the confinement factor for a GaAs laser of active region thickness 1.5 μm, refractive index 3.6 and critical angle at the active to non-active boundary of 85°. Assume the C constant to be 8×10^7 m^{-1}. Repeat the calculation for a GaAs/AlGaAs DH laser, where all the factors remain unchanged except for the critical angle, which is now 75°.

13. Calculate the gain coefficient for the two cases of problem 12, if the cavity length is 100 μm, the absorption coefficient is 10^4 m^{-1} and the end mirrors are cleaved. How much shorter can the cavity be, and still produce the same gain, if one end mirror is metallized to produce a reflectivity of 0.99?

14. Assuming that the gain calculated in problem 13 corresponds to a threshold current of 1.0 A, calculate the power emitted from the main output facet of the metallized laser for an internal efficiency of 0.8 and emission wavelength 0.82 μm if the drive current is 1.07 A.

15. What are the main differences between the perceived output intensity from an LED and a laser? How would this affect coupling of these sources to an optical fiber?

16. Why is the suppression of lateral and transverse modes in a laser deemed to be desirable?

17. What are the main design criteria that allow only the fundamental lateral, transverse or longitudinal modes to resonate?

18. A short optical cavity is one means of obtaining single frequency operation. What are its drawbacks over other approaches?

19. What would be the simplest way of physically transforming a laser into a superradiant diode?

20. What is the difference between an index guided and a gain guided laser?

21. Calculate typical stimulated emission lifetimes for the lasers discussed in problems 12 and 13.

22. A particular laser diode is considered to be past its useful life when its output power falls by a half. If its operating temperature is 60 °C, the degradation mechanism has an activation energy of 0.92 eV and $\beta_0 = 1.7 \times 10^7$ h^{-1}, estimate the useful lifetime of the diode, to the nearest year.

23. Compare the ratio of threshold current densities for an AlGaAs laser with $T_0 = 160$ K and an InGaAsP laser with $T_0 = 55$ K, at operating temperatures

of 25 °C and 65 °C. Which device would be more likely to degrade at the higher temperature, and why?

4.13   References

1. R N Hall, G E Fenner, J D Kingsley, T J Soltys and R O Carlson, 'Coherent Light Emission from GaAs Junctions', *Phys. Rev. Lett.* **9**, 366 (1962).

2. J Wilson and J F B Hawkes, *Optoelectronics: an Introduction*, 2nd ed., Prentice-Hall International, 1989, p. 169ff.

3. K A Jones, *Introduction to Optical Electronics*, Wiley, 1987, p. 287ff.

4. A R Goodwin and G H B Thompson, 'Superlinear Dependence of Gain on Current Density in GaAs Injection Lasers', *IEEE J. Quantum Electron.* **QE-6**, 311 (1970).

5. F Stern, 'Calculated Spectral Dependence of Gain in Excited GaAs', *J. Appl. Phys.* **47**, 5382 (1976).

6. H Kressel, M Ettenberg, J P Wittke and I Ladany, 'Laser Diodes and LEDs for Fiber Optical Communication', in Topics in Applied Physics, vol. 39: *Semiconductor Devices for Optical Communication*, Springer Verlag, 1980, p. 18.

7. W T Tsang, R A Logan and J P van der Ziel, 'Low Current Threshold Strip Buried Heterostructure Lasers with Self-Aligned Current Injection Stripes', *Appl. Phys. Lett.* **34**, 644 (1979).

8. See [6], p. 21.

9. J E Geusic, W B Bridges and J I Pankove, 'Coherent Optical Sources for Communications', *Proc. IEEE* **58**, 1419 (1970).

10. M I Nathan, 'Semiconductor Lasers', *Proc. IEEE* **54**, 1276 (1966) and refs therein, esp. [37]–[49].

11. H Kressel and M Ettenberg, 'Low Threshold Double Heterojunction Al-GaAs/GaAs Laser Diodes: Theory and Experiment', *J. Appl. Phys.* **47**, 3533 (1976).

12. H Kressel, Introduction to [6], p. 4.

13. M B Panish, I Hayashi and S Sumski, 'Double Heterostructure Injection Lasers with Room Temperature Thresholds as Low as 2300 A/cm^2', *Appl. Phys. Lett.* **16**, 326 (1970).

14. A G Milnes and D L Feucht, *Heterojunctions and Metal–Semiconductor Junctions*, Academic Press, 1972, p. 9.

15. S S Vishnubhatla, B Eyglunet and J C Woolley, 'Electroreflectance Measurements in Mixed III–V Alloys', *Can. J. Phys.* **47**, 1661 (1969).

16. R C Goodfellow and R Davis, 'Optical Source Devices' in *Optical Fibre Communications*, M J Howes and D V Morgan, eds, Wiley, 1980, p. 32.

17. T H Glisson, J R Hauser, M A Littlejohn and C K Williams, 'Energy Bandgap and Lattice Constant Contours of III–V Quaternary Alloys', *J. Electronic Mat.* **7**, 1 (1978).

18. H F Lockwood, H Kressel, H S Sommers. Jr, and F Z Hawrylo, 'An Efficient Large Optical Cavity Injection Laser', *Appl. Phys. Lett.* **17**, 499 (1970).

19. G H B Thompson and P A Kirkby, '(GaAl)As Lasers with a Heterostructure for Optical Confinement and Additional Heterojunctions for Extreme Carrier Confinement', *IEEE J. Quantum Electron.* **QE-9**, 311 (1973).

20. H Kressel and J K Butler, 'Heterojunction Laser Diodes', in Semiconductors and Semimetals, vol. 14: *Lasers, Junctions, Transport*, R K Willardson and A C Beer, eds, Academic Press, 1979, p. 139ff.

21. J C Dyment, 'Hermite–Gaussian Mode Patterns in GaAs Junction Lasers', *Appl. Phys. Lett.* **10**, 84 (1967).

22. B W Hakki, 'Carrier and Gain Spatial Profiles in GaAs Stripe Geometry Lasers', *J. Appl. Phys.* **44**, 5021 (1973).

23. P K Cheo, *Fibre Optics and Optoelectronics*, 2nd ed., Prentice-Hall International, 1990, p. 241.

24. W P Dumke, 'Current Thresholds in Stripe Contact Injection Lasers', *Solid State Electron.* **16**, 1279 (1973).

25. See [6], p. 31.

26. H Kressel and J K Butler, *Semiconductor Lasers and Heterojunction LEDs*, Academic Press, 1977, p. 218.

27. H Yonezu, I Sakuma, K Kobayashi, T Kamejima, M Ueno and Y Nannichi, 'A GaAs-Al_xGa_{1-x}As Double Heterostructure Planar Stripe Laser', *Jpn. J. Appl. Phys.* **12**, 1585 (1973).

28. D D Cook and F R Nash, 'Gain-Induced Guiding and Astigmatic Output Beam of GaAs lasers', *J. Appl. Phys.* **46**, 1660 (1975).

29. K Petermann, 'Calculated Spontaneous Emission Factor for Double Heterostructure Injection Lasers with Gain Induced Waveguiding', *IEEE J. Quantum Electron.* **QE-15**, 566 (1979).

30. P A Kirkby, A R Goodwin, G H B Thompson and P R Selway, 'Observations of Self Focusing in Stripe Geometry Semiconductor Lasers and the Development of a Comprehensive Model of their Operation', *IEEE J. Quantum Electron.* **QE-13**, 705 (1977).

31. K Itoh, M Inoue and I Teramoto, 'New Heteroisolation Stripe Geometry Visible Light Emitting Lasers', *IEEE J. Quantum Electron.* **QE-11**, 421 (1975).

32. J C Dyment, L A d'Asaro, J C North, B I Miller and J E Ripper, 'Proton Bombardment Formation of Stripe Geometry Heterostructure Lasers for 300 K CW Operation', *Proc. IEEE* **60**, 726 (1972).

33. J M Blum, J C McGroddy, P G McMullin, K K Shih, A W Smith and J F Ziegler, 'Oxygen Implanted Double Heterojunction GaAs/GaAlAs Injection Lasers', *IEEE J. Quantum Electron.* **QE-11**, 413 (1975).

34. T Tsukada, H Nakashima, J Umeda, S Nakamura, N Chinone, R Ito and O Nakada, 'Very Low Current Operation of Mesa Stripe Geometry Double Heterostructure Injection Lasers', *Appl. Phys. Lett.* **20**, 344 (1972).

35. See [6], p. 25.

36. T Tsukada, 'GaAs–Ga$_{1-x}$Al$_x$As Buried Heterostructure Injection Lasers', *J. Appl. Phys.* **45**, 4899 (1974).

37. K Aiki, M Nakamura, T Kuroda and J Umeda, 'Channeled Substrate Planar Structure (AlGa)As Injection Lasers', *Appl. Phys. Lett.* **30**, 649 (1977).

38. D Botez and P Zory, 'Constricted Double Heterostructure (AlGa)As Diode Lasers', *Appl. Phys. Lett.* **32**, 261 (1978).

39. E Oomura, T Murotani, H Higuchi, H Namizaki and W Susaki, 'Low Threshold InGaAsP/InP Buried Crescent Laser with Double Current Confinement Structure', *IEEE J. Quantum Electron.* **QE-17**, 646 (1981).

40. H Ishikawa, H Imai, T Tanahashi, K-I Hori and K Takahei, 'V-Grooved Substrate Buried Heterostructure InGaAsP/InP Laser Emitting at 1.3 μm Wavelength', *IEEE J. Quantum Electron.* **QE-18**, 1704 (1982).

41. W H Cheng, C B Su, K D Buehring, J W Ure, D Perrachione, D Renner, K L Hess and S W Zehr, 'Low Threshold and Wide Bandwidth 1.3 μm InGaAsP Buried Crescent Injection Lasers with Semi-Insulating Current Confinement Layers', *Appl. Phys. Lett.* **51**, 155 (1987).

42. K Imanaka, H Imamoto, F Sato, M Asai and M Shimura, 'Inner Stripe AlGaAs/GaAs Laser Diode by Single Step Molecular Beam Epitaxy', *Elec. Lett.* **23**, 209 (1987).

43. S Yamamoto and T Hijikata, 'Very Low Threshold V-Channeled Substrate Inner Stripe Lasers Using High Resistive Al$_{0.85}$Ga$_{0.15}$As Burying Layer', *J. Appl. Phys.* **61**, 3108 (1987).

44. T Murakami, K Ohtaki, H Matsubara, T Yamawaki, H Saito, K Isshiki, Y Kokubo, A Shima, H Kumabe and W Susaki, 'A Very Narrow Beam AlGaAs Laser with a Thin Tapered Thickness Active Layer (T^3 Laser)', *IEEE J. Quantum Electron.* **QE-23**, 712 (1987).

45. I P Kaminow, L W Stulz, J S Ko, A G Dentai, R E Nahory, J C deWinter and R L Hartman, 'Low Threshold InGaAsP Ridge Waveguide Lasers at 1.3μm', *IEEE J. Quantum Electron.* **QE-19**, 1312 (1983).

46. A Yoshikawa, A Yamamoto, M Hirose, T Sugino, G Kano and I Teramoto, 'A Novel Technology for Formation of a Narrow Active Layer in Buried Heterostructure Lasers by Single Step MOCVD', *IEEE J. Quantum Electron.* **QE-23**, 725 (1987).

47. J Gowar, *Optical Communication Systems*, Prentice-Hall International, 1984.

48. T E Bell, 'Single Frequency Semiconductor Lasers', *IEEE Spectrum* **20 (12)**, 38 (1983).

49. R Wyatt and W J Devlin, '10 kHz Linewidth 1.5 μm InGaAsP External Cavity Laser with 55 nm Tuning Range', *Elec. Lett.* **19**, 110 (1983).

50. H Kogelnik and C V Shank, 'Stimulated Emission in a Periodic Structure', *Appl. Phys. Lett.* **18**, 152 (1971).

51. H Kogelnik and C V Shank, 'Coupled Wave Theory of Distributed Feedback Lasers', *J. Appl. Phys.* **43**, 2327 (1972).

52. D R Scifres, R D Burnham and W Streifer, 'Distributed Feedback Single Heterostructure GaAs Diode Laser', *Appl. Phys. Lett.* **25**, 203 (1974).

53. M Nakamura, K Aiki, J Umeda, A Yariv, H W Yen and T Morikawa, 'GaAs–$Ga_{1-x}Al_xAs$ Double Heterostructure Distributed Feedback Diode Lasers', *Appl. Phys. Lett.* **25**, 487 (1974).

54. H C Casey, Jr, S Somekh and M Ilegems, 'Room Temperature Operation of Low Threshold Separate Confinement Heterostructure Injection Laser with Distributed Feedback', *Appl. Phys. Lett.* **27**, 142 (1975).

55. A Doi, T Fukuzawa, M Nakamura, R Ito and K Aiki, 'InGaAsP/InP Distributed Feedback Injection Lasers Fabricated by One Step Liquid Phase Epitaxy', *Appl. Phys. Lett.* **35**, 441 (1979).

56. K Utaka, S Akiba, K Skai and Y Matsushima, 'Room Temperature CW Operation of Distributed Feedback Buried Heterostructure InGaAsP/InP Laser Emitting at 1.57 μm', *Elec. Lett.* **17**, 961 (1981).

57. S R Chinn, 'Effects of Mirror Reflectivity in a Distributed Feedback Laser', *IEEE J. Quantum Electron.* **QE-9**, 574 (1973).

58. S Akiba, K Utaka, K Sakai and Y Matsushima, 'Distributed Feedback InGaAsP/InP Lasers with Window Region Emitting at 1.5 μm Range', *IEEE J. Quantum Electron.* **QE-19**, 1052 (1983).

59. H A Haus and C V Shank, 'Antisymmetric Taper of Distributed Feedback Lasers', *IEEE J. Quantum Electron.* **QE-12**, 532 (1976).

60. J E Midwinter and Y L Guo, *Optoelectronics and Lightwave Technology*, Wiley, 1992, p. 219.

61. K Utaka, S Akiba, K Sakai and Y Matsushima, '$\lambda/4$ Shifted InGaAsP DFB Lasers', *IEEE J. Quantum Electron.* **QE-22**, 1042 (1986).

62. L D Westbrook, I D Henning, A W Nelson and P J Fiddyment, 'Spectral Properties of Strongly Coupled 1.5 μm DFB Laser Diodes', *IEEE J. Quantum Electron.* **QE-21**, 512 (1985).

63. A Yariv and M Nakamura, 'Periodic Structures for Integrated Optics', *IEEE J. Quantum Electron.* **QE-13**, 233 (1977).

64. S Takigawa, T Uno, M Kume, K Hamada, N Yoshikawa, H Shimizu and G Kano, '50 mW Stable Single Longitudinal Mode Operation of a 780 nm GaAlAs DFB Laser', *IEEE J. Quantum Electron.* **QE-25**, 1489 (1989).

65. Y Suematsu, S Arai and K Kishino, 'Dynamic Single Mode Semiconductor Lasers with a Distributed Reflector', *IEEE J. Lightwave Technol.* **LT-1**, 161 (1983).

66. T Tanbun-ek, S Suzaki, W S Min, Y Suematsu, F Koyama and S Arai, 'Static Characteristics of 1.5–1.6 μm GaInAsP/InP Buried Heterostructure Butt Jointed Built-in Integrated Lasers', *IEEE J. Quantum Electron.* **QE-20**, 131 (1984).

67. T P Lee, C A Burrus, J A Copeland, A G Dentai and D Marcuse, 'Short Cavity InGaAsP Injection Lasers: Dependence of Mode Spectra and Single

Longitudinal Mode Power on Cavity Length', *IEEE J. Quantum Electron.* **QE-18**, 1101 (1982).

68. R Lang and K Kobayashi, 'Suppression of the Relaxation Oscillation in the Modulated Output of Semiconductor Lasers', *IEEE J. Quantum Electron.* **QE-12**, 194 (1976).

69. J Yamada, S Kobayashi, H Nagai and T Kimura, 'Modulated Single Longitudinal Mode Semiconductor Laser and Fibre Transmission Characteristics at 1.55 μm', *IEEE J. Quantum Electron.* **QE-17**, 1006 (1981).

70. N K Dutta, E I Gordon, T M Shen, P J Anthony and G Zydzik, 'Single Longitudinal Mode Operation of a Semiconductor Laser using a Metal Film Reflection Filter', *IEEE J. Quantum Electron.* **QE-21**, 559 (1985).

71. L A Coldren, K J Ebeling, B I Miller and J A Rentschler, 'Single Longitudinal Mode Operation of Two Section GaInAsP/InP Lasers Under Pulsed Excitation', *IEEE J. Quantum Electron.* **QE-19**, 1057 (1983).

72. W T Tsang, 'The Cleaved Coupled Cavity Laser', in Semiconductors and Semimetals, vol. 22B: *Semiconductor Lasers I*, W T Tsang, ed., Academic Press, 1985, p. 263.

73. W Streifer, D Yevick, T L Paoli and R D Burnham, 'An Analysis of Cleaved Coupled Cavity Lasers', *IEEE J. Quantum Electron.* **QE-20**, 754 (1984).

74. N Holonyak, Jr, R M Kolbas, R D Dupuis and P D Dapkus, 'Quantum Well Heterostructure Lasers', *IEEE J Quantum Electron.* **QE-16**, 170 (1980).

75. J S Blakemore, *Solid State Physics*, 2nd ed., Cambridge University Press, 1985, p. 364.

76. L W James and J L Moll, 'Transport Properties of GaAs Obtained from Photoemission Measurements', *Phys. Rev.* **183**, 740 (1969).

77. J H Lee, K Y Hsieh, Y L Hwang and R M Kolbas, 'Stimulated Emission from Monolayer Thick $Al_xGa_{1-x}As$–GaAs Single Quantum Well Heterostructures', *Appl. Phys. Lett.* **56**, 626 (1990).

78. J P van der Ziel, R Dingle, R C Miller, W Wiegmann and W A Nordland, Jr, 'Laser Oscillation from Quantum States in Very Thin GaAs–$Al_{0.2}Ga_{0.8}As$ Multilayer Structures', *Appl. Phys. Lett.* **26**, 462 (1975).

79. E A Rezek, N Holonyak, Jr, B A Vojak, G E Stillman, J A Rossi, D L Keune and J D Fairing, 'LPE $In_{1-x}Ga_xP_{1-z}As_z$ ($x \sim 0.12$, $z \sim 0.26$) DH Laser with Multiple Thin Layer (< 500 Å) Active Region', *Appl. Phys. Lett.* **31**, 288 (1977).

80. E D Jungbluth, 'MAGIC laser emits at 15 wavelengths', *Laser Focus World* **29(5)**, 20 (1993).

81. K Varhala, L C Chiu, S Margalet and A Yariv, 'On the Linewidth Enhancement Factor α in Semiconductor Injection Lasers', *Appl. Phys. Lett.* **42**, 631 (1983).

82. R Chin, N Holonyak, Jr, B A Vojak, K Hess, R D Dupuis and P D Dapkus, 'Temperature Dependence of Threshold Current for Quantum Well $Al_xGa_{1-x}As$–GaAs Heterostructure Laser Diodes', *Appl. Phys. Lett.* **36**, 19 (1980).

83. W T Tsang, 'Extremely Low Threshold (AlGa)As Modified Multiquantum Well Heterostructure Lasers Grown by Molecular Beam Epitaxy', *Appl. Phys. Lett.* **39**, 786 (1981).

84. W T Tsang, 'A Graded Index Waveguide Separate Confinement Laser with Very Low Threshold and a Narrow Gaussian Beam', *Appl. Phys. Lett.* **39**, 134 (1981).

85. W T Tsang, 'Extremely Low Threshold (AlGa)As Graded-Index Waveguide Separate Confinement Heterostructure Lasers Grown by Molecular Beam Epitaxy', *Appl. Phys. Lett.* **40**, 217 (1982).

86. M M Leopold, A P Specht, C A Zmudzinski, M E Givens and J J Coleman, 'Temperature Dependent Factors Contributing to T_0 in Graded Index Separate Confinement Heterostructure Single Quantum Well Lasers', *Appl. Phys. Lett.* **50**, 1403 (1987).

87. I J Fritz, S T Picraux, L R Dawson, T J Drummond, W D Laidig and N G Anderson, 'Dependence of Critical Layer Thickness on Strain for $In_xGa_{1-x}As/GaAs$ Strained Layer Superlattices', *Appl. Phys. Lett.* **46**, 967 (1985).

88. W D Leidig, P J Caldwell, Y F Lin and C K Peng, 'Strained Layer Quantum Well Injection Laser', *Appl. Phys. Lett.* **44**, 653 (1984).

89. D Feketa, K T Chan, J M Ballantyne and L F Eastman, 'Graded-Index Separate Confinement InGaAs/GaAs Strained Layer Quantun Well Laser Grown by Metalorganic Chemical Vapor Deposition', *Appl. Phys. Lett.* **49**, 1659 (1986).

90. S E Fischer, D Feketa, G B Feak and J M Ballantyne, 'Ridge Waveguide Injection Laser with GaInAs Strained Layer Quantum Well ($\lambda = 1\,\mu$m)', *Appl. Phys. Lett.* **50**, 714 (1987).

91. T Hayakawa, T Suyuma, K Takahashi, M Kondo, S Yamamoto and T Hijikata, 'Low Current Threshold AlGaAs Visible Laser Diodes with an $(AlGaAs)_m(GaAs)_n$ Superlattice Quantum Well', *Appl. Phys. Lett.* **49**, 636 (1986).

92. H Temkin, T Tanbuk-ek and R A Logan, 'Strained InGaAs/InP Quantum Well Lasers', *Appl. Phys. Lett.* **56**, 1210 (1990).

93. N Chand, E E Becher, J P van der Ziel, S N G Chu and N K Dutta, 'Excellent Uniformity and Very Low (< 50 A/cm^2) Threshold Current Density Strained InGaAs Quantum Well Diode Lasers on GaAs Substrate', *Appl. Phys. Lett.* **58**, 1704 (1991).

94. P M Petroff, A C Gossard, R A Logan and W Wiegmann, 'Towards Quantum Well Wires: Fabrication and Optical Properties', *Appl. Phys. Lett.* **41**, 635 (1982).

95. A Yariv, 'Scaling Laws and Minimum Threshold Currents for Quantum Confined Semiconductor Lasers', *Appl. Phys. Lett.* **53**, 103 (1988).

96. E Kapon, S Simhony, R Bhat and D M Hwang, 'Single Quantum Wire Semiconductor Lasers', *Appl. Phys. Lett.* **55**, 2714 (1989).

97. K Vahala, Y Arakawa and A Yariv, 'Reduction of the Field Spectrum Linewidth of a Multiple Quantum Well Laser in a High Magnetic Field – Spectral Properties of Quantum Dot Lasers', *Appl. Phys. Lett.* **50**, 365 (1987).

98. See [23], p. 258.

99. See [26], p. 231–3.

100. N Chinone, K Saito, R Ito, K Aiki and N Shige, 'Highly Efficient (GaAl)As Buried Heterostructure Lasers with Buried Optical Guide', *Appl. Phys. Lett.* **35**, 513 (1979).

101. D Botez, 'CW High Power Single Mode Operation of Constricted Double Heterojunction AlGaAs Lasers with a Large Optical Cavity', *Appl. Phys. Lett.* **36**, 190 (1980).

102. J C Zhong, B R Zhu, R H Li, Y J Zhao and R Pillai, 1.55 μm High Power Large Optical Cavity Lasers, *Appl. Phys. Lett.* **59**, 3087 (1991).

103. J K Butler and D Botez, 'Lateral Mode Discrimination and Control in High Power Single Mode Diode Lasers of the Large Optical Cavity (LOC) Type', *IEEE J. Quantum Electron.* **QE-20**, 879 (1984).

104. K Hamada, M Wada, H Shimizu, M Kume, F Susa, T Shibutani, N Yoshikawa, K Itoh, G Kano and I Teramoto, 'A 0.2 W CW Laser with Buried Twin-Ridge Substrate Structure', *IEEE J. Quantum Electron.* **QE-21**, 623 (1985).

105. T Shibutani, M Kume, K Hamada, H Shimuzu, K Itoh, G Kano and I Teramoto, 'A Novel High Power Laser Structure with Current-Blocked Regions Near Cavity Facets', *IEEE J. Quantum Electron.* **QE-23**, 760 (1987).

106. D F Welch, P S Cross, D R Scifres, W Streifer and R D Burnham, 'High Power AlGaAs Buried Heterostructure Lasers with Flared Waveguides', *Appl. Phys. Lett.* **50**, 233 (1987).

107. K Shigihara, Y Nagai, S Karakida, A Takami, Y Kokubo, H Matsubara and S Kakimoto, 'High Power Operation of Broad Area Laser Diodes with GaAs and AlGaAs Single Quantum Wells for Nd:YAG Laser Pumping', *IEEE J. Quantum Electron.* **QE-27**, 1537 (1991).

108. R G Waters, R J Dalby and M A Emanuel, 'Full Aperture, High Power Semiconductor Laser', *Appl. Phys. Lett.* **54**, 2534 (1989).

109. D Z Garbuzov, N Yu Antonishkis, A D Bondarev, A B Gulakov, S N Zhigulin, N I Katsavets, A V Kochergin and E V Rafailov, 'High Power 0.8 μm InGaAsP–GaAs SCH SQW Lasers', *IEEE J. Quantum Electron.* **QE-27**, 1531 (1991).

110. D R Scifres, R D Burnham and W Streifer, 'Phase Locked Semiconductor Laser Array', *Appl. Phys. Lett.* **33**, 1015 (1978).

111. J K Butler, D E Ackley and D Botez, 'Coupled Mode Analysis of Phase Locked Injection Laser Arrays', *Appl. Phys. Lett.* **44**, 293 (1984).

112. J K Butler, D E Ackley and M Ettenberg, 'Coupled Mode Analysis of Gain and Wavelength Oscillation Characteristics of Diode Laser Phased Arrays', *IEEE J. Quantum Electron.* **QE-21**, 458 (1985).

113. J Katz, E Kapon, C Lindsey, S Margalit, U Shreter and A Yariv, 'Phase Locked Semiconductor Array with Separate Contacts', *Appl. Phys. Lett.* **43**, 521 (1983).

114. D E Ackley, D Botez and B Bogner, 'Phase Locked Injection Laser Arrays with Integrated Phase Shifters', *RCA Review* **44**, 625 (1983).

115. D E Ackley, Phase Locked Injection Laser Arrays with Nonuniform Stripe Spacing, *Elec. Lett.* **20**, 695 (1984).

116. E Kapon, C Lindsey, J Katz, S Margalit and A Yariv, 'Chirped Arrays of Diode Lasers for Supermode Control', *Appl. Phys. Lett.* **45**, 200 (1984).

117. M Taneya, M Matsumoto, H Kawanishi, S Matsui, S Yano and T Hijikata, 'Phased Array with the 'YY' Shaped Symmetrically Branching Waveguide (SBW)', *Jpn. J. Appl. Phys.* **25**, L432 (1986).

118. W Streifer, B F Welch, P S Cross and D R Scifres, 'Y-Junction Semiconductor Laser Arrays, Parts I and II', *IEEE J. Quantum Electron.* **QE-23**, 744 (1987).

119. M Sakamoto, D F Welch, J G Endriz, D R Scifres and W Streifer, '76 W cw Monolithic Laser Diode Arrays', *Appl. Phys. Lett.* **54**, 2299 (1989).

120. H Soda, K Iga, C Kitahara and Y Suematsu, 'GaInAsP/InP Surface Emitting Lasers', *Jpn. J. Appl. Phys.* **18**, 2329 (1979).

121. I Watanabe, F Koyama and K Iga, 'Low Temperature CW Operation of GaInAsP/InP Surface Emitting Laser with Circular Buried Heterostructure', *Elec. Lett.* **22**, 1325 (1986).

122. A Ibakari, K Kawashima, K Furusawa, T Ishikawa, T Yamaguchi and T Niina, 'Buried Heterostructure GaAs/AlGaAs Distributed Bragg Reflector Surface Emitting Laser with Very Low Threshold (5.2 mA) under Room Temperature CW Conditions', *Jpn. J. Appl. Phys.* **28**, L667 (1989).

123. J L Jewell, J P Harbison, A Scherer, Y H Lee and L T Florez, 'Vertical Cavity Surface Emitting Lasers: Design, Growth, Fabrication, Characterisation', *IEEE J. Quantum Electron.* **QE-27**, 1332 (1991).

124. A J SpringThorpe, 'A Novel Double Heterostructure p-n Junction Laser', *Appl. Phys. Lett.* **31**, 524 (1977).

125. Z L Liau and J N Walpole, 'Surface Emitting GaInAsP/InP Laser with Low Threshold Current and High Efficiency', *Appl. Phys. Lett.* **46**, 115 (1985).

126. Z L Liau and J N Walpole, 'Large Monolithic Two-Dimensional Arrays of GaInAsP/InP Surface Emitting Lasers', *Appl. Phys. Lett.* **50**, 528 (1987).

127. T H Windhorn and W D Goodhue, 'Monolithic GaAs/AlGaAs Diode Laser/Reflector Devices for Light Emission Normal to the Surface', *Appl. Phys. Lett.* **48**, 1675 (1986).

128. J Puretz, R K deFreez, R A Elliott, J Orloff and T L Paoli, '300 mW Operation of a Surface-Emitting Phase-Locked Array of Diode Lasers', *Elec. Lett.* **23**, 130 (1987).

129. D R Scifres, R D Burnham and W Streifer, 'Highly Collimated Laser Beams From Electrically Pumped SH GaAs/GaAlAs Distributed Feedback Lasers', *Appl. Phys. Lett.* **26**, 48 (1975).

130. K Kojima, S Noda, K Mitsunaga, K Kyuma and K Hamanaka, 'Continuous Wave Operation of a Surface-Emitting AlGaAs–GaAs Multiquantum Well Distributed Bragg Reflector Laser', *Appl. Phys. Lett.* **50**, 1705 (1987).

131. G A Evans, N W Carlson, J M Hammer, M Lurie, J K Butler, S L Palfrey, R Amantea, L A Carr, F Z Hawrylo, E A James, C J Kaiser, J B Kirk and W F Reichert, 'Two-Dimensional Coherent Laser Arrays using Grating Surface Emission', *IEEE J. Quantum Electron.* **QE-25**, 1525 (1989).

132. G A Evans, D P Bour, N W Carlson, R Amantea, J M Hammer, H Lee, M Lurie, R C Lai, P F Pelka, R E Farkas, J B Kirk, S K Liew, W F Reichert, C A Wang, H K Choi, J N Walpole, J K Butler, W F Ferguson, Jr, R K deFreez and M Felisky, 'Characteristics of Coherent Two-Dimensional Grating Surface Emitting Diode Laser Arrays during CW Operation', *IEEE J. Quantum Electron.* **QE-27**, 1594 (1991).

133. M Ikeda, Y Mori, H Sato, K Kaneko and N Watanabe, 'Room Temperature Continuous Wave Operation of an AlGaInP Double Heterostructure Laser Grown by Atmospheric Pressure Metalorganic Chemical Vapour Deposition', *Appl. Phys. Lett.* **47**, 1027 (1985).

134. H B Serreze, Y C Chen and R G Waters, 'High Power, Very Low Threshold, GaInP/AlGaInP Visible Diode Lasers', *Appl. Phys. Lett.* **58**, 2464 (1991).

135. H Jeon, J Ding, W Patterson, A V Nurmikko, W Xie, D C Grillo, M Kobayashi and R L Gunshor, 'Blue–Green Injection Laser Diodes in (Zn,Cd)Se/ZnSe Quantum Wells', *Appl. Phys. Lett.* **59**, 3619 (1991).

136. D Fluck, J Moll, P Günter, M Fleuster and Ch Buchal, 'Blue Light Generation by Frequency Doubling CW Diode Laser Radiation in $KNbO_3$ Channel Waveguides', *Elec. Lett.* **28**, 1092 (1992).

137. T P Lee, 'Effect of Junction Capacitance on the Rise Time of LEDs and on the Turn-on Delay of Injection Lasers', *Bell System Tech. J.* **54**, 53 (1975).

138. See [26], p. 555ff.

139. R C Goodfellow and R Davis, 'Optical Source Devices', in *Optical Fibre Communications*, M J Howes and D V Morgan, eds, Wiley, 1980, p. 84.

140. V Ostoich, P Jeppesen and N Slaymaker, 'Direct Modulation of D.H. GaAlAs Lasers with GaAs M.E.S.F.E.T.s', *Elec. Lett.* **11**, 515 (1975).

141. P W Schumate and M DiDomenico, Jr, 'Lightwave Transmitters', in Topics in Applied Physics, vol. 39: *Semiconductor Devices for Optical Communication*, Springer Verlag, 1980, p. 184.

142. M A Karr, T C Rich and M DiDomenico, Jr, 'Lightwave Fiber Tap', *Appl. Opt.* **17**, 2215 (1978).

143. See [47], p. 559.

144. W van Etten and J van der Plaats, *Fundamentals of Optical Fiber Communications*, Prentice-Hall International, 1991, p. 179.

145. See [26], p. 533ff.

146. See [6], p. 52.

147. B A Dean and M Dixon, 'The Functional Reliability of Semiconductor Lasers as Optical Transmitters', in Semiconductors and Semimetals, vol 22C: *Semiconductor Injection Lasers II, Light Emitting Diodes*, W T Tsang, ed, Academic Press, 1985, p. 153ff.

148. M Ettenberg, H S Sommers, Jr, H Kressel and H F Lockwood, 'Control of Facet Damage in GaAs Laser Diodes', *Appl. Phys. Lett.* **18**, 571 (1971).

149. B W Hakki and F R Nash, 'Catastrophic Failure in GaAs Double-Heterostructure Injection Lasers', *J. Appl. Phys.* **45**, 3907 (1974).

150. C H Henry, P M Petroff, R A Logan and F R Merritt, 'Catastrophic Damage of $Al_xGa_{1-x}As$ Double Heterostructure Laser Material', *J. Appl. Phys.* **50**, 3721 (1979).

151. R F Murison, A J N Houghton, A R Goodwin, A J Collar and I G A Davies, 'CW Performance and Life of 1.3 μm InGaAsP/InP Lasers Emitting at High Facet Power Densities', *Elec. Lett.* **23**, 601 (1987).

152. M Ettenberg, H Kressel and H F Lockwood, 'Degradation of $Al_xGa_{1-x}As$ Heterojunction Electroluminescent Devices', *Appl. Phys. Lett.* **25**, 82 (1974).

153. I Ladany and H Kressel, 'Influence of Device Fabrication Parameters on Gradual Degradation of (AlGa)As CW Laser Diodes', *Appl. Phys. Lett.* **25**, 708 (1974).

154. M Fukuda, K Wakita and G Iwane, 'Dark Defects in InGaAsP/InP Double Heterostructure Lasers under Accelerated Ageing', *J. Appl. Phys.* **54**, 1246 (1983).

155. O M Hirao, K Mizuichi and M Nakamura, 'High Reliability Semiconductor Lasers for Optical Communications', *IEEE J. Selected Areas in Commun.* **SAC-4**, 1494 (1986).

156. P W Shumate, 'Semiconductor Laser Transmitters', in *Optoelectronic Technology and Lightwave Communication Systems*, C Lin, ed., Van Nostrand Reinhold, 1989, p. 422.

157. I Ury, S Margalit, M Yust and A Yariv, 'Monolithic Integration of an Injection Laser and a Metal Semiconductor Field Effect Transistor', *Appl. Phys. Lett.* **34**, 430 (1979).

158. U Koren, K L Yu, T R Chen, N Bar-Chaim, S Margalit and A Yariv, 'Monolithic Integration of a Very Low Threshold GaInAsP Laser and Metal Insulator Semiconductor Field Effect Transistor on Semi-Insulating InP', *Appl. Phys. Lett.* **40**, 643 (1982).

159. J Shibata, I Nakao, Y Sasai, S Kimura, N Hase and H Serizawa, 'Monolithic Integration of an InGaAsP/InP Laser Diode with Heterojunction Bipolar Transistors', *Appl. Phys. Lett.* **45**, 191 (1984).

160. T Horimatsu, T Iwama, Y Oikawa, T Touge, O Wada and T Nakagami, '400 Mbits/s Transmission Experiment Using Two Monolithic Optoelectronic Chips', *Elec. Lett.* **21**, 319 (1985).

161. H Nakano, S Yamashita, T P Tanaka, M Hirao and M Maeda, 'Monolithic Integration of Laser Diodes, Photomonitors and Laser Driving and Monitoring Circuits on Semi-Insulating GaAs', *J. Lightwave Technol.* **LT-4**, 574 (1986).

162. Y Kawamura, K Wakita, Y Yoshikuni, Y Itaya and H Asahi, 'Monolithic Integration of a DFB Laser and an MQW Optical Modulator in the 1.5 μm Wavelength Range', *IEEE J. Quantum Electron.* **QE-23**, 915 (1987).

163. W J Grande, J E Johnson and C L Tang, 'GaAs/AlGaAs Photonic Integrated Circuits Fabricated using Chemically Assisted Ion Beam Etching', *Appl. Phys. Lett.* **57**, 2537 (1990).

5

Photoconductors

This is the simplest type of photodetector to be reviewed in this book. It is simple to make because the detector consists of only one type of semiconductor, i.e. no junctions, and two associated ohmic contacts (which take no part in the photoconductivity process – they act merely as charge collectors). This chapter reviews the photoconductivity process, the types of material used in devices and the applications found for these structures. A section on noise is also included as this is also of interest for subsequent chapters on other detectors.

5.1 Photoconductivity

5.1.1 The photoconductivity process

This was outlined in section 1.3.5, where it was noted that a photon of energy $h\nu$ will be absorbed by a semiconductor of band gap E_g if $h\nu \geq E_g$. This leads to a fundamental absorption edge as shown in Figure 1.17, with typical examples for semiconductors of main interest shown in Figure 5.1 [1]. Whilst interband transitions are the most dominant absorbing mechanism, there are others involving transitions to or from centres within the band gap. These centres can be provided by external means, e.g. doping, and hence the terms intrinsic and extrinsic photoconductor are used to denote a pure or doped material respectively.

Simple photoconductor structures are shown in Figure 5.2. For the commonly described, if not commonly made, device as in Figure 5.2(a) the whole semiconductor slab is the photoconductor, and so should be at least the penetration depth $(1/\alpha)$ in thickness to ensure maximum light absorption. However, if the device is too thick, only the upper part will absorb and the rest will form a shunt resistance. Noise considerations (section 5.2) also have an influence on the thickness. An antireflection coating on the top surface is often used to minimize losses. Once electron–hole pairs have been generated (assuming an intrinsic semiconductor) the

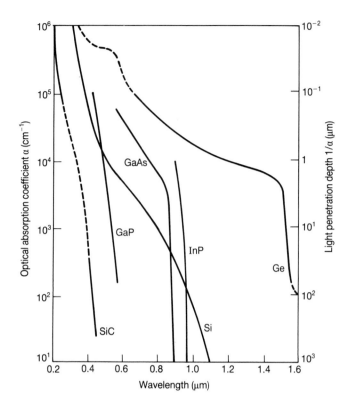

Figure 5.1 Absorption vs wavelength characteristics for the main elemental and binary semiconductors (ⓒNorth-Holland Publishing: reproduced by kind permission).

carriers must have sufficient mobility and lifetime to carry charge to the ohmic contacts for collection. An external field is usually provided to move charge carriers through the material. Figure 5.2(b) shows a planar photoconductive detector where the active region is formed near the semiconductor surface.

A detection circuit is usually of the form shown in Figure 5.3, with a d.c. blocking capacitor if an a.c. voltage source is used. Obviously a change in conductivity of the detector will lower its resistance, leading to an increase in potential difference measured across the load resistor R_L. The choice of R_L is important, as to maintain a linear response between input light level and output voltage the potential drop across the load resistor V_L must be less than that across the detector V_D, i.e. $R_D \gg R_L$. The nature of the device in operation often leads to the alternative name of photoresistor.

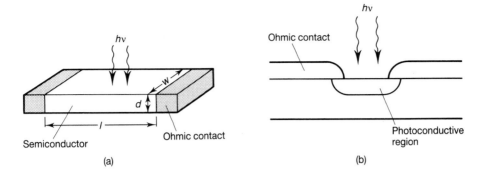

Figure 5.2 (a) Simple, and (b) planar photoconductor structure.

5.1.2 Electrical parameters

5.1.2.1 Photocurrent

In a practical photoconductor, the densities of photogenerated electrons and/or holes are determined by a dynamic balance between the generation rate and carrier losses. Losses can occur by recombination (reviewed in section 1.3.6), hence terminating the life of these carriers, traps (section 1.3.7), where carriers are temporarily removed from their appropriate band for later emission and 'sweep-out', where carriers recombine at the external ohmic contacts.

In its non-illuminated state, a photoconductor in a circuit as in Figure 5.3 will pass a steady current, and the internal generation of electron–hole pairs will be balanced by a similar recombination. When the device is illuminated, there will be an initial rise in current indicating that the generation rate is greater than the recombination rate. The recombination rate will then increase until again a steady state is reached. Once the illumination is removed, the generation rate falls, recombination dominates and the current level falls. A subsequent fall in the recombination rate will again produce non-illuminated equilibrium. The mathematics of this are described in section 1.3.6. The important equation from that section to be used here is (1.28).

Let us assume an intrinsic photoconductor of n-type conductivity. The total number of electron–hole pairs generated by illumination of incident power P_0 is

$$\frac{\eta P_0}{h\nu} \, . \tag{5.1}$$

The generation rate per unit volume as a function of depth is

$$g_0(x) \;=\; \frac{\eta \alpha P_0}{h\nu wld} \exp(-\alpha x) \, . \tag{5.2}$$

where w, l and d are as shown in Figure 5.2(a). Over the whole thickness of the semiconductor, the generation rate per unit volume is

$$g_0 \;=\; \int_0^d g_0(x)\mathrm{d}x$$

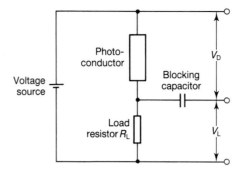

Figure 5.3 Basic optical detection circuit using a photoconductor.

$$= \frac{\eta \alpha P_0}{h\nu wld}[1 - \exp(-\alpha d)]. \tag{5.3}$$

Not forgetting what we said earlier about d being of the order of $1/\alpha$, the arithmetic of (5.2) is simplified if we consider $d \gg 1/\alpha$. Then (5.2) becomes

$$g_0(x) = \frac{\eta P_0}{h\nu wld}. \tag{5.4}$$

The photogeneration mechanism in this case relies on a band to band transition, and so illumination will provide a change in each carrier concentration such that

$$\Delta n = \Delta p. \tag{5.5}$$

The subsequent change in conductivity σ can then be related to a change in current density J which directly leads on to the photocurrent I_0. Using (1.41) and (1.42) for J gives

$$\begin{aligned} I_0 &= eE(\mu_e \Delta n + \mu_h \Delta p)\, wd \\ &= eE\Delta p(\mu_e + \mu_h)wd \end{aligned} \tag{5.6}$$

from (5.5). Using (1.28) and (5.6):

$$I_0 = eg_0\tau_p E(\mu_e + \mu_h)wd, \tag{5.7}$$

and, from (5.4),

$$I_0 = \frac{e\eta P_0 \tau_p E}{h\nu l}(\mu_e + \mu_h). \tag{5.8}$$

The transit time t for a carrier to cross the device is

$$t = \frac{l}{v}. \tag{5.9}$$

Using this and (1.33), (5.8) can be rearranged to give

$$I_0 = \frac{e\eta P_0}{h\nu} \tau_p \left(\frac{1}{t_n} + \frac{1}{t_p}\right) \tag{5.10}$$

in terms of the minority carrier lifetime and transit times.

Example 5.1

Calculate the current generated when 1 μW of optical power is shone on to a photoconductor of $\eta = 0.8$ and minority carrier lifetime 0.5 ns, if the material has values of electron and hole mobilities of 2500 cm^2/V s and 500 cm^2/V s respectively, and in operation 5 V is dropped across the conductor length of 10 μm.

Solution: carrier velocities are given by $v = \mu E$, and so

$$\text{for electrons} \quad v = 2500 \times \frac{5}{10^{-3}} = 1.25 \times 10^8 \text{ cm s}^{-1}$$

$$\text{and for holes} \quad v = 500 \times \frac{5}{10^{-3}} = 2.5 \times 10^7 \text{ cm s}^{-1}. \tag{5.11}$$

From these values and (5.9), transit times can be calculated as:

$$\text{for electrons} \quad t_n = \frac{10^{-3}}{1.25 \times 10^8} = 8 \text{ ps}$$

$$\text{and for holes} \quad t_p = \frac{10^{-3}}{2.5 \times 10^7} = 40 \text{ ps}. \tag{5.12}$$

From these values and (5.10)

$$I_0 = \frac{e \times 10^{-6} \times 1.55 \times 10^{-6}}{hc} \times 5 \times 10^{-10} \times \left(\frac{1}{8 \times 10^{-12}} + \frac{1}{40 \times 10^{-12}}\right)$$

$$= 75 \, \mu\text{A}. \tag{5.13}$$

5.1.2.2 *Gain*

This can be defined as the ratio of the carrier collection rate at the contacts to the carrier generation rate. Thus

$$G = \frac{I_0/e}{g_0 wld}. \tag{5.14}$$

From (5.7) and (5.14)

$$G = \frac{\tau_p(\mu_e + \mu_h)V}{l^2} \tag{5.15}$$

for an applied voltage $V\,(= El)$. So a high gain device can be obtained by any combination of increasing τ_p, μ_e, μ_h or V and decreasing the device length l. For a long lifetime and small device length, gains of up to 10^6 are possible. If the carrier transit times t_n and t_p are very dissimilar then (5.4), (5.10) and (5.14) can be combined to give a simple form for G. For instance, if $t_n \ll t_p$, because $\mu_e \gg \mu_h$, then rearrangement of these equations gives

$$G = \frac{\tau_p}{t_n}, \tag{5.16}$$

i.e. the gain is the ratio of the minority carrier lifetime to the majority carrier transit time. This may help to explain the gain phenomenon, i.e. how can a simple semiconductor act to amplify current? After an electron–hole pair is generated, the (usually) more mobile electrons are rapidly swept out of the semiconductor to the anode ohmic contact. Another electron is attracted in to the semiconductor at the cathode to maintain charge neutrality. Electrons are drawn in at the cathode and removed at the anode until the hole is removed, either at the cathode or by recombination. Hence, the gain relationship between the recombination time and electron transit time.

Example 5.2

Find the gain of the device in example 5.1.

Solution: using the results obtained from example 5.1 in (5.16)

$$G = \frac{5 \times 10^{-10}}{8 \times 10^{-12}} = 62.5. \tag{5.17}$$

Note that if the device is an extrinsic photoconductor, i.e. only either electrons or holes are created, the same analysis leads to the minority carrier lifetime in (5.16) being replaced by the majority carrier lifetime.

5.1.2.3 *Response speed and bandwidth*
These factors will depend on how fast the photocurrent can decay after illumination has been removed. As shown in section 1.3.6, the current will decay with a

time constant equal to the minority carrier lifetime. Thus for holes the carrier concentration at time t after illumination is removed is

$$p(t) = p_0 + \tau_p g_0 \exp\left(\frac{-t}{\tau_p}\right) \tag{5.18}$$

where p_0 is the non-illuminated carrier concentration. Thus, a large value of τ_p is detrimental to response speed. As can be seen in these last two sections, the gain and response speed (hence the bandwidth) are intimately linked, and one cannot be maximized without detriment to the other. The upper frequency limit placed on the device's operation f_{max} is given by

$$f_{max} = \frac{1}{2\pi\tau_p}. \tag{5.19}$$

Note also that from (5.16) and (5.19) the gain depends on the lifetime and the transit time, whereas the speed is only dependent on lifetime. A result of this, in terms of device design and operation, is something that may initially seem surprising: the response speed of a photoconductor is independent of the device dimensions and the applied bias voltage. However, for devices with a long minority carrier lifetime, and hence negligible trapping in the material, the speed is determined by the rapid sweep-out of electron–hole pairs by the electric field. In this case τ_p in (5.19) is replaced by the time the pair spend in the high field region of the device [2]. This leads to two types of photoconductive devices: lifetime limited, independent of applied voltage and geometry, and transit-time limited, dependent on bias but only valid when the photoconductive length is very small (of the order of a few microns or less depending on the particular semiconductor).

5.1.3   Response spectrum

The nature of the absorption coefficient as shown in Figure 5.1 means that more of the carriers are generated near the surface of the device as the wavelength decreases. Near surface effects such as defects increase the density of traps in this region, leading to a much higher probability of generated carriers being lost to the photoconductivity process, leading to the real response spectrum of Figure 5.4. Other surface phenomena arise from the zero-bias surface potential associated with a semiconductor. Careful surface passivation techniques are needed to minimize the effects of traps and other surface states, as surface effects are also thought to be responsible for an anomalous low frequency gain mechanism in photoconductors [3]. Alternatively, surface doping by ion implantation can decrease the depth of the depletion layer associated with the zero-bias surface potential so that there is an active channel between the ohmic contacts to the photoconductor [4].

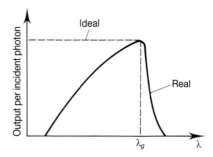

Figure 5.4 Wavelength response characteristic of both an ideal and a real photoconductor.

5.1.4   Transient response

The time-dependent response of a photoconductor depends on characteristics such as the semiconductor material parameters, device geometry, the external circuit and the input optical pulse shape and intensity. Using the continuity equations as described previously in section 1.4.3 ((1.58) and (1.60), with appropriate generation and recombination rate terms), the current densities can be calculated using (1.50) and (1.51). This has been done elsewhere [5], and using Poisson's equation (2.7) leads to equations for current which are solved numerically. The details are beyond the space available in this book, but typical results are shown in Figure 5.5.

As seen in Figure 5.5(a), the response is sublinear with intensity. The pulse fall contains both fast electron and slow hole components. The decay tail relaxes faster at high intensities, because the increased hole trapping rate is faster at reducing the hole current, the dominant mechanism for the production of the tail. The current density is also seen to be bias dependent (Figures 5.5(b) and (c) for low and high optical intensities respectively). Finally, Figures 5.5(d) and (e) show the effect of varying the device length, whilst keeping the electric field constant (i.e. proportionately changing the applied bias). The explanations of these phenomena are related to the interaction between charge states of deep level traps, the electric field characteristics, transport of carriers and the optical excitation spectrum, and are modelled and experimentally verified in [5].

5.2   Noise and sensitivity

Although gain has been treated in some detail in section 5.1.2.2, it is the application of gain in noise situations that is important. We shall introduce two terms as figures of merit for photoconductors: the detectivity and the sensitivity. Whilst being introduced here these terms are important for all types of optical receivers, and will be used in Chapters 6 and 7. We start this section by introducing the

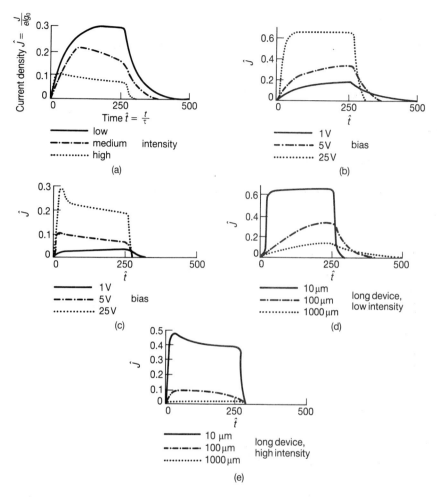

Figure 5.5 Time-dependent response of a photoconductor; the effect of (a) incident optical intensity, (b) and (c) applied bias, (d) and (e) device length (©1987 IEEE: reproduced by kind permission).

application of a photoconductor as a front end receiver for optical communication, followed by an equivalent circuit and a description of the relevant noise sources. The treatment of noise in a complete way is beyond the scope of this book in terms of both mathematical rigour and sheer volume; for such a treatment textbooks more suited to the electronics aspect of detection should be referred to (e.g. [6–9]).

5.2.1 Photoreceiver circuit

As will be seen in section 5.3, a common type of integration involves a photo-conductor with a high-impedance amplifier employing a FET as the first stage. This is shown in Figure 5.6(a), where the other basic circuit components such as a pre-amplifier, equalizer and filter are included [9]. Such a circuit could be used for either analog or digital signals, although for the latter some additional decision circuitry would be required.

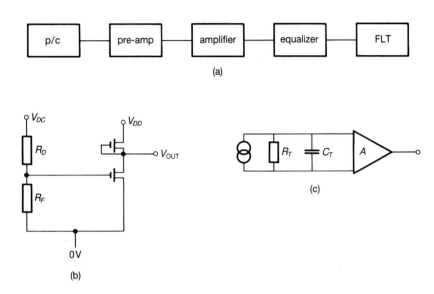

(a)

(b)

(c)

Figure 5.6 (a) System representation of photoconductor-based receiver. (b) Typical front end circuit. (c) Equivalent circuit of (b).

A circuit of the front end part is shown in Figure 5.6(b), with its equivalent circuit in Figure 5.6(c). R_T is the total input resistance, consisting of the parallel combination of the photoconductor dark resistance R_D and the front end resistance. This latter term is replaced by a feedback resistance R_F in a transimpedance amplifier [10]. C_T is a stray capacitance associated with the detector/amplifier interconnections. Series resistance and shunt conductance effects are usually negligible. How the circuit in Figure 5.6(c) is modified to include noise sources is now given.

5.2.2 Noise sources

The sources of noise in the detector of Figure 5.6(c) are:

(i) Johnson noise,

(ii) shot noise associated with recombination,
(iii) flicker noise,
(iv) intersymbol interference.

In addition the FET has associated shot and flicker noise effects, as well as an additional channel noise term. The rest of the receiver circuit elements will also have their own noise terms. Notice the use of different symbols for the frequency of the optical power (ν) and the signal modulation (f). Also notice the use of the terms $\langle v^2 \rangle$ and $\langle i^2 \rangle$ to represent the average value of the square of voltage or current respectively.

5.2.2.1 *Johnson noise*

Also called thermal noise, the r.m.s. value of this term was first determined experimentally in 1928 [11]. It is a result of the random motion of carriers within a resistive material due to their temperature stimulated kinetic energy. As this motion is random, the current generated by the carrier movement will fluctuate about a mean value of zero, and hence lead to a fluctuating voltage across a resistance.

The theoretical basis for this noise was developed at the same time as it was observed. Nyquist developed a generalized theorem [12] which describes the spectral intensities of the voltage fluctuations in terms of a second order differential equation, where for an electrical system the damping constant is just the resistance. Rigorously derived, the expression for the Johnson noise voltage v_j in a resistance R at a temperature T is

$$\langle v_j^2 \rangle (f) \;=\; \frac{4Rhf\Delta f}{e^{hf/kT} - 1} \tag{5.20}$$

where Δf is a frequency interval. If $hf \ll kT$, the exponential term in the denominator can be approximated by

$$\exp\left(\frac{hf}{kT}\right) \;=\; 1 + \frac{hf}{kT}. \tag{5.21}$$

and so (5.20) becomes the term more familiar to electronic engineers

$$\langle v_j^2 \rangle (f) \;=\; 4kTR\Delta f. \tag{5.22}$$

We can treat this noise source as a voltage source $(\langle v_j^2 \rangle)^{1/2}$ and a noiseless resistor R. For such a circuit, as shown in Figure 5.7 with a load resistor R_L, the noise current $\langle i_j^2 \rangle$ will be given by

$$\langle i_j^2 \rangle \;=\; \frac{\langle v_j^2 \rangle (f)}{(R + R_L)^2}. \tag{5.23}$$

If the resistors are equal $(R = R_L)$, maximum power will be dissipated in R_L. This is known as the available noise power P_j and is given by

$$P_j(f) \;=\; \langle i_j^2 \rangle R_L. \tag{5.24}$$

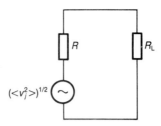

Figure 5.7 Circuit representation of a Johnson noise source.

Hence, using (5.22) and (5.23), (5.24) becomes

$$P_j(f) \ = \ kT\Delta f. \tag{5.25}$$

From (5.25), P_j is independent of the frequency (and the resistance) at which the noise is measured, i.e. there is the same amount of noise per unit of frequency interval anywhere in the spectrum. Hence it is known as white noise (as in white light – no colour, c.f. frequency, dependence).

For the circuit of Figures 5.6(b) and (c), if we assume that $R_F = R_D = 2R_T$, then the noise current is given by the sum of the contributions of both the photoconductor and the feedback resistor R_F

$$\langle i_j^2 \rangle(f) \ = \ \frac{4kTR_D}{(R_D)^2}\Delta f + \frac{4kTR_F}{(R_F)^2}\Delta f = \frac{8kT}{R_D}\Delta f. \tag{5.26}$$

If however $R_F \gg R_D$, then the noise current would be lowered and would asymptotically approach $4kT/R_D$. However, the sensitivity of the amplifier used will decrease if this occurs. Thus the optimum performance is when $R_F = R_D$.

For a frequency spectrum of bandwidth B, the total noise voltage, current or power is found by integrating Δf over B. This is straightforward, as

$$\int_0^B \Delta f \ = \ B. \tag{5.27}$$

Hence (5.22), (5.23) and (5.25) become, over the whole frequency spectrum,

$$\langle v_j^2 \rangle \ = \ 4kTRB, \tag{5.28}$$

$$\langle i_j^2 \rangle \ = \ \frac{4kTRB}{(R + R_L)^2}, \tag{5.29}$$

$$\text{and} \quad P_j \ = \ kTB. \tag{5.30}$$

So although a white noise source has a magnitude independent of frequency, the total noise voltage (or current, power) increases linearly with available bandwidth. This means that for high frequency analog, or high bit rate digital, signals there is an increase in the noise level compared to low frequency, or low bit rate, signals.

5.2.2.2   Shot noise

Thermal noise is generated due to the random movement of a number of carriers; shot noise is due to random fluctuations in the number of carriers themselves. For instance, the arrival of photons at a photoconductor surface, and hence the associated carrier generation, is a random process. The theoretical value for the noise current i_s associated with this type of phenomenon was developed by Schottky in 1918 (hence the alternative name Schottky noise), and is given by

$$\langle i_s^2 \rangle (f) \;=\; 2eI_0 \Delta f \tag{5.31}$$

where I_0 is the average photogenerated d.c. current flowing. Again this is a white noise source, and again this expression can be integrated over the whole bandwidth B to give

$$\langle i_s^2 \rangle \;=\; 2eI_0 B. \tag{5.32}$$

Example 5.3

Compare the room temperature ratio of noise current associated with Johnson noise with that of shot noise for a photoconductor of photocurrent 2.5 μA and resistance 5 Ω, with a load resistance of 5 Ω.

Solution: from (5.29) and (5.32)

$$
\begin{aligned}
\frac{\langle i_j^2 \rangle}{\langle i_s^2 \rangle} &= \frac{2TRk}{eI_0(R+R_L)^2} \\
&= \frac{2 \times 293 \times 5 \times k}{e \times 2.5 \times 10^{-6} \times 10^2} \\
&= 1010.
\end{aligned}
\tag{5.33}
$$

Sometimes the device does not give 'pure' shot noise, and an additional constant factor is introduced in the right hand side of (5.31) and (5.32) to take account of this. This constant is known as the noise suppression factor, and has a value between zero and one. An example of how this factor could be introduced is where there is some correlation between the random processes involved in the noise generation, such as mutual interactions between incoming photons. The situation is slightly more complicated for a photoconductor. For such a device, the current consists of a set of random pulses whose arrival types are predictable (Poisson distribution) but whose pulse widths fluctuate because of the statistical nature of recombination. It can be shown [13] that the shot noise current i_{SGR} associated with the generation–recombination process is given by

$$\langle i^2_{SGR}\rangle(f) \;\; = \;\; \frac{4GeI_0}{1 + 4\pi^2 f^2 \tau_p^2}. \tag{5.34}$$

Note that this is not now a white noise source, as there is a clear frequency dependence. If, as is usual, $t_n \ll t_p$, then the $1/t_p$ term in (5.10) can be ignored to give

$$I_0 \;\; = \;\; \frac{e\eta P_0}{h\nu}\frac{\tau_p}{t_n} = \frac{e\eta P_0 G}{h\nu} \tag{5.35}$$

using (5.16). Equations (5.34) and (5.35) can then be combined to give

$$\langle i^2_{SGR}\rangle(f) \;\; = \;\; \frac{4e^2\eta P_0}{h\nu}\frac{\tau_p^2}{t_n^2}\left(\frac{1}{1 + 4\pi^2 f^2 \tau_p^2}\right). \tag{5.36}$$

Integrating over the bandwidth B gives a total generation–recombination shot noise contribution of

$$\langle i^2_{SGR}\rangle \;\; = \;\; \frac{2e^2\eta P_0}{\pi h\nu}\frac{\tau_p}{t_n^2}\,\tan^{-1}\left(2\pi B\tau_p\right). \tag{5.37}$$

Noting that $\tan x \simeq x$ when x is very small, then for $B\tau_p \ll 1$, (5.37) reduces to

$$\langle i^2_{SGR}\rangle \;\; = \;\; 4eI_0 GB \tag{5.38}$$

using (5.16) and (5.35). This is similar to (5.32), with the gain G included, and a factor 4 instead of 2 as a multiplier (because both generation and recombination contribute equally to the noise). Notice also that for $x \gg 1$, $\tan^{-1}x$ is $\pi/2$. So for very high frequencies (or bit rates) or long detector response times, the shot noise current approaches an asymptotic value. This can be calculated using (5.10), (5.16) and (5.37):

$$\lim_{B\tau_p \to \infty}\left(\langle i^2_{SGR}\rangle\right) \;\; = \;\; \frac{eI_0 G}{t_n}. \tag{5.39}$$

Example 5.4

Calculate the ratio of Johnson noise current to generation–recombination noise current for the photoconductor of the previous examples at bit rates of both 5 Mb s^{-1} and 5000 Mb s^{-1}. Take the photocurrent to be as in example 5.3.

Solution: at 5 Mb s^{-1}, the term in the tan^{-1} bracket of (5.37) can be calculated as 0.0157, whose tan^{-1} value is also 0.0157: equation (5.38) can then be used for $\langle i^2_{SGR} \rangle$. Equations (5.29) and (5.38) then give

$$
\begin{aligned}
\frac{\langle i^2_j \rangle}{\langle i^2_{SGR} \rangle} &= \frac{TRk}{eI_0(R + R_L)^2 G} \\
&= \frac{293 \times 5 \times k}{e \times 2.5 \times 10^{-6} \times 10^2 \times 62.5} \\
&= 8.1.
\end{aligned}
\tag{5.40}
$$

For the high bit rate case, the term in the tan^{-1} bracket of (5.37) is now 15.7, whose tan^{-1} value is 1.507, or 0.96 $\times \pi/2$. In this case equations (5.29) and (5.39) will give

$$
\begin{aligned}
\frac{\langle i^2_j \rangle}{\langle i^2_{SGR} \rangle} &= \frac{4TRBkt_n}{eI_0(R + R_L)^2 G} \\
&= \frac{4 \times 293 \times 5 \times 5 \times 10^9 \times k \times 8 \times 10^{-12}}{e \times 2.5 \times 10^{-6} \times 10^2 \times 62.5} \\
&= 1.3.
\end{aligned}
\tag{5.41}
$$

5.2.2.3 Flicker noise

In addition to the noise sources already mentioned, there is one that is present in all measurement systems. This noise component shows a power spectral density that varies as K/f^n, where K is a constant and n lies in the range 0.8 to 1.4. This phenomenon was first observed in 1925 [14], and has been experimentally verified in a frequency range varying from 10^{-6} Hz to over 10^6 Hz. It occurs in all electronic materials and devices, with the term flicker noise originating from observations of thermionic valves. It is also known as contact noise (although in general it is not a contact effect), current noise, excess noise and, very commonly, $1/f$ noise. Several models, both empirical and theoretical, have been put forward to explain this phenomenon but all seem to have only limited applicability [15]. Besides problems with contacts, surface effects have also been suggested; this could explain why a silicon JFET (active channel buried away from the semiconductor surface) displays virtually no flicker noise compared to a GaAs MESFET (a near surface channel region). However, a comprehensive explanation for all manifestations of flicker noise current i_f has not yet been found.

5.2.2.4 Intersymbol interference

This term arises in digital systems if a slow photoconductor is used to detect a high bit rate signal. In this case, the device's response to bits arriving in previous time

Noise Source	Symbol	Dependence on Bandwidth B
Johnson	$\langle i_j^2 \rangle$	B
FET Gate Leakage Shot	$\langle i_g^2 \rangle$	B
Intersymbol Interference	$\langle i_{isi}^2 \rangle$	B
Flicker	$\langle i_f^2 \rangle$	B^2
FET Channel	$\langle i_c^2 \rangle$	B^3
Generation–Recombination Shot	$\langle i_{SGR}^2 \rangle$	B at low values of B, limiting value at high B

Table 5.1 Sources of noise current and the dependence of their average square values on bandwidth.

slots will overlap into the decision interval, giving rise to a shot noise generated background photocurrent. The magnitude of the noise current i_{isi} depends on the duration of the response as well as the previously transmitted bit pattern; a term similar to shot noise can be generated for this phenomenon [10].

5.2.2.5 *Importance of noise terms*
We have now covered all the main sources of noise in the photodetector, but the FET-based amplifier will also have flicker noise and intersymbol interference terms. It will also have gate leakage shot noise i_g^2 and additional channel noise terms i_c^2. Table 5.1 lists the relative dependence on bandwidth of the noise terms described here [10].

The overall effect of all the noise terms can be calculated and plotted as a function of signal frequency or, as shown in Figure 5.8, bit rate [10]: $\langle i_n^2 \rangle$ is the total noise current. It can be readily seen, for the two examples of photoconductive gain shown, that the Johnson noise term as given by (5.29) is the dominant factor over almost the whole of the currently available optical communication spectrum; only when bit rates > 3–4 Gb s^{-1} are used does any other term, in this case the FET channel noise, become important. Indeed, because this latter term has a cubic dependence on bandwidth it will rapidly dominate the Johnson, and any other, noise terms for high (> 5 Gb s^{-1}) bit rate applications. Readers familiar with bipolar devices will know that the noise current increases with the square of the bandwidth (except when the base resistance noise dominates), and so it might be expected that such a device would be better as an amplifying stage than a FET. For high bandwidth applications this is true ('crossover' point for Si FET/bipolar devices is around 50–200 Mb s^{-1}) depending on the parameter values of the device, but for low bandwidths the high impedance level of the FET gives a superior input stage amplifier by not loading the detector. For GaAs based devices the same is true, but the frequency 'crossover' point is much higher than for Si. The exact point is difficult to determine as technology improvements shift the value ever upwards, but it is well into the Gb s^{-1} region [16].

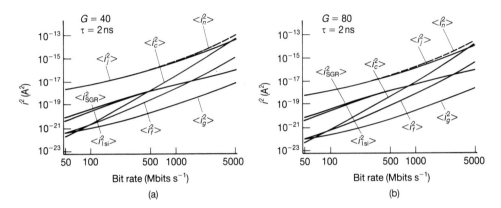

Figure 5.8 Photoconductive noise current contributions assuming a series dark resistance of 400 Ω and (a) a gain of 40, (b) a gain of 80 (©1985 IEEE: reproduced by kind permission).

5.2.3   Sensitivity, noise equivalent power (NEP) and detectivity

These terms are important for all photodetectors. Noise equivalent power (NEP) is defined as the value of the optical input power necessary to give a signal to noise ratio of one. As an example, we can see from Figure 5.8 that at low bit rates Johnson noise dominates all other noise sources. From (5.29) the Johnson noise current for a stand alone detector ($R_L = 0$) is given by

$$\langle i_j^2 \rangle = \frac{4kTB}{R}, \tag{5.42}$$

and so from (5.35) and (5.42) the power signal to noise ratio (the ratio of the square of the currents) is

$$\left(\frac{S}{N}\right)_p = \frac{I_0^2}{\langle i_j^2 \rangle}$$

$$= \frac{e^2 \eta^2 P_0^2 G^2}{h^2 \nu^2} \frac{R}{4kTB}. \tag{5.43}$$

For $(S/N)_p$ to be equal to one, the input power P_0 must be given by

$$P_0 = \frac{2h\nu}{e\eta G} \left(\frac{kTB}{R} \right)^{1/2} = (NEP)_{SL} \tag{5.44}$$

where the subscript SL implies that the system is signal noise limited. P_0 is known as the sensitivity of the device. There are other limiting factors, such as when the background noise is greater than the signal noise, where the expression for NEP will be different from that in (5.44). Other examples of limiting situations are amplifier noise and dark current. The relevant expressions are derived and discussed in [17].

The detectivity, D, is simply the inverse of NEP and is specified for a 1 Hz bandwidth at a given wavelength, modulation frequency and source radiation temperature. The specific detectivity, D^*, is the value of D normalized to a detector area of 1 cm^2. The value of the theoretical limit is derived in [18], and is given by

$$D^* = 1.3 \times 10^{11} \left(\frac{300}{T} \right)^{5/2} \frac{\exp\left(x_c/2\right)}{x_c \left(x_c^2 + 2x_c + 2\right)^{1/2}} \text{ cm Hz}^{1/2} \text{ W}^{-1} \tag{5.45}$$

for a photodetector able to absorb photons within a solid angle of 2π, and where $x_c = h\nu_c/kT$, where ν_c is the minimum detectable frequency.

To calculate the minimum power level needed to detect a signal, the expressions for D^* or NEP are used with appropriate material values.

Example 5.5

Calculate the minimum power level needed to detect a 6.25 MHz signal for the case of a Johnson noise limited photoconductor, assuming $\lambda = 1.55$ μm, $T = 300$ K, $\eta = 1$, $R = 10$ Ω and $G = 40$. Also calculate the minimum power required to obtain a signal to noise ratio of 50 dB.

Solution: for a Johnson noise limited photoconductor, (5.44) applies. Hence

$$P_0 = \frac{2 \times h \times 2.1 \times 10^{14}}{e \times 40} \left(\frac{k \times 300 \times 6.25 \times 10^6}{10} \right)^{1/2} = 2.21 \text{ nW}. \tag{5.46}$$

However, for a system requiring a good quality signal, this figure has to be multiplied by the appropriate signal/noise ratio. For a S/N ratio of 50 dB, the previously calculated value would have to be multiplied by 10^5, making P_0 equal to 221 μW.

5.2.4 Bit error rate

Ideal digital signals have only two signal levels, '0' and '1'. However, real digital signals will have a spread of levels around these idealized values. If we assume that these spreads can be represented by a Gaussian function, then their form can be readily calculated and their individual contributions summed to give a total error probability. For a two-level signal, this probability is given by [19]:

$$P(e) \ = \ \frac{1}{2} \, \text{erfc} \, \left(\frac{(S/N)^{1/2}}{2\sqrt{2}} \right) \tag{5.47}$$

where erfc represents the complementary error function ($\text{erfc}(y) = 1 - \text{erf}(y)$, where $\text{erf}(y) = 2/\sqrt{\pi} \int_0^y \exp(-x^2) \mathrm{d}x$), whose numerical value is usually found from look up tables. (More on the properties of error functions are given in Chapter 8, and in particular Table 8.6).

Example 5.6

A telecommunications industry standard is to have $P(e) = 10^{-9}$, i.e. a bit error rate of 1 in 10^9 ($BER = 10^{-9}$). Given that $\text{erfc}(4.24) = 2 \times 10^{-9}$, calculate the signal to noise ratio required to obtain this standard.

Solution: from (5.47)

$$\left(\frac{S}{N} \right)^{1/2} = 2\sqrt{2} \times 4.24 = 144, \tag{5.48}$$

or 21.6 dB. Figure 5.9 shows the S/N ratio required as a function of bit error rate.

5.2.5 Minimum detectable signal

Irrespective of the efficiency or the gain of a photoconductor, there must be a lower limit to the optical power which can be detected. It also follows that the lower the incoming power, the more chance there is of noise becoming dominant over signal. Although the average power in an optical pulse can be readily determined, the power in any particular pulse cannot; there is an uncertainty in this as a result of the statistical nature of photon emission. It is then easier to discuss number of photons rather than optical power, and the statistical function that governs the

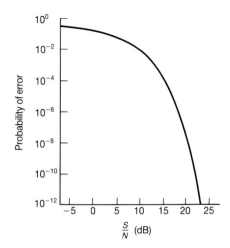

Figure 5.9 Required signal to noise (S/N) ratio as a function of bit error rate.

number of photons in a pulse stream is the Poisson distribution. The probability $P(n)$ of receiving n photons in a pulse of average number N photons is given by

$$P(n) \quad = \quad \frac{N^n \exp(-N)}{n!}. \tag{5.49}$$

As we saw in the last section, a bit error rate of 10^{-9} is usually required for communication systems. If we assume that:

(i) there is no noise,
(ii) a signal contains on average equal amounts of '1' and '0' levels,
(iii) '0' is represented by no photons, whereas one or more photons will be interpreted as a '1',

then because of the exact nature of the '0' detection (no photons only) the probability of error is zero. As both '1' and '0' levels exist in equal amounts, the probability of error in the '1' level should not exceed 2×10^{-9} for a BER of 10^{-9}. An error in '1' will only occur when no photons ($n = 0$) is interpreted as a '1'. Therefore

$$2 \times 10^{-9} \quad = \quad \frac{N^0}{0!} \exp(-N). \tag{5.50}$$

From this equation $N = 20$. As there are equal numbers of '1' and '0' levels in the signal the average number of photons per bit in the minimum detectable signal is 10. This 10 photons per bit is the quantum limit on detection. (Note: some calculations similar to that shown above ignore the zero error in the '0' level detection and set the error in the '1' level to be equal to that of the BER, 10^{-9}. In this case $N = 20.7$, or 21, and the 10 photons per bit level becomes 10.35 or 10.5. As most detectors have limits well away from these figures (in the upper hundreds of photons per bit at best) the difference in the calculation method is not of any practical significance.)

In terms of optical power, the 10 photons per bit level can be readily assessed. This wil be given by

$$P_0 \quad = \quad \frac{h\nu}{\eta} \quad \times \quad 10 \quad \times \quad \text{bit rate.} \quad (5.51)$$

average	=	average energy	average number
power		per absorbed	of photons
		photon	needed per bit

Example 5.7

Calculate the value of P_0 in terms of W and dB for a photoconductive detector with the following parameters: $\lambda = 0.85\ \mu m$, $\eta = 1$ and a bit rate of 100 Mb s^{-1}.

Solution: from (5.51)

$$P_0 = h \times 3.5 \times 10^{14} \times 10 \times 100 = 23.4\,\text{pW}, \quad (5.52)$$

or, for a standard power reference level of 1 mW, $P_0 = -76.4$ dB m.

5.3 Fabrication and integration

5.3.1 Fabrication

The fabrication of photoconductive detectors is the simplest of all the procedures needed to make optoelectronic devices described in this book. The basic device has already been described in section 5.1.1 and shown in Figure 5.2. If the photoconductive region is the whole bulk of the semiconductor (Figure 5.2(a)) then, after sawing the wafer into die, ohmic contacts can be evaporated on and bond wires attached. More usually the photoconductor is only a small surface part of the bulk (Figure 5.2(b)), and typical fabrication procedures are suggested in Figure 5.10 for this kind of structure.

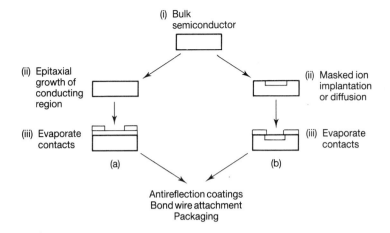

Figure 5.10 Typical fabrication procedure for a photoconductor where the active region is (a) epitaxially grown, and (b) formed by ion implantation or diffusion.

5.3.2   Integration

Integration of photoconductive elements has followed two paths: the first on silicon wafers, to interface with MOSFET based circuitry, and the second in III–V wafers, where detectors are either multiplexed together or matched with optical waveguides.

5.3.2.1   *Silicon substrates*

As with all integration of this type, the need is for close proximity of optical detection/emission to advanced signal processing. This allows interchip and intrachip signals to be transmitted optically, improving on the margins a circuit designer has for considerations such as signal skew, clock frequency and pin count. As always, the lattice mismatch between Si and III–V semiconductors can limit growth quality. Although photoconductive semiconductor thin films have been deposited on insulating substrates by various means such as sputtering, evaporation, plating or electrochemical deposition, growth techniques such as MBE or MOVPE were only successful from the mid-1980s onwards (e.g. [20] and references therein). One of the first reported uses of MBE for growth of a GaAs photoconductor on a silicon substrate is shown in Figure 5.11 [21]; even though the GaAs material was polycrystalline a reasonable device was demonstrated. Figure 5.12 shows a cross-section and an SEM of an InAsSb detector, grown on top of a GaAs seeding layer which was grown in a well etched in a Si substrate [22]. After growth the top polycrystalline part of the InAsSb was removed and metal contacts made to the detector. Such a detector is useful in the 3–5 μm region of the spectrum.

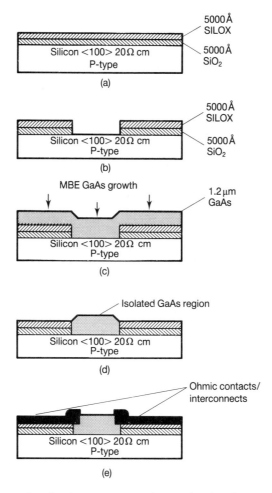

Figure 5.11 Molecular beam epitaxial growth of a GaAs photoconductor on a Si substrate (©1989 IEEE: reproduced by kind permission).

5.3.2.2 *III–V substrates*

An array of photoconductive elements with a pitch of only 19 μm has been reported and used as a detector in a Raman multichannel spectrometer [23]. A cross-section of one device is shown in Figure 5.13. There is no reason why this system could not be fabricated on a Si substrate, where the amplifiers (one for each detector) and multiplexing circuits could readily be integrated into the same device.

The integration of a short InGaAs photoconductor with a GaAs/AlGaAs waveguide using MOVPE is shown in Figure 5.14(a) [24]. The light is injected in the direction shown, where the relative refractive indices of the AlGaAs/GaAs/InGaAs

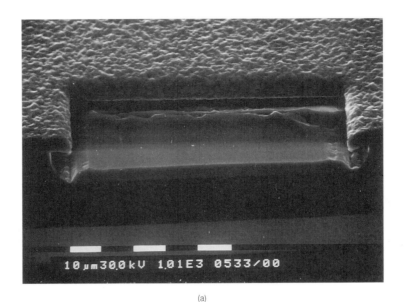

(a)

(b)

Figure 5.12 InAsSb photodetector, grown on a GaAs seeded layer. (a) SEM photograph (©IEE: photo courtesy of IMEC). (b) Device cross-section.

structure act largely to confine the optical power within the GaAs rib (Figure 5.14(b)). However the amount of leakage into the InGaAs is such that only 100μm of this material is needed to absorb 90% of the incoming power.

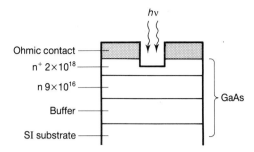

Figure 5.13 One element of a photoconductive array.

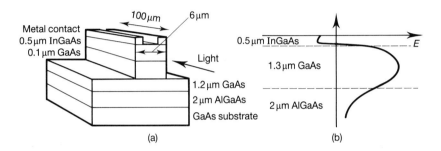

Figure 5.14 InGaAs photoconductor integrated with a GaAs/AlGaAs waveguide. (a) Device structure. (b) Electric field confinement (©AIP: reproduced by kind permission).

5.4 Problems

1. Show that maximum power will be dissipated in the load resistor of Figure 5.3(b) if the photodetector has the same value of resistance.

2. Calculate values for the photogenerated current, the gain and the maximum operating frequency of a photoconductor of length 20 μm if a potential of 10V is dropped across the device and 5 μW of optical power at a wavelength of 0.85 μm is shone on the active surface. Assume the internal efficiency is 0.8, the material is n-type with $\mu_e = 1000$ cm^2/V s and the minority carrier lifetime is 8 μs.

3. Calculate the generation rate of electron–hole pairs in problem 2 if the area of the device facing the incoming light is 0.5 mm^2. How is the calculation altered if the absorption coefficient is low, e.g. 1 cm^{-1}, for a device thickness of 100 μm?

4. For the photoconductor of problem 2, what is the maximum operating frequency if the material is altered to produce a gain of 1?

5. Compare the values of the room temperature Johnson, shot and shot generation–recombination noise terms for the photoconductor of problem 2, using calculated values for photocurrent and maximum operating frequency (as the bandwidth of the incoming signal). Assume a load resistance of 50 Ω is used.

6. What is the signal to noise ratio calculated from problems 2 and 5? Hence calculate the sensitivity of the device.

7. For a digital signal with a bit rate of 1 Gbit/s calculate the average power needed at a wavelength of 1.55 μm in order to obtain a bit error rate of 10^{-9}. Give your answer in dB.

5.5   References

1. H Melchior, 'Demodulation and Photodetection Techniques', in *Laser Handbook*, vol. 1, F T Arecchi and E O Schulz-Dubois, eds, North-Holland, 1972, p. 732.

2. H S Sommers, Jr. and W B Teutsch, 'Demodulation of Low-Level Broad Band Optical Signals with Semiconductors: Part II - Analysis of the Photoconductive Detector', *Proc. IEEE* **52**, 144 (1964).

3. K Iizuka, J Akasaka, T Tsubata and H Hesegawa, 'Surface Recombination in InGaAs Photoconductive Detectors and its Reduction by a Novel Passivation Scheme Using an MBE Si Layer', *Inst. Phys. Conf. Ser.* 106, IOP Publishing, 1990, p. 743.

4. G Wood Anderson, N A Papanicolaou, P E Thompson, J B Boos, T F Carruthers, D I Ma, I A G Mack, J A Modolo and F J Kub, 'High Speed Planar GaAs Photoconductors with Surface Implant Layers', *Appl. Phys. Lett.* **53**, 312 (1988).

5. A Evan Iverson and D L Smith, 'Mathematical Modelling of Photoconductor Transient Response', *IEEE Trans. Electron. Dev.* **ED-34**, 2098 (1987).

6. R H Kingston, *Detection of Optical and Infrared Radiation*, Springer Series in Optical Sciences, vol. 10, Springer Verlag, 1978.

7. T E Jenkins, *Optical Sensing Techniques and Signal Processing*, Prentice Hall International, 1987.

8. M J Buckingham, *Noise in Electronic Devices and Systems*, Ellis Horwood Ltd., 1983.

9. R G Smith and S D Personick, 'Receiver Design for Optical Fibre Communication Systems', in Topics in Applied Physics, vol. 39: *Semiconductor Devices for Optical Fibre Communication*, 2nd ed., H Kressel, ed., Springer Verlag, 1982, p. 90.

10. S R Forrest, 'The Sensitivity of Photoconductor Receivers for Long Wavelength Optical Communications', *IEEE J. Lightwave Tech.* **LT-3**, 347 (1985).

11. J B Johnson, 'Thermal Agitation of Electricity in Conductors', *Phys. Rev.* **32**, 97 (1928).
12. H Nyquist, 'Thermal Agitation of Electric Charges in Conductors', *Phys. Rev.* **32**, 110 (1928).
13. See [6], p. 56.
14. J B Johnson, 'The Schottky Effect in Low Frequency Circuits', *Phys. Rev.* **26**, 71 (1925).
15. See [8], p. 143.
16. See [9], p. 112ff.
17. See [6], p. 60.
18. See [6], p. 22.
19. J M Senior, *Optical Fiber Communications – Principles and Practice*, 2nd ed., Prentice-Hall International, 1992, p. 625.
20. A M Johnson, R M Lum, W M Simpson and J Klingert, 'Picosecond OMVPE GaAs/SiO$_2$ Photoconductive Devices and Applications in Materials Characterisation', *IEEE J. Quantum Electron.* **QE-23**, 1180 (1987).
21. J D Morse, R Mariella, G D Anderson and R W Dutton, 'Picosecond GaAs Photoconductors on Silicon Substrates for Local Integration with Silicon Devices and Circuits', *IEEE Electron. Dev. Lett.* **EDL-10**, 7 (1989).
22. W Dobbelaere, J de Boeck, M van Hove, K Deneffe, W DeRaedt, R Mertens and G Borghs, 'Long Wavelength Infra-red Photoconductive InAsSb Detectors Grown in Si Wells by Molecular Beam Epitaxy', *Elec. Lett.* **26**, 259 (1990).
23. M Constant, L Boursekey, D Decoster and J P Vilcot, 'GaAs Photodetector Array as new Detector in Multichannel Spectroscopic System', *Elec. Lett.* **26**, 56 (1990).
24. F Mallecot, J F Vinchant, M Razeghi, D Vandermoere, J P Vilcot and D Decoster, 'Monolithic Integration of a Short Length GaInAs Photoconductor with a GaAs/AlGaAs Optical Waveguide on a GaAs Semi-insulating Substrate', *Appl. Phys. Lett.* **53**, 2522 (1988).

6

PIN diodes

The operation of a pn junction under forward bias has been used to describe light emitting diodes and semiconductor lasers, reviewed in Chapters 3 and 4 respectively. Reverse bias characteristics form the background to a pn junction as a light detector. In this chapter we will review the basics of reverse bias operation, and see how the incorporation of an intrinsic (i, or lightly doped region) between the p- and n-regions improves the efficiency of the device considerably, leading to the almost universal structure for the basic reverse bias detector, the PIN diode. In the next chapter the characteristics are extended out to high values of reverse bias, and form the basis of another type of device, the avalanche photodiode (APD).

After a review of device operation, the design and material characteristics of PIN diodes are described, and it will be no surprise to learn that, considering what has already been discussed about light emitters, heterojunctions play an important role in maximizing performance. A different type of detector, the Schottky barrier photodiode, is then reviewed. Building on what has already been learnt in Chapter 5 on photoconductors, aspects of frequency response, noise and amplification are then discussed. It should then be clear why PIN devices need integration with their amplifying circuitry to be fully exploited.

Before starting the main part of this chapter, though, it is worth reviewing why solid state photodiodes have become much in demand by briefly describing other means of photodetection. The use of photoconductors is described in Chapter 5, and details of phototransistors can be found in more specialist texts, e.g. [1]. Devices such as photomultipliers may be familiar to many readers, and provide high sensitivity in their wavelength regions. Compared to a photodiode, however, they are bulky, costly and require high voltages to operate. Photoemissive devices [2] have low efficiencies, especially at wavelengths greater than 1 μm. Only solid state devices offer the right combination of low cost, high performance, high reliability and ease of operation that is required in most optical communication detection systems.

6.1   pn junction on reverse bias

This was described in detail in section 2.1.5, where we saw that reverse bias prevented majority carriers being injected across the junction, and that current flow was fed by minority carrier extraction at the edge of the depletion region in both the n- and p-sides. This led to an expression for reverse bias current density J given by (2.71) for diffusion dominated current, and (2.75) if generation effects are included.

6.1.1   Illumination and absorption

Figure 6.1 shows photons incident on a reverse biased pn junction region and being absorbed by various mechanisms. There are eight different examples shown, but only the latter three are important for us; hence we will briefly cover the first five, and then discuss mechanisms 6–8 in more detail.

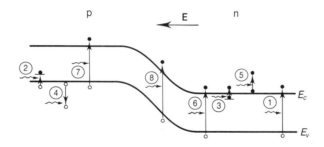

Figure 6.1 The various photon absorption mechanisms in a reverse biased pn junction (see text for details).

1. Absorption in the bulk semiconductor, well away from the depletion region edge. Although it is only shown in the n-type material, it can obviously also happen in the p-type. Absorption of a photon of energy greater than or equal to the band gap creates an electron–hole pair. Because this pair are well away from the depletion region edge, they will move only by diffusion, and will recombine with another hole/electron within an average distance given by the diffusion length. Because of this recombination within the material, no charge is picked up at an external contact unless the absorption happens within a diffusion length of the contact.

2. Absorption in the p-region to release a hole via an acceptor state. Obviously the photon energy required to do this is much less than for case 1, but the same constraints on recombination apply. This is not likely to be a significant term, as most acceptor states will already be full.

3. The same as case 2, except that a donor state is being ionized in n-type material. The same constraints as in case 2 apply.

4. Free carrier absorption within the p-type material valence band, this raises an electron to a higher energy position (hence a hole to a lower position). No extra carriers are created, and so there is no effect on measured current.

5. The same as case 4, except that the free carrier absorption is within the conduction band of the n-type material. The same constraints as in case 4 apply.

6. The same as case 1, except now the absorption is near the depletion region edge. The majority carrier electron will diffuse away into the bulk n-type, but the minority carrier hole has a strong probability of diffusing to the edge of the depletion region if the point at which it is generated is less than a diffusion length away. The electric field within the depletion region sweeps the hole across to the other side. This adds to the minority carrier extraction which already feeds the current in a reverse biased pn junction. Hence the generated hole contributes an additional charge e to this current.

7. The same as case 6, except that the majority carrier hole recombines on the p-side and the minority carrier electron is swept across the junction, again contributing an additional charge e to the minority carrier extracted current.

8. Generation of an electron–hole pair within the depletion region. Both carriers are swept out of this region to the n (electron) and p (hole) side of the device. At first sight it might be thought that this process contributes a charge $2e$ to the current, because of the two carrier nature of this mechanism. But each carrier only moves across part of the junction region. The net flow of charge across the whole depletion region width is only equivalent to e, the same as in cases 6 and 7.

From the above considerations, only mechanisms 6–8 contribute to the external photocurrent. Of these, 8 is the most desirable because it is not limited by the relatively long time needed for carriers to diffuse to the depletion region edge – this is considered in more detail in section 6.2 on PIN diodes. The important characteristics of absorption noted in the above discussion are:

(i) incoming photons must have an energy at least equal to the band gap,
(ii) only separated carriers contribute to photocurrent.

This leads on to the reverse bias $J–V$ characteristics under illumination as shown in Figure 6.2. Because the current under 'dark' conditions (hence the term 'dark current' when describing the reverse bias leakage current of photodiodes) is very small, the change in current produced by the correct illumination is very large. (The processes outlined above also happen on forward bias, but because in this case the forward current is so large any photogenerated current tends not to be noticed.) Equation (2.71) can now be modified to take account of the photocurrent density J_0:

$$J = -J_s - J_0. \qquad (6.1)$$

How the photocurrent is calculated is shown in the next section.

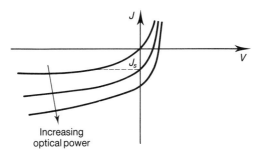

Figure 6.2 The effect of input optical power on the J–V characteristics of a reverse biased pn diode.

6.1.2   Photocurrent

6.1.2.1   Absorption characteristics
We will first consider how to determine the optical power level P at any point in the device. Consider Figure 6.3. On reaching the surface of the semiconductor light of incident power P_0 will have its level reduced to $P_0(1 - R)$ on entering the material, where R is the air–semiconductor reflection coefficient. On passing through the semiconductor the light will be absorbed, and so at any depth x the amount of residual optical power $P(x)$ is given by

$$P(x) = P_0(1 - R)\exp(-\alpha x) \tag{6.2}$$

where α is the absorption coefficient.

Example 6.1

For an absorption coefficient of 10^4 cm^{-1} and a surface reflectivity of 0.1, calculate the depth at which half the incident optical power has been absorbed in a material.

Solution: rearranging (6.2) gives

$$
\begin{aligned}
x &= \frac{-1}{\alpha}\log_e\frac{P(x)}{P_0(1 - R)} \\
&= -10^{-4}\log_e\frac{1}{2 \times 0.9} \\
&= 0.59\,\mu\text{m}. \tag{6.3}
\end{aligned}
$$

This example shows the importance of keeping the bulk part of the semiconductor that is facing the incident radiation very thin.

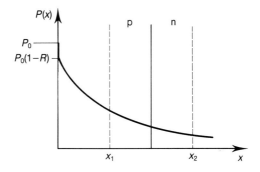

Figure 6.3 The optical intensity as a function of distance from the surface of a photodiode.

6.1.2.2   Depletion region current

In early considerations of pn junctions this factor was thought to be negligible. It was only in 1959 that its importance was realized [3]. It now forms the major part of junction region photogeneration, especially in the PIN diode, and in many texts is given as the sole source of photocurrent. If in Figure 6.3 x_1 and x_2 represent the beginning and the end of the depletion region respectively, then the power absorbed in this region is given from (6.2) as

$$P(x_1) - P(x_2) = P_0(1 - R) \left[\exp(-\alpha x_1) - \exp(-\alpha x_2)\right] . \tag{6.4}$$

The current density generated in the depletion region $J_0(DL)$ then becomes

$$J_0(DL) = \frac{e\eta_i}{h\nu} \, \Phi_0 \, (1 - R) \left[\exp(-\alpha x_1) - \exp(-\alpha x_2)\right] \tag{6.5}$$

where η_i is the internal efficiency, defined as the ratio of the number of electron–hole pairs generated in the depletion region volume to the number of photons absorbed in this region. We have used the term current density J_0 as opposed to current I_0, and input optical power flux Φ_0 instead of power P_0. Replacing the equivalent terms in (6.5) will still validate the equation, but more often than not expressions are seen in terms of current and power densities. This avoids the use of device areas in calculations, and makes easier the incorporation of the diffusion current terms derived in the next section. To maximize this current obviously η_i should be large and R should be small. The first point we have already mentioned, and the latter is obtained using a suitable antireflection coating. Two further very important points come out of (6.5): to maximize $J_0(DL)$, x_1 should be small, and the difference $x_2 - x_1$ should be large. This means that the start of the depletion region should be close to the air–semiconductor interface, and the depletion region should be very wide. Only by realizing this latter point were PIN diodes proposed, where the depletion region generated current dominates over the diffusion current. As mentioned in section 6.1.1, this is preferable because depletion region current is not diffusion time limited.

Increasing the reverse bias, under constant illumination, has the effect of increasing the photogenerated current because of the dependence of depletion region width on bias ($w \propto V^{1/2}$ from (2.79)). Thus increasing the value of reverse bias has the effect of increasing the separation $x_2 - x_1$, leading to an increase in current as shown in Figure 6.4. Nevertheless, for a fixed value of bias (6.5) shows that there is a linear dependence of current on input power, a point that has been experimentally verified over many orders of magnitude of current. This is why this part of the $J-V$ characteristic is called the photoconductive mode of operation. J_{sc} (short circuit) and V_{oc} (open circuit) are the crossover points on the current density and applied voltage axes respectively. In the quadrant where J is negative and V is positive the device is a consumer of negative power, i.e. a generator of power. This leads to the familiar term solar cell, with the diode operating in the photovoltaic mode.

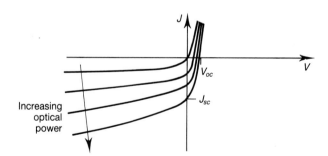

Figure 6.4 The $J-V$ characteristics of a pn junction under various levels of illumination.

6.1.2.3 *Efficiency and responsivity*

Equation (6.5) can be used to define an external efficiency, η_e:

$$\eta_e = \frac{\text{no. of carriers producing current}}{\text{no. of incident photons}} \tag{6.6}$$

$$\eta_e = (1 - R)\,\eta_i\,[\exp(-\alpha x_1) - \exp(-\alpha x_2)]. \tag{6.7}$$

Example 6.2

Calculate the external efficiency for a pn photodiode using the following parameters: absorption coefficient and surface reflectivity as in example 6.1, internal efficiency 0.8, and p and depletion region thicknesses both of 1 μm.

Solution: in (6.7) x_2 becomes 2 μm. So

$$\eta_e = 0.9 \times 0.8 \times \left[\exp\left(-10^6 \times 10^{-6}\right) - \exp\left(-10^6 \times 2 \times 10^{-6}\right) \right]$$
$$= 0.168. \tag{6.8}$$

Clearly pn diodes have a low external efficiency compared to the internal value.

Another figure of merit for a photodiode is its responsivity R_s, defined as the ratio of output current I_0 to input optical power P_0:

$$R_s = \frac{I_0}{P_0} \text{AW}^{-1}. \tag{6.9}$$

A relationship between η_e and R_s can now be found. If η_e is expressed in terms of current and power, then

$$\eta_e = \frac{I_0/e}{P_0/h\nu}. \tag{6.10}$$

Using (6.9) and (6.10)

$$\eta_e = R_s \frac{hc}{e\lambda}. \tag{6.11}$$

Example 6.3

Calculate the responsivity and hence the photocurrent when 5 μW of optical power at a wavelength of 1.55 μm is incident on the device of example 6.2.

Solution: from (6.11)

$$R_s = \frac{e\eta_e\lambda}{hc}$$
$$= \frac{e \times 0.168 \times 1.55 \times 10^{-6}}{hc}$$
$$= 0.210 \text{ A W}^{-1}. \tag{6.12}$$

Using (6.9)

$$I_0 = 0.210 \times 5 \times 10^{-6} = 1.05\,\mu\text{A}. \tag{6.13}$$

It is clear from (6.11) that the responsivity is directly proportional to the wavelength for energies above the band gap. This represents an ideal case, and tells us that even under these situations the output decreases with decreasing wavelength. It is important then to choose the material carefully to tailor the band gap to as close to the detection wavelength as possible, in order to maintain a high output current. In reality the situation is less than ideal, because for instance the absorption coefficient is a function of wavelength, as shown in Figure 5.1.

6.1.2.4 *Diffusion current*

Diffusion current will be generated on both sides of the depletion region; within a diffusion length L_p of x_2 on the n-side, and L_n of x_1 on the p-side respectively. If the device is optimized for absorption in the depletion region, then x_1 is likely to be small. The diffusion term on the p-side is included in (6.20) for completeness, but the analysis here concentrates on the n-side. The minority carrier hole density p on this side is given from the continuity equation (1.63), where in this case an additional term $g(x)$ has been added to represent optical generation of carriers:

$$D_p \frac{\mathrm{d}^2 p}{\mathrm{d}x^2} - \frac{p - p_0}{\tau_p} + g(x) = 0 \tag{6.14}$$

where D_p is the diffusion coefficient, τ_p the hole lifetime and p_0 the equilibrium hole concentration. $g(x)$ is the optical generation term and, using (6.5), is given by

$$g(x) = \frac{\eta_i \Phi_0 (1-R)\alpha}{h\nu}\, \exp(-\alpha x)\,. \tag{6.15}$$

The following boundary conditions apply in order to solve (6.14):

$$
\begin{aligned}
p &= p_0 \ \text{ for } \ x = \infty \\
\text{and} \quad p &= 0 \ \text{ for } \ x = x_2
\end{aligned}
\tag{6.16}
$$

because the semiconductor is in equilibrium well away from the depletion region and minority carriers are extracted at the depletion region edge. The solution is then given by [3]

$$p = p_0 - [p_0 + B\,\exp\left(-\alpha x_2\right)]\exp\left(\frac{x_2 - x}{L_p}\right) + B\,\exp\left(-\alpha x\right) \tag{6.17}$$

where we have used (1.64), and B is given by

$$B = \frac{\eta_i \, \Phi_0 \, (1 - R)}{h\nu D_p} \frac{\alpha^2 L_p^2}{\alpha \left(1 - \alpha^2 L_p^2\right)} . \tag{6.18}$$

The diffusion current density at $x = x_2$ is then calculated by (1.49)

$$J(diff) = -eD_p \frac{\mathrm{d}p}{\mathrm{d}x} \tag{6.19}$$

to give

$$J(diff) = \frac{-e\eta_i \Phi_0 (1 - R)}{h\nu} \frac{\alpha L_p}{1 + \alpha L_p} \exp(-\alpha x_2) - \frac{ep_0 D_p}{L_p} . \tag{6.20}$$

The latter term on the right hand side of (6.20) is the familiar term for saturation current density due to holes in a reverse bias non-illuminated diode, if we compare (2.41) with (2.71). Thus the previous term represents the optical generation of diffusion current.

A similar equation representing current generated on the p-side of the junction would be

$$J(diff) = \frac{-e\eta_i \Phi_0 (1 - R)}{h\nu} \frac{\alpha L_n}{1 + \alpha L_n} \exp\left(-\alpha \left(x_1 - L_n\right)\right) - \frac{en_0 D_n}{L_n} . \tag{6.21}$$

Equations (6.5), (6.20) and (6.21) describe the total optical current plus the reverse bias saturation current. Usually only (6.5) is used, as PIN diodes, which are dominated by depletion region generation, are the device in most common use today. These are discussed in more detail in the next section.

6.2   PIN junction

For any photodetecting device it is important to maximize the light absorption within the material. For a reverse biased diode we have seen from section 6.1.2.2 that maximizing absorption in the depletion region is the most desirable way of increasing device performance. This is done by noting that, from (6.4), the distance x_1 from the light input should be small and the absorption region thickness $x_2 - x_1$ should be large. It is the latter concept that led to the development of the PIN diode. Because the depletion region of a pn junction is very small, usually less than 1 μm, making the depletion region wider is a priority in improving device efficiency. If a region of very lightly doped, called intrinsic, material is placed between the p and n regions the depletion region extends over the whole volume of this part of the device, as in Figure 6.5. From (6.7) the external efficiency is greatly increased, leading to a greater responsivity from (6.11). The first PIN diode was reported in 1962 [4], and was made in germanium. Since then this type of construction has virtually eliminated the standard reverse biased pn junction.

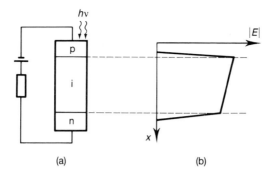

Figure 6.5 (a) The reverse biased PIN junction, and (b) its associated electric field and depletion region.

Example 6.4

Recalculate the external efficiency, responsivity and photocurrent obtained if a PIN diode with an intrinsic region thickness of 50 μm is used in examples 6.2 and 6.3, with all other parameters remaining the same.

Solution: in (6.7), x_2 becomes 51 μm. So

$$\begin{aligned} \eta_e &= 0.9 \times 0.8 \times \left[\exp\left(-10^6 \times 10^{-6}\right) - \exp\left(-10^6 \times 5.1 \times 10^{-5}\right)\right] \\ &= 0.265, \end{aligned} \tag{6.22}$$

giving R_s from (6.11) as

$$\begin{aligned} R_s &= \frac{e \times 0.265 \times 1.55 \times 10^{-6}}{hc} \\ &= 0.331 \text{ A W}^{-1}. \end{aligned} \tag{6.23}$$

Using (6.9)

$$I_0 = 0.331 \times 5 \times 10^{-6} = 1.66\,\mu\text{A}. \tag{6.24}$$

an improvement of 48.6%. The dominant factor in increasing the efficiency further is now the reduction in thickness of the near surface p-region, although this can lead to other effects such as surface state trapping and surface leakage currents.

Because the depletion region is so wide in PIN diodes, typically 10–100 μm, the transit time for carriers to cross the depletion region is a factor to consider in device high frequency response. This is illustrated in Figure 6.6 [5], where increasing the depletion layer width of a silicon PIN diode results in increased absorption efficiency at a given wavelength, at the expense of a fast carrier transit time. Fortunately, the use of intrinsic material ensures the highest possible mobility for a particular type of semiconductor.

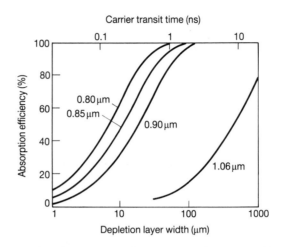

Figure 6.6 The absorption efficiency as a function of both incident wavelength and depletion region width for a silicon PIN diode (©Bellcore: reproduced by kind permission).

6.2.1   Electric field

So far we have considered two aspects of the material that are important for a particular PIN diode:

 (i) The band gap should be, in energy terms, just less than the energy of the incoming photons,
 (ii) the mobility should be as high as possible.

The former we shall return to in the next two sections on homojunction and heterojunction detectors. A high mobility ensures a high carrier drift velocity v from (1.33). This equation is usually only valid over a limited range of E, and past a certain critical value v starts to saturate. This is illustrated with several examples in Figure 6.7. Although the characteristics of each semiconductor are unique, they all tend to show this saturation effect. A well designed PIN diode should then seek to maintain the electric field throughout the depletion region at a value above that of saturation. From Poisson's equation (2.7), dE/dx is a constant in the depletion region, as seen in Figure 6.5. The change in E across the depletion region is then given by

$$\Delta E = \frac{e N_D (x_2 - x_1)}{\epsilon \epsilon_0}. \tag{6.25}$$

Example 6.5

Calculate the value of N_D in a GaAs PIN diode (relative permittivity 13) with an intrinsic region thickness of 10 μm, and a permitted ΔE of 1×10^5 V m^{-1}.

To reach the saturation region an electric field of 5×10^5 V m^{-1} is needed. Calculate the bias voltage.

Solution: from (6.25)

$$\begin{aligned} N_D &= \frac{1 \times 10^5 \times 13 \times \epsilon_0}{10^{-5} \times e} \\ &= 7 \times 10^{12} \, \text{cm}^{-3}. \end{aligned} \tag{6.26}$$

The bias voltage is easily calculated by assuming that it is all dropped across the 10 μm thick intrinsic region. Hence

$$V = 5 \times 10^5 \times 10^{-5} = 5 \, \text{V}. \tag{6.27}$$

6.2.2 Single and binary material

The absorption coefficients of important semiconductors have previously been shown in Figure 5.1. Silicon and germanium, having indirect gaps, do not have as sharp an absorption edge as direct gap GaAs, but germanium has a response range covering all the useful wavelengths for photodetection. It does have a high value of dark current, however, which tends to limit its photoresponse in low light level situations. Each of these materials is now discussed, but before that one point is worth mentioning that applies to all three, and to heterojunction devices as well. Because absorption coefficient increases with decreasing wavelength even after the band gap has been reached, the amount of light being absorbed in the top part of the device, i.e. before it reaches the depletion region, also increases. This has an additional effect in that the extra minority carriers being generated near the surface have a greater chance of being trapped in surface states without contributing to the photocurrent. This is known as surface recombination. Thus external

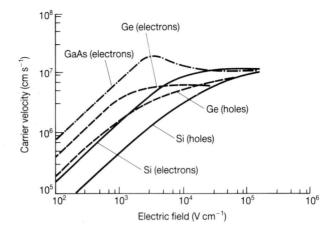

Figure 6.7 Drift velocity vs applied electric field for both electrons and holes in silicon, germanium and gallium arsenide.

efficiency, as defined in (6.7) will decrease with decreasing wavelength, as will responsivity. The addition of this factor to the ideal responsivity of (6.11) gives a real diode case as in Figure 6.8.

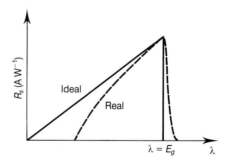

Figure 6.8 The ideal and real characteristics of responsivity as a function of wavelength for a constant incident energy.

Figure 6.9 shows typical efficiencies gained from homojunctions in Si, Ge, InAs and GaSb. It can be seen that these materials more than adequately cover the range of interest in optoelectronic communications, and so there is no volume demand for detectors based on GaAs or InP. Si diodes can be cheaply and reliably made, and their high efficiency at the short wavelength end (0.85 μm) of the fiber optic communication spectrum has made them an automatic choice in this application for many years. At the higher wavelength end, germanium has been a popular choice, with the extended spectral response of GaSb proving useful in some applications. Further gains in this respect are obtained by using InAs. All these latter three materials, however, suffer from a problem of high dark current. As we shall show in section 6.2.2.1, a reduction in dark current is important for an improvement in minimum detectable power.

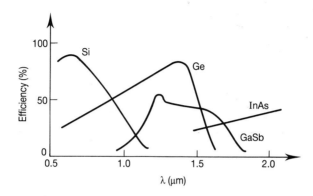

Figure 6.9 Typical efficiencies of homojunction pn photodiodes as a function of wavelength for various materials.

6.2.2.1 Dark current

The ideal diode equation on reverse bias has already been given by (2.71). Also noted in section 2.1.8, however, was that this was over simplified because of two additional factors which contributed to the dark current. These were (i) generation–recombination currents, and (ii) tunnelling currents.

The incorporation of generation–recombination currents led to an expression for reverse bias current density given by (2.76). The interesting point to note from this equation is that the diffusion current is dependent on n_i^2, whereas the generation current was proportional to n_i. This means that the diffusion current will have a much greater dependence on band gap and temperature, via (1.10), than the generation–recombination current. The temperature effect can be seen from Figure 6.10(a) [6]. At low temperatures, J_{gr} dominates and the total reverse current I_R is proportional to the reverse voltage V_R by $I_R \propto V_R^{1/2}$, because the depletion region width is also given by the same dependence. Above 175 °C, however, the current tends to saturate at which point the diffusion current becomes dominant. Figure 6.10(b) shows relative values of dark current, at the same temperature, for the three materials Si, Ge and GaAs.

Tunneling currents are also present in reverse biased diodes, but, because they are only significant at high fields, their discussion is only relevant to avalanche photodiodes (APDs), as will be seen in Chapter 7.

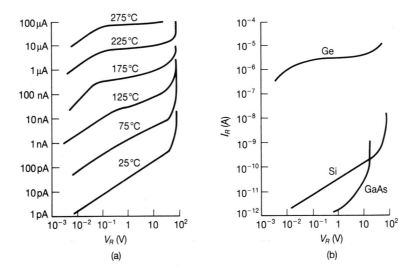

Figure 6.10 The dark current in a reverse biased diode: (a) as a function of temperature for a particular silicon diode, and (b) at a constant temperature for otherwise identical diodes made of different semiconductors (©John Wiley & Sons: reproduced by kind permission).

6.2.2.2 Basic structure

The basic PIN device is shown in Figure 6.11(a). It consists of an n-type substrate, on top of which is grown a lightly doped (intrinsic) layer. SiO_2 is then deposited and patterned to form windows for a subsequent high temperature diffusion of a p-type dopant. The n-region can then be thinned back and metal contacts placed on both the front and back surfaces. The front contact is patterned to allow light into the device, whilst the back is a planar contact. An antireflection coating on the front completes the structure. Typically p-region thicknesses should be very small compared to that of the intrinsic region. This design forms the basis of all single and binary semiconductor devices, although sometimes it is made 'upside down', i.e. p-substrate, intrinsic epitaxy and then n-diffusion.

A side entry structure is shown in Figure 6.11(b). This has the advantage of eliminating the unwanted p-region absorption, minimizing light losses. By placing a reflection coating on the right hand side a large absorption volume is created, which is particularly useful for detecting a wavelength close to the band gap without having to resort to very wide intrinsic regions, and necessarily a high applied voltage to fully deplete it.

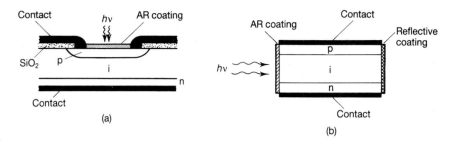

Figure 6.11 Different mechanisms of light admission to a PIN diode: (a) top entry, and (b) side entry.

6.2.3   Ternary, quaternary and heterostructure detectors

As can be seen from Figure 6.9, Si devices adequately cover the short wavelength end of the optical communication spectrum. Germanium is a good choice for the 1.55 μm region. Only GaSb has a peak response in the 1.3 μm region, and even then not a particularly good one. As with lasers and LEDs, the use of lattice matched ternary and quaternary compounds offers the possibility of optimizing a detector for a particular wavelength, and it is 1.3 μm that is of the most interest to us here. Two systems have been proposed for this wavelength, each using a III–V based alloy: InGaAsP and AlGaSb. The former is grown on InP substrates and the latter on GaSb. As noted in Chapters 3 and 4, both materials have been used to make light emitting devices.

$Al_xGa_{1-x}Sb$ is a direct material for $x < 0.2$ as shown in Figure 6.12 [7]. The lattice matching and band gap nature of InGaAsP/InP has been reviewed in section 4.2.5, and the $Al_xGa_{1-x}Sb$ ternary shows only a slight mismatch to GaSb which is not significant. These two systems are reviewed in more detail in sections 6.2.3.2 and 6.2.3.3 but first the advantages of a heterostructure are outlined.

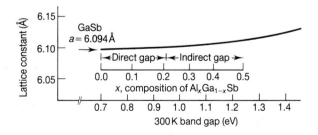

Figure 6.12 The lattice constant and band gap of the ternary $Al_xGa_{1-x}Sb$ range of compounds (©John Wiley & Sons: reproduced by kind permission).

6.2.3.1 Heterostructure PIN diode

A typical example is shown in Figure 6.13(a) [8]. It consists of an intrinsic layer
of $In_{1-x}Ga_xAs$ grown on top of an n-type InP substrate ($x = 0.47$ ensures lattice
matching, and gives a response out to 1.65 μm). A top layer of p-InP completes
the semiconductor part of the structure and the rest is as in Figure 6.11(a). From
Figure 6.13(b), InP is transparent to all wavelengths above 0.92 μm. Thus there
will be no absorption in the p-region, and maximum absorption in the i-region right
up to 1.65 μm. The efficiency will be flat in this wavelength range because of the
lack of near surface absorption. Also, because absorption is in the depletion region
only, no light generated diffusion currents occur, and there is no waiting time for
carriers generated within a diffusion length of the depletion region to diffuse to its
edge. As will be shown in section 6.4.1.4, this absence of diffusion effects produces
a very fast device. Above 1.65 μm the InGaAs becomes transparent, and below
0.92 μm the InP becomes highly absorbing; both result in the efficiency falling
quickly to zero. This type of device is known as a backwall diode.

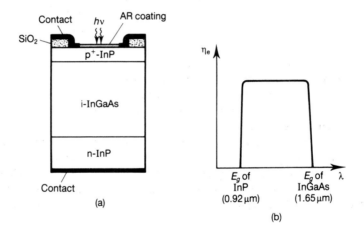

Figure 6.13 An InGaAs/InP PIN diode: (a) structure, and (b) efficiency
characteristics.

The constant efficiency of the device as a function of wavelength in the absorption
range is only true if the depletion region thickness w is much greater than an
absorption length. For narrow depletion region thicknesses, the lower absorption
at longer wavelengths would tend to decrease efficiency in this area. This is clearly
illustrated in Figure 6.14 [9] for two different values of w. For $w = 2.5$ μm, the
efficiency is high and fairly constant, only dropping away significantly at the band
edge. However, for a much thinner depletion region, $w = 0.5$ μm, there is a
clear wavelength dependency, showing that this thickness is not optimized for the
absorption coefficient characteristics of $In_{0.53}Ga_{0.47}As$.

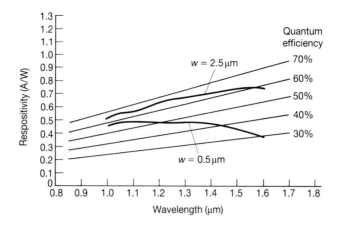

Figure 6.14 The responsivity and quantum efficiency of a photodiode with InGaAs as both p$^+$ and i region (©1987 IEEE: reproduced by kind permission).

6.2.3.2 AlGaAsSb system

Although this system usually contains just AlGaSb, with no arsenic, the latter material is sometimes incorporated to take up some lattice strain. Although the lattice constant mismatch between AlSb and GaSb is small, about 0.65%, it is greater than is found in the AlAs–GaAs system (only 0.13%). For aluminium concentrations of $x > 0.2$ a small amount of arsenic is incorporated ($y < 0.02$) to avoid a significant mismatch. The material is grown on GaSb substrates in a temperature range of 350–500 °C for LPE; the lower temperature produces heavily doped p-type, the high temperature n-type. Additional n- and p-type doping is obtained using tellurium and germanium respectively [10].

The first photodiode made using this material system had a GaSb/AlGaSb heterojunction as in Figure 6.15(a) [11]. The efficiency was high (up to 54%) and constant from 1 to 1.7 µm. By making a PIN structure using AlGaSb as the intrinsic layer a sharp cut off at 1.3 µm can be achieved. The structure is shown in Figure 6.15(b) [12] and the spectal responses of the two devices of Figures 6.15(a) and (b) compared in Figure 6.15(d). Also contained in Figure 6.15(d) is the response of the structure shown in Figure 6.15(c). This latter device is a heterojunction of two different stoichiometries of AlGaAsSb. The reason for investigating this type of structure is the dark current. AlGaAsSb devices show a particularly large, and hence undesirable, value of this parameter, possibly due to leakage currents along unpassivated or reactive surfaces. The structure in Figure 6.15(b) is prone to this problem. The planar structure of Figure 6.15(c), and the guard ring employed to increase the breakdown voltage, reduce the dark current substantially to densities of 25–35 µA cm^{-2}; although these figures are comparable to InGaAs devices, they are much worse that those of InGaAsP. AlGaAsSb, as a material for PIN diodes in the 1–1.6 μm region, has largely been replaced by alloys from the InGaAsP system.

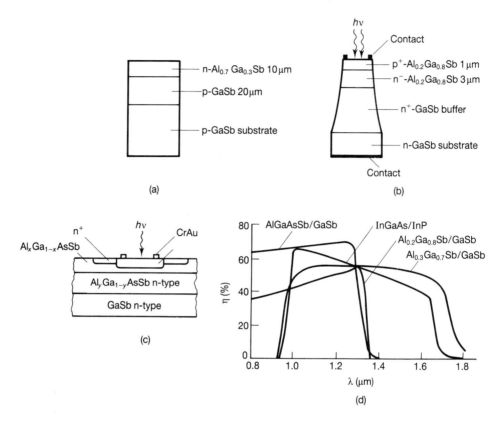

Figure 6.15 The AlGaAsSb photodiode: (a) an AlGaSb/GaSb pn junction, (b) an AlGaSb/GaSb PIN junction, (c) an AlGaAsSb/GaSb PIN junction, and (d) the efficiencies of the various devices (the efficiency of InGaAs/InP is also plotted for comparison).

6.2.3.3 InGaAsP system

The quaternary system of $In_{1-x}Ga_xAs_{1-y}P_y$ can be grown epitaxially, and with perfect lattice matching, on to an InP substrate. All that is needed is an optimization of x, y and the band gap using Figures 4.22 and 4.25. If a ternary material is required, $In_{0.53}Ga_{0.47}As$ is perfectly matched to InP, and has a band gap of 1.65 μm. For this reason, InGaAs is often used to cover all the 1–1.65 μm region, and InGaAsP, with its more difficult fabrication technology, not as widely applied. Besides the added difficulty of fabricating a quaternary rather than a ternary, the growth of phosphorus containing compounds of uniform composition is a problem for all epitaxial techniques. Growth of InGaAs is at a much higher temperature (600–700 °C), using LPE, than for AlGaSb. Doping is straightforward, with Sn for n-type and Zn for p-type being the most commonly used elements.

The first InGaAs detector was reported in early 1978 [13], with InGaAsP devices appearing slighly earlier [14]. However, the efficiency of the first InGaAsP device was low, and high performance devices were not made until after the first InGaAs detector was reported [15]. Figure 6.16(a) compares the efficiencies of these early detectors, and shows how, by varying the stoichiometry of the InGaAsP system, the spectral response can be narrowed or extended. Dark currents even of these early devices were very low (down to 5 μA cm^{-2} for some InGaAsP structures). A heterostructure device was also reported in [15]. This had a In$_{0.69}$Ga$_{0.31}$As$_{0.66}$P$_{0.34}$ i-layer and In$_{0.78}$Ga$_{0.22}$As$_{0.47}$P$_{0.53}$ p-layer, and produced a narrow spectral response centred at 1.36 μm because of the wide band gap ($E_g = 1.22$ μm) nature of the p-layer (Figure 6.16(c)).

Early devices were made using mesa structures, as these were the simplest to fabricate. There are many different ways of forming the junction in this type of structure; Figure 6.17 [16] shows the main techniques based on growth, diffusion or ion implantation. As we shall see later in section 6.6.4, for ease of fabrication of optoelectronic integrated circuits (OEICs) planar devices are far more preferable. Planar structures also have the advantages of reduced dark current due to surface leakage. A typical structure is shown in Figure 6.18(a). Care has to be taken with both the material and mode of deposition of the surface 'passivating' dielectric. The correct choice can result in the surface leakage current densities being as low as a few μA cm^{-2}; the incorrect choice may see leakage currents orders of magnitude higher [17].

Another type of structure has been made in InGaAs devices. We have seen the standard 'top entry' device in many guises, and a 'side entry' system was shown in Figure 6.11(b). If we take the same material structures and redesign the metallization procedures to make the incoming light enter through the substrate (Figure 6.18(b)), then surface recombination effects caused by top entry are removed, and all the light is absorbed within the depletion region.

The design parameters of an InGaAs PIN photodiode are shown in Figure 6.19 [18]. The effect of junction capacitance on the device performance we shall return to in section 6.4.1.3, but the other important factors of depletion region width, applied bias and doping, and their effect on device efficiency, are shown. For instance, if a low voltage device (say < 10 V) is required to operate with a depletion width of 10 μm, the i-layer doping can be no greater than 10^{14} cm^{-3}. The device efficiency will be extremely high (almost 100%), and the capacitance less than 0.1 pF. Such low doping densities are difficult to achieve reproducibly, however, and a more usual compromise will require an increase in doping density, a reduction in depletion region width and hence in efficiency.

Dark currents in InGaAsP systems are obviously a major consideration. Besides the effect of surface passivation mentioned earlier, the other contributions of diffusion, generation–recombination and tunnelling need to be taken into account. It

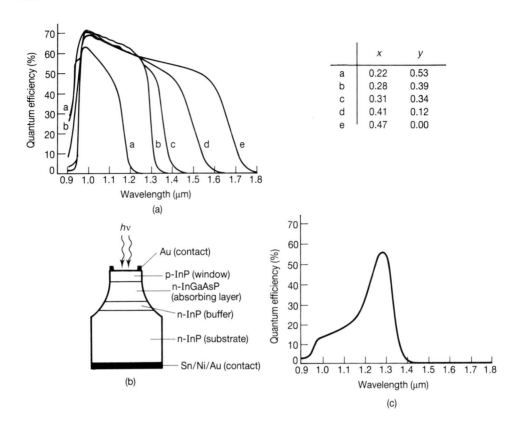

Figure 6.16 The InGaAsP/InP photodiode: (a) external quantum efficiency for five different quaternary compositions, (b) cross-section of a typical device, and (c) a narrow spectral response from an $In_{0.69}Ga_{0.31}As_{0.66}P_{0.34}$ absorbing layer and an $In_{0.78}Ga_{0.22}As_{0.47}P_{0.53}$ window layer ((a) and (c) ©AIP: reproduced by kind permission).

has been shown [19] that it is generation–recombination effects that dominate at low reverse biases, with tunnelling only becoming significant above 100 V. Even the small level of dark current contributed by generation–recombination can be a problem for receiver sensitivity. A way around this is to design a structure where narrow band gap alloys are only used where necessary; elsewhere being wide gap. Equations (1.10) and (2.76) show that generation–recombination currents are band gap dependent, and so a wide gap detector should show significant reductions in leakage current. A device which can reduce these currents by an order of magnitude over a conventional InGaAs diode is shown in Figure 6.20 [20]. It consists of an InGaAs/InP structure with the pn junction, and hence the depletion layer and its associated generation–recombination currents, inside the InP. The optical

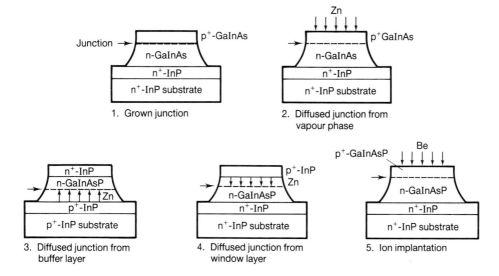

Figure 6.17 Schematics of mesa type photodiodes with the pn junction formed by various methods (©T P Pearsall: reproduced by kind permission).

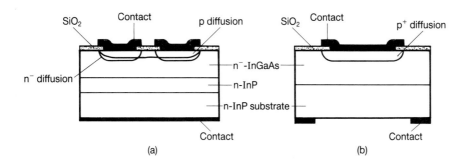

Figure 6.18 Two different planar structures in InGaAs photodiodes: (a) top or side entry, and (b) substrate entry.

absorption region is the p-InGaAs. The p-InP region is to ensure that the InGaAs and heterojunction are contained in a region of zero field so that the depletion region is all in the wide gap InP. Heavy doping of the InGaAs ensures a small contribution from this side to the diffusion current, further improving the reverse characteristics.

Double heterostructures, to further reduce the diffusion current, have been employed [21]. An example is shown in Figure 6.21, where the use of graded band

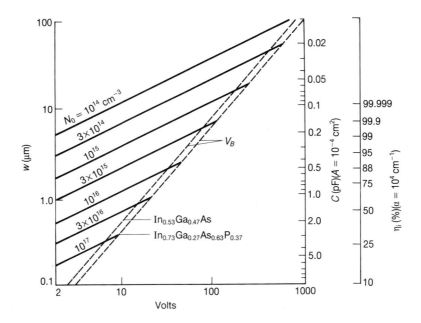

Figure 6.19 Capacitance (C), depletion region width (w) and internal efficiency (η_i) vs applied voltage (V) and doping density (N_D) of two In-GaAsP photodiodes. Breakdown voltage V_B is shown by the dashed lines (©1981 IEEE: reproduced by kind permission).

gap superlattices reduces carrier trapping effects. Response times, to be discussed in section 6.4, are thus extremely fast.

6.2.3.4   Long wavelength detectors

In this section the term 'long wavelength' is used to denote the region well beyond 1.55 μm, where fiber-based communication systems currently in use do not operate. Here we will be looking at detectors in the mid and far infra-red regions, with wavelengths in the range 2–14 μm. The shorter end of this spectrum is of research interest to optical communications. Glasses based on zirconium fluoride are being developed which have much lower losses at 2.55 μm than silica fibers at 1.55 μm, largely because of the dependence of Rayleigh scattering. The binary semiconductor InAs, with a band gap of 3.44 μm (0.36 eV) can be used as a detector in this wavelength range. However, as we have seen previously, optimum detector performance is obtained when the band gap is at the detection wavelength. A quick look at the energy gap vs composition diagram (Figure 4.25) shows that a material based on InGaAs would be suitable; unfortunately it also shows that for the optimum composition $(In_{0.82}Ga_{0.18}As)$ there is no lattice matched substrate. A

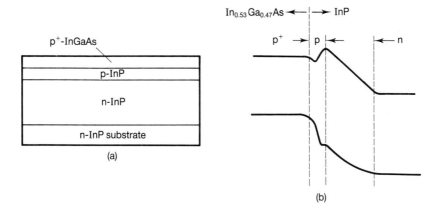

Figure 6.20 A low dark current photodiode: (a) cross-section, and (b) band diagram.

substrate of InP has been used to fabricate such a detector, with a grading layer (varying x in $In_{1-x}Ga_xAs$ from 0 at the InP interface to 0.18 at the $In_{0.82}Ga_{0.18}As$ interface) to take up the strain [22].

For even longer wavelengths, the interest is in free space optical communication. There are two windows in the atmosphere's absorption spectrum, corresponding approximately to 3–5 μm and 8–14 μm. Detectors (and sources) for these wavelengths open up many applications besides communication: infra-red imaging, pollution monitoring and range finding are but a few. Up until recently, II–VI material based around the $Hg_xCd_{1-x}Te$ system had a virtual monopoly in this area. Although other materials such as InSb, PbTe, etc. could be used, the HgCdTe system has the tremendous flexibility of being wavelength tunable from CdTe at 770 nm (1.6 eV) to HgTe which is a semimetallic compound with a 'negative band gap' of 0.3 eV. The bandgap of the alloy $Hg_xCd_{1-x}Te$ is zero at $x = 0.85$ and is nearly linear over the range $x = 0$ to 0.85. It could then be used in the near infra-red ($\sim$ 1 μm) range, but other more established Si, Ge and III–V detectors ensure that it is not competitive in this region. However, over the 3–5 μm and 8–14 μm region it has been used extensively. The main difficulty is in fabricating devices: both material preparation and device technology are very undeveloped compared to III–V devices. Material growth problems are primarily due to the high vapour pressure of mercury, which makes solution grown techniques based on LPE very difficult. More advanced methods such as MBE and MOVPE are more reliable, but are not without their problems and considerably more expensive. Doping is difficult and only predictable within an order of magnitude, and device metallization and etching are other problems. Although some progress is now being made in dry etching of HgCdTe, it is still immature compared to III–Vs, and is unlikely ever to reach the same level of predictability. The etching is also known to inter-

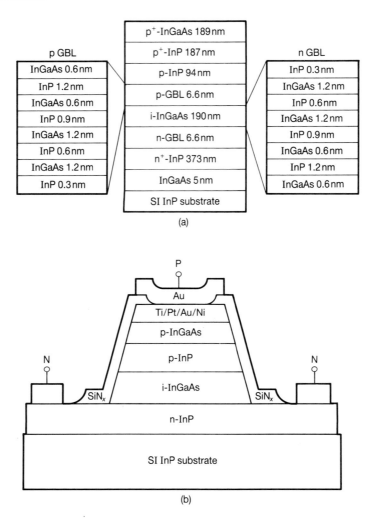

Figure 6.21 A graded DH InGaAs/InP photodiode: (a) graded band gap layer (GBL) detail, and (b) device cross-section (©AIP: reproduced by kind permission).

fere with the device itself, often causing type conversion by some as yet unknown mechanism. Although this can be put to an advantage by creating pn junctions and subsequently detectors, the lack of understanding of the process does not lend itself to exploitation by device engineers. In addition, because of the narrow band gap of HgCdTe alloys in the infra-red regions the devices often have to be cooled to give noise-free operation, and room temperature can be enough to destroy the device by allowing mercury outdiffusion or precipitation.

All of these problems were acknowledged in the development of long wavelength detectors simply because there was no other alternative with the required flexibility to HgCdTe. However, AlGaAs compounds have now begun to be used in this region, but obviously not using a direct band to band transition. The devices here used the multiple quantum well structures discussed in the context of semiconductor lasers in section 4.5. The mechanism is discussed in detail in [23], and is shown in Figure 6.22. Figure 6.22(a) shows the band structure of an AlGaAs/GaAs superlattice with only two confined states. For a bias per well larger than the ground state bandwidth, tunnelling through the ground state is not possible. The structure then separates into a low field region on the left hand side of Figure 6.22(a), and a high field region on the right hand side. When this happens the process of sequential resonant tunnelling allows electron movement from the ground state of one well into the localized excited state of a neighbouring well. This is illustrated in Figures 6.22(c) and (d) [24]. Figure 6.22(c) shows tunnelling from the level E_1 (ground state) of one well to E_2 (first excited state) of the adjacent well. Non-radiative relaxation to the ground state in this well occurs before the electron tunnels to the next well. As in Figure 6.22(d) tunnelling can also occur between a ground state and a second excited state for a sufficiently high field. Because this process only occurs for certain values of energy level differences it is a resonant effect. Resonant tunnelling devices have also been made in many forms as purely electrical devices.

Here, device operation as a photodetector can be seen using Figure 6.22(b). Incoming light that is resonant with the transition $E_2 - E_1$, which happens to be in the infra-red, excites an electron from a doped ground state to the excited state where it can tunnel out of the well through the thin top of the barrier. This photogenerated electron can travel a mean free path L before being recaptured by a well, and hence generates a photocurrent. The first device detected radiation at 10.8 μm with a good responsivity (0.52 A W^{-1}) and a high response speed of 30 ps [23]. Broadband operation over the 8–12 μm region has been demonstrated with subsequent devices [25]. Using the same basic approach, multiple quantum well detectors have also been made in InGaAs/InAlAs [26] and InGaAs/InP [27] structures, with peak detection wavelengths of 4 μm and 8 μm respectively. Tunable detectors have also been made by exploiting the quantum confined Stark effect [28]. By grading the composition of AlGaAs in an AlGaAs/GaAs single quantum well detector, an applied voltage tunability of 0.25 meV/kV cm^{-1} has been obtained, with a peak responsivity at 5.3 μm.

6.3   Schottky barrier photodiodes

Up until this point all the photodiodes we have considered have been based around a pn junction. As detailed in section 2.2.1 metal–semiconductor junctions have some properties similar to pn structures. Although the current mechanisms involved, and

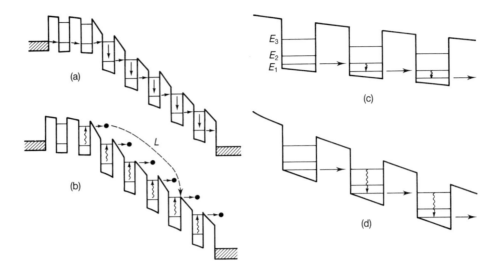

Figure 6.22 Sequential resonant tunnelling. (a) High field domain (right hand side) and through the ground state (left hand side). (b) Photoconductivity produced by absorption of intersubband radiation followed by tunnelling out of well. (c) Tunnelling for a potential drop across the superlattice period equal to the energy difference between the first excited state and the ground state of the wells. (d) As for (c), except that the energy difference is between the second excited state and the ground state (©AIP: reproduced by kind permission).

hence the current constant J_s, are quite different between the two types of junction, for the rectifying metal–semiconductor contact (the Schottky barrier contact) the J–V characteristics follow that of the pn junction, i.e. exponential dependence of J on V for forward bias, and a near constant value of J on reverse bias. In this section we will see how the Schottky barrier diode can be used as a photodetector.

6.3.1 Principle of operation

As the wavelength decreases from the band gap, the absorption coefficient of the material in a pn or PIN diode increases, as in Figure 5.1. More light is then absorbed in the near surface region with the resultant photogenerated carriers recombining before they can cross the depletion region and cause a photocurrent. This results in a decrease in both responsivity (Figure 6.8) and quantum efficiency (Figure 6.9) at wavelengths lower than the band gap. If no suitable device exists, the detection of radiation well away from the band gap may result in so much surface absorption that the device efficiency is very low; for instance, below 0.5 μm this will certainly be the case in a silicon detector. If a metal replaces the p-semiconductor, this surface photogeneration–recombination will not take place, leaving the light to be absorbed in the metal–semiconductor depletion region. Of course, the introduction of a metal brings its own disadvantages; metal films are characterized by high reflectivity and low transmission in the visible part of the spectrum. By making the metal very thin (200 Å or less) and coating with an antireflection dielectric the device can be made to be highly transmitting [29]. The basic structure is shown in Figure 6.23(a). Contact to the Schottky metal is either made through a hole in the antireflection coating or, as shown here, via a large pad adjacent to the contact and isolated from the semiconductor. Gold is often used as the contact metal, though the use of transparent materials such as indium tin oxide (ITO) allows much more light to pass through. Surface damage of the semiconductor can sometimes happen as a result of deposition of this material, however, and junction formation is not as reliable and predictable as for standard metallizations. Great care needs to be taken to match the thicknesses of the metal and anti-reflection coating, as these form two coupled dielectrics on top of a third (the semiconductor) for light transmission purposes. Calculations on this phenomenon have been performed, and two examples are shown in Figure 6.23(b). It can be seen that the transmittance as a function of gold thickness is very different for the three cases, although all show high transmission for thin gold layers and virtually no transmission beyond 1000 Å.

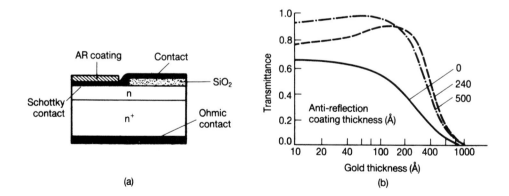

Figure 6.23 (a) Cross-section of a Schottky photodiode. (b) Transmittance of a thin gold film with various antireflection coatings.

At the long wavelength end of the spectrum, Schottky photodiodes do not find any particular advantages until a wavelength of several μm has been reached. Small area W–GaAs diodes have been used to detect 0.1–1 mm radiation, and point contact structures based on W–Ge have been used at a somewhat shorter 10 μm wavelength [30]. The use of Schottky contacts has been otherwise fairly limited however, because, apart from the two extremes of high and low wavelength, the pn and PIN junction detectors offer a better performance. Even at the long (i.e. several μm) end, detectors using only semiconductors are well established with extensively studied, if not extensively understood, growth and fabrication procedures.

6.3.2   Metal–semiconductor–metal structures

A metal–semiconductor–metal (MSM) photodetector is an essentially planar structure, and has the two metal contacts on the 'top' of the device; this is in contrast to the normal Schottky photodiode which has a 'top' and a 'bottom' metal contact. The structure of an MSM diode is shown in Figure 6.24. An undoped layer of, in this case, GaAs is grown by epitaxial techniques on top of a semi-insulating substrate. The undoped layer will typically be 3 μm thick. Schottky metal contacts are then made to the undoped GaAs in an interdigitated fashion. The device then represents two diodes in series, one forward biased and the other reverse biased. The device should be biased to give complete depletion of the GaAs epitaxial layer, in order to maximize both the absorption volume and the response characteristics. The size, spacing and number of fingers should also aim to give complete depletion, but too large a contact area for the metallization will give insufficient light sensitive area for the MSM diode. Typical metallizations occupy 25–50% of the available surface area.

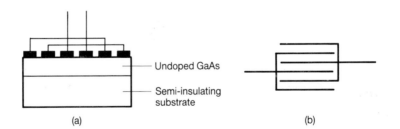

Undoped GaAs

Semi-insulating
substrate

(a)   (b)

Figure 6.24 An MSM diode: (a) cross-section, and (b) top view.

The MSM diode has several advantages over the standard Schottky photodiode. First, because the structure, and in particular the metallization, is planar the fabrication is simple and leads to high yields. The parasitic capacitances between contacts are much smaller than for a vertical diode of the same active area because only half of the spacing between the contacts is filled with the semiconductor; there is then the equivalent of two capacitances in parallel, one with an air dielectric and the other with a semiconductor dielectric. The net effect is to reduce the overall capacitance, leading to a fast device. Speed is further increased by the spacings between the fingers being smaller than for a vertical diode, giving short carrier transit times.

MSM diodes, also called DSI (double Schottky interdigitated) diodes, were, like most optoelectronic devices, made on GaAs [31]. For long wavelength detectors, the use of InGaAs as the semiconductor presents a problem; the very low Schottky barrier height on this material (0.2 eV as opposed to 0.7–0.8 eV for GaAs) gives a very large value of dark current. The way around this problem is to have a barrier enhancement layer between the metal and semiconductor, as shown in Figure 6.25 [32]. Here the use of a large band gap AlInAs layer followed by a superlattice of AlInAs/InGaAs gives a device of high barrier height and hence low dark current. These structures have been made lattice matched to InP substrates, but non-lattice matched InGaAs devices on GaAs substrates have also been fabricated [33]. The resultant structure is more involved because of the need for buffer layers to take up the strain caused by mismatch, but GaAs substrates are cheaper, and also provide for easier integration with amplifiers. This ease of integration has been demonstrated using GaAs based MSM diodes, initially with a diode/FET amplifier combination [34] and later using the same structure to give a four-channel optical receiver array [35]. The essentially planar structure of these devices leads to very low stray capacitances and a straightforward fabrication procedure. We shall return to integration in section 6.6.3 on PINFETs, where the MSM diode is replaced by a PIN device.

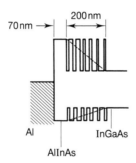

Figure 6.25 Cross-section of an InGaAs MSM photodiode incorporating a AlInAs/InGaAs graded superlattice (©AIP: reproduced by kind permission).

In addition to the integration with electronics, MSM diodes have also been integrated optically with waveguides. Such a device is shown in Figure 6.26 [36]. By coupling the light into the side of the detector, near complete absorption is obtained without the need for a very thick active region. Besides being more difficult to grow, thick regions are also unlikely to be fully depleted and hence have a slow response. This butt-coupling approach has also been used for other types of detectors, notably PIN diodes.

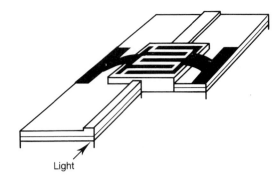

Light

Figure 6.26 An integrated waveguide/MSM photodetector (©AIP: reproduced by kind permission).

6.4   Frequency response

This section considers the limitations placed on the response of a PIN diode by the physical and electrical characteristics of the system, and notes the trade-offs to be made between high speed response and other factors.

6.4.1   Equivalent circuit

Consider Figure 6.27(a), which shows the physical phenomena involved in PIN diode photodetection. Light enters the device through the p-layer, which is sufficiently thin so as not to cause significant absorption away from the depletion region. Electron–hole pairs are generated in the depletion region, or within a diffusion length of its edges, and are separated by the reverse biased electric field. This gives a current flow that is measured in an external circuit. A simple external circuit is as in Figure 6.27(b), with the equivalent circuit of the whole system as in Figure 6.27(c). The photodiode is a current generator with a parallel (and high value) junction resistor R_j and capacitor C_j, and a series (low value) bulk resistance R_B. Because of the relative values of the resistances ($R_j \gg R_L > R_B$) and their position in the circuit all but R_L can usually be neglected (amplifier impedances are considered in section 6.5).

There are three factors which have an influence on the frequency response of the detector:

(i)   the drift time of carriers through the depletion region,
(ii) the RC time constant of the equivalent circuit,
(iii) the diffusion time of carriers generated outside the depletion region in reaching the edge of this part of the device.

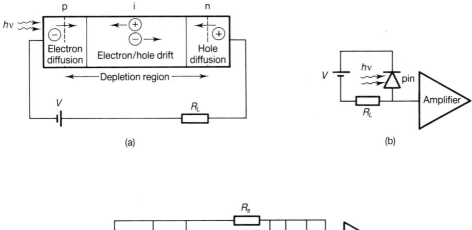

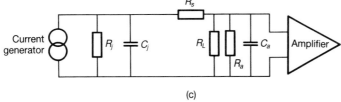

Figure 6.27 The PIN photodiode receiver: (a) optical generation of current, (b) simple amplifier circuit, and (c) equivalent circuit of the receiver.

Each of these factors is now considered in more detail.

6.4.1.1 Drift time

Also known as the charge collection time, t_c is related to the physical characteristics of the device by the simple expression

$$t_c = \frac{w}{v} \qquad (6.28)$$

where w is the depletion region width and v is the carrier saturation velocity if the device is biased to operate in the saturated part of the velocity–field characteristic. The value of t_c represents the maximum time taken to cross the depletion region, and hence leads to a low value of the maximum frequency response; other authors take the average time to cross the depletion region, which is given by $t_c = w/2v$. In terms of measurable components (6.28) becomes

$$t_c = \frac{w^2}{\mu V} \qquad (6.29)$$

where μ is the carrier mobility and V is the applied bias. Generally μ (direct gap) $> \mu$ (indirect gap), and so t_c (direct) $< t_c$ (indirect), leading to a faster device for direct gap materials.

6.4.1.2 Diffusion time

For photodiodes constructed so that the top p region is very thin, and biased such that it is fully depleted, the diffusion time t_d is not important. However, for weakly absorbing structures, or those with thick p-regions (i.e. whenever the diffusion length is less than the absorption depth) the diffusion time needs to be considered. The value of t_d can be found from the following expressions [37]:

$$\text{p–on–n} \quad t_d = \frac{1}{13} \left(\frac{3}{\alpha} - 0.54 \rho_n^{1/2} \left(V_{bi} + V \right)^{1/2} \times 10^{-4} \right)^2 \qquad (6.30)$$

$$\text{and n–on–p} \quad t_d = \frac{1}{36.4} \left(\frac{3}{\alpha} - 0.32 \rho_p^{1/2} \left(V_{bi} + V \right)^{1/2} \times 10^{-4} \right)^2 \qquad (6.31)$$

where α is the absorption coefficient in cm^{-1}, ρ_n and ρ_p are respectively the n- and p-type resistivities in $\Omega\,\text{cm}$, and V_{bi} is the junction built-in potential.

6.4.1.3 RC time constant

This time t_{RC} is the time taken to discharge the junction capacitance C_j through the load resistance R_L. Taking this as the time taken to discharge from 90% of a maximum value V_0 to 10% of V_0, then from the standard expression for an *RC* system ($V = V_0 \exp(-t/RC)$)

$$t_{RC} = 2.2 R_L C_j . \qquad (6.32)$$

As already mentioned, only R_L is included here from the different resistance sources. If the junction capacitance C_j is small, then other parasitic elements such as packaging and external wiring capacitances need to be included in (6.32).

Example 6.6

Calculate the values of the three elements affecting diode response time using the following parameters: the material is grown p-on-n, p-region resistivity 0.012 $\Omega\,\text{cm}$, material absorption coefficient 10^4 cm^{-1}, intrinsic region thickness and mobility 50 μm and 4000 cm^2/Vs respectively, applied bias 15 V, junction potential 0.6 V, load resistance 250 Ω and junction capacitance 1.5 pF.

Solution: from (6.29)

$$t_c = \frac{\left(50 \times 10^{-4} \right)^2}{4000 \times 15} = 4.17 \times 10^{-10}\,\text{s}. \qquad (6.33)$$

The diffusion time t_d is given by (6.30)

$$\begin{aligned} t_d &= \frac{1}{13} \left(\frac{3}{10^4} - 0.54 \times 0.012^{1/2} \times (0.6 + 15)^{1/2} \times 10^{-4} \right)^2 \\ &= 5.87 \times 10^{-9}\,\text{s}. \end{aligned} \qquad (6.34)$$

Finally the time associated with discharging the load resistance through the device capacitance t_{RC} is given from (6.32)

$$t_{RC} = 2.2 \times 250 \times 1.5 \times 10^{-12} = 8.25 \times 10^{-10} \text{ s.} \tag{6.35}$$

6.4.1.4 Response time and bandwidth

Combining the three times t_c, t_{RC} and t_d in one response, t, gives, to a good approximation [37]

$$t = \left(t_c^2 + t_d^2 + t_{RC}^2\right)^{1/2} . \tag{6.36}$$

Obviously t needs to be minimized by the choice of material, dimensions and applied bias. Because t_d has a very high value, the device is usually designed to eliminate the diffusion component. This will make the rise and fall characteristics of a photodetector symmetrical, as shown in Figure 6.28(a), in response to a step input of optical radiation: the rise time t_r equals the fall time t_f ($t_r = t_f = t$). The shape of the response is because the absorption of light in the material is an exponentially decaying function of distance. If the absorption rate was uniform within the depletion region, the rise and fall edges would be linear. If absorption was at one or other edge of the depletion region only, the rise and fall edges would be vertical. However, if the device is not fully depleted, as might happen for instance at low bias levels, the response from the slowly diffusing carriers leads to a very long rise time, as shown in Figure 6.28(b).

If we assume that the diffusion time t_d has been eliminated, then we now notice that the charge collection time t_c is determined by the saturated velocity of the slowest carrier, whereas for a photoconductor, as we saw in section 5.1.2, a transit-time limited device is constrained by the peak velocity of the fastest carrier. For a material such as silicon, where the saturated and peak velocities of both electrons and holes are similar, this distinction is unimportant. However it is very important for III–V materials, where the velocity-field characteristics usually give a peak electron velocity substantially greater than the high field saturated velocity, and where electrons have a velocity 2–3 times greater than that of holes.

In practice a PIN diode is usually response limited by the third factor, the RC time constant, and it is in the optimization of this parameter that trade-offs against other factors need to be considered. For an efficient device we have already seen that the depletion width needs to be as great as possible, certainly such that $w > 1/\alpha$. Because capacitance C_j is inversely proportional to w, this will result in a low value of C_j. The response to an input pulse will then be dominated by the charge collection time, t_c, and will be symmetric as shown in Figure 6.28(a). For a given material, a large surface area will give more collected light, but a greater

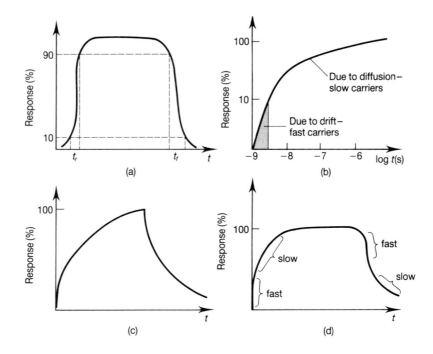

Figure 6.28 The response of a PIN diode photoreceiver: (a) no diffusion, (b) diffusion extending the rise time, (c) RC limited, and (d) rise and fall of diffusion limited device.

dark current and a larger capacitance C_j. The response will then be RC limited, and will appear as in Figure 6.28(c).

If the depletion region is narrow, such that $w < 1/\alpha$, the diffusion components become important. Figure 6.28(b) for the rise time then becomes Figure 6.28(d) for the complete response, as a slowly decaying tail on the end of the fast response component is a result of photogenerated carriers diffusing to the depletion region edge. Also, if w is too thin the capacitance will become large and RC effects again will dominate. Any electrical system giving an output voltage V as a function of signal frequency f is governed by a simple relationship from electrical circuit analysis:

$$V_{out} = \frac{V_{DC}}{\sqrt{1 + 4\pi f^2 R^2 C^2}} \tag{6.37}$$

where $V_{DC} = V_{out}$ when $f=0$. The half power (3 dB) point is when $V = V_{DC}/2$, and is given by

$$B = \frac{1}{2\pi RC} \tag{6.38}$$

where B is the bandwidth. If the device is dominated by RC effects, then substituting RC with $R_L C_j$, and comparing (6.32) and (6.38) gives

$$t = t_{RC} = \frac{0.35}{B} \, . \tag{6.39}$$

If the diffusion or drift effects dominate, substitution of either (6.30), (6.31) or (6.29) for t_d or t_c in place of RC in (6.38) will give a value for the bandwidth. If factors have to be combined, then (6.36) should also be used.

Example 6.7

Assuming the diffusion component of example 6.6 has been eliminated by device design, calculate the bandwidth of the photodiode.

Solution: in this case (6.36) should be used to calculate the response time in terms of just t_c and t_{RC}. Hence

$$t = \left(t_c^2 + t_{RC}^2\right)^{1/2} = 9.2 \times 10^{-10} \text{ s.} \tag{6.40}$$

This result can now be put into (6.39) to give the bandwidth:

$$B = \frac{0.35}{9.2 \times 10^{-10}} \simeq 3.8 \times 10^8 \text{ s}^{-1}. \tag{6.41}$$

The bandwidth B is then $\simeq 380$ Mb s^{-1}.

6.5   Detection circuitry and noise

In section 5.2 we introduced a basic photoreceiver circuit, the problems of noise, sensitivity and minimum detectable signal. All the various noise sources and their relative importance were discussed. Errors, in terms of a bit error rate (BER) and the quantum limit of detection, were also introduced. All those principles are equally valid both here and in the next chapter on avalanche diodes; the major difference is obviously that the current generator in this case is a diode without gain as opposed to a resistor with a gain mechanism; amplification and associated circuitry is then different and the relative importance of the noise terms are also dissimilar from the photoconductor. We start this section by looking at some of the various photoreceiver circuit implementations when using PIN diodes.

6.5.1   Receiver design

There are three basic types of 'front end' to an optical receiver using a PIN diode: low impedance, high impedance and transimpedance. These are shown schematically in Figure 6.29. We saw in section 5.2.2.1 how impedance (in this case in the form of a pure resistance) affected the noise generated by a receiver; a low impedance generates a lot of thermal noise (equation (5.23)). However, in the last section (6.38) told us that for a high bandwidth the impedance should be kept to a minimum. The choice of impedance is then a compromise between bandwidth and noise sensitivity.

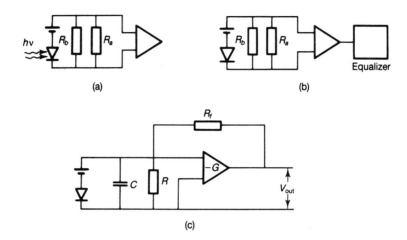

Figure 6.29 Three front ends of a photoreceiver: (a) low impedance, (b) high impedance, and (c) transimpedance.

A low impedance design is shown in Figure 6.29(a), and is similar to that of the photoconductor receiver in Figure 5.7. The PIN diode here is loaded with a bias resistor R_b before the amplifier input resistance R_a, giving a load resistance R_L equivalent to R_a and R_b in parallel. If R_a and R_b are low, then R_L is low giving a low input impedance. The signal is readily amplified and requires no equalization, but the output does need to be filtered to regenerate the original pulse shape. The resultant noise penalty of this design makes it unsuitable for low light level situations, such as where the distance between repeater stations in a communication system is very large.

If noise is the major consideration, a system with a low input capacitance in conjunction with a low dark current detector should be used. A high value of R_L can then be used to minimize the thermal noise current. Because the capacitance is now dominant, the signal current is integrated over a large time constant (hence the alternative name for a high impedance front end: integrating front end). A post-amplification equalizer (differentiator) must then be used (Figure 6.29(b)). Equalization in this type of system is not a simple problem, as first of all the zero position of the equalizer needs to be calibrated to compensate for the zero of the input admittance. This will depend on the individual device as well as C and R_L. The precision with which equalization must be achieved also depends on the proportion of the signal spectrum near the equalizer's cut-in frequency. The low dynamic range (ratio of maximum to minimum input currents) is another drawback; this happens because the charge on the input capacitance can build up over a duration of time slots. High input signals can then saturate the amplifier, leading to a heavy distortion of the output signal. The dynamic range of the system is then dependent on the input capacitance and the equalizer design.

A third approach, the transimpedance amplifier, is shown in Figure 6.29(c). It is also called a shunt feedback amplifier, and its basic function is to act as a current-to-voltage converter. Its advantage over the high impedance design is that within the bandwidth limitations given by [38]

$$B \leq \frac{G}{2\pi R_f C} \tag{6.42}$$

where G is the amplifier gain, no output equalization is needed. Also apparent from (6.42), when compared with (6.38) for a non-transimpedance design, is the greater bandwidth available. The design allows a greater dynamic range than a high impedance amplifier, because in the transimpedance design the low frequency components are amplified by the closed loop gain, instead of the open loop as in other amplifiers. The improvement in dynamic range is then given by the ratio of closed to open loop gains. It can be shown [39] that when $R_f \ll R_L$, the major source of noise is thermally generated in R_f, which can be minimized by making R_f large. Unfortunately, too high a value of R_f will make the closed loop amplifier unstable, and will also reduce the bandwidth from (6.42). In practice, the chief disadvantage of the transimpedance design is one of compromising noise performance against amplifier stability.

Irrespective of the receiver design, the choice of any particular amplifier is important. The importance of amplifier noise, particularly FET channel noise, was discussed in section 5.2.2.5 and shown in Figure 5.8. The salient conclusions of this section were that the channel noise becomes important only at high bit rates, it has a cubic dependency on bandwidth (square dependency for bipolar amplifiers) and GaAs FETs offer a superior performance to Si FETs. An illustrative example of receiver sensitivity for particular bit rates is shown in Figure 6.30 [40].

6.5.2 Importance of noise terms

All the separate noise terms were discussed in section 5.2.2, and relevant expressions were derived for each source. For a PIN diode, the main sources of noise are dark current noise and quantum noise, which can both be regarded as photocurrent

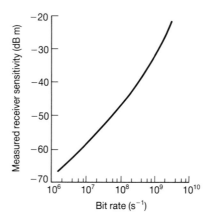

Figure 6.30 Receiver sensitivity as a function of bit rate (ⒸAcademic Press, Inc.: reproduced by kind permission).

shot noise, and Johnson noise generated within the load resistor R_L. The shot and Johnson noise currents i_s and i_j are given from (5.31) and (5.42) by

$$\langle i_s^2 \rangle = 2eB\,(I_0 + I_d + I_G) \tag{6.43}$$

$$\text{and} \quad \langle i_j^2 \rangle = \frac{4kTB}{R} \tag{6.44}$$

where I_0 is the photocurrent, I_d the dark current, I_G the amplifier gate leakage current and B the bandwidth. If the diode is illuminated with continuous light, the term I_0 is important; however, if the incoming light signal is at a high frequency the time averaged value of I_0 is often small and is sometimes neglected. Unlike the usual case of a photoconductor, for a PIN diode there is a noise current i_{amp} associated with the amplifier. This is a combination of various elements associated with the amplifier, and can be represented as a series voltage noise source $\langle v_a^2 \rangle$ and a parallel current noise source $\langle i_a^2 \rangle$. Combining these gives

$$\langle i_{amp}^2 \rangle = \int_0^B \left(\langle i_a^2 \rangle + \langle v_a^2 \rangle\, |Y|^2 \right)\, \mathrm{d}f \tag{6.45}$$

where we use the integration of f because we can no longer assume that i_a and v_a are independent of frequency f (Y is the shunt admittance). The power signal to noise ratio $(S/N)_p$ is found in exactly the same way as for the photoconductor:

$$\left(\frac{S}{N} \right)_p = \frac{I_0^2}{(\text{total noise current})^2}. \tag{6.46}$$

Incorporation of the noise terms gives

$$\left(\frac{S}{N} \right)_p = \frac{I_0^2}{2eB\,(I_0 + I_d + I_G) + 4kTB/R_L + \langle i_{amp}^2 \rangle}. \tag{6.47}$$

Often the noise current for an amplifier has been measured and referred to a load resistor value, enabling the noise figure F_n of the amplifier to be incorporated with the Johnson noise term. This gives a simplified form of (6.47)

$$\left(\frac{S}{N}\right)_p = \frac{I_0^2}{2eB\left(I_0 + I_d + I_G\right) + 4kTBF_n/R_L} \,. \tag{6.48}$$

The noise equivalent power (NEP), i.e. the value of optical input power necessary to make either side of (6.48) equal to unity, can be found by substituting P_0 from (6.10) into (6.48). The detectivity $D\ (= 1/NEP)$, and specific detectivity D^*, can also be found (section 5.2.3).

Figure 6.31(a) [41] is the PIN receiver equivalent of Figure 5.8(a) for a photo-conductor, i.e. the relative importance of noise currents as a function of bit rate (i_n is the total noise current). Also shown is the sensitivity in terms of the device efficiency η_i and the mean incident optical power $\overline{P}$. It can be seen that the dominant contributor to i_n is the noise current i_{amp} due to the amplifier. At very low bit rates shot noise is important, and at higher bit rates Johnson noise and flicker noise currents i_f have greater prominence (discussed in section 5.2.2.3). Besides the previously mentioned cubic dependence of amplifier noise on bit rate, it can also be shown [41] that the amplifier noise is given by

$$\langle i_{amp}^2 \rangle = H_1 B + H_2 \frac{C_T^2}{g_m} B^3 \tag{6.49}$$

where H_1 and H_2 are constants for a given device and temperature, g_m is the mutual transconductance of the amplifier and C_T is the total input capacitance given by

$$C_T = C_j + C_{GS} + C_{GD} + C_S \tag{6.50}$$

with C_{GS} and C_{GD} being the gate–source and gate–drain capacitances of the amplifier respectively, and C_S the stray capacitances due to packaging and wire bonding. As it is the amplifier noise that dominates at all but low bit rates, the use of short gate length GaAs MESFETs ($g_m \propto 1/$gate length, and g_m of GaAs MESFET $> g_m$ of equivalent Si MOSFET) has enabled low noise currents to be achieved. Even so, a comparison of Figures 5.8(a) and 6.31(a) will show that photoconductors have a lower noise current, and hence a higher sensitivity.

The reduction of the capacitance terms associated with C_T has been a major factor in pin-receiver development over the last few years. Some reductions are easily achieved, such as lowering C_j by employing a smaller area device, but there are obviously physical limits to what can be achieved in this way. A lot of attention has focused on the stray capacitance elements, and it is the desire to reduce the effect of these that has driven the development of hybrid and then integrated PINFET receivers. An illustration of how a reduction in total capacitance C_T can lead to greater sensitivity of a pin-receiver is shown in Figure 6.31(b) [41].

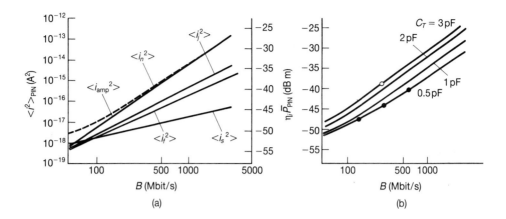

Figure 6.31 (a) Noise current components as a function of bit rate in a PIN receiver. (b) Receiver sensitivity as a function of total capacitance C_T and bit rate (©Academic Press, Inc.: reproduced by kind permission).

6.5.3   Optical feedback

This is a technique used primarily to extend the dynamic range of a transimpedance amplifier. A typical design is shown in Figure 6.32 [42]. As can be seen when comparing this design with a typical non-optical transimpedance amplifier, as in Figure 6.29(c), there is no feedback resistor. The elimination of this component, to be replaced by an LED/pin diode combination, also eliminates thermally generated noise and a parasitic shunt capacitance due to interconnects. Both greater sensitivity and higher bandwidth result. As the LED is a high current device driven by a low output voltage, there is little chance of amplifier saturation and hence the dynamic range is increased.

6.6   Integration

With most high performance photodiodes being made from materials that are readily grown on substrates such as GaAs or InP, the possibility of optoelectronic integrated circuits (OEICs) becomes very real. In an OEIC a photodetector, usually a diode, is integrated with a receiver amplifier and associated signal processing circuitry. The resultant signal can then be either sent to other circuits electrically, or reconverted to light for transmission via an (on-chip) LED or laser diode. These circuits have been realized, but aside from the achievement of demonstrating such a circuit there are several other factors that need to be taken into account before they have an obvious advantage over discrete components. The most obvious of these are cost, which is related to both development time and process yield, and

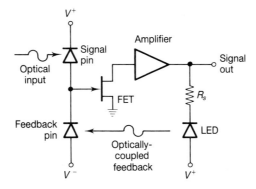

Figure 6.32 An optical feedback transimpedance amplifier (ⓒ1988 IEEE: reproduced by kind permission).

performance, where as we shall see when discussing integrated PINFETs the minimization of parasitics such as stray capacitances is a major factor. Other criteria include long term reliability, device size and functionality. We shall start this review of integrated photodiodes by looking at detector arrays, which do lead the way to a particular type of communication system, namely wavelength division multiplexing (WDM).

6.6.1   Photodiode arrays

Wavelength division multiplexing is a means of optimizing the available bandwidth of an optical fiber, by sending different communication signals at different wavelengths in parallel. Thus the amount of information transmitted is greatly increased without increasing the bit rate of any channel, with its associated noise penalty. For more on the details of WDM, the interested reader is referred to [43].

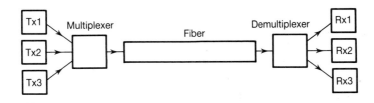

Figure 6.33 The principle of wavelength division multiplexing.

A simple version of WDM is shown in Figure 6.33, with three sources/detectors. The sources of light can either be LEDs, which would have emission wavelengths spaced far apart, or lasers, with emission wavelengths very close together. A simple example of a two-level system based on LEDs is shown in Figure 6.34, using a two-wavelength photodiode [44]. This has the advantage of demultiplexing two wavelengths in one detector without the need for additional components. Photons of the band gap of the quaternary (Q) are absorbed first, whereas those of a lower energy, equal to the ternary (T) band gap, pass right through to the InGaAs where they are subsequently absorbed.

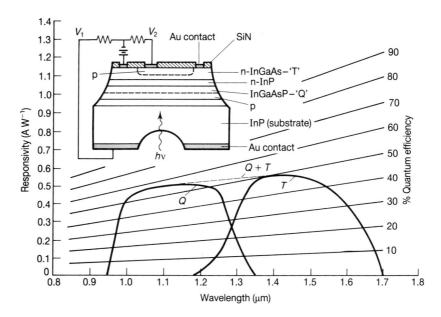

Figure 6.34 A two-wavelength photodiode and its associated characteristics (ⒸIEE: reproduced by kind permission).

This system, whilst demonstrating the principle of WDM, is not really of great advantage in practice. WDM is only of real importance if large arrays of closely spaced (in wavelength) lasers are used with some form of demultiplexing into a receiver array. Solutions to the multiplexing problem have generally come first, with the development of single frequency lasers. Demultiplexing has followed, but based on a diffractive arrangement into an array of identical photodiodes. These lead to another set of design considerations with such an array. Crosstalk is now a problem, arising from optical leakage (quite small), resistance and capacitance. The effect of the latter on crosstalk becomes more important as the bit rate increases, for similar reasons to that of receiver noise. Alignment of the incoming fiber and packaging design are other considerations. Device reliability is a major concern, with the problem of process yield and what to do should a device fail in operation being of great importance. As the latter could mean a replacement of the complete array, it is important that the possibility of this is minimized by using highly reliable materials and fabrication techniques.

The achievement of a good array yield can be obtained in two ways [45]. If we required, say, an array of n working devices, and the individual yield y is low, then a sequential test of every device on a wafer would seem to be the best strategy. Alternatively, the wafer could be diced into $1 \times m$ arrays, with $m > n$, before testing. Statistical considerations will give the probability that such an array will contain at least one functional $1 \times n$ array:

$$P(n,m,y) = y^n + \sum_{i=0}^{m-n-1} P(n, m-i-1)y^i(1-y) \qquad (6.51)$$

where y is given by

$$y \leq 1 - 1/n. \qquad (6.52)$$

The statistical nature of (6.51), suggesting that defective elements are randomly placed, is not often found in practice as most material or fabrication based failures tend to be localized. Equation (6.51) tends to be overly pessimistic, and so if $m \leq 2n$, it can be approximated by

$$P(n,m,y) = y^n \left[1 + (m-n)(1-y)\right]. \qquad (6.53)$$

The result of this strategy is shown in Figure 6.35, where it can be seen that the probability of obtaining a working array depends on the extra number of devices in an array, but more especially on the device yield. The philosophy from this type of graph is then clear; if the device yield is low, increasing m over n will strongly increase the yield of arrays. However, if the device yield is high, the redundancy of extra devices in an array does not have a significant effect, and the overall number of working arrays obtained per wafer, i.e. the wafer yield, will be lower.

Detector arrays, in the form of just two devices, are especially useful in coherent optical transmission. A dual detector balanced optical receiver can achieve a sensitivity close to the quantum limit by cancelling excess local oscillator noise [46]. Integration of the twin diodes with a semiconductor 3 dB directional coupler and a local oscillator have realized a compact and high performance receiver [47].

Integration of a waveguide and a single photodiode has been achieved by many laboratories, but the disadvantage of such a system is the long detector length (> 1mm) for significant absorption. This leads to a high capacitance, and hence low bandwidth, device. Vertical impedance matching (VIM), by using intermediate layers between the waveguide and the detector which act in a similar manner to antireflection coatings, has been used to reduce the absorption length to a few hundred microns, an improvement of over 500% compared with non-VIM devices [48].

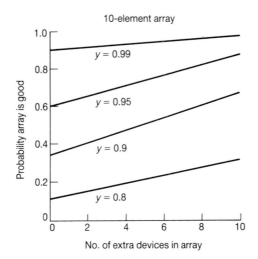

Figure 6.35 A typical array yield as a function of both the number of extra devices in a 10-element array and the individual device yield y (©Academic Press, Inc.: reproduced by kind permission).

6.6.2   Hybrid PIN-FET

Section 6.5 on noise, and in particular the equations (6.49) and (6.50), showed how important capacitance and amplifier noise were in PIN receiver sensitivity. Low noise amplifiers can be obtained using short gate length GaAs MESFETs, but the stray capacitances have also to be minimized. The first step to doing this is to integrate a PIN diode with a FET amplifier on a thick film board, analagous to a printed circuit board (PCB). The thick film board is usually made of alumina with conducting tracks etched on its surface to connect the devices.

Early devices integrated silicon PIN diodes with FETs, but soon long wavelength devices sensitive to 1.3 and 1.55 μm were developed [49]. The PIN diode was based on InGaAs/InP, with a substrate entry fiber to provide good optical alignment. Total input capacitance was less than 0.5 pF, and the final hybrid receiver was able to demonstrate better sensitivity at a bit rate of 565 Mbit/s than a germanium APD.

The early amplifier design of a FET/bipolar cascode preamplifier was replaced in later systems [50] with a FET/FET cascode stage for high bit rates. The reasons for this are that the FET/bipolar configuration provides too large a value of drain capacitance C_{GD}, and the bond wire inductances and stray metallization capacitances begin to be important at high rates. Care needs to be taken also in the circuit layout and grounding of any package to a PCB. In the final implementation of the high bit rate receiver, the PIN-FET, differentiator and second stage capacitor were all contained in one standard 14-pin DIL package. Further improvements can be made by incorporating high gain devices, such as HEMT (high electron mobility transistor) amplifiers based on GaAs/AlGaAs, and/or low capacitance devices, because C_{GS} tends to dominate numerically over other terms in (6.50). The reduction in the number of trapping centres in the construction of the FET is a way of doing this. It is clear that obtaining optimum sensitivity from a PIN-FET hybrid depends critically on the design and performance of the FET, and this is given further consideration in [51].

6.6.3   Integrated PINFET

From the previous discussion it is clear that the ideal way to reduce the amplifier input capacitance to a minimum is to integrate the PIN diode and FET on the same chip; there is no problem with leads and bond wires, and stray capacitances due to metallization are minimized. The great problem with this, at least for long wavelength optical detection, is that the highest performance amplifiers are made out of GaAs, whereas the detectors are InGaAs or InGaAsP on InP substrates. Clearly GaAs detectors are unsuitable for 1.3 or 1.55 μm, and so FETs have to be made on InP. The MESFET, as used in GaAs, is unsuitable because the metal–InP barrier height is so low, typically 0.45–0.50 eV for InP compared to 0.70–0.75 eV in GaAs. For this reason JFETs or MISFETs are used, which have a lower value of transconductance but a higher barrier height, giving greater margin for error in logic applications.

Most research on integrating PIN diodes with amplifiers has taken this route, though ironically enough the first integration was reported using a PIN/bipolar combination [52]; this was a device made in silicon. The approach does not seem to have caught on, however, with the advantages previously mentioned of the FET giving this type of device priority: it is also clear that silicon would be unsuitable for wavelengths > 1.1 μm. The first long wavelength system was demonstrated in 1980 [53] using an InGaAs PIN diode and JFET; an alternative structure using a higher performance InP MISFET and InGaAs PIN diode was reported in 1984 [54]. The problem with these early structures and similar contemporary examples was in fabrication, with material quality and uniformity, channel layer mobility and short gate length realization. Substantial development was put into these areas in the 1980s, resulting in major advancements and the realization of devices that were at first equal to and subsequently better than hybrid PIN-FETs in performance; an example is the InGaAs PINFET shown in Figure 6.36, where a thin layer of AlInAs is used to enhance the barrier height of the FET [55]. The input capacitance of this device was very low ($\sim$ 0.2 pF), giving a minimum detectable power of -18.5 dB m at a bit error rate of 10^{-9} for a NRZ signal at a very high bit rate of 2 Gbit/s.

Recent advances in crystal growth techniques, particularly with regard to growing one semiconductor on a substrate of a dissimilar material, have led to the idea of proposing InGaAs photodetectors integrated with epitaxially grown GaAs MESFETs. This would give the best detector/amplifier combination without sacri-

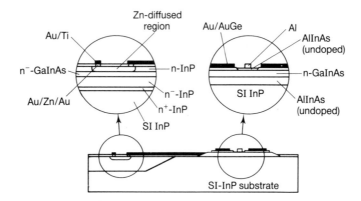

Figure 6.36 Cross-section of a monolithic InGaAs PINFET (©IEE: reproduced by kind permission).

ficing the benefits of monolithic integration. Further details on this type of crystal growth is given in section 8.5.6; it is very difficult, but GaAs MESFETs have been demonstrated on an InP substrate [56].

As with the PIN-FET hybrid, proper design of all the components in the system are necessary for optimum performance of an integrated PINFET; further details of design are given in [57].

For shorter wavelength applications, a Schottky photodiode has been integrated with a GaAs MESFET [58]. This is shown in Figure 6.37. Such a device is readily optimized for the amplifier part of the receiver, and the photodetector is quite simple to make. Extension of this technique into longer wavelengths has not caught on, however, but it should be possible to make optoelectronic integrated circuits (OEICs) at $\lambda \sim 0.85$ μm using this approach.

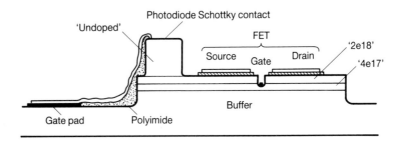

Figure 6.37 An optoelectronic integrated circuit consisting of a Schottky photodiode and a FET (©IEE: reproduced by kind permission).

6.6.4   Optoelectronic integrated circuit (OEIC)

OEICs are of course the next logical extension of integrating the PIN and FET. The term OEIC covers all aspects of integrating a photodevice with an electronic device, not just photodetectors. Aspects of integrating other devices such as lasers and LEDs have been discussed in each relevant chapter, but it is worth mentioning here some of the problems relevant to all integration methods:

(i) optical devices are usually based on bulk properties, and hence require thick (few μm) active regions. Electronic devices usually require narrow (<0.5 μm) channels for effective operation. There is then likely to be a topography problem when trying to interconnect integrated devices, as lithographic techniques do not work well over steep contours.

(ii) Material constraints on stoichiometry and doping are usually different for each type of device, leading to optical and electronic components being fabricated on different areas of the substrate, usually in different processing steps.

(iii) Layout of components needs to be considered, to 'make room' for all the devices; this may lead to a non-optimal interconnect.

(iv) Cost, with regard to device yield and benefits of integration. If the circuit is complicated, and hence has a low yield, the performance of the resultant package needs to be considerably better than a hybrid to justify the greatly increased cost. As OEICs do not at present show substantial advantages over hybrid systems, it has been suggested [59] that the lowest module cost for a photoreceiver is obtained by integrating only two functions on any chip, the rest of the module being assembled in a hybrid fashion.

Nevertheless, the 1980s saw substantial progress in the maturity of optoelectronic integration, particularly when the photodevice was a PIN diode; a particular target was the one-chip transmitter/receiver. Most receiver circuits have been based around the InGaAs/InP systems of PIN diode and JFET, although some have used depletion mode FETs. Some authors have used exclusively epitaxial growth techniques to form the active layers of both detector and amplifier [60]; others have used additional doping techniques such as implantation and/or diffusion [61]. Results are good for both approaches, with a sensitivity of -32.7 dB m at 560 Mbit/s in the former case and -36.4 dB m at 200 Mbit/s for the latter, both for a BER of 10^{-9}. The design of one of the integrated circuits is shown in Figure 6.38 [61].

6.7   Problems

1. Why do only separated carriers contribute to photocurrent?
2. What is the dominant current carrying mechanism in a PIN diode?

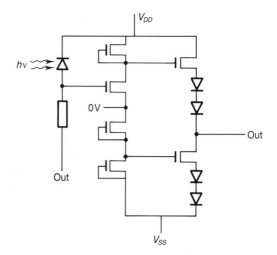

Figure 6.38 An optoelectronic integrated circuit based on a PIN diode, several FETs and level shifting diodes.

3. Explain the role of diffusion length in PIN diode design.

4. Calculate the thickness of silicon dioxide required as an antireflection coating on a GaAs photodiode for zero reflection at a wavelength of 1.3 μm, if the relative refractive index of SiO_2 is 3.9.

5. Consider a pn homojunction photodiode made on a GaAs n-type substrate doped with 10^{15} donors cm^{-3}, with light incident on the p-type material. Calculate the doping required in the p-region to make sure 95% of the depletion volume is contained within n-type material. Also calculate the diffusion length, and hence the thickness of p-region required to make sure all incoming photons are absorbed within either the junction or a diffusion length of its edge in the p-type material.

6. What are the consequences of altering the

   (i) p-region thickness,

   (ii) p-region surface area,

   (iii) intrinsic region thickness,

   on the characteristics of a PIN diode where the illumination enters through the p -surface?

7. Estimate the values of x and y in an $In_{1-x}Ga_xAs_{1-y}P_y$ photodiode that has a maximum efficiency at 1.3 μm.

8. Given that the absorption coefficient and reflectivity in a particular pin diode are 7×10^4 m^{-1} and 0.07 respectively at the operating wavelength of 0.9 μm, calculate the minimum thickness of the intrinsic layer required to obtain an

external quantum efficiency of 0.8. Assume the p-region has a thickness of 1μm. Hence calculate the responsivity of the diode.

9. What form would a graph of output current vs wavelength take, assuming an ideal photodiode and constant incident energy?

10. For an equivalent circuit of a PIN diode, why does the junction resistance dominate over other resistances? What is the dominant resistance when the detector is connected across a load?

11. Consider a particular silicon PIN photodiode where the light enters through the p-region and all light is absorbed at the p–i interface. Sketch the form of the impulse response of the photodiode, if the drift velocities of electrons and holes in silicon are 7×10^4 m s^{-1} and 5×10^4 m s^{-1} respectively at the operating voltage of the diode. The thickness of the i-layer is 13 μm. Hence calculate the maximum bit rate available to a communication system using this diode.

12. Consider an ideal PIN photodiode, which has a value of responsivity R_s of 0.4 A W^{-1} at a wavelength of 0.9 μm, and zero responsivity at 0.4 μm. If the photodiode is used to measure the power output from an 850 nm semiconductor laser of minimum output power 10 nW, calculate the load resistance required to give a signal to noise ratio of 35 dB if the signal bandwidth is 1 GHz. Assume that the device is operated at room temperature, the amplifier has a noise figure of 10^{13} J, and the dark current and gate leakage current represent 3% and 1% of the photocurrent respectively.

13. Consider an InGaAs PIN photodiode with a relative permittivity of 11.8 and a surface area of 500 μm^2. Calculate the equivalent noise bandwidth of the circuit when the diode is connected to an amplifier with an input impedance of 2 kΩ.

14. Explain why InP based photodiodes are more likely to use a JFET than any other type in a PINFET structure.

6.8   References

1. J C Campbell, 'Phototransistors for Lightwave Communications', in Semiconductors and Semimetals, vol. 22D: *Photodetectors*, W T Tsang, ed., Academic Press, 1985, p. 393.

2. J Wilson and J F B Hawkes, *Optoelectronics: an Introduction*, 2nd. ed., Prentice-Hall International, 1989, p. 261.

3. W W Gartner, 'Depletion Layer Photoeffects in Semiconductors', *Phys. Rev.* **116**, 84 (1959).

4. R P Riesz, 'High Speed Semiconductor Photodiodes', *Rev. Sci. Instr.* **33**, 994 (1962).

5. T P Lee and T Li, 'Photodetectors', in *Optical Fiber Telecommunications*, S E Miller and A G Chynoweth, eds, Academic Press, 1979, p. 596.

6. A S Grove, *Physics and Technology of Semiconductor Devices*, Wiley, 1967, p. 178.

7. T Pearsall, 'Photodetectors for Communication by Optical Fibres', in *Optical Fibre Communications*, M J Howes and D V Morgan, eds, Wiley, 1980, p. 154.

8. S Sakai, M Umeno and Y Amemiya, 'InGaAs/InP Double Heterostructure Photodiodes', *Jpn. J. Appl. Phys.* **17**, 1701 (1978).

9. J E Bowers and C A Burrus, Jr, 'Ultrawide Band Long Wavelength p-i-n Photodetectors', *IEEE J. Lightwave Technol.* **LT-5**, 1339 (1987).

10. T P Pearsall and M A Pollack, 'Compound Semiconductor Photodiodes', in [1], p. 218.

11. T Sukegawa, T Hiraguchi, A Tanaka and M Hagino, 'Highly Efficient p GaSb-n $Ga_{1-x}Al_xSb$ Photodiodes', *Appl. Phys. Lett.* **32**, 376 (1978).

12. F Capasso, A L Hutchinson, P W Foy, C Bethea and W A Bonner, 'Very Low Reach-Through Voltage, High Performance $Al_xGa_{1-x}Sb$ p-i-n Photodiodes for 1.3 μm Fiber Optical Systems', *Appl. Phys. Lett.* **39**, 736 (1981).

13. K J Bachmann and J L Shay, 'An InGaAs Detector for the 1.0–1.7 μm Wavelength Range', *Appl. Phys. Lett.* **32**, 446 (1978).

14. H H Wieder, A R Clawson and G E McWilliams, '$In_xGa_{1-x}As_yP_{1-y}$/InP Heterojunction Photodiodes', *Appl. Phys. Lett.* **31**, 468 (1977).

15. M A Washington, R E Nahory, M A Pollock and E D Beebe, 'High Efficiency $In_{1-x}Ga_xAs_yP_{1-y}$/InP Photodetectors with Selective Wavelength Response Between 0.9 and 1.7 μm', *Appl. Phys. Lett.* **33**, 854 (1978).

16. Y Matsushima and K Sakai, 'Photodetectors', in *GaInAsP Alloy Semiconductors*, T P Pearsall, ed, Wiley, 1982, p. 419.

17. See [16], p. 424.

18. S R Forrest, 'Performance of $In_xGa_{1-x}As_yP_{1-y}$ Photodiodes with Dark Current Limited by Diffusion, Generation–Recombination and Tunneling', *IEEE J. Quantum Electron.* **QE-17**, 217 (1981).

19. S R Forrest, R F Leheny, R E Nahory and M A Pollock, '$In_{0.53}Ga_{0.47}As$ Photodiodes with Dark Current Limited by Generation–Recombination and Tunneling', *Appl. Phys. Lett.* **37**, 322 (1980).

20. T P Pearsall, M Piskorski, A Brochet and J Chevrier, 'A $Ga_{0.47}In_{0.53}As$/InP Heterophotodiode with Reduced Dark Current', *IEEE J. Quantum Electron.* **QE-17**, 255 (1981).

21. Y G Wey, D L Crawford, K Giboney, J E Bowers, M J Rodwell, P Silvestre, M J Hafich and G Y Robinson, 'Ultrafast Graded Double-Heterostructure GaInAs/InP Photodiode', *Appl. Phys. Lett.* **58**, 2156 (1991).

22. R U Martinelli, T J Zamerowski and P A Longeway, '2.6 μm InGaAs Photodiodes', *Appl. Phys. Lett.* **53**, 989 (1988).

23. B F Levine, K K Choi, C G Bethea, J Walker and R J Malik, 'New 10 μm Infrared Detector Using Intersubband Absorption in Resonant Tunneling GaAlAs Superlattices', *Appl. Phys. Lett.* **50**, 1092 (1987).

24. F Capasso, K Mohammed and A Y Cho, 'Sequential Resonant Tunneling through a Multiquantum Well Superlattice', *Appl. Phys. Lett.* **48**, 478 (1986).

25. B F Levine, G Hasnain, C G Bethea and N Chand, 'Broadband 8–12 μm High Sensitivity GaAs Quantum Well Infrared Photodetector', *Appl. Phys. Lett.* **54**, 2704 (1989).

26. G Hasnain, B F Levine, D L Sivco and A Y Cho, 'Mid-Infrared Detectors in the 3–5 μm Band using Bound to Continuum State Absorption in InGaAs/InAlAs Multiquantum Well Structures', *Appl. Phys. Lett.* **56**, 770 (1990).

27. S D Gunapala, B F Levine, D Ritter, R Hamm and M B Panish, 'InGaAs/InP Long Wavelength Quantum Well Infrared Photodetectors', *Appl. Phys. Lett.* **58**, 2024 (1991).

28. S R Parihar, S A Lyon, M Santos and M Shayegan, 'Voltage Tunable Quantum Well Infrared Detector', *Appl. Phys. Lett.* **55**, 2417 (1989).

29. M V Schneider, 'Schottky Barrier Photodiodes with Antireflection Coating', *Bell System Tech. J.* **45**, 1611 (1966).

30. D Tsang and S E Schwarz, 'Detection of 10 μm Radiation with Point Contact Schottky Diodes', *Appl. Phys. Lett.* **30**, 262 (1977).

31. W Roth, H Schumacher, J Kluge, H J Geelen and H Beneking, 'The DSI Diode – A Fast Large Area Optoelectronic Detector', *IEEE Trans. Electron. Dev.* **ED-32**, 1034 (1985).

32. O Wada, H Nobuhara, H Hamaguchi, T Mikawa, A Tackeuchi and T Fujii, 'Very High Speed GaInAs Metal–Semiconductor–Metal Photodiode Incorporating an AlInAs/GaInAs Graded Superlattice', *Appl. Phys. Lett.* **54**, 16 (1989).

33. D L Rogers, J M Woodall, G D Pettit and D McInturff, 'High-Speed 1.3 μm GaInAs Detectors Fabricated on GaAs Substrates', *IEEE Electron. Dev. Lett.* **EDL-9**, 515 (1988).

34. M Ito, O Wada, K Nakai and T Sakurai, 'Monolithic Integration of a Metal–Semiconductor–Photodiode and a GaAs Preamplifier', *IEEE Electron. Dev. Lett.* **EDL-5**, 531 (1984).

35. O Wada, H Hamaguchi, M Makiuchi, T Kumai, M Ito, K Nakai, T Horimatsu and T Sakurai, 'Monolithic Four-Channel Photodiode/Amplifier Receiver Array Integrated on a GaAs Substrate', *J. Lightwave Technol.* **LT-4**, 1694 (1986).

36. J B D Soole, H Schumacher, H P LeBlanc, R Bhat and M A Koza, 'Butt-Coupled InGaAs Metal–Semiconductor–Metal Waveguide Photodetector Formed by Selective Area Regrowth', *Appl. Phys. Lett.* **56**, 1518 (1990).

37. P K Cheo, *Fiber Optics and Optoelectronics*, 2nd. ed., Prentice-Hall International, 1990, p. 368.

38. J Gowar, *Optical Communication Systems*, Prentice-Hall International, 1984, p. 421.

39. J L Hullett and T V Muoi, 'Referred Impedance Noise Analysis for Feedback Amplifiers', *Elec. Lett.* **13**, 387 (1977).

40. See [10], p. 179.

41. S R Forrest, 'Sensitivity of Avalanche Photodetector Receivers for High-Bit-Rate Long-Wavelength Optical Communication Systems', in [1], p. 341.

42. B L Kasper, A R McCormick, C A Burrus, Jr and J R Talman, 'An Optical Feedback Transimpedance Receiver for High Sensitivity and Wide Dynamic Range at Low Bit Rates', *J. Lightwave Technol.* **6**, 329 (1988).

43. J Senior, *Optical Fiber Communications: Principles and Practice*, 2nd. ed., Prentice-Hall International, 1992, pp. 262–70 and 674–7.

44. K Ogawa, T P Lee, C A Burrus, J C Campbell and A G Dentai, 'Wavelength Division Multiplexing Experiment Employing Dual Wavelength LEDs and Photodetectors', *Elec. Lett.* **17**, 857 (1981).

45. See [10], p. 229.

46. O Wada, S Miura, T Mikawa, O Aoki and T Kiyonaga, 'Fabrication of Monolithic Twin-GaInAs PIN Photodiode for Balanced Dual-Detector Optical Coherent Receivers', *Elec. Lett.* **24**, 514 (1988).

47. S Chandrasekhar, J C Campbell, F G Storz, A G Dentai, C H Joyner and G J Qua, 'Balanced Dual Photodiodes Integrated with a 3 dB Directional Coupler for Coherent Lightwave Receivers', *Elec. Lett.* **24**, 1457 (1988).

48. R J Deri, N Yasuoka, M Makiuchi, O Wada, A Kuramata, H Hamaguchi and R J Hawkins, 'Integrated Waveguide/Photodiodes using Vertical Impedance Matching', *Appl. Phys. Lett.* **56**, 1737 (1990).

49. D R Smith, A K Chatterjee, M A Z Rejman, D Wake and B R White, 'P.I.N./FET Hybrid Optical Receiver for 1.1–1.6 μm Optical Communication Systems', *Elec. Lett.* **16**, 750 (1980).

50. M C Brain, P P Smyth, D R Smith, B R White and P J Chidgey, 'PINFET Hybrid Optical Receivers for 1.2 Gbit/s Transmission Systems Operating at 1.3 and 1.55 μm Wavelength', *Elec. Lett.* **20**, 894 (1984).

51. R A Minasian, 'Optimum Design of a 4 Gbit/s GaAs MESFET Optical Preamplifier', *J. Lightwave Technol.* **5**, 373 (1987).

52. S Hata, T Sugeta, Y Mizushima, K Asatani and K Nawata, 'Silicon p-i-n Photodetectors with Integrated Transistor Amplifiers', *IEEE Trans. Electron. Dev.* **ED-26**, 989 (1979).

53. R F Leheny, R E Nahory, M A Pollock, A A Bullman, E D Beebe, J C DeWinter and R J Martin, 'Integrated $In_{0.53}Ga_{0.47}As$ p-i-n FET Photoreceiver', *Elec. Lett.* **16**, 353 (1980).

54. K Kasahara, J Hayashi, K Makita, K Taguchi, A Suzuki, H Nomura and S Matsushita, 'Monolithically Integrated $In_{0.53}Ga_{0.47}As$-PIN/InP-MISFET Photoreceiver', *Elec. Lett.* **20**, 314 (1984).

55. S Miura, T Mikawa, T Fujii and O Wada, 'High Speed Monolithic GaInAs pinFET', *Elec. Lett.* **24**, 394 (1988).

56. K Asano, K Kasahara and T Itoh, 'GaAs MESFETs Fabricated on InP Substrates', *IEEE Electron. Dev. Lett.* **EDL-8**, 289 (1987).

57. G P Vella-Coleiro, 'Optimisation of the Optical Sensitivity of p-i-n FET Receivers', *IEEE Electron. Dev. Lett.* **9**, 269 (1988).

58. H Verriele, J L Lorriaux, P Legry, J P Gouy, J P Vilcot and D Decoster, 'GaAs Monolithic Integrated Photoreceiver for 0.8 μm Wavelength: Association of Schottky Photodiode and FET', *IEE Proc. J: Optoelectronics* **135**, 92 (1988).

59. R J Schuelke and K P Pande, 'Manufacturing Cost Analysis of Optoelectronic Integrated Circuits', *IEEE Trans. Semi. Manuf.* **2**, 29 (1989).

60. D A H Spear, P J G Dawe, G R Antell, W S Lee and S W Bland, 'New Fabrication Technology for Long Wavelength Receiver OEICs', *Elec. Lett.* **25**, 156 (1989).

61. S J Kim, G Guth, G P Vella-Coleiro, C W Seabury, W A Sponsler and B J Rhoades, 'Monolithic Integration of InGaAs p-i-n Photodetector with Fully Ion-Implanted InP JFET Amplifier', *IEEE Electron. Dev. Lett.* **9**, 447 (1988).

7

Avalanche photodiodes

The avalanche multiplication effect, which is a particular phenomenon of pn junctions under certain reverse biased and doping conditions, was referred to in section 2.1.8 but not described in any detail. Only the other types of reverse breakdown phenomena, tunnelling and Zener breakdown, were discussed. The avalanche effect is deliberately left to this chapter in order to be described in more detail, as this mechanism is behind one particular family of photosensitive devices.

The avalanche photodiode came to prominence as a useful device for optical communication once the noise limiting factors of PIN diodes were realized. As seen in the last chapter, this is usually noise in the amplification section. If a device could be made that had its own built-in gain mechanism, then the need for an external amplifier, and its associated noise, could be much reduced or even eliminated. As we shall shortly see, the avalanche diode fulfils this criterion and rapidly became the main type of photodetector used in optical communication. Only from the 1980s, with the combination of a PIN diode with a FET amplifier to form a hybrid and then an integrated PINFET, have PIN devices challenged this supremacy.

We start this chapter by looking at the simple avalanche process, its history and other applications. Reviews of theoretical work are included, and the extension to optical detectors is introduced. Avalanche diode materials and structures are then described, noise effects are discussed and finally the chapter ends with a comparison of PIN and avalanche photodiode performance.

7.1 The avalanche effect

As discussed in Chapter 2, a pn junction under a high reverse bias can show catastrophic breakdown from the normally associated low values of leakage current. The Zener effect and quantum mechanical tunnelling have been discussed in section 2.1.8, but in 1953 a different mechanism was noticed [1]. It happened under different bias and doping conditions to the other two breakdown mechanisms, and was identified as a solid state analog of the Townsend avalanche breakdown effect in gases. What made this observation different from tunnelling or the Zener effect is that, although these two mechanisms cause a large increase in current, there is no multiplication effect in their description. The avalanche effect does rely on multiplication, leading to the full description of avalanche multiplication (and the popular term 'avalanching', which strictly speaking is incorrect).

7.1.1 The multiplication mechanism

As shown in Chapter 2 and used in Chapter 6 on PIN diodes, almost all of the potential applied to a pn junction on reverse bias is dropped across the depletion region. Thus the electric field is considered to be formed only in this region and elsewhere it is zero. As shown in (2.81), the width w of the depletion region increases with the square root of the applied potential V. As electric field E will increase linearly with V in the absence of any depletion region width change, it follows that increasing the value of the reverse bias will lead to a sublinear increase in E at any point. Under the influence of an electric field, carriers in the depletion region acquire a velocity v ($= \mu E$ from (1.33)) and hence drift into the neutral regions of the device. With the velocity is an associated momentum (m^*v, where m^* is the carrier's effective mass) and kinetic energy ($m^*v^2/2$). If a carrier has sufficient kinetic energy it may, on collision with a crystal atom located in the depletion region, knock an electron out of the atomic structure and give it sufficient energy for the released electron to be promoted from its previous position in the valence band to a new one in the conduction band. This will then release a hole into the valence band. The process is illustrated in Figure 7.1(a), and it can be seen that one carrier (an electron) has released two further carriers (an electron and a hole) giving a multiplication in carrier concentration (and hence current) of three. The process is then one of collision based momentum transfer and particle release, leading to the alternative name for the avalanche process, impact ionization. If both energy and momentum are to be conserved, then the following equations must hold:

$$\frac{1}{2}m_e^*v_1^2 \;=\; E_g + m_e^*v_{2e}^2 + \frac{1}{2}m_h^*v_{2h}^2 \tag{7.1}$$

$$m_e^*v_1 \;=\; 2m_e^*v_{2e} + m_h^*v_{2h} \tag{7.2}$$

where m_e^* and m_h^* are the electron and hole effective masses respectively, v_1 and v_2 represent before and after collision velocities, and the subscripts e and h on v_2 refer to electrons or holes. Without knowing any relationships between the factors in (7.1) and (7.2) there are too many unknowns for a solution to be found. If we introduce simplifying terms $m_e^* = m_h^*$, and $v_{2e} = v_{2h}$, then (7.1) and (7.2) become

$$\frac{1}{2}m_e^*v_1^2 \;=\; E_g + \frac{3}{2}m_e^*v_{2e}^2 \tag{7.3}$$

and $m_e^* v_1 = 3m_e^* v_{2e}$.   (7.4)

These can now be solved by isolating v_{2e} from (7.4)

$$v_{2e}^2 = \frac{v_1^2}{9}$$ (7.5)

and substituting (7.5) into (7.3) to give

$$\frac{1}{2}m_e^* v_1^2 = \frac{3}{2}E_g \, .$$ (7.6)

If the left hand side of (7.6) is the minimum energy required to initiate the avalanche process, then the relationship to the semiconductor band gap can be clearly seen. Because the mobility of holes is usually less than that of electrons, a higher value of electric field is needed to accelerate holes to a given velocity. This, and the fact that holes generally have a higher effective mass than electrons, combine to give a different value to the minimum energy required for impact ionization for the two carrier types, electrons and holes. This will then lead to different ionization rates, as discussed in section 7.1.3.

Example 7.1

Calculate the minimum electric field required to cause (i) electron, and (ii) hole ionization multiplication in a sample of GaAs with the following material parameters:

(a) electron and hole effective masses of 0.07 m_0 and 0.48 m_0 respectively,
(b) electron and hole mobilities of 2000 cm^2/V s and 350 cm^2/V s respectively,
(c) band gap of 1.42 eV.

Solution: rearranging (7.6) gives

$$v = \left(\frac{3E_g}{m_e^*}\right)^{1/2} \, .$$ (7.7)

(i) This means that for electrons

$$\begin{aligned} v &= \left(\frac{3 \times 1.42 \times e}{0.07 \times m_0}\right)^{1/2} \\ &= 3.27 \times 10^7 \text{ m s}^{-1} \end{aligned}$$ (7.8)

giving an electric field

$$\begin{aligned} E &= \frac{v}{\mu} \\ &= 1.64 \times 10^8 \text{ V m}^{-1}. \end{aligned}$$ (7.9)

(ii) Similarly for holes

$$v = \left(\frac{3 \times 1.42 \times e}{0.48 \times m_0}\right)^{1/2}$$
$$= 1.25 \times 10^7 \text{ m s}^{-1}$$

giving $E = 3.57 \times 10^8$ V m^{-1}. \hfill (7.10)

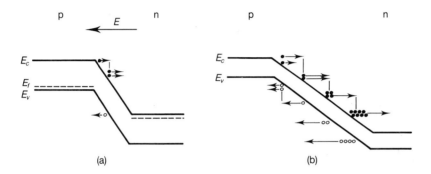

(a) \hspace{8cm} (b)

Figure 7.1 (a) A single avalanche multiplication. (b) Electron and hole multiplication, leading to an avalanche effect.

Of course, after the ionization process shown in Figure 7.1(a), the resultant carriers will be accelerated by the depletion region field and may individually cause further ionizations, as shown in Figure 7.1(b). The process will lead to a rapid multiplication of the carrier concentration, and hence the current, as carriers are swept across the depletion region. The origin of the term 'avalanche multiplication' then becomes clear. Only one hole ionization process is shown in Figure 7.1(b) for clarity, but all of the holes produced could contribute to further ionizations.

7.1.2 Breakdown voltage

As shown in section 2.1.2, the electric field across a pn junction varies in either a linear or a parabolic fashion (abrupt or linearly graded junctions respectively; Figures 2.4(b) and (d)). For either case, the magnitude of the electric field will have a maximum value at the metallurgical junction. As the avalanche process is field related, it is useful to determine the value of the maximum field for any junction, as for an avalanche diode this value will turn out to be the critical field for the ionization process. As shown in section 2.1.2, the potential in the depletion region is found from a solution of Poisson's equation (2.7). The maximum magnitude of the field E_0 is given by (2.13) and (2.14) for an abrupt junction. Integrating these equations gives expressions for the potential in the n and p regions of the junction, equations (2.15) and (2.16). If the junction is doped so that $N_A \gg N_D$, then (2.13)–(2.16) give

$$E_0 = -\frac{eN_D w}{\epsilon\epsilon_0} \tag{7.11}$$

$$\text{and} \quad V = -\int_0^w E_0\,\mathrm{d}x = \frac{eN_D w^2}{2\epsilon\epsilon_0}. \tag{7.12}$$

The depletion width w depends on applied potential V, and so we must arrange (7.12) to include only constant terms in order to determine their effect on breakdown voltage. Combining (7.11) and (7.12) gives a dependence of V on E_0, and if we introduce the terms breakdown voltage V_B and critical field E_c, then

$$V_B = \frac{\epsilon\epsilon_0 E_c^2}{2eN_D}. \tag{7.13}$$

This relationship is shown in Figure 7.2 [2] for a wide range of dopant densities in four common semiconductors. It can be seen that the inverse dependence of (7.13) holds over several orders of magnitude, until high doping densities are encountered – here the tunnelling mechanism takes over as the dominant term in determining breakdown voltage.

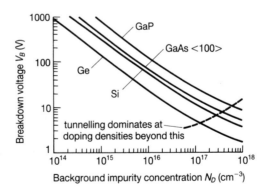

Figure 7.2 The breakdown voltage as a function of background doping density for four common semiconductors (©AIP: reproduced by kind permission).

As mentioned in section 2.1.2, $w \propto V_{bi}^{1/3}$ for a linearly graded junction, and going through the same analysis as that used to produce (7.13) will give a similar relationship between V_B and E_c for this type of structure:

$$V_B = \left(\frac{32}{9}\frac{\epsilon\epsilon_0 E_c^3}{ea}\right)^{1/2} \tag{7.14}$$

where a is the doping gradient. Note that V_B in this case is a much slower varying function of the doping term. Equations (7.13) and (7.14) can be combined in the case of a junction doped as in Figure 7.3(a), which has a constant doping concentration in the bulk semiconductor with graded doping at the junction. For large a and low N_D, V_B is dominated by the value of N_D, whereas for small a and high N_D, (7.14) dominates and V_B is more linear with N_D. The result of various combinations of a and N_D is shown in Figure 7.3(b) [3].

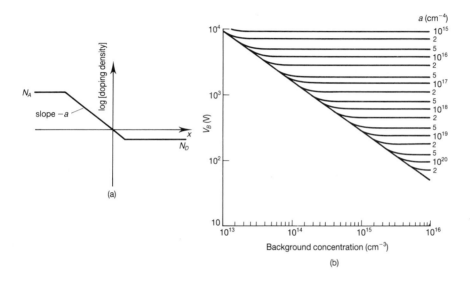

Figure 7.3 A linearly graded junction: (a) doping profile, and (b) breakdown voltage as a function of background doping density and doping gradient (©John Wiley & Sons: reproduced by kind permission).

7.1.3 Ionization rate

As mentioned in the last section, carriers can cause several impact ionizations as they cross the depletion region. This leads to the term ionization rate α, defined as the number of ionizing collisions per unit distance; α will be different for each type of carrier, leading to two terms α_e and α_h, and will be dependent on both the material and the applied electric field. (Describing α as a rate is not strictly correct, as rates usually apply to unit time rather than unit distance; the term ionization coefficient is less often seen, although it is the correct one.)

Ionization rates as functions of applied field and/or doping densities have been measured for many different semiconductors. The measurement of α_e and α_h themselves require a stringent set of conditions, and care must be taken to ensure that the end results are accurate. This is described in some detail in [4], but the salient points are:

(i) Pure electron and hole injection must be obtained in the same, and not complimentary, structure(s). One type of device should be used, rather than p$^+$n and n$^+$p. This method of injection is best done optically.

(ii) The photocurrent prior to the onset of avalanche multiplication needs to be known accurately.

(iii) The electric field profile should be accurately known and only vary slightly with distance so that α_e and α_h are functions only of the field.

(iv) The avalanche gain should be uniform across the active area of the device. As we shall see in section 7.3.1, early avalanche photodiodes were made of poor quality material, which led to local avalanche regions being initiated (microplasmas) before the critical field had been reached.

The most studied element in terms of ionization rate is silicon, although most data is usually referenced to the original work in [5] and shown in Figure 7.4(a). It can be seen that the electron ionization rate is significantly greater than that of holes.

Gallium arsenide shows a dependency of α_e and α_h on the orientation of the crystal. Figure 7.4(b) shows this effect for three different directions $\langle 100 \rangle$, $\langle 111 \rangle$, and $\langle 110 \rangle$ [6]. The hole ionization rate shows a negligible anisotropy, but clearly the electron term is different for each orientation. The mechanism for this is unclear, as different ideas have been put forward and subsequently challenged [7].

Ionization rates have also been published for Ge, InAs, InGaAs, InAlAs, GaAsSb, InP, InGaAsP, GaP, GaSb, AlGaSb, InSb and InGaSb. A full review of these results is given in [8], and a few selected results for important semiconductors shown in Figures 7.4(c) and (d).

7.2   Multiplication factor

The multiplication factor M is an important parameter, as it is from this that the ionization rates and the ultimate gain of the device are determined. The problem of calculating α_e from M has always centred on solving the integral equations relating these parameters. Presented in this section is a review of the attempts made to do this.

7.2.1   Equal ionization rates

Early attempts at theoretical models of avalanche diodes were based on very limited experimental data. The first work was presented in 1954 [9], and its basis is shown in Figure 7.5(a). Consider a pn junction with no minority carriers being extracted

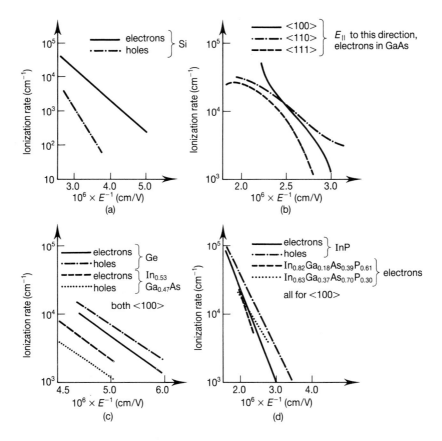

Figure 7.4 Electron and hole ionization rates in (a) Si, (b) GaAs, (c) In$_{0.53}$Ga$_{0.47}$As, and (d) InP, In$_{0.82}$Ga$_{0.18}$As$_{0.39}$P$_{0.61}$ and In$_{0.63}$Ga$_{0.37}$As$_{0.70}$P$_{0.30}$ ((a) ©APS, (b) ©Pergamon Press Ltd. (T P Pearsall, F Capasso, R E Nahory, M A Pollack and J R Chelikowsky, 'The Band Structure Dependence of Impact Ionization by Hot Carriers in Semiconductors: GaAs', *Solid State Electron.* **21**, 297 (1978)), (c) and (d) ©Academic Press, Inc.: reproduced by kind permission).

at the edge of the depletion region on the p-side. If the diode is operated in the avalanche multiplication mode, these electrons can produce more carriers by impact ionization. Let the number of electrons produced by electrons or holes between 0 and x be n_1, and similarly between x and w be n_2. If the electron and hole ionization rates are the same, i.e. $\alpha_e = \alpha_h = \alpha$, then the number of electrons produced between x and $x + dx$ is

$$
\begin{aligned}
dn_1 &= (n_0 + n_1)\alpha dx + n_2 \alpha dx \\
&= n\alpha dx
\end{aligned}
\tag{7.15}
$$

where n, the total number of electrons arriving in the n-region, is the sum of n_0, n_1 and n_2. Note that because the ionization rates of electrons and holes are considered to be equal, we need only consider carriers of one particular sign. Equation (7.15) can then reduce to

$$\frac{\mathrm{d}n_1}{n} = \alpha \mathrm{d}x. \tag{7.16}$$

This can now be integrated between $x = 0$ and $x = w$. At $x = 0$, $n_1 = 0$ and, for $x = w$, $n_2 = 0$, and so $n_1 = n - n_0$. Equation (7.16) then becomes

$$\frac{n - n_0}{n} = \int_0^w \alpha \, \mathrm{d}x. \tag{7.17}$$

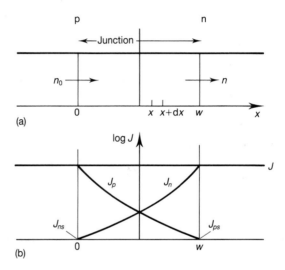

(a)

(b)

Figure 7.5 The pn junction on reverse bias: (a) electron flow, and (b) current distribution.

If we now introduce the multiplication factor M, defined as the ratio of the number of electrons leaving the junction to those entering it, then substituting

$$M = \frac{n}{n_0} \tag{7.18}$$

into (7.17) gives

$$1 - \frac{1}{M} = \int_0^w \alpha \, \mathrm{d}x. \tag{7.19}$$

When the right hand side of (7.19) equals unity, $M = \infty$ and avalanche breakdown occurs. This equation can be used to determine relationships between α and the

breakdown field for both abrupt and graded junctions. The resultant relationships
are, for an abrupt junction [9]:

$$\alpha(E_0) = \frac{2}{w_1^2} \frac{\mathrm{d}(1 - 1/M)}{\mathrm{d}E_0} \tag{7.20}$$

$$\text{and} \quad \alpha(E_c) = -\frac{4}{w_1^3} \frac{\mathrm{d}w_1}{\mathrm{d}E_c} \tag{7.21}$$

$$\text{where} \quad w_1 = \left(\frac{2\epsilon\epsilon_0}{e(N_A - N_D)} \right)^{1/2} \tag{7.22}$$

and the built-in voltage of the junction V_{bi} is included in the applied voltage term.
Equation (7.20) gives a method of measuring M vs maximum field E_0 on a single
junction of constant width: (7.21) measures critical field E_c vs junction width
parameter w_1 for $M = \infty$. The equivalent equations to (7.20) and (7.21) for a
graded junction are

$$\alpha(E_0) = \frac{2}{\pi} \left(\frac{1.5}{w_1^3} \right)^{1/2} \frac{\mathrm{d}}{\mathrm{d}E_0} \int_0^{E_0} \frac{(1 - 1/M)}{(E_0 - E)^{1/2}} \, \mathrm{d}E \tag{7.23}$$

$$\text{and} \quad \alpha(E_c) = \frac{2}{\pi} (1.5)^{1/2} \frac{\mathrm{d}}{\mathrm{d}E_c} \int_0^{E_c} \frac{\mathrm{d}E}{w_1^{3/2}(E_c - E)^{1/2}} \, . \tag{7.24}$$

7.2.2   Unequal ionization rates

It was not long into the development of avalanche diodes that it was realized that
ionization rates were different for electrons and holes, and the relative ratios of α_e
to α_h varied from material to material. This is graphically illustrated in the series
of diagrams in Figure 7.4. The next theoretical analysis [10] modified the equation
given in the last section to produce, as an analogy to (7.19):

$$1 - \frac{1}{M} = \int_0^w \alpha_e \exp\left[-\int_0^x (\alpha_e - \alpha_h) \, \mathrm{d}x' \right] \mathrm{d}x \tag{7.25}$$

with the equations (7.20) and (7.21) for an abrupt junction being suitably modified
by (7.25). A graded junction, or any other type of profile, was not considered.
These more difficult problems were attempted by subsequent authors using various
simplifications. Unfortunately most work proved to have considerable error when
compared with experiment.

A particularly successful approach was first published in 1964 [5], and has been
reviewed by many authors since. It has become the standard approach for analyzing
avalanche diodes of different electron and hole ionization rates. It is an extension of
the work in [10], and considers the introduction of both electron and hole current, as
shown in Figure 7.5(b). If the analogous differential equation to (7.15) is expressed
in terms of current, then

$$\frac{\mathrm{d}J_n}{\mathrm{d}x} = -\frac{\mathrm{d}J_p}{\mathrm{d}x}$$

$$= \alpha_e |J_n| + \alpha_h |J_p|. \tag{7.26}$$

As $J = J_n + J_p$, (7.26) readily reduces to

$$\frac{\mathrm{d}J_n}{\mathrm{d}x} - (\alpha_e - \alpha_h)\, J_n = \alpha_h J. \tag{7.27}$$

This equation is one of a standard form

$$\frac{\mathrm{d}y}{\mathrm{d}x} + Ay = B \tag{7.28}$$

where $y \equiv J_n$, and A and B are constants. The standard solution is

$$y = \frac{\int_0^x B \exp\left(\int_0^x A\,\mathrm{d}x'\right)\,\mathrm{d}x + C}{\exp\left(\int_0^x A\cdot\mathrm{d}x'\right)}. \tag{7.29}$$

The boundary condition on (7.27) is $J_n(w) = M_n J_{ns}$, where M_n is the electron multiplication factor. Combining this with the solution given by (7.29), and noting that $A \equiv \alpha_h - \alpha_e$ and $B \equiv \alpha_h J$ leads to an equation for $J_n(x)$:

$$J_n(x) = J\frac{\left(1/M_n + \int_0^x \alpha_h \exp\left[-\int_0^x (\alpha_e - \alpha_h)\,\mathrm{d}x'\right]\,\mathrm{d}x\right)}{\exp\left[-\int_0^x (\alpha_e - \alpha_h)\,\mathrm{d}x'\right]}. \tag{7.30}$$

The electron multiplication factor M_n can be written as

$$M_n = \frac{J_n(w)}{J_n(0)} \tag{7.31}$$

and because the total current density $J \equiv J_n(w)$ several simplifications can be made to (7.30). Equation (7.31) then becomes

$$M_n = \frac{1 + M_n \int_0^w \alpha_h \exp\left[-\int_0^x (\alpha_e - \alpha_h)\,\mathrm{d}x'\right]\,\mathrm{d}x}{\exp\left[-\int_0^w (\alpha_e - \alpha_h)\,\mathrm{d}x'\right]}. \tag{7.32}$$

The current density terms have now been replaced by appropriate multiplication factors. The equation still looks complex, however, and further reminders of standard forms of integrals are needed. Remember that

$$\frac{\mathrm{d}(e^z)}{\mathrm{d}x} = e^z \frac{\mathrm{d}z}{\mathrm{d}x} \tag{7.33}$$

$$\text{and thus} \quad e^z = \int \mathrm{d}(e^z)$$

$$= \int e^z \frac{\mathrm{d}z}{\mathrm{d}x}\,\mathrm{d}x + C. \tag{7.34}$$

Then equating

$$z \equiv -\int_0^x (\alpha_e - \alpha_h)\,\mathrm{d}x' \tag{7.35}$$

$$\text{and so} \quad \frac{\mathrm{d}z}{\mathrm{d}x} = -(\alpha_e - \alpha_h), \tag{7.36}$$

the denominator of (7.32) can now be assessed. In the general case

$$\exp\left[-\int_0^x \alpha_{e-h}\,\mathrm{d}x'\right] = -\int_0^x \alpha_{e-h}\exp\left[-\int_0^x \alpha_{e-h}\,\mathrm{d}x'\right]\mathrm{d}x + C\,. \qquad (7.37)$$

where $\alpha_{e-h} = \alpha_e - \alpha_h$. In the specific case of $x = 0$ all integrals becomes zero and hence $C = 1$, and so

$$\exp\left[-\int_0^w \alpha_{e-h}\,\mathrm{d}x'\right] = 1 - \int_0^w \alpha_{e-h}\exp\left[-\int_0^x \alpha_{e-h}\,\mathrm{d}x'\right]\mathrm{d}x\,. \qquad (7.38)$$

Placing (7.38) in (7.32), and rearranging to give only numerators, gives similar terms on either side of the equation:

$$M_n\left[1 - \int_0^w \alpha_e\,\mathcal{I}\,\mathrm{d}x + \int_0^w \alpha_h\,\mathcal{I}\,\mathrm{d}x\right] = 1 + M_n\int_0^w \alpha_h\,\mathcal{I}\,\mathrm{d}x \qquad (7.39)$$

$$\text{where}\quad \mathcal{I} = \exp\left[-\int_0^x \alpha_{e-h}\,\mathrm{d}x'\right]\,. \qquad (7.40)$$

The integrals involving α_h cancel out and final rearranging gives an expression for M_n:

$$M_n = \frac{1}{1 - \int_0^w \alpha_e\exp\left[-\int_0^x \alpha_{e-h}\,\mathrm{d}x'\right]\mathrm{d}x} \qquad (7.41)$$

or, as it is sometimes seen,

$$1 - \frac{1}{M_n} = \int_0^w \alpha_e\exp\left[-\int_0^x \alpha_{e-h}\,\mathrm{d}x'\right]\mathrm{d}x\,. \qquad (7.42)$$

There is an equivalent equation for hole multiplication:

$$1 - \frac{1}{M_p} = \int_0^w \alpha_h\exp\left[-\int_x^w \alpha_{e-h}\,\mathrm{d}x'\right]\mathrm{d}x\,. \qquad (7.43)$$

Note the form of the inside integral in (7.43); the limits on this have been changed, as well as replacing α_e by α_h in the outside integral. Early analyses missed this point when considering multiplication caused by only one carrier type; consideration of both types of carriers must be done interactively, not independently. Expressions for graded junctions were also developed in [5], and solution methods were also suggested for other forms of doping profile. Subsequent analyses, especially [11] which has become popularly accepted as the simplest presentation, have used multiplication factor M throughout rather than current to arrive at the same expressions as for (7.41)–(7.43).

Comparing (7.42) and (7.43) with (7.19), the same condition for avalanche breakdown occurs, i.e. $M = \infty$; obviously the right hand sides of the equations are differently formulated in that the breakdown condition depends on phenomena within the depletion region and not on the nature of the charge carriers.

If the ionization rates can be assumed to vary in the same way with electric field (generally a good approximation), then they can be related by

$$k = \frac{\alpha_h}{\alpha_e}\,. \qquad (7.44)$$

Substituting this in (7.41) gives

$$M_n = \frac{1}{1 - \int_0^w \alpha_e \exp\left(-\int_0^x \alpha_e \left(1 - k\right) \mathrm{d}x'\right) \mathrm{d}x} \cdot \tag{7.45}$$

If we assume that we have a diode where the electric field in the avalanche region is uniform, then α_e is independent of x. Evaluating (7.45) gives

$$
\begin{aligned}
M_n &= \frac{1}{1 - \int_0^w \alpha_e \exp\left(-\alpha_e \left(1 - k\right) x\right) \mathrm{d}x} \\
&= \frac{1}{1 + 1/(1 - k)\left[\exp\left(-\alpha_e \left(1 - k\right) w\right) - 1\right]} \\
&= \frac{(1 - k)}{\exp\left(-\alpha_e \left(1 - k\right) w\right) - k} \cdot
\end{aligned}
\tag{7.46}
$$

Example 7.2

Calculate the multiplication factor for an avalanche diode with a uniform electric field in a breakdown region of width 5 μm and an electron ionization coefficient of 5000 cm^{-1} (which is 50 times higher than that of the hole ionization coefficient).

Solution: from (7.46)

$$
\begin{aligned}
M &= \frac{(1 - 1/50)}{\exp\left(-5000 \times (1 - 1/50) \times 5 \times 10^{-4}\right) - 1/50} \\
&\simeq 15.
\end{aligned}
\tag{7.47}
$$

If the electric field is non-uniform, the integral form of α_e must be retained. We can do this by letting

$$\int_0^w \alpha_e \mathrm{d}x = \delta, \tag{7.48}$$

so that (7.45) becomes

$$M = \frac{(1 - k)}{\exp\left(-\left(1 - k\right) \delta\right) - k} \cdot \tag{7.49}$$

For $\alpha_e \gg \alpha_h$, i.e. $k = 0$, this simplifies to

$$M \simeq \exp \delta. \tag{7.50}$$

In this case the carrier multiplication is increasing exponentially with δ; however, it will remain finite as long as $\alpha_h = 0$, and thus the diode will be prevented from reaching the breakdown condition. Figure 7.6 shows the effect of k, δ, and E on the electron multiplication in a particular diode structure [12]. As mentioned, the gain remains finite for $k = 0$, but shows a rapid increase with E for other values of k. The slope of these gain vs E curves give some idea as to how difficult avalanche diodes are to make reliably. The doping levels in the devices control the electric field, and only slight variations in doping can be seen to produce enormous changes in gain, especially for high k values. An example from this curve is that a 0.5% variation in doping (and hence in field) would produce a 320% variation in gain for $k = 1$.

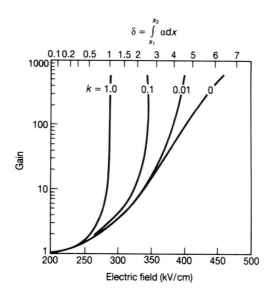

Figure 7.6 The dependence of gain on electric field, δ and k for a 1 μm Si PIN avalanche diode (©1974 RCA: reproduced by kind permission of General Electric).

7.2.3 Dependence on breakdown voltage

The relationship between multiplication factor M and breakdown voltage V_B was first investigated empirically [13], using a complementary set of abrupt pn$^+$ and np$^+$ junctions. These all had the same dopant concentration on the high resistivity side, and this led to different values of the breakdown voltage for each structure.

Typical graphs of breakdown characteristics are shown in Figure 7.7. An empirical relationship can be obtained from a plot of this type:

$$M = \frac{1}{1 - (V/V_B)^n} \tag{7.51}$$

where n is an index in the range 1.4–4 (for the data obtained in [13]). A theoretical expression for n was obtained in [14], which numerically was in broad agreement with experimental data. It was noted, however, that a phenomenon which plagued early avalanche diode work, the formation of microplasmas (see section 7.3.1), could lead to n increasing dramatically from the computed values.

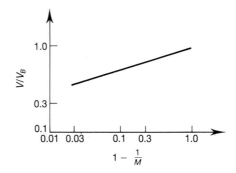

Figure 7.7 A typical relationship between breakdown voltage V_B and multiplication factor M.

7.2.4   Temperature effects

Figure 7.8(a) shows the reverse bias characteristics as a function of temperature for a typical silicon avalanche photodiode [15]. There are two things to note from this type of graph: (i) the breakdown voltage and (ii) the dark current both increase with operating temperature. The reasons for the former will be considered first. As the temperature increases, so more heat is being given to the lattice in the form of vibrational energy – this is quantized by phonons. The increasing number of phonons will give an increase in related scattering of electrons or holes. This reduces the energy of the carriers and hence decreases their ionization coefficients with increasing temperature. The original formula put forward [16] to relate α to electric field E was

$$\alpha = A \exp\left(-\frac{b}{E}\right) \tag{7.52}$$

where both A and b are constants. This is used to model the data of Figure 7.4. The temperature dependence of α was incorporated into (7.52) by letting b have the form

$$b = b_0 + \frac{\mathrm{d}b}{\mathrm{d}T} \, . \tag{7.53}$$

Plots of α_e and α_h are shown in Figure 7.8(b) [17], and from these the following values for silicon are obtained:

$$\alpha_e = 6.2 \times 10^5 \exp\left[-\frac{(1.05 \times 10^6 + 1.3 \times 10^3 T)}{E} \right] \tag{7.54}$$

$$\text{and} \quad \alpha_h = 2.0 \times 10^6 \exp\left[-\frac{(1.95 \times 10^6 + 1.1 \times 10^3 T)}{E} \right] \tag{7.55}$$

where E is the electric field strength and T is the temperature in °C. For a given temperature increase, the electric field will have to increase to maintain breakdown, and thus:

$$\frac{\mathrm{d}V_B}{V_0} \frac{1}{\mathrm{d}T} = \gamma \tag{7.56}$$

where V_0 is the breakdown voltage at 25 °C, and γ is an index [15]. An experimental plot of γ is shown in Figure 7.8(c) [18]. The multiplication factor M as a function of breakdown voltage V_B also varies with temperature, as shown in Figure 7.8(d) [15]. The dependence of M and V_B on T is given by

$$\left. \frac{\mathrm{d}V_B}{\mathrm{d}T} \right|_{M=M_0} = \left. \frac{\mathrm{d}V}{\mathrm{d}E_m} \frac{\mathrm{d}E_m}{\mathrm{d}T} \right|_{M=M_0}$$
$$= \gamma V_0 \tag{7.57}$$

which is similar to (7.56). Thus, as might be intuitively expected, the voltage necessary to sustain a multiplication has an identical temperature dependence to breakdown voltage.

The other temperature dependent factor is the dark current. As we have seen in section 6.2.2.1 when discussing PIN diodes, this current contains several components which each have an exponential dependence on T. For avalanche diodes, at high temperature, the dark current is determined by the diffusion currents from the neutral region, which have an $I \propto \exp\left(-E_g/kT\right)$ dependence. For temperatures less than about 70 °C, where most avalanche diodes operate, the generation–recombination currents dominate ($I \propto \exp\left(-E_g/2kT\right)$) giving very low values of dark current. Typical temperature dependencies are shown in Figure 7.8(e) [15].

7.2.5   Other theoretical considerations

In section 7.2 we have considered impact ionization as a means of obtaining current multiplication. Ionization rates and multiplication factors have been presented.

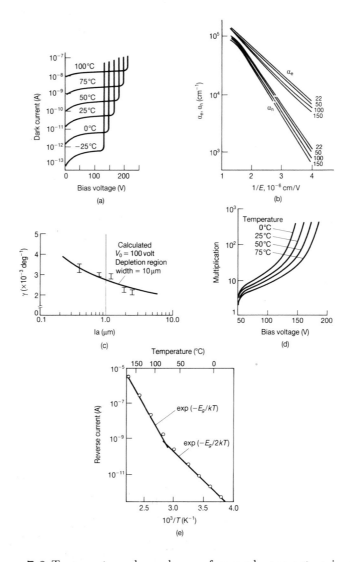

Figure 7.8 Temperature dependence of several parameters in avalanche photodiodes: (a) silicon device dark current, (b) silicon ionization rates, (c) γ parameter as a function of avalanche region width, (d) multiplication factor, and (e) components of reverse current ((a), (d) and (e) ©Academic Press, Inc., (b) ©Pergamon Press Ltd. (W N Grant, 'Electron and Hole Ionisation Rates in Epitaxial Silicon at High Electric Fields', *Solid State Electron.* **16**, 1189 (1973)), (c) ©AIP: reproduced by kind permission).

The theory of impact ionization has not been covered, being more appropriate to a solid state physics book than to one dedicated to applying physics to device operation. A full consideration of this phenomenon is given in [19], where impact ionization is related to the band structure, phonon scattering, distribution functions and the related theories of Schockley, Wolff and Baraff. The interested reader is recommended to study this work for a deeper insight into the basic concepts of the impact ionization process.

7.3   Structures

As the theoretical understanding of avalanche diodes has developed, so has the incorporation of these ideas into device structures. Paralleling this has been a steady improvement in the control of material growth and doping which has led to more uniform and predictable devices. This section takes the development of avalanche photodiodes from the earliest structures to the creation of very sophisticated devices.

7.3.1   Microplasmas

We start this study of structures by noting one of the first observations in early avalanche diodes. Material quality was poor in the 1950s and early 1960s, even in elemental semiconductors, and there were may defects in fabricated devices. The first report of an unexpected phenomenon was in 1955, when a silicon pn junction emitted a yellowish-white light on *reverse bias* [20]. It was subsequently shown that this light was emitted only from certain spots in the junction region, and it was associated with electron–hole recombination at the breakdown voltage [21]. The spots were termed microplasmas, and once initiated they remained localized in the crystal; any further increase in current was accompanied by an increased density of microplasmas. Later it was shown that the formation of the microplasmas tended to be at dislocations [22]. Although the mechanism for this was unclear, what was clear was the need for a dislocation free structure to make the device breakdown uniform across the junction area. This broad area breakdown was first confirmed in 1960 [23] when it was compared with a junction containing defects. The former showed a smooth $I-V$ breakdown characteristic, whereas the latter had two kinks in it associated with the formation of microplasmas. As microplasmas were obviously an undesirable phenomenon, work in material growth enabled the defects causing them to be eliminated. Microplasmas soon became nothing more than a sign of poor grade material, as broad area breakdown became the observed characteristic of most devices.

7.3.2   Avalanche photodiode

Up until the early 1960s the avalanche effect was used purely as a current multiplier and, ironically enough, as a poor light emitter as shown in the previous section. The first reported avalanche photodiode was in 1965 [24], using a silicon PIN structure (both mesa etched and planar devices were made) biased into breakdown. Obviously the carriers used to initiate the ionization process in an avalanche photodiode are optically generated in the depletion region, rather than obtained by extraction from the depletion region edge.

Shortly afterwards several different types of structures were developed. One consideration is that the electric field in a device will be higher at the edge than at the centre. To make sure that the current goes through the central part of the structure, some method of increasing the breakdown voltage V_B and/or reducing the edge field strength is necessary. Mesa shaped structures, which have exposed surfaces, have an additional constraint on the electric field at the surface. Some of the earliest structures are shown in Figure 7.9 [25].

A popular structure is the guard ring arrangement of Figure 7.9(a) [26]. This is a planar device, and it needs two separate diffusions to form the n-type guard ring and the n$^+$p junction. The guard ring is there to minimize the field at the edge of what would otherwise be only an n$^+$p junction; the np junction extends the depletion region into the n guard ring thus minimizing the field strength. Breakdown then occurs only at the n$^+$p junction, the high field region, directly underneath the light window.

Example 7.3

A particular APD has a quantum efficiency of 0.6. Input radiation at 1.3 μm produces 6 μA of photocurrent for an optical power of 0.1 μW. Calculate the responsivity R_s, the photocurrent before multiplication I_i and hence the multiplication factor M.

Solution: from (6.9)

$$R_s = \frac{6}{0.1} = 60 \text{ A W}^{-1} \tag{7.58}$$

We will call this value the 'external' responsivity R_{se}. If the device was a PIN diode without gain, then the 'internal' responsivity R_{si} could be calculated from (6.11). Hence

$$
\begin{aligned}
R_{si} &= \frac{0.6 \times 1.3 \times 10^{-6} \times e}{hc} \\
&= 0.63 \text{ A W}^{-1}.
\end{aligned}
\tag{7.59}
$$

Equation (6.9) can now be used to calculate the photocurrent before multiplication:

$$I_i = 0.63 \times 0.1 \times 10^{-6} = 6.3 \times 10^{-8} \, \text{A}. \tag{7.60}$$

Hence the multiplication factor is just the ratio of the two photocurrents, i.e. before and after multiplication:

$$M = \frac{6 \times 10^{-6}}{6.3 \times 10^{-8}} = 95. \tag{7.61}$$

Obviously the ratio of the two responsivities would give the same result.

An unfortunate side effect of a guard ring is the addition of both parasitic capacitance and resistance to the device which, as we shall see later in section 7.5, limit its high frequency performance. An alternative device that eliminates the guard ring is shown in Figure 7.9(b) [27]. The fabrication starts with an n-layer epitaxially grown across the whole of a p$^+$ substrate. Selective diffusion is then used to form first the p-region and then the n$^+$. This inverted diode has both low series resistance and no additional capacitance.

A third type of structure is shown in Figure 7.9(c), and involves shaping the device so that the field in the junction region at the surface is less than in the bulk, because of the extra width of the depletion region along the bevelled edge [28]. The initial diffusion to form the p$^+$n junction is followed by lapping and etching to produce the desired structure.

7.3.3   Reach-through structures

This type of device was developed very early in avalanche photodiode research, and it has continued, after various refinements, to be useful in more modern APDs based on compound semiconductors. It is then important enough to merit a separate section on its operation.

The cross-section of such a device is shown in Figure 7.10(a). It has a material structure of p$^+\pi$pn$^+$, where π stands for lightly doped p-type (a complementary structure of n$^+\nu$np$^+$ is also available, where ν means lightly doped n-type). For an applied reverse bias, most of the voltage will be dropped across the depletion region of the pn$^+$ junction, i.e. where the charge imbalance is greatest (Figures 7.10(b) and (c)). As the reverse bias is increased, the depletion layer gradually widens into the π-region, until it eventually traverses the whole of this lightly doped layer. On reaching the surface p$^+$ region the depletion region will rapidly terminate. Hence the depletion region, and its associated electric field, 'reach through' from the n$^+$p junction to the p$^+$ surface across the whole intrinsic region volume – this gives the name 'reach-through APD', or RAPD to the structure (because the device is

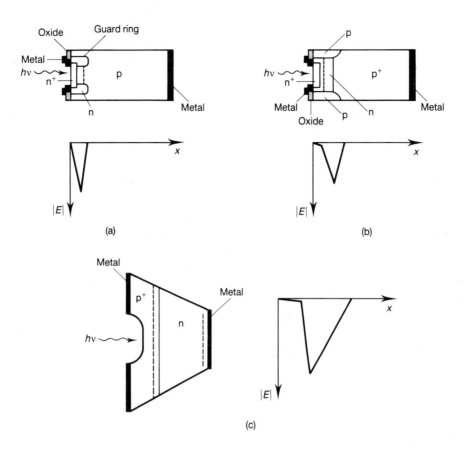

Figure 7.9 Various avalanche photodiode structures and their associated electric field distributions: (a) guard ring, (b) inverted diode, and (c) mesa etch (©Academic Press Inc.: reproduced by kind permission).

similar to a Read diode, the 'R' in RAPD was in the early days often attributed to 'Read' rather than 'reach through'). Any excess applied bias above the reach-through voltage will establish a constant field in the intrinsic region. The device and operating voltage should then be designed to provide a carrier saturation velocity in the intrinsic region, and multiplication at the pn^+ junction. The principle of the device is then as follows. First, light incident on the photodetector is absorbed within the very large intrinsic volume. Here photogenerated carriers are created and separated. Under the bias conditions holes will be swept to the p^+ region, and hence a pure electron current will be directed towards the pn^+ junction. Because of the value of the electric field in the intrinsic region, the electrons will move towards the pn$^+$ junction at maximum velocity. At this junction, the field is high enough to cause current multiplication.

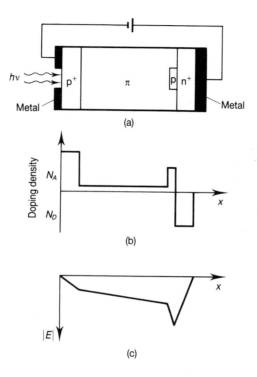

Figure 7.10 The reach-through photodiode: (a) structure, (b) doping profile, and (c) electric field distribution.

There are many benefits to this type of device in relation to other APD structures, which were all noted at the time of its first design [29]. The most important problem which led to the RAPD first being proposed was that previous APDs had a very strong dependence of multiplication factor on bias voltage. This has two sources: (i) a positive feedback effect due to the presence of two types of ionizing carriers, and (ii) the ionization rates increasing exponentially with field intensity. Such an effect would make a linear photodetector very difficult to operate, particularly when bias sensitivity and temperature stability are taken into account. The RAPD structure eliminates one of the problems by only having multiplication due to one type of carrier – in the diagram (Figure 7.10(a)) these are electrons because in silicon (the material of early APDs) electrons have a higher ionization rate than holes. In order to minimize the second factor, it is necessary to minimize the variation in field intensity in the multiplication region with applied bias, i.e. a structure should show little change in the field in the multiplication region over the operating range despite any change in applied bias. As the field in the structure is built up in the manner described earlier in this section, and the intrinsic region is much wider than the p-region, it follows that this second condition is satisfied by the RAPD structure.

The RAPD also has other important advantages. As we saw for the PIN diode, high speed operation is limited by the carrier collection mechanism. Carriers generated within the depletion region are no problem, but those formed by absorption within a diffusion length of the depletion region edge will take a long time to diffuse to the high field region before being swept across. It is then advantageous to have all carriers absorbed in a region of electric field. This function the RAPD does, and also the carriers are separated out at maximum velocity, giving the fastest possible response. Absorption can be made much more efficient than for a normal APD with a necessarily small depletion region because the intrinsic volume of the RAPD is large. However, the intrinsic region should not be so thick as to limit the high speed response due to the carriers having a long distance to travel. A further advantage of the RAPD is the small parasitic capacitance associated with the device because of the wide depletion region.

For all of these reasons, RAPDs have become the most popular manifestation of the avalanche photodiode. They are quite difficult to make, and many early devices failed to live up to expectations because of the need to create both a buried highly doped p-region and a large volume intrinsic region – the latter often broke down because of microplasma formation. The RAPD does form the principle of operation of the SAM-APD (separate absorption and multiplication APD) described in section 7.4 on compound semiconductor devices, and a similar structure has been made using a MOS (metal oxide semiconductor) as the replacement for the n^+p junction [30]. Early problems with fabricating large area RAPDs led to the development of this device, shown in Figure 7.11. The top aluminium layer, through which the light enters, is made very thin so as to be semi-transparent. Obviously a thin layer of SiO_2 is transparent to most optical communication wavelengths, and so absorption occurs within the bulk, lightly doped silicon. Formation of the SiO_2 layer during growth does, in this device, produce an inversion layer, which is necessary to ensure some conduction across the oxide. Good quality large area diodes were fabricated using this technique, but improvements in conventional RAPDs meant that it didn't really develop in a significant commercial way.

7.4   Materials

Having now described the basic physics and structures of avalanche photodiodes, we are now in a position to apply the devices in particular wavelength regions using appropriate materials. As has already been mentioned, most early work centred on either silicon (short wavelength, <1.1 μm) or germanium (long wavelength, <1.65 μm) based detectors because of the ready availability of good quality material and the ease of manufacture. With the maturity of III–V material growth and

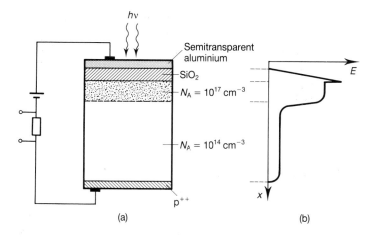

Figure 7.11 MOS photodiode: (a) structure, and (b) electric field distribution (©AIP: reproduced by kind permission).

doping came detectors using compound semiconductors, particularly InP-based, as a replacement for germanium. As for other devices, heterostructures and more recently superlattices have had an important role in III–V based APD development. This section summarizes all the main advances in materials used in avalanche photodiodes.

7.4.1   Silicon

This is the most studied of all semiconductor materials, and because a silicon APD could find ready applications as a detector of both visible and near infrared wavelengths, all of the device structures described in the previous section and shown in Figures 7.9 and 7.10 were developed for silicon based devices. For reasons already mentioned, the reach-through diode (RAPD) has proved to be the most superior in terms of performance. As shown in Figure 7.10, a typical structure has the light entering through a thin p^+ contact before being absorbed in a thick π-region. This means that, in fabrication terms, the devices must be bulk structures thinned to 50–100 μm before metallization, or epitaxial devices forming p and π-layers on an n^+ substrate. This has proved difficult to control, and a device that can be more readily fabricated is shown in Figure 7.12(a) [31]. Here the light is incident through the n^+ region (either formed by diffusion or ion implantation). There is an additional guard ring formed around the central region to incorporate the benefits of this kind of structure, i.e. a higher breakdown field at the junction edge than in the centre. The p^+ channel stop diffusions surrounding the device limit the lateral spread of the depletion region. This type of structure has become the main one employed in silicon RAPDs, as a near 100% quantum efficiency can be obtained. Figure 7.12(b) shows a typical curve for a silicon based device. Because of the reach-through nature, diffusion currents are limited and a fast responding device can be obtained, with rise and fall times below about 2 ns. Operating voltages are very high, however, with 100–500 V being common and some devices needing as much as 1500–2000 V.

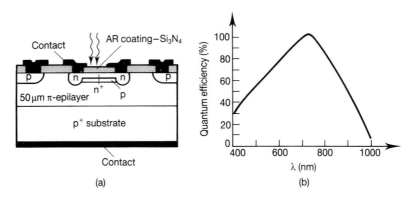

Figure 7.12 A typical silicon RAPD: (a) structure, and (b) efficiency.

Other types of silicon APDs have also been made, including the single photon avalanche diode (SPAD). Such a device is shown in Figure 7.13 and is not dissimilar to the guard ring RAPD, except that there is no π-region [32]. Light enters through the thin n^+ layer and the avalanche region is the small area n^+p junction. The very deep n^- diffusion ensures only a 'plug' of p-material reaches this junction, and so most carriers generated in the neutral p-region, including thermal generation, are drained by the wide n^-p junction. Only the electrons generated close to the n^+p junction contribute to the avalanche current. The device efficiency is then poor, but the dark current is minimal, leading to the ability of one photon to trigger an avalanche current, the leading edge of which marks the arrival of the photon. An external circuit can then quench the current by lowering the bias below threshold, and the device is ready to detect another photon after a very short dead time. In this respect the SPAD works in a non-proportional, Geiger-like mode. Improved versions of the SPAD [33] make it look even more like a guard ring RAPD; the differences are in the relative doping and physical geometry of the devices. SPADs are useful in the detection of ultrashort optical pulses, with a timing resolution as low as 20 ps when made from silicon [34]. These devices have also been made in germanium and III–V materials for optical communication purposes, but with a somewhat lower resolution [35].

A heterostructure device has been made in silicon, using an amorphous silicon/hydrogen doped silicon carbide structure [36]. In a superlattice, as we shall see later, the characteristics of multiplication are different from those of a bulk semiconductor. As carriers move across a heterobarrier step they gain kinetic

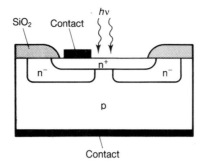

Figure 7.13 The single photon avalanche photodiode (SPAD) (©AIP: reproduced by kind permission).

energy from the band gap discontinuity, thus effectively reducing the impact ionization energy and leading to an enhanced ionization rate. A high optical gain can then be obtained.

7.4.2 Germanium

From a knowledge of the band gap of germanium (0.67 eV) it is clear that it is a suitable detector up to a wavelength of 1.65 μm – enough to cover all optoelectronic telecommunication wavelengths of primary interest. It is also clear that this low band gap will give a high value of the dark current, as seen from the $I \propto \exp(-E_g)$ dependencies mentioned in section 6.2.2.1. This will limit the sensitivity and gain of any APD device. Cooling will lower the dark current because of the $I \propto \exp(-1/T)$ dependence, but then the bandgap and its associated absorption edge will also shift.

Other characteristics of germanium include a ratio of ionization coefficients that is close to one: an increase in noise factor (section 7.5.2.2) over that of silicon is then to be expected ($\alpha_e \gg \alpha_h$ for Si). Germanium APD performance is then not as sensitive to device structure as for silicon, although it still has to be optimized.

The first germanium APD was reported in 1966 and is shown in Figure 7.14(a) [37]. The avalanche region is a shallow n^+p junction and a guard ring structure is employed – some devices were subsequently etched from planar to mesa structures. This structure is satisfactory for short wavelengths, but close to the band edge, as the absorption coefficient falls off rapidly with increasing wavelength, the proportion of electrons injected into the junction region increases. As will be shown in section 7.5.2.2, this results in increased excess noise. The n^+ layer could be made thicker to compensate for this, but the quantum efficiency and response speed will suffer because of increased surface recombination and carrier diffusion respectively.

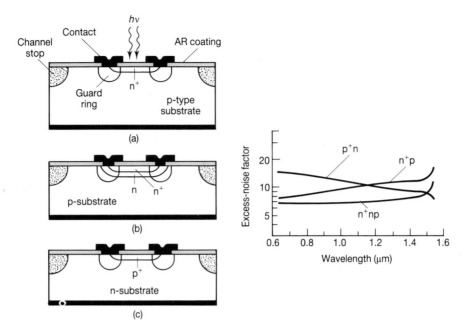

Figure 7.14 Typical structures for germanium avalanche photodiodes: (a) n^+p, (b) n^+np, (c) p^+n (©1966, 1980 IEEE) and (d) their relative noise performance (©Academic Press, Inc.: reproduced by kind permission).

Other structures based on an n^+np or p^+n junction have been proposed [38]. In the former case (Figure 7.14(b)) the thin n^+ layer ensures that long wavelength light is absorbed almost entirely in the thick n-layer. The depletion region extends from the n^+n boundary to well into the p-layer, and avalanche multiplication takes place at the high field junction between n and p. Since the light has been mainly absorbed by this depth, carrier injection into the junction is largely characterized by holes.

In Figure 7.14(c) the p^+n structure is shown. The thin p^+-layer gives a one-sided abrupt junction that ensures almost all incoming light is absorbed in the depletion region formed in the n-layer. Hole injection will then predominate over electron injection from the p^+-layer. A comparison of the performance, in terms of excess noise factor, of the three structures in Figures 7.14(a)–(c) is shown in Figure 7.14(d) [39]. In the original n^+p device, excess noise increases as wavelength increases because of the previously mentioned increase in electron injection. For the p^+n device, the trend is reversed because the hole/electron injection ratio increases with λ, corresponding to the decrease in absorption coefficient. The n^+np device shows the best performance because almost all incident light is absorbed in the thick n-region, resulting in pure hole injection.

At 1.55 μm, the wavelength of minimum absorption in a typical optical fiber, the absorption coefficient in germanium is so low that a wide depletion region is needed for optimized efficiency. The structures outlined above, and particularly the lowest noise p$^+$n structure, would need a depletion region of at least 10 μm thickness, which is difficult to fabricate reliably and still have an effective guard ring. Using a low dopant concentration in the substrate, a so-called Hi–Lo (actually a p$^+$nn$^-$) structure can be used. This is shown in Figure 7.15 [40]. This structure ensures a sufficiently wide depletion region and hence high efficiency.

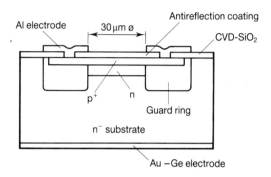

Figure 7.15 A Hi–Lo (p$^+$nn$^-$) photodiode (©IEE: reproduced by kind permission).

The dark current of germanium APDs is substantially higher than for silicon devices, largely because of the low value of the band gap in germanium. In an APD the dark current consists of a leakage component flowing around the periphery of the guard ring and a multiplied component across the high field junction – dark current as well as photocurrent is multiplied in an APD. It has been shown that in germanium the dark current is largely due to generation–recombination effects [41]. The leakage current around the guard ring, usually generated by a surface effect, can be reduced by improving the surface passivation. Unlike silicon, the native oxides of germanium are unstable and therefore unsuitable for surface passivation: either silicon dioxide or nitride is used instead.

A reach-through structure has also been made in germanium [42], and is shown in Figure 7.16. Unlike the silicon p$^+\pi$pn$^+$ construction, the doping is reversed in germanium to give n$^+\nu$np$^+$. A guard ring and channel stop are employed as in Figure 7.12(a). As for silicon, the performance of the device is superior to that of other structures; it took longer to make a prototype in germanium because of the increased difficulty in processing the semiconductor.

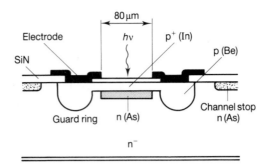

Figure 7.16 A reach-through germanium photodiode (©1984 IEEE: reproduced by kind permission).

7.4.3   GaAs based devices

APDs based on GaAs have not found widespread applications because of the acceptance of silicon devices. Early avalanche photodiodes based on GaAs, as for most III–V semiconductors, used a Schottky junction rather than a pn structure as the high field region. A cross-section of the first reported device is shown in Figure 7.17(a) [43]. A semi-transparent platinum layer forms the Schottky contact to an epitaxially grown n-layer. A guard ring was formed either by proton bombardment for a planar structure or by epitaxial growth of high resistivity GaAs for mesa devices. Schottky photodiodes were also used for early InGaAs avalanche detectors, and a comparison of the responsivity of GaAs and InGaAs devices is shown in Figure 7.17(b) [44]. As can be seen, the GaAs device has a similar responsivity to that of silicon, whilst the InGaAs devices, for the values of x chosen, extend the response out to 1.2 μm; further increases in x can take the response much further.

Most of the recent work in GaAs based devices has been as a vehicle for proving the concepts in an easier technology before transferring the idea to a more difficult material, such as InP based quaternaries. An obvious example of this is the multiquantum well (MQW) structure, first noted in Chapter 4 on lasers. The aim of an MQW avalanche detector is to increase the ionization coefficient of one or other carrier, thus reducing the noise factor. Most compound semiconductors, including those of interest to long wavelength applications, have $\alpha_e \sim \alpha_h$, and so the end result of increasing one or other of these is desirable. The effect arises from two factors, which can be understood in relation to Figure 7.18(a), which is a band diagram of a GaAs/Al$_{0.45}$Ga$_{0.55}$As superlattice [45]. The field across this structure is constant because of the use of low doped material. Consider an electron accelerating in a (wide gap) AlGaAs layer. When it enters the (narrow gap) GaAs layer, it abruptly gains an energy equal to the conduction band discontinuity, in this case $\Delta E_c = 0.48$ eV. The electron then 'sees' that the bulk ionization energy

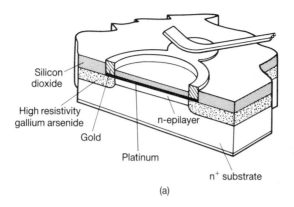

Silicon dioxide

High resistivity gallium arsenide

Gold

Platinum

n-epilayer

n$^+$ substrate

(a)

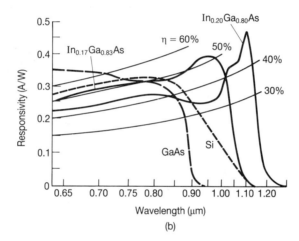

(b)

Figure 7.17 (a) An early GaAs APD. (b) A comparison of the responsivities of Si, GaAs and InGaAs APDs (©AIP: reproduced by kind permission).

of GaAs (~ 2.0 eV) has been reduced to ~ 1.5 eV. A large increase in α_e then occurs because of the exponential dependency of α_e on ionization energy. Something is never for nothing, however, and on entering the next AlGaAs layer the effect is reversed: the electron loses an energy equivalent to ΔE_c, it 'sees' an increased value of ionization energy and α_e for AlGaAs is then decreased. However, because α_e (GaAs) $\gg \alpha_e$ (AlGaAs) the average value for α_e, $\overline{\alpha}_e$, is increased because of the exponential dependence. $\overline{\alpha}_e$ is given by [45]:

$$\overline{\alpha}_e = \frac{\alpha_e(GaAs)L(GaAs) + \alpha_e(AlGaAs)L(AlGaAs)}{L(GaAs) + L(AlGaAs)} \qquad (7.62)$$

where L is the width of one quantum well. Besides the increased electron ionization rate, the hole ionization rate α_h is not substantially increased because the valence band discontinuity ΔE_v is only 0.08 eV, much lower than ΔE_c. The net result is an increase in the ratio of α_e/α_h. A cross-section of the first superlattice APD is shown in Figure 7.18(b).

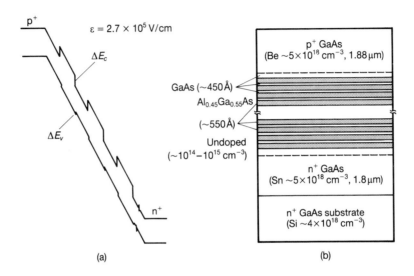

(a)   (b)

Figure 7.18 (a) The band diagram of a GaAs/Al$_{0.45}$Ga$_{0.55}$As superlattice. (b) The first superlattice APD (©AIP: reproduced by kind permission).

7.4.4   InP based devices

For longer wavelengths at 1.55 μm where germanium characteristics are far from ideal, there has been a lot of activity in InP based devices. Here we try and present a picture of a field that, like many others in semiconductor optoelectronics, is rapidly changing. The term 'InP based' in this context means in reality detectors sensitive to wavelengths in the 1.2–1.6 μm region, where ternary or quaternary compounds based around InGaAsP as the sensitive material are grown on InP substrates. Lattice matching and band structure characteristics are detailed in section 4.2 on heterostructure lasers. This and subsequent sections highlight the important characteristics and milestones in the development of InP based avalanche photodetectors as a competitive rival to germanium devices.

InGaAs, the first material to be studied here, was in fact first grown on GaAs substrates, with a graded composition transition region between the substrate and the active region. As already mentioned in the last section, at first InGaAs devices were based on Schottky barriers, not pn junctions [44]. The device was only made sensitive out to 1.2 μm, and the responsivity is shown in Figure 7.17(b).

The first lattice matched InGaAsP/InP avalanche photodiode was reported in 1978 [46]. This was a pn junction structure, and the device cross-section is shown in Figure 7.19(a). It consists of a p$^+$-InP substrate, an n-Ga$_{0.24}$In$_{0.76}$As$_{0.58}$P$_{0.42}$ layer ($E_g = 1.0$ eV) and an n$^+$-InP capping layer. Doping of the InGaAsP to form a pn junction was done by diffusing zinc from the substrate. Mesa structures were etched before metallization. The device is thus a double heterostructure, with wide gap (i.e. transparent to 1.0 eV) top and bottom layers of low resistance. This performs two functions. First, either carrier may be preferentially injected into the high field region, essential for low noise operation. Second, the band structure as shown in Figure 7.19(b) prevents photogenerated minority carriers diffusing to the surface where they would be lost by recombination.

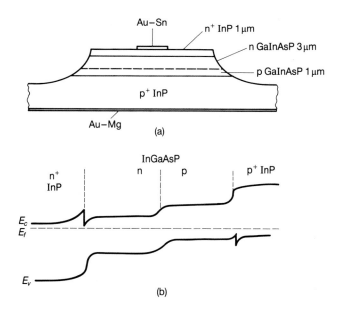

Figure 7.19 (a) Structure of the first lattice matched InGaAsP/InP APD (©AIP: reproduced by kind permission). (b) Band diagram of the device.

7.4.4.1 Dark current

One problem immediately identified with these types of devices was a high dark current. Experiments on spacing between the heterointerface and the pn junction suggested that carrier generation centres at the InGaAs/InP boundary were responsible for the dark current, although their identity could not be found [47]. In a series of papers published in the early 1980s [48–50] it was shown that tunnelling was the dominant source of dark current for these types of avalanche diodes, at least at high bias: for low bias the generation–recombination term already mentioned dominates the reverse characteristics. Band to band tunnelling in reverse biased, direct gap semiconductors is given by [48]:

$$I_{tun} = \frac{(2m^*)^{1/2} \, e^3 EVA}{4\pi^2\hbar^2 E_g^{1/2}} \exp\left(-\frac{\theta m_0^{1/2} E_g^{3/2}}{e\hbar E}\right) \tag{7.63}$$

where m^* is the effective mass of the tunnelling carrier, E the electric field, V the applied voltage to a junction of area A, m_0 the free electron mass and θ is given by

$$\theta = \beta \left(\frac{m^*}{m_0}\right)^{1/2} \tag{7.64}$$

where β is a dimensionless quantity whose value depends on the detailed shape of the tunnelling barrier; in reality $\beta \sim 1$ for band to band processes. The exponential term in (7.63) is the probability that a valence band carrier will tunnel into the conduction band, and the exponential prefactor depends on the density and occupancy of states in both bands. Equation (7.63) is valid when $|V + V_{bi}| \geq E_g/e$. Note that $I_{tun} \propto \exp\left(-E_g^{3/2}/E\right)$, and so tunnelling can account for the experimentally found exponential dependence of dark current I_D on applied voltage.

Figure 7.20(a) shows the theoretical reverse bias characteristics of In$_{0.53}$Ga$_{0.47}$As, detailing the various components [50]. As can be seen, the combination of diffusion (I_{diff}) and generation–recombination (I_{gr}) current is dominant up to an applied bias of typically 30–40 V. It is shown in [42] that $I_{gr} \gg I_{diff}$ for typical medium doped devices. At higher values of applied bias, tunnelling becomes dominant. The term cross-over voltage, V_x, at which $I_{tun} = I_{gr}$, can be approximated by

$$V_x = 5.5 \times 10^{15} \frac{T\theta^2 E_g^2 V}{N_D \tau_{eff}^{0.06}} \tag{7.65}$$

where N_D is the n-type doping density and τ_{eff} is the effective carrier lifetime. V_x then has a value that must be kept below that of V_B, the breakdown voltage, otherwise avalanche multiplication will be accompanied by a large tunnelling current that is also multiplied, increasing the noise factor. Thus for low noise devices $V_B < V_x$, and so

$$N_D < 1.4 \times 10^{18} \frac{\theta^2 E_g^2}{\tau_{eff}^{0.24}} \text{ cm}^{-3} \tag{7.66}$$

using an empirical formula for V_B [51]:

$$V_B = 60 \left(\frac{E_g}{1.1}\right)^{3/2} \left(\frac{N_D}{10^{16}}\right)^{-3/4} \tag{7.67}$$

with E_g in eV, N_D in cm^{-3} and V_B in V. Figures 7.20(b) and (c) plot V_x vs N_D for the materials In$_{0.73}$Ga$_{0.27}$As$_{0.63}$P$_{0.37}$ and In$_{0.53}$Ga$_{0.47}$As, over a range of carrier

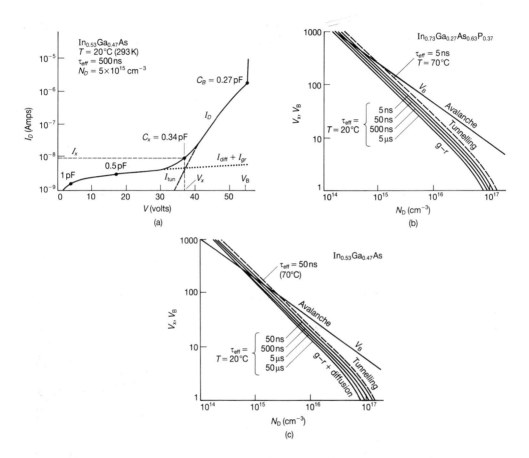

Figure 7.20 (a) The components of reverse bias in $In_{0.53}Ga_{0.47}As$. Tunnelling and avalanche dependences in (b) $In_{0.73}Ga_{0.27}As_{0.63}P_{0.37}$ and (c) $In_{0.53}Ga_{0.47}As$. (©1981 IEEE: reproduced by kind permission.)

lifetimes. There are three regions to each graph: (i) the avalanche region, where $V \geq V_B$, (ii) the tunnelling region where $V < V_B$, and (iii) the low voltage region where $V < V_x$. It can be seen, for instance, that for the InGaAsP device to have a low tunnelling current before breakdown, $N_D < 10^{15}$ cm^{-3}; similarly for InGaAs $N_D < 2 \times 10^{15}$ cm^{-3}.

Example 7.4

Calculate the breakdown voltage associated with an InGaAsP based APD (band gap of 0.95 eV) with n doping densities of (i) 10^{15} cm^{-3}, and (ii) 10^{16} cm^{-3}.

Solution: (i) from (7.67)

$$V_B = 60\left(\frac{0.95}{1.1}\right)^{3/2}\left(\frac{10^{15}}{10^{16}}\right)^{-3/4}$$
$$= 267\,\text{V}.$$

(ii) Similarly $V_B = 48\,\text{V}.$ (7.68)

7.4.4.2 SAM-APD

One method of reducing the tunnelling current, and which has proved to be so popular that it has been adopted for many III–V heterostructure avalanche diodes, is the separate absorption and multiplication (SAM) device. This is similar in principle to the reach-through silicon diode discussed in section 7.3.3. A cross-section of the first SAM device is shown in Figure 7.21(a) [52], with the electric field distribution in Figure 7.21(b). The device has a transparent top InP layer, as for the device in Figure 7.19(a). The difference in the SAM structure is that the InP has a pn junction built into it, and the InGaAsP is solely of one conductivity type; the device in Figure 7.19(a) is the other way around, i.e. single conductivity InP and a pn junction in InGaAsP. The result is that the SAM diode behaves as a reach-through device, with absorption taking place in the wide InGaAsP region, and subsequent separation of carriers by a sub-breakdown electric field. The carriers are swept to the high field pn junction in InP where avalanche multiplication takes place. The use of InP as a substrate as well as a top layer means that incoming light can enter via the top or bottom of the device, depending on the metallization. InP has a large band gap, and so from (7.63) the tunnelling current will be reduced, and the condition $V_B < V_x$ can be satisfied with the n-InP doping density being in the range 5–50 $\times$ 10^{15} cm^{-3}.

Other constraints on this device are [53]:

(i) tunnelling currents in the InGaAsP should be negligible, obtained by reducing the maximum value of the interface field E_I in Figure 7.20(b) to below 1.5 $\times$ 10^5 V cm^{-1},

(ii) the maximum field at the pn junction E_m should be above 4.5×10^5 V cm^{-1} for significant multiplication,

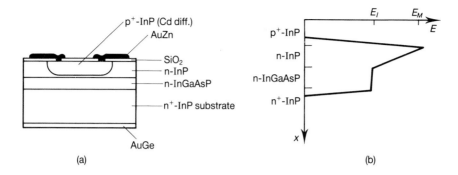

Figure 7.21 A separate avalanche and multiplication (SAM) device: (a) structure, and (b) electric field distribution (©AIP: reproduced by kind permission).

(iii) for a fast response and high efficiency the depletion region should be two absorption lengths wide; this translates to 2 μm at $\lambda < 1.65$ μm for InGaAs.

From Gauss' law

$$E_I = \frac{e}{\epsilon_T \epsilon_0} \sigma_T \qquad (7.69)$$

where ϵ_T is the relative permittivity of the ternary (or quaternary) layer and σ_T is the total number of charges per unit area swept out in the ternary layer. Putting in the values of constants and constraint (i) leads to the result that $\sigma_T \leq 1.0 \times 10^{12}$ cm^{-2} at breakdown. In a similar way, constraint (ii) leads to

$$E_m = \frac{e}{\epsilon_0} \left(\frac{\sigma_T}{\epsilon_T} + \frac{\sigma_B}{\epsilon_B} \right) \qquad (7.70)$$

and hence $\sigma_B + \sigma_T \geq 3 \times 10^{12}$ cm^{-2} if $\epsilon_T \sim \epsilon_B$ (true to within 2%). The constraints on σ_B and σ_T just described are related to device operation for an InP/InGaAs device in Figure 7.22. At low voltages the applied bias is dropped across the pn junction as for the RAPD diode. This moves the operating point along the axis at $\sigma_T = 0$. Increasing the value of the reverse bias will eventually fully deplete the InP, at which value the operating point moves parallel to the σ_T axis at a value of σ_B equal to the total integrated sheet charge in InP. Further increases in reverse bias mean either the operating point crosses the vertical line denoted by $\sigma_T = 1.0 \times 10^{12}$ cm^{-2}, in which case tunnelling in InGaAs occurs, or for $\sigma_B > 2 \times 10^{12}$ cm^{-2} avalanche breakdown occurs prior to tunnelling. However, for $\sigma_B > 3 \times 10^{12}$ cm^{-2} the InP layer is never fully depleted at breakdown, giving an optimum operating region shown by the shaded part of Figure 7.22(a).

Figure 7.22(a) is a somewhat idealized graph, as several parameters such as V_B and η depend on the explicit form of the doping profiles in the binary ($N_B(x)$) and

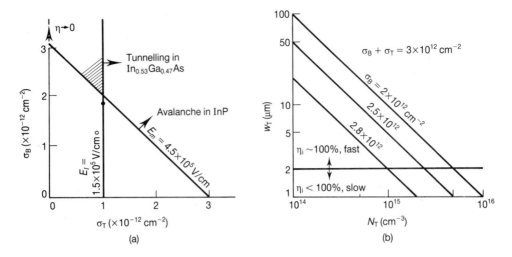

Figure 7.22 Design characteristics of an $In_{0.53}Ga_{0.47}As$ APD: (a) idealized, and (b) more realistic (for explanation see text) (©1982 IEEE: reproduced by kind permission).

ternary $(N_T(x))$ regions. The values of σ_B and σ_T are related to $N_B(x)$ and $N_T(x)$ by

$$\sigma_B = \int_0^{x_I} N_B(x)\,\mathrm{d}x \tag{7.71}$$

$$\text{and} \quad \sigma_T = \int_{x_I}^{w} N_T(x)\,\mathrm{d}x \tag{7.72}$$

where x_I is the position of the heterointerface and w is the depletion region width. For an abrupt junction with uniform doping in the separate layers, $N_B(x)$ and $N_T(x)$ can be replaced by N_B and N_T respectively. Under these conditions, (7.69)–(7.72) can be used to find V_B:

$$V_B = \frac{e}{2\epsilon\epsilon_0}\left[\frac{1}{N_T}\left(\frac{\epsilon\epsilon_0 E_m}{e} - N_B x_I\right)^2 + x_I\left(\frac{2\epsilon\epsilon_0 E_m}{e} - N_B x_I\right)\right] \tag{7.73}$$

with the depletion width at breakdown w_B given by

$$w_B = \left[\frac{2\epsilon\epsilon_0 V_B}{e N_T} + x_I^2\left(1 - \frac{N_B}{N_T}\right)\right]^{1/2}. \tag{7.74}$$

Depletion region penetration into the InGaAs layer, as a function of N_T for several values of σ_B, is shown in Figure 7.22(b). The diagonal lines follow the multiplication condition that $\sigma_B + \sigma_T = 3 \times 10^{12}$ cm^{-2}, and the horizontal line is constraint (iii) that $w_T \geq 2$ μm. The intersection points of diagonal and horizontal lines determine the maximum value of N_T for $w_T = 2$ μm. For N_T greater than these values w_T would be less than 2 μm, resulting in a decrease in internal efficiency.

7.4.4.3 SAGM-APD

Another factor to consider in InGaAs/InP photodiodes is the optical response time. Early research showed that the response contained both slow and fast components, and that the speed of response was limited by the pile-up of photogenerated holes at the heterointerface [54]. This pile-up occurs because of the large valence band discontinuity, as shown in Figure 7.23(a). As the bias voltage increases, this discontinuity decreases, resulting in an increase in operating speed. But at $V \sim V_B$ there is still a substantial residual discontinuity, limiting ultimate performance. A graded InGaAsP region, grown between the n-InP and the n-InGaAs was suggested as a way of reducing this problem. Figure 7.23(b) shows how the valence band discontinuity, ΔE_v, is reduced as a function of both applied bias and thickness L of the grading layer. Depending on operating conditions, especially V_B, L obviously has to be at least several hundred Å. The structure is known as a separate absorption, grading and multiplication (SAGM) APD. It can be shown [53] that L is given by

$$L \geq L_{min} = \frac{3.8 \times 10^{10}}{\sigma_T} \mu m \qquad (7.75)$$

for a minimal valence band discontinuity. This is shown in Figure 7.23(c), with the shaded region giving the most practical range when related to dark current, response time and doping levels. It can be seen that 400 Å $\leq L \leq$ 2000 Å for most practical APDs.

7.4.4.4 Planar structures

Up until the early 1980s almost all SAM and SAGM avalanche photodiodes were made by mesa structures because of ease of low volume fabrication and the reduction of surface leakage effects. Typical examples of SAM and SAGM-APDs are shown in Figures 7.24(a) and (b) respectively [55, 56]. A planar structure is desirable for two reasons: (i) ease of volume manufacturability, and (ii) full utilization of surface passivation techniques. However, a planar device needs a guard ring, and this complicates the structure of an already difficult to fabricate device. Such a planar SAM-APD is shown in Figure 7.25(a) [57]. The guard ring is formed by ion implantation into a two-step InP region, n⁻ and n. This gives a linearly graded guard ring junction, which has a higher breakdown voltage than an abrupt system.

A buried structure, using compositional layers similar to the device described previously, is shown in Figure 7.25(b) [58]. Here the n-InP region has two steps in its horizontal dimension, in order to provide electric field control around the periphery of the multiplication region. The result is a device with uniform multiplication over the central region. The top surface is fully passivated with silicon nitride.

A device made using separate guard rings is shown in Figure 7.26 [59]. As can be seen, the device is somewhat different from those of Figure 7.25 in that the p⁺ guard rings are physically separated from the p⁺n junction and are allowed

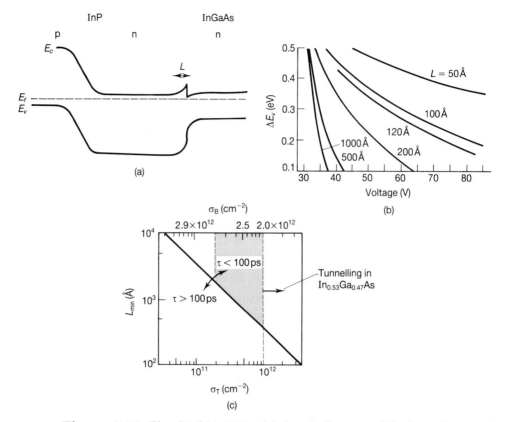

Figure 7.23 The SAGM-APD: (a) band diagram, (b) dependence of valence band discontinuity on applied bias and grading layer thickness (©AIP: reproduced by kind permission), and (c) designed operating region of such a device (©1982 IEEE: reproduced by kind permission).

to 'float' electrically by having no contact made. In this way edge breakdown effects are reduced while at the same time there is a minimal electric field at the semiconductor/passivating layer interface. This latter term is important because it has been shown [60] that there is a degradation mechanism at this interface that is bias driven; positive charge starts to accumulate in the passivating layer followed by localized avalanche multiplication at the guard ring periphery.

7.4.4.5 *Superlattice structures*

As with other types of optoelectronic devices, the principles of superlattices have been applied to avalanche diodes, although as one would expect this has not been to the same extent as for lasers. One of the first applications of this was in a graded InGaAs/InP superlattice region in a SAGM structure, as shown in Figure 7.27(a)

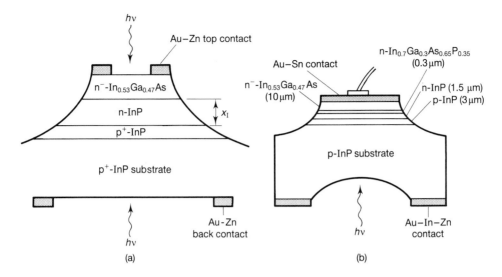

Figure 7.24 Mesa realizations of (a) SAM (©AIP: reproduced by kind permission), and (b) SAGM-APDs (©IEE: reproduced by kind permission).

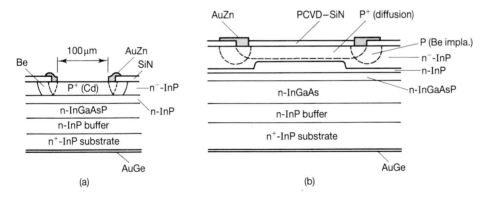

Figure 7.25 Two realizations of planar SAM-APDs: (a) guard ring approach, and (b) buried structure (©1982, 1984 IEEE: reproduced by kind permission).

[61]. The 'standard' SAGM structure will have an InGaAsP region forming the layers between the InGaAs and InP, thus grading the valence band discontinuity of the device in Figure 7.27(a). A graded composition region would increase the operational speed of the device, and the InGaAs/InP superlattice method is one

way of achieving this without having to keep careful control on the stoichiometry of a quaternary compound.

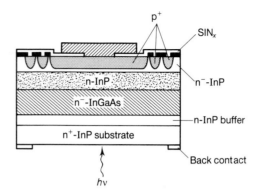

Figure 7.26 A SAM-APD with two separate guard rings (©AIP: reproduced by kind permission).

The same group then extended the idea to make a multiquantum well (MQW) detector, essentially replacing the SAGM structure with an MQW system to enhance the ionization coefficient of one type of carrier (Figure 7.27(b) – [62]), as detailed earlier on the AlGaAs system [45]. The use of another type of superlattice, the strained layer structure, has also been used in the InGaAs/InP system, and extends the photodiode response out to 2 μm [63].

7.4.5   AlGaAsSb devices

The wavelength response of materials based on this technology is somewhere in between that of Si and InGaAsP devices, centring around 1.1–1.2 μm, although 1.3 μm devices have been made. As such their spectral properties have no advantages over those of other materials, and most work on PIN photodiodes in AlGaAsSb has largely disappeared. Avalanche photodiodes, however, have for a particular composition an ionization ratio α_e/α_h of about 20, leading to an extremely low noise factor. The high value of dark current in this material is, however, a problem that limits potential commercial interest.

7.5   Noise

The detection circuitry considerations for an avalanche photodiode are the same in principle as for a PIN diode – these were discussed in section 6.5.1. The main differences for an APD are the use of a much higher bias voltage and the likelihood of a temperature compensation mechanism.

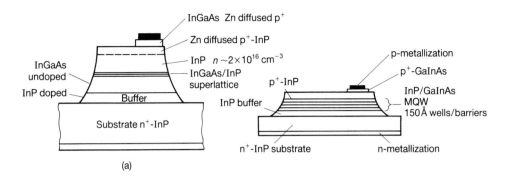

Figure 7.27 Two applications of superlattices in APDs: (a) grading of the valence band discontinuity, and (b) using a MQW as the detecting region (©IEE: reproduced by kind permission).

Noise considerations are again similar. The sources of noise were introduced in section 5.2.2, and applied to the PIN-receiver combination in section 6.5.2. The equations developed in that section need only a minimal amount of changes to make them relevant to the APD. The amplifier and Johnson noise terms will remain the same, but the big difference in comparing a PIN diode with an APD is the shot noise.

7.5.1   Shot noise

The expression for a PIN diode given by (6.43) is modified, in the case of an APD, to [64]

$$\langle i_s^2 \rangle = 2eB\left(I_{du} + M^2 F(M)I_{dm}\right). \tag{7.76}$$

This contains two current terms; an unmultiplied current, represented as a dark current I_{du} containing I_s and I_R, and a multiplied dark current I_{dm}. Here we are assuming that the shot noise is multiplied by the same gain M as the photocurrent. The random nature of the gain introduces an additional excess noise factor $F(M)$. Because of the multiplication factor involving I_{dm} it is expected that this noise term dominates that of I_{du}, and so the latter is often neglected. $F(M)$ is usually a power law of M, with an index x between 0.3 and 1 depending on the material used. Thus (7.76) can be simplified to

$$\langle i_s^2 \rangle = 2eBI_{dm}M^{2+x}. \tag{7.77}$$

The power signal to noise ratio can then be calculated as for a PIN diode:

$$\left(\frac{S}{N}\right)_P = \frac{M^2 I_0^2}{2eBI_{dm}M^{2+x} + 4kTBF_n/R_L}. \tag{7.78}$$

The multiplying factor in the signal current shows that avalanche gain can be used to increase the SNR if the shot noise is less than the amplifier noise. Differentiating (7.78) will give an optimum avalanche gain $\hat{M}$ necessary to maximize the SNR:

$$\hat{M} = \left(\frac{4kTF_n}{xeR_L I_{dm}} \right)^{1/(2+x)} \tag{7.79}$$

Thus the optimum gain becomes larger if the amplifier noise is increased or if the multiplied dark current is decreased. The excess noise factor will ensure that the increase in SNR for an APD is always much less than the optimum gain. The sensitivity improvement, or 'real gain' G, is given approximately by [65]

$$G = \frac{\hat{M}}{F(\hat{M})} . \tag{7.80}$$

7.5.2   PIN vs APD noise comparison

PIN and avalanche diodes are the most mature of all semiconductor photodetector structures, and so it is useful that a comparison of performance in terms of sensitivity is given. There are other factors to consider as well in overall system design, and PIN vs APD is a subject we shall return to in section 7.7. For the moment, however, we limit ourselves to a consideration of noise effects on sensitivity; this section is based on a more detailed account given in [66].

7.5.2.1   Zero dark current
In this section we consider the effect on APD receiver noise of $I_{dm} = 0$ – the next section considers $I_{dm} > 0$. As we have seen previously, sensitivity depends on both BER (bit error rate) and bandwidth or bit rate, B. Thus any comparison between the two diodes has to be at equal values of BER and B. A series of curves of comparable sensitivity of each device for various values of B is given in [66], and the overall comparison is plotted in Figure 7.28(a). Data for a PIN diode represents the optimum available at the time. η_i is the device efficiency and $\bar{P}$ is the mean optical power incident on the receiver. The ordinate shows the ratio of minimum power needed for each device, and the abscissa is a PIN sensitivity normalized to a given bit rate. Curves for several k (equation (7.44)) values are given, together with values of $\hat{M}$ in parentheses. Depending on which parameters are chosen, the sensitivity improvement in using an APD over a PIN is between 4 and 18 dB. This superior performance can be translated into less light being needed for a given sensitivity, giving either a lower constraint on light source power, greater spacing between repeaters or the use of an inferior amplifier.

7.5.2.2   Non-zero dark current
For the more likely case of $I_{dm} > 0$, similar calculations to those in the previous section can result in similar graphs. A summary of the results is given in Fig-

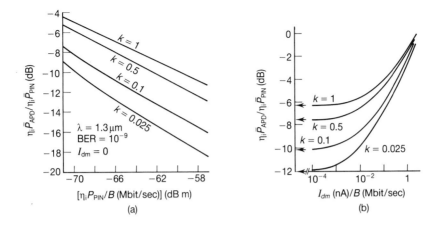

Figure 7.28 The relative sensitivities of a PIN diode and an APD as a function of (a) bit rate, and (b) normalized dark current (©Academic Press Inc.: reproduced by kind permission).

ure 7.28(b). In this case, the ordinate is the same as for Figure 7.28(a), i.e. a ratio of sensitivities, but the abscissa is a dark current normalized to a bit rate. Again curves for several values of k are plotted, and values of $\hat{M}$ are indicated in parentheses. As for the case of $I_{dm} = 0$, the greatest advantage of an APD over a PIN occurs when k is small, and not surprisingly the margin increases for lower values of dark current. To estimate the amount of primary dark current that can be tolerated, we can calculate the normalized dark current I_{dm}/B at which the APD receiver sensitivity is decreased by 1 dB from its value for zero dark current. These values are listed as maxima in Table 7.1 for several values of k and B [66]. Again the PIN sensitivity represents one of the best available, –67 dB m. If the specification is decreased, the allowable APD dark currents will be allowed to increase. It should be noted that the values given in Table 7.1 must be satisfied over the whole operating temperature of an APD. As dark current is thermally activated (section 7.2.4), this means that the values in Table 7.1 must be satisfied at the maximum operating temperature, generally 70 °C. At room temperature the maximum allowable dark currents will be ∼10 times smaller than those indicated. These extremely low dark currents are quite difficult to achieve in APDs. Germanium, because of its high intrinsic dark current, is unlikely ever to be a material to meet these specifications.

7.5.2.3   Comparison with non-ideal PIN

The two previous sections have looked at the effect of dark current when comparing the sensitivity of an avalanche photodetector with a noiseless PIN detector. Figure 7.29 shows the result of making the dark current I_{dm} of equal value for the diodes, where the sensitivity ratio is plotted vs bit rate for several values of k. It is

B (Mbit/s)	$\eta_i \bar{P}_{pin}$ (dB m)	I_{dm} (nA)			
		$k = 1$	0.5	0.1	0.025
50	−50	1.0	0.7	0.3	0.1
100	−47	2.0	1.6	0.6	0.2
500	−38	13	9.5	3.5	1.9
1000	−34	27	19	7.0	3.2
2000	−30	67	45	16	8.1

Table 7.1 The values of dark current at which an APD sensitivity is decreased by 1 dB from its value for zero dark current for several values of bit rate and ionization rate ratios.

clear that an increasing dark current has a dramatic effect on the APD sensitivity advantage, particularly for low bit rates. Indeed, the high dark current typical of germanium APDs ($>$ 100 nA, and $k = 1.0$) gives no advantage to this type of diode over a PIN at bit rates $<$ 100–300 Mbit/s. This bit rate range will be even higher if higher operating temperatures are demanded, due to the thermally activated nature of the dark current mentioned above. For a low dark current device, such as one made from $In_{0.53}Ga_{0.47}As/InP$, APDs should have significant sensitivity advantages over PIN diodes, especially at high bit rates.

7.5.2.4   PIN vs APD, Ge vs InGaAs for long wavelength

It should be clear from all that has been said during this and the previous chapter that there are only three material/device systems that satisfy the necessary requirements for efficient detection at the two important wavelengths of 1.3 and 1.55 μm: Ge and $In_{0.53}Ga_{0.47}As/InP$ APDs, and $In_{0.53}Ga_{0.47}As$ PIN diodes. Germanium devices have been available for over two decades, and in that respect represent a mature feature in the market. The InGaAs devices are really a 1980s phenomenon, and the APD is especially immature in this respect.

As shown in the last section, a germanium APD with its high dark current is less desirable as a photodetector than a PIN diode at low bit rates. A clearer comparison is shown in Figure 7.30(a) [67], where two values of the input capacitance C_T to an InGaAs PIN diode are shown. As noted in section 6.5.2, the amplifier noise so important in a PIN receiver increases with increasing input capacitance, giving reduced sensitivity as shown. The PIN diode has greater sensitivity over the APD for low bit rates, with the crossover point being $\sim$ 500 Mbit/s for $C_T = 1.5$ pF and $\geq$ 2 Gbit/s for a high performance PIN with $C_T = 0.45$ pF. It is clear that even a high quality germanium APD gives only a marginal improvement at the high bit rate end, and a significant degradation at the low end. Considering also that the

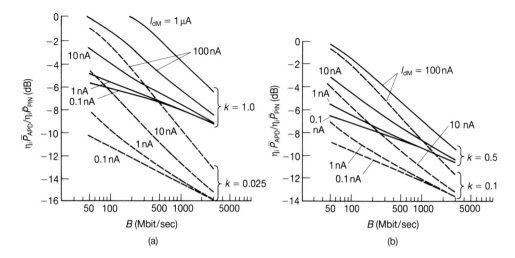

Figure 7.29 The relative sensitivities of a PIN diode and an APD for a fixed value of dark current (©Academic Press Inc.: reproduced by kind permission).

APD is far more temperature sensitive, both in terms of bias circuitry and dark current, and that APDs are more difficult to fabricate than PIN diodes it appears that an $In_{0.53}Ga_{0.47}As$ PIN detector has the overall advantage where maximum bit rate is not the primary system requirement. Another disadvantage of germanium is that it is significantly less sensitive to 1.55 μm than to 1.3 μm, whereas $In_{0.53}Ga_{0.47}As$ has a fairly flat absorption characteristic over this wavelength range.

When comparing similar materials but different diode structures, it is clear that an APD usually has an advantage over a PIN diode. This is illustrated in Figure 7.30(b) for $In_{0.53}Ga_{0.47}As$, comparing a heterostructure APD with a PIN detector using the same GaAs FET transimpedance amplifier [68]. For a fixed bit rate of 45 Mbit/s, the maximum sensitivity advantage of the APD was 4.8 dB over that of the PIN diode. Further improvements could be expected with the heterostructure design optimized for minimum dark current.

7.6   Integration

In section 6.6 we covered details of integration advantages and difficulties when discussing PIN diodes. In particular we noted the importance of yield when fabricating diode arrays. Avalanche photodetectors have a low yield, and so device arrays based on this type of diode tend to be avoided. For similar reasons integration with other components has not been extensively investigated. However,

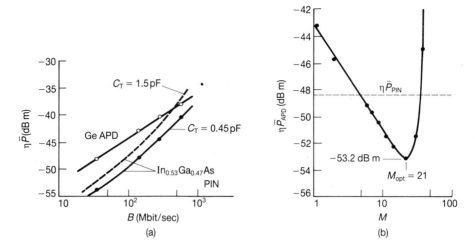

Figure 7.30 (a) The sensitivity of Ge or $In_{0.53}Ga_{0.47}As$ as an APD material. (b) The sensitivity of $In_{0.53}Ga_{0.47}As$ as a PIN diode or an APD (©Academic Press Inc.: reproduced by kind permission).

one successful example used an InGaAs/InGaAsP/InP APD followed by a hybrid GaAs preamplifier, with direct coupling eliminating the stray capacitance to ground and improving the preamplifier bandwidth [69]. The whole system operated at 8 Gbit/s.

7.7   PIN vs APD detector

From a noise perspective comparisons have already been made between these two devices in section 7.5.2. As shown, an APD usually has a significant sensitivity advantage over the PIN diode. When comparing different materials as well as different devices, however, this isn't always true, as Figure 7.30(a) shows. To summarize this and all the other comparisons between the two devices, the following points are made:

(i) APDs have greater sensitivity for a given material, and hence can be used to detect weaker signals over longer distances of fiber at a higher bit rate, or some combination of these three factors.

(ii) APDs have a multiplied dark current, which means that for long wavelength detection a PIN diode may have greater sensitivity than an APD of a different material – the InGaAs PIN vs the Ge APD in section 7.5.2.4 is an example of this.

(iii) Only PIN diodes are useful in coherent detection systems, where the input signal is boosted by a local oscillator.

(iv) PIN diodes are easier to fabricate, and hence produce higher yield devices and arrays at lower cost.

(v) PIN diodes are easier to integrate, and PINFETs can offset some of the sensitivity advantage of an APD over a PIN diode.

(vi) APDs are very temperature sensitive, not just for dark current (also affects PINs) but also for the multiplication factor. Some stabilization is usually required.

(vii) APDs require a high (tens or hundreds of volts) operating voltage.

As is usually the case, the choice of one or other type of photodetector is a balance between all the factors that contribute to the cost, performance, complexity and in-use reliability.

7.8 Problems

1. Why are avalanche photodiodes (APDs) far more temperature sensitive than PIN diodes?

2. Clearly an APD power supply works at much higher voltages than that required by a PIN diode. What other constraints are put on an APD supply?

3. How would you expect the ionization coefficients of a semiconductor to depend on the value of the band gap?

4. Calculate the multiplication factor for an APD with a gain region width of 40 μm if the electron ionization rate is 50 times greater than that of the holes, and the electron ionization coefficient is 600 cm^{-1}.

5. The quantum efficiency of a particular APD is 0.7 for detection at 0.85 μm. For an incident optical power of 0.3 μW the output current is 8 μA. Determine the responsivity, the photocurrent before multiplication and hence the multiplication factor of the device.

6. A particular silicon p$^+\pi$pn$^+$ RAPD has its four regions formed with 5×10^{18}: 10^{13}: 10^{15}: 10^{18} dopants cm^{-3}. If V_{bi} for silicon is 0.7 V, calculate the reverse bias required to fully deplete the structure if the p-region is 4 μm thick. Hence calculate the values of the maximum electric field and the electric field in the intrinsic region if the latter is 100 μm thick.

7. What are the advantages of a separate avalanche and gain (SAG) structure over a conventional APD?

8. What are the main differences between an RAPD, a SAM-APD and a SAGM-APD?

9. Why would the formation of microplasmas on reverse bias never be likely to be exploited as a light source?

10. A particular InGaAs APD used to detect 1.55 μm radiation has a multiplication factor of 30. If the responsivity is 0.9 A W^{-1} and a single frequency

source produces 10^{11} photons per second incident on the APD, calculate the quantum efficiency and photocurrent.

11. Calculate the likely breakdown voltage in an $In_{0.53}Ga_{0.47}As$ APD for doping densities of 10^{14}, 10^{15} and 10^{16} cm^{-3}.

7.9   References

1. K G McKay and K B McAfee, 'Electron Multiplication in Silicon and Germanium', *Phys. Rev.* **91**, 1079 (1953).
2. S M Sze and G Gibbons, 'Avalanche Breakdown Voltages of Abrupt and Linearly Graded p-n Junctions in Ge, Si, GaAs and GaP', *Appl. Phys. Lett.* **8**, 111 (1966).
3. S K Ghandhi, *Semiconductor Power Devices*, Wiley, 1977, p. 56.
4. G E Stillman and C M Wolfe, 'Avalanche Photodiodes', in Semiconductors and Semimetals, vol. 12: *Infrared Detectors II*, R K Willardson and A C Beer, eds, Academic Press, 1977, p. 330.
5. C A Lee, R A Logan, R L Batdorf, J J Kleimack and W Wiegmann, 'Ionisation Rates of Holes and Electrons in Silicon', *Phys. Rev.* **134**, A761 (1964).
6. T P Pearsall, F Capasso, R E Nahory, M A Pollack and J R Chelikowsky, 'The Band Structure Dependence of Impact Ionization by Hot Carriers in Semiconductors: GaAs', *Solid State Electron.* **21**, 297 (1978).
7. F Capasso, 'Physics of Avalanche Photodiodes', in Semiconductors and Semimetals, vol. 22D: *Photodetectors*, W T Tsang, ed., Academic Press, 1985, p. 52.
8. See [7], p. 79–105.
9. K G McKay, 'Avalanche Breakdown in Silicon', *Phys. Rev.* **94**, 877 (1954).
10. S L Miller, 'Avalanche Breakdown in Germanium', *Phys. Rev.* **99**, 1234 (1955).
11. R J McIntyre, 'Multiplication Noise in Uniform Avalanche Photodiodes', *IEEE Trans. Electron. Dev.* **ED-13**, 164 (1966).
12. P P Webb, R J McIntyre and J Conradi, 'Properties of Avalanche Photodiodes', *RCA Review* **35**, 234 (1974).
13. S L Miller, 'Ionisation Rates for Holes and Electrons in Silicon', *Phys. Rev.* **105**, 1246 (1957).
14. W Schockley, 'Problems Related to p-n Junctions in Silicon', *Solid State Electron.* **2**, 35 (1961).
15. T Kaneda, 'Silicon and Germanium Avalanche Photodiodes', in Semiconductors and Semimetals, vol. 22D: *Photodetectors*, W T Tsang, ed., Academic Press, 1985, p. 282ff.
16. A G Chynoweth, 'Ionisation Rates for Electrons and Holes in Silicon', *Phys. Rev.* **109**, 1537 (1958).

17. W N Grant, 'Electron and Hole Ionisation Rates in Epitaxial Silicon at High Electric Fields', *Solid State Electron.* **16**, 1189 (1973).

18. T Kaneda, H Matsumoto and T Yamaoka, 'A Model for Reach-Through Avalanche Photodiodes (RAPDs)', *J. Appl. Phys.* **47**, 3135 (1976).

19. Ref. 7, p. 1-66.

20. R Newman, 'Visible Light from a Silicon p-n Junction', *Phys. Rev.* **100**, 700 (1955).

21. A G Chynoweth and K G McKay, 'Photon Emission from Avalanche Breakdown in Silicon', *Phys. Rev.* **102**, 369 (1956).

22. A G Chynoweth and G L Pearson, 'Effect of Dislocations on Breakdown in Silicon p-n Junctions', *J. Appl. Phys.* **29**, 1103 (1958).

23. R L Batdorf, A G Chynoweth, G C Dacey and P W Foy, 'Uniform Silicon p-n Junctions. I. Broad Area Breakdown', *J. Appl. Phys.* **31**, 1153 (1960).

24. K M Johnson, 'High Speed Photodiode Signal Enhancement at Avalanche Breakdown Voltage', *IEEE Trans. Electron. Dev.* **ED-12**, 55 (1965).

25. See [4], p. 358.

26. L K Anderson, P G McMullin, L A D'Asaro and A Goetzberger, 'Microwave Photodiodes Exhibiting Microplasma-free Carrier Multiplication', *Appl. Phys. Lett.* **6**, 62 (1966).

27. W T Lynch, 'Elimination of the Guard Ring in Uniform Avalanche Photodiodes', *IEEE Trans. Electron. Dev.* **ED-15**, 735 (1968).

28. R J Locker and G C Huth, 'A New Ionising Radiation Detection Concept which Employs Semiconductor Avalanche Amplification and the Tunnel Diode Element', *Appl. Phys. Lett.* **9**, 227 (1966).

29. H W Ruegg, 'An Optimised Avalanche Photodiode', *IEEE Trans. Electron. Dev.* **ED-14**, 239 (1967).

30. N A Foss and S A Ward, 'Large Area Metal-Oxide-Semiconductor Avalanche Photodiodes', *J. Appl. Phys.* **44**, 728 (1973).

31. H Melchior, A R Hartman, D P Schinke and T E Seidel, 'Planar Epitaxial Silicon Avalanche Photodiode', *Bell System Tech. J.* **57**, 1791 (1978).

32. S Cova, A Longoni and A Andreoni, 'Towards Picosecond Resolution with Single Photon Avalanche Diodes', *Rev. Sci. Instrum.* **52**, 408 (1981).

33. M Ghioni, S Cova, A Lacaita and G Ripamonti, 'New Silicon Epitaxial Avalanche Diode for Single Photon Timing at Room Temperature', *Elec. Lett.* **24**, 1476 (1988).

34. A Lacaita, M Ghioni, F Zappa, G Ripamonti and S Cova, 'Recent Advances in the Detection of Optical Photons with Silicon Photodiodes', *Physics Research A: Nuclear Instruments and Methods* **A326**, 290 (1993).

35. A Lacaita, S Cova, F Zappa and P A Francese, 'Subnanosecond Single-Photon Timing with Commercially Available Germanium Photodiodes', *Optics Lett.* **18**, 75 (1993).

36. S C Jwo, M-T Wu, Y-K Fang, Y-W Chen, J-W Hong and C-Y Chang, 'Amorphous Silicon/Silicon Carbide Superlattice Avalanche Photodiodes', *IEEE Trans. Electron. Dev.* **ED-35**, 1279 (1988).

37. H Melchior and W T Lynch, 'Signal and Noise Response of High Speed Germanium Avalanche Photodiodes', *IEEE Trans. Electron. Dev.* **ED-13**, 829 (1966).

38. O Mikami, H Ando, H Kanbe, T Mikawa, T Kaneda and Y Toyama, 'Improved Germanium Avalanche Photodiodes', *IEEE J. Quantum Electron.* **QE-16**, 1002 (1980).

39. See [15], p. 295.

40. M Niwa, Y Tashiro, K Minemura, and H Iwasaki, 'High Sensitivity Hi–Lo Germanium Avalanche Photodiode for 1.5 μm Wavelength Optical Communication', *Elec. Lett.* **20**, 552 (1984).

41. H Ando, H Kanbe, T Kimura, T Yamaoka and T Kaneda, 'Characteristics of Germanium Avalanche Photodiodes in the Wavelength Region of 1–1.6 μm', *IEEE J. Quantum Electron.* **QE-14**, 804 (1978).

42. T Mikawa, S Kagawa and T Kaneda, 'Germanium Reachthrough Avalanche Photodiodes for Optical Communication Systems at 1.55 μm Wavelength Region', *IEEE Trans. Electron. Dev.* **ED-31**, 971 (1984).

43. W T Lindley, R J Phelan, Jr, C M Wolfe and A G Foyt, 'GaAs Schottky Barrier Avalanche Photodiodes', *Appl. Phys. Lett.* **14**, 197 (1969).

44. G E Stillman, C M Wolfe, A G Foyt and W T Lindley, 'Schottky Barrier $In_xGa_{1-x}As$ Alloy Avalanche Photodiodes for 1.06 μm', *Appl. Phys. Lett.* **24**, 8 (1974).

45. F Capasso, W T Tsang, A L Hutchinson and G F Williams, 'Enhancement of Electron Impact Ionisation in a Superlattice: A New Avalanche Photodiode with a Large Ionisation Rate Ratio', *Appl. Phys. Lett.* **40**, 38 (1982).

46. C E Hurwitz and J J Hsieh, 'GaInAsP/InP Avalanche Photodiodes', *Appl. Phys. Lett.* **32**, 487 (1978).

47. Y Takanashi and Y Horikoshi, 'InGaAsP/InP Avalanche Photodiode', *Jpn. J. Appl. Phys.* **17**, 2065 (1978).

48. S R Forrest, M DiDomenico, Jr, R G Smith and H J Stocker, 'Evidence for Tunneling in Reverse Biased III–V Photodetector Diodes', *Appl. Phys. Lett.* **36**, 580 (1980).

49. S R Forrest, R F Leheny, R E Nahory and M A Pollack, '$In_{0.53}Ga_{0.47}As$ Photodiodes with Dark Current Limited by Generation–Recombination and Tunneling', *Appl. Phys. Lett.* **37**, 322 (1980).

50. S R Forrest, 'Performance of $In_xGa_{1-x}As_yP_{1-y}$ Photodiodes with Dark Current Limited by Diffusion, Generation Recombination and Tunneling', *IEEE J. Quantum Electron.* **QE-17**, 217 (1981).

51. S M Sze, *Physics of Semiconductor Devices*, 2nd ed., Wiley, 1981, p. 104.

52. K Nishida, K Taguchi and Y Matsumoto, 'InGaAsP Heterostructure Avalanche Photodiodes with High Avalanche Gain', *Appl. Phys. Lett.* **35**, 251 (1979).

53. S R Forrest, R G Smith and O K Kim, 'Performance of $In_{0.53}Ga_{0.47}As/InP$ Avalanche Photodiodes', *IEEE J. Quantum Electron.* **QE-18**, 2040 (1982).

54. S R Forrest, O K Kim and R G Smith, 'Optical Response Time of In$_{0.53}$Ga$_{0.47}$As/InP Avalanche Photodiodes', *Appl. Phys. Lett.* **41**, 95 (1982).

55. O K Kim, S R Forrest, W A Bonner and R G Smith, 'A High Gain In$_{0.53}$Ga$_{0.47}$As/InP Avalanche Photodiode with no Tunneling Leakage Current', *Appl. Phys. Lett.* **39**, 402 (1981).

56. J C Campbell, A G Dentai, W S Holden and B L Kasper, 'High Performance Avalanche Photodiode with Separate Absorption, 'Grading' and Multiplication Regions', *Elec. Lett.* **19**, 818 (1983).

57. T Shirai, S Yamazaki, H Kawata, K Nakajima and T Kaneda, 'A Planar InP/InGaAsP Heterostructure Avalanche Photodiode', *IEEE Trans. Electron. Dev.* **ED-29**, 1404 (1982).

58. K Yasuda, Y Kishi, T Shirai, T Mikawa, S Yamazaki and T Kaneda, 'InP/InGaAs Buried Structure Avalanche Photodiodes', *Elec. Lett.* **20**, 158 (1984).

59. Y Liu, S R Forrest, V S Ban, K M Woodruff, J Colosi, G C Erikson, M J Lange and G H Olsen, 'Simple, Very Low Dark Current, Planar Long-Wavelength Avalanche Photodiode', *Appl. Phys. Lett.* **53**, 1311 (1988).

60. H Sudo and M Suzuki, 'Surface Degradation Mechanism of InP/InGaAs APDs' *J. Lightwave Technol.* **6**, 1496 (1988).

61. A J Moseley, J Urquhart, P D Hodson, J R Riffat and J I Davies, 'InGaAs/InP SAGM Avalanche Photodiodes Incorporating a Pseudoquaternary Superlattice Graded Heterojunction Grown by Atmospheric Pressure MOCVD', *Elec. Lett.* **23**, 914 (1987).

62. A J Moseley, J Urquhart and J R Riffat, 'High Speed GaInAs/InP Multiquantum Well Avalanche Photodiodes Grown by Atmospheric Pressure MOCVD', *Elec. Lett.* **24**, 313 (1988).

63. D Gershoni, H Tomkin and M B Panish, 'Strained Layer Ga$_{1-x}$In$_x$As/InP Avalanche Photodetectors', *Appl. Phys. Lett.* **53**, 1294 (1988).

64. R G Smith and S R Forrest, 'Sensitivity of Avalanche Photodetector Receivers for Long Wavelength Optical Communications', *Bell System Tech. J.* **61**, 2929 (1982).

65. T P Pearsall and M A Pollack, 'Compound Semiconductor Photodiodes', in Semiconductors and Semimetals, vol. 22D: *Photodetectors*, W T Tsang, ed, Academic Press, 1985, p. 183.

66. S R Forrest, 'Sensitivity of Avalanche Photodetector Receivers for High Bit-Rate Long-Wavelength Optical Communication Systems', in Semiconductors and Semimetals, vol. 22D: *Photodetectors*, W T Tsang, ed, Academic Press, 1985, p. 344ff.

67. D R Smith, R C Hooper, P P Smyth and D Wake, 'Experimental Comparison of a Germanium Avalanche Photodiode and InGaAs PINFET Receiver for Longer Wavelength Optical Communication Systems', *Elec. Lett.* **18**, 453 (1982).

68. S R Forrest, G F Williams, O K Kim and R G Smith, 'Excess Noise and Receiver Sensitivity Measurements of $In_{0.53}Ga_{0.47}As/InP$ Avalanche Photodiodes', *Elec. Lett.* **17**, 917 (1981).

69. B L Kasper, J C Campbell, J R Talman, A H Gnauck, J E Bowers and W S Holden, 'An APD/FET Optical Receiver Operating at 8 Gbit/s', *IEEE J. Lightwave Technol.* **LT-5**, 344 (1987).

8

Materials

From a materials point of view, the integrated circuit industry has been built up on the basis of an understanding of single crystal silicon, refinement of growth techniques to produce large crystals, and the ability to selectively dope parts of a silicon wafer. With the exception of some silicon and germanium photodetectors, semiconductor optoelectronic devices rely on compound materials, usually III–V based, as their starting point for device fabrication. Here single crystal and doping studies are important, but are complicated by the two-element nature of the crystal. The success of large volume crystal growth has been especially held back by a lack of complete understanding of two-element systems.

However, where optoelectronic devices really differ from silicon ICs is in the emphasis on epitaxial techniques; the ability to grow a three or four element single crystal compound semiconductor using a two-element substrate as both the seed for growth and the physical support of the new material has been the key issue in realizing the current maturity of optoelectronic devices. Silicon relies on epitaxy for just a few specialist applications, although the volume and diversity of these is continually increasing.

This chapter looks at the main bulk crystal growth techniques, leading on to the three different systems of epitaxy. Doping techniques, both high temperature diffusion and ion implantation, are then discussed and finally a section on chemical etching is included.

8.1 Bulk crystal growth

The success of large volume single crystal compound semiconductor growth has not kept pace with its equivalent in silicon. Whilst the latter has continually increased available device area, such that 4" wafers were the norm in 1980 and 8" in 1993 for new IC fabrication plants, gallium arsenide wafers, arguably the most characterized of the compound semiconductor materials, were at the 2" stage in 1980, 3" by 1985 and 4" diameter GaAs by 1990. There are two main reasons for the difference in progress:

(i) the growth of a compound semiconductor is always more difficult than that of a single-element system, and hence GaAs wafer size will always trail that of Si given the same effort,

(ii) the demand from device manufacturers for large area compound semiconductors is lacking. Although 4" is available, most optoelectronic fabrication plants are quite happy with 2" or 3", as the volume of device sales does not justify increased production with its associated costs. A few GaAs IC foundries use 4" wafers.

The growth techniques mentioned here, whilst applicable to, and indeed derived from, silicon, are all mentioned in the context of the important III–V compound semiconductors. Whatever the technique, the desired outcome is the same: uniformity and reproducibility of electrical characteristics and the minimization of unwanted impurities and defects. Silicon parameters can be used as the 'reference' for the III–V materials, and this elemental semiconductor has comparatively high values for thermal conductivity, critically resolved sheer stress and stacking fault energy. This means that silicon will have lower thermal gradients and dislocation densities during growth, and under a given set of conditions can form a larger crystal with fewer faults than compound semiconductors. Also to be considered, however, for III-V materials are the constitution and phase diagram of a binary system.

8.1.1   Phase diagram

The base elements (Ga, As, In and P) used to make wafers can now all be obtained with a high degree of purity (99.9999% or 6N (six nines)). In determining the correct growth conditions from these elements a phase diagram is essential. These are given for GaAs, InP and GaP in Figure 8.1 [1–3], and show the relative phases (gas, liquid, solid) of the two element combination as a function of stoichiometry, i.e. relative atomic ratios, and temperature. Consideration of these systems and vapour pressure vs temperature curves help to determine the optimum conditions for melt-originated growth, a feature of both the liquid encapsulated Czochralski (LEC) and Bridgmann techniques. For instance, at any given temperature arsenic has a higher vapour pressure than gallium, and so will be preferentially lost from a liquid Ga–As mixture. Suitable overpressure and/or encapsulation techniques, discussed in more detail in the forthcoming sections, are needed to prevent this happening and maintain stoichiometry.

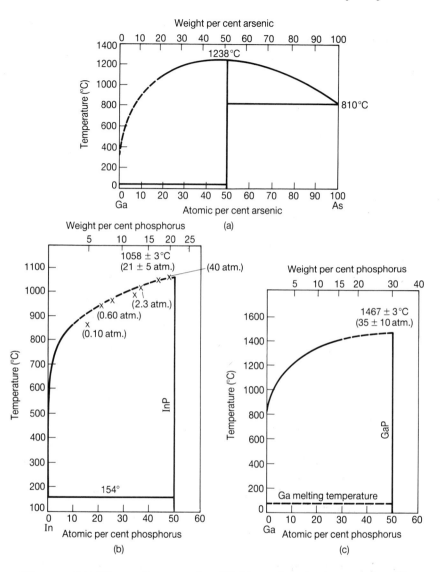

Figure 8.1 Phase diagrams for III–V semiconductors: (a) gallium arsenide, (b) indium phosphide, and (c) gallium phosphide (©McGraw Hill: reproduced by kind permission).

8.1.2 Liquid encapsulated Czochralski (LEC) method

This is a variation on the basic Czochralski method for growing silicon wafers, with a layer of high temperature stable liquid floating on top of the melt, held in place by an ambient overpressure. It is used to grow GaAs, InP and GaP, with gallium arsenide being the first material synthesized by this technique [4].

A fuller and more detailed revision of LEC growth can be found in [5] and [6], but the basic equipment used in this technique is shown in Figure 8.2. A molten mixture of, in this case, gallium and arsenic is heated in a crucible by resistance and/or r.f. heating. The crucible is pyrolytic boron nitride (PBN), as it has been found that this material can be used several times over (unlike quartz) and does not act as a source of unintentional silicon dopants (again unlike quartz). The melt is contained by a layer of boric oxide, which is an inert liquid with both a low melting point and vapour pressure. The whole system is contained in a pressure vessel, with an inert gas ambient providing an overpressure to the melt. The first users of this technique reported growth under pressures of up to 50 atm; more recently low (< 3 atm) and medium (3–10 atm) pressure ranges have been used. A comparison between high and low pressure systems with regard to GaAs wafer specifications is shown in Table 8.1.

Property	HP-LEC	LP-LEC
Environmental heat loss	High	Low
Temperature gradient	Abrupt	Gradual
Arsenic loss	Large	Small
Purity	Comparable	Comparable
Ingot yield	Better	Worse
Electrical properties	Comparable	Comparable
Etch pit density	Large	Small
Maintenance	Difficult	Easy
Modifications	Difficult	Easy
As-grown mechanical properties	Worse	Better

Table 8.1 A comparison of the features of high pressure (HP-LEC) and low pressure (LP-LEC) grown GaAs.

A seed single crystal material, usually of low dislocation density, is dipped into the melt through the liquid B_2O_3 and pulled out again (hence the alternative name for such a growth system – puller). The rotational speed of the seed ($\sim$ 6 r.p.m.) and its pull rate (7 mm h^{-1}) are crucial to the success of the technique. The crucible is generally rotated too, either in a counter- or iso-direction to that of the seed. The whole process can be monitored by a video camera through a window in the pressure vessel (the transparency of B_2O_3 is helpful in this way) and microprocessor

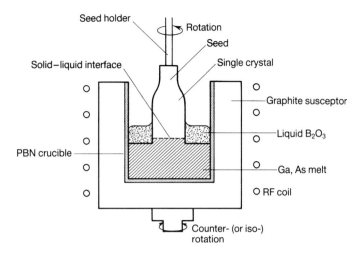

Figure 8.2 Liquid encapsulated Czochralski (LEC) growth of GaAs.

control of temperature, rotational speeds and pull rate help to minimize errors in the growth procedure. After the crystal has been pulled, it is slowly cooled at $\sim 50\ °C\,h^{-1}$ to minimize the possibility of temperature induced stress causing dislocations in the material.

Crystals are not defect free, however, and the dislocation density produced by this method (around 10^4 to $10^5\ cm^{-2}$) is its major disadvantage when compared to the Horizontal Bridgmann (HB) technique. Dislocations can be highlighted by etching sliced wafers from a crystal in hot KOH, which preferentially etches at these defects. The resulting etch pit density (dislocation density) often follows a 'W' shape across the wafer (Figure 8.3), peaking at the edge of the slice [7]. This is thought to be a thermal problem due to convection in the melt, with temperature non-uniformity (greater at the edge of the crystal) leading to an increase in dislocation density.

As well as GaAs, GaP and InP can be grown this way. In fact, it is the only growth technique for GaP, as the HB method relies on the use of quartz, which cannot withstand the temperatures/pressures (1470 °C at 2.3 atm). For indium phosphide, the low melting point associated with the growth (1062 °C) leads to the In/P melt sticking to the B_2O_3 because of the latter's higher viscosity at low temperatures. This, and a lower stacking fault energy in InP, tends to form twin crystals very readily, which is obviously undesirable.

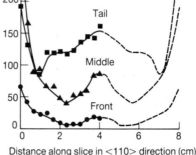

Figure 8.3 Etch pit density as a function of position across a wafer (©John Wiley & Sons: reproduced by kind permission).

8.1.3   Horizontal Bridgmann (HB) method

This technique has been in use for longer than the LEC method and, as we shall see, produces wafers of very different characteristics to those formed in a puller.

A schematic of a HB growth system is shown in Figure 8.4. A quartz ampoule several feet long contains a quartz boat in which the growth takes place. This assembly is placed inside a zoned heating system, with the ability to move the heater/quartz assemblies relative to each other. A GaAs seed crystal is placed at one end of the quartz boat, and molten GaAs is maintained in the bulk of the boat region (T_1 zone $\sim 1250\,°C$). An arsenic overpressure is provided by the elemental source at one end of the ampoule. As the seed end of the melt moves out of the T_1 zone to the cooler T_2 zone, it solidifies into single crystal GaAs.

The seed crystal is usually chosen to give a $\langle 111 \rangle$ direction parallel to the growth axis. If wafers were sawn from this crystal perpendicular to this axis, (111) material would result. It is more usual, especially for epitaxial applications, to have (100) material. Hence HB grown crystals are sawn at an angle of 54.7° to the axis to give a (100) slice. The growth and sawing method then gives rise to the unique geometry of HB grown material. As grown, the crystal cross-section follows that of its boat container, giving a characteristic part flat/part circular section as shown in Figure 8.5(a), corresponding to the form of a liquid not quite filling a cylindrical boat. After the angled sawing, the wafers are shaped as in Figure 8.5(b), in a much larger area and a characteristic D-shape. These can be ground to give a

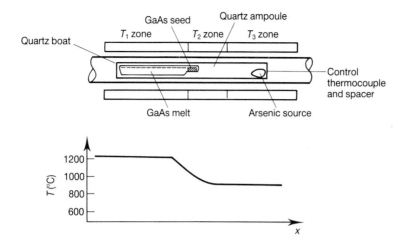

Figure 8.4 Horizontal Bridgmann (HB) growth system.

circular shape as in Figure 8.5(c), but obviously a lot of material is lost in doing this. Excessive thermal gradients in the melt have prevented the extension of HB techniques beyond a maximum of about 65 mm along the flat part of a D-shaped wafer; after this the result tends to be twin crystal or even polycrystalline material.

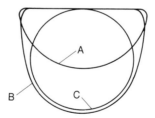

Figure 8.5 Horizontal Bridgmann slices cut at various orientations: (a) normal to the crystal axis (111), (b) cut at 54.7°(100), and (c) circular slice after shaping from (b).

The lack of circular wafers of a suitable size has led to a reluctance by device manufacturers to take HB grown wafers for IC fabrication. But as semi-insulating material is usually required for this application, a more serious problem than geometry manifests itself with the doping properties of HB grown wafers. Because they are grown in a quartz boat, it is easy to incorporate unwanted amounts of silicon into the melt (a graphite boat can be used, but this leads to a similar problem with carbon). A large amount of chromium (10^{17} cm^{-3}) is usually added to the melt to compensate for the silicon donor levels and make the material semi-insulating, but it has been found that annealing HB wafers grown in this way redistributes the chromium, leading to a conductive p-layer at the surface after annealing; this has important ramifications for ion implantation or diffusion doping.

The HB technique does have two important advantages over LEC growth: dislocation densities are usually lower ($1\text{--}3 \times 10^4$ cm^{-2}) and, because of the lessons learned from chromium doping, the ability is there to deliberately incorporate dopants and give a conducting wafer if semi-insulating material is not required. Table 8.2 compares typical electrical properties of LEC and HB grown material using GaAs, InP and GaP as examples.

Semiconductor	Technique	Dopant	Concentration (cm^{-3})	Resistivity (Ω cm)
GaAs	LEC	–	intrinsic	1.0×10^7
	HB	Cr		5×10^8
	HB	(n) Si, Te	$1\text{--}5 \times 10^{18}$	$0.8\text{--}2.0 \times 10^{-3}$
	HB	(p) Zn	$1\text{--}5 \times 10^{18}$	$1.0\text{--}4.0 \times 10^{-2}$
InP	LEC	Fe		$> 1.0 \times 10^7$
	LEC	(n) S, Sn	$1\text{--}8 \times 10^{18}$	$10^{-4}\text{--}10^{-2}$
	LEC	(p) Zn, Cd		
GaP	LEC	(n) S, Te	$2\text{--}7 \times 10^{17}$	
	LEC	(p) Zn	$2\text{--}7 \times 10^{17}$	

Table 8.2 Electrical characteristics of LEC and HB grown substrates. Note that the HB technique is not normally used to produce InP and GaP because of the very high vapour pressure over the melt.

If deliberate doping is incorporated, the impurity distributions can be calculated from the following equation [8]:

$$C_s = k_0 C_0 \left[1 - \frac{M}{M_0} \right]^{k_0 - 1} \tag{8.1}$$

$$\text{and} \quad k_e = \frac{k_0}{k_0 + (1 - k_0) \exp(-\nu\delta/D)} \tag{8.2}$$

where C_0 is the initial doping concentration in the melt (weight for weight), C_s is the equivalent concentration of dopant in the solid, k_0 and k_e are respectively the equilibrium and effective segregation coefficients, M and M_0 are respectively the mass of grown crystal and original melt, ν is the crystal growth velocity, δ is the distance into the liquid from the melt interface, i.e. where $C_l(x) = C_l$, and D is the dopant diffusion coefficient in the melt. The term k_0 is replaced in (8.1) by the term k_e if the value of C_s is less than its liquid equivalent C_l, and the rejection rate of dopants at the melt-interface is greater than the removal rate by diffusion. This situation leads to a concentration gradient of dopants starting at this interface (Figure 8.6).

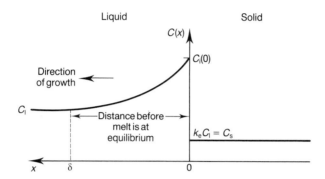

Figure 8.6 Concentration of dopants at a liquid–solid interface.

8.1.4 Wafer shaping

Once a solid piece of compound semiconductor has been formed (alternatively called the crystal, boule or ingot) it has to be sawn into individual wafers. A HB grown crystal will have the shape already discussed in the last section, and LEC grown material will be cylindrical in form with a taper at the seed end of the crystal. 'Coracle' control of the diameter, where the growing crystal is pulled through a diameter-defining ring floating at the interface between the GaAs melt and B_2O_3 encapsulant [9], can provide good diameter control, although the formation of twin crystals can be a problem. An alternative is to apply a magnetic field (~ 0.3 T) along the axis of the growing crystal – this helps reduce the convection currents induced by temperature gradients in the melt [10]. After cooling, the ingot is ground to the correct diameter. The weight of the ingot is generally in the range of a few kilograms, and about 150 wafers can be obtained from a 3 kg 50 mm diameter GaAs crystal.

A flow chart for post-growth processing and characterization is shown in Figure 8.7. The seed and tail end of the crystal are removed and the quality material is tested for electrical (carrier concentration, resistivity, mobility) and physical (etch pit density) characteristics. X-ray techniques determine the crystal's orientation and specific 'flats' are ground along the length of the ingot to mark particular crystal directions. At least one 'major flat' is defined along a (110) plane, and an optional secondary flat is placed at 90° to this around the wafer (Figure 8.8 – note that American and European/Japanese (E–J) sourced material have two different standards for wafer orientation). The crystal is then sawn into slices, of thickness depending on diameter of slice and the material itself. The slices are edge bevelled to facilitate handling and polished using an Al_2O_3/glycerine mixture; polishing may be on one or both sides, depending on the application. A wet chemical etch can then be performed to remove any damage induced in the surface region by the preparation procedure, although this is often done a second time by the wafer buyer as part of the processing schedule. Typical mechanical characteristics are shown in Table 8.3; many variations on diameter/thickness are available.

After final inspection, round wafers are usually shipped in individual inert plastic carriers, whereas D-shaped wafers are placed in individual polythene envelopes and shipped in styrofoam boxes.

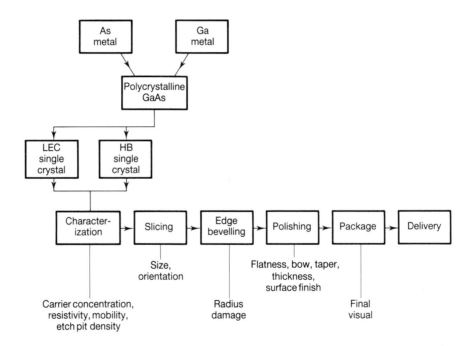

Figure 8.7 Process flow for GaAs wafer production from the purified elements Ga and As.

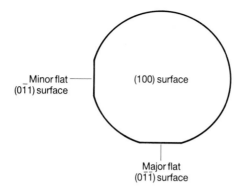

Figure 8.8 Orientation flats ground on a (100) wafer (E–J standard).

Material	Diameter (mm)	Thickness (μm)	Flatness (μm/25 mm of surface)	Bow (μm)
LEC GaAs	50.8 ± 0.4	500 ± 25	<2	<20
HB GaAs	50 mm along flat	400 ± 25	<2	<20
LEC InP	50.8 ± 0.4	350 ± 10	<2.5	<10

Table 8.3 Typical physical specifications of III–V substrates.

8.2 Epitaxy

The origin of the word 'epitaxy' is a combination of Greek terms (*epi* = upon, *taxis* = arrangement), and is used to denote the growth of crystalline material from a fluid phase onto a seed crystal, where the growing layer has the same crystal structure as the seed. Bulk crystals, i.e. those formed by HB or LEC methods, can rarely be used for optimized optoelectronic devices, for the following reasons:

(i) Emitters operating at different wavelengths are required. This requires different band gaps for the emitting region, implying the availability of many different semiconductors. Until recently, only wafers of one or two elements were available; growth techniques were needed to produce the AlGaAs, InGaAs, GaAsP, InGaAsP, etc. range of semiconductors needed for emitter technology. Whilst this reasoning is also true for detectors, often materials are used to detect photons away from their optimal wavelength, i.e. they operate with a reduced efficiency. A semiconductor such as $In_{1-x}Ga_xAs$ has only been fabricated in 1" diameter wafer form and with variable composition [11].

(ii) Material quality for bulk crystals is generally lower than that of epitaxial layers for compound semiconductors (the reverse is true for silicon). Defects such as vacancies and dislocations occur in higher densities in bulk material because of the higher temperatures, and hence steeper thermal gradients, involved.

Bulk grown crystals of III–V semiconductors are used as a seed for the epitaxial growth of other compound semiconductors; the wafers also act as physical support for the epitaxial layers which are no more than a few microns thick. The wafers are usually cut 2° off the [100] direction; this is the orientation that gives optimum surface morphology. Despite this, surface etching in appropriate solutions (see section 8.8.1.3) is necessary prior to growth. The first layer to be grown is often a buffer layer – this is a non-electrically active layer several microns thick which acts to take out any dislocations present on the surface of the bulk crystal. The active epilayers can then be grown on high quality material, and the chance of defect related performance degradation is minimized.

8.3   Liquid phase epitaxy (LPE)

Liquid phase epitaxy has some similarities with bulk crystal growth: both rely on a seed crystal that is in contact with a melt of the required composition, and temperature gradient techniques are used to produce material of the correct sto-ichiometry. The difference is that LPE uses comparatively transient phenomena, measured over minutes rather than hours, to deposit each layer in a sequence; bulk growth is a continuous phenomenon.

LPE was the first of the epitaxial techniques to be described and is the simplest. It provided much of the material for the early work on LEDs and lasers, and to this day is the volume method used for standard LED production.

8.3.1   Growth techniques

As with all growth systems, the key to understanding LPE is the phase diagram (Figure 8.1 for two-element III–V semiconductors). The region of concern here is shown in more detail in Figure 8.9 for GaAs. As low a process temperature as possible is used to minimize the formation of defects, bearing in mind that the tangent to the solid–liquid interface increases its slope rapidly at low temperatures. Consider a point on this interface, which has a certain atomic percentage of As in a Ga–As melt. If the temperature is lowered to the point b, solidification takes place until equilibrium can again be reached (point c). If the conditions are right, this solidification takes place epitaxially on the seeding substrate. This leaves a gallium rich solution, and arsenic diffusion through the melt to the solid–liquid interface must occur to maintain the growth of the layer. If the cooling rate is too fast, GaAs nucleation within the solution occurs, and a consideration of temperature dependent diffusion constants shows that the cooling rate should be about $1\,°\text{C}\,\text{min}^{-1}$ to avoid this. There are four different temperature–time regions used in LPE: step cooling, equilibrium cooling, supercooling and two-phase solution cooling [12]. A schematic of these is shown in Figure 8.10. All regimes begin with the substrate and solution physically separate, and at a higher temperature than the liquidus temperature T_l of the solution. Cooling then takes place and the indicators in Figure 8.10 show when each regime brings substrate and solution into contact.

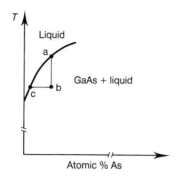

Figure 8.9 GaAs phase diagram of interest in LPE.

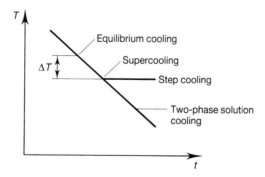

Figure 8.10 Temperature–time regimes used in LPE.

The equilibrium cooling technique has a constant cooling rate throughout the growth process, starting at the temperature when the growth solution is saturated (hence at equilibrium). It can be shown [12] that the grown layer thickness d is a function of temperature T and time t given by

$$d \;=\; \frac{4}{3C_s m}\left(\frac{D}{\pi}\right)^{1/2}\frac{\mathrm{d}T}{\mathrm{d}t}\,t^{3/2} \tag{8.3}$$

where D is the diffusion coefficient of arsenic in a gallium solution, C_s is the concentration of arsenic in the LPE grown solid, and m is the gradient of the liquidus curve at the time of contact.

The step and supercooling techniques are used where the chance of nucleation within the solution is negligible. Both involve an initial constant cooling rate to below T_l, but the step cooling technique then maintains a constant temperature on contact whereas the supercooling method continues to reduce temperature. Growth thicknesses are given by

$$d = \frac{2}{C_s m} \left(\frac{D}{\pi}\right)^{1/2} \Delta T_0 \, t^{1/2} \tag{8.4}$$

for step cooling, and

$$d = \frac{2}{C_s m} \left(\frac{D}{\pi}\right)^{1/2} \left(\Delta T_0 t^{1/2} + \frac{2}{3} \frac{dT}{dt} \, t^{3/2}\right) \tag{8.5}$$

for supercooling. It can be seen that, because supercooling is a combination of step-cooling and equilibrium cooling, the solution to the linear differential equation describing its growth is the sum of the separate solutions (8.3) and (8.4).

Two-phase solution cooling requires lowering the initial temperature sufficiently (below T_l) for spontaneous nucleation, and hence precipitation, to occur. The substrates are then brought into contact and cooling is continued. The precipitation reduces the solute concentration in the solution to the equilibrium value, and hence is an extension of the equilibrium cooling technique, but with a lower value of T_l.

The same principles apply to other III–V systems, although the phase diagrams for ternary and quaternary semiconductors are much more complicated. Hence compositional control during the epitaxial process is even more difficult, and it is normally only possible to achieve very thin layers of a fixed stoichiometry [13].

8.3.2   Growth equipment

8.3.2.1   Tipping system
This was the first reported of the LPE techniques [14], and consists of a graphite boat assembly which is rotated through a certain angle perpendicular to its main axis in order to bring the growth solution into contact with the substrate for a finite growth time (Figure 8.11) before being tipped back. A high purity ambient of hydrogen fills the atmosphere around the boat, which is placed in a quartz tube. This system, like the next one, is simple and straightforward in its operation, but is limited to the formation of a layer of fixed stoichiometry on a single substrate.

8.3.2.2   Vertical dipping system
This allows the even growth of an epilayer on several substrates simultaneously by moving the wafers into a stationary solution, as shown in Figure 8.12 [15]. Again,

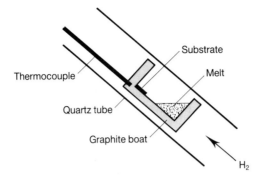

Figure 8.11 Tipping system for LPE.

a graphite boat is placed in a hydrogen atmosphere inside a quartz tube, and again only one solution may be used. However, pn junctions have been formed in GaAs this way by exploiting the temperature dependent doping properties of silicon. At a growth temperature below 820 °C silicon is incorporated as a donor, above 820 °C it becomes an acceptor. By using a solution containing silicon, and operating above and below this temperature threshold in one growth operation, an n-layer and p-layer can be epitaxially grown. Unfortunately, its application is limited to GaAs:Si and $Al_xGa_{1-x}As$:Si [16].

8.3.2.3 *Horizontal sliding system*
This is used to produce several successive epilayers of varying stoichiometry, and does so by bringing the substrate underneath various growth solutions, all enclosed in the same apparatus (Figure 8.13 and [16]). The substrate holder and slider are both made of graphite, and the atmosphere inside the quartz tube is again hydrogen. By appropriate control of temperature profiles along the LPE system, alloy composition, doping levels and layer thicknesses can be readily estimated.

8.3.2.4 *Melt-back method*
This was developed primarily for green LEDs based on GaP:S/GaP:Zn junctions (Figure 8.14 [17]). A GaP substrate, in contact with a gallium melt, is heated past its liquidus point until about 50 μm of the substrate surface is dissolved. Subsequent cooling results in an epitaxial layer growing on the remaining substrate, and during this cooling stage three types of gases are introduced into the hydrogen ambient:

  (i) H_2S, to provide sulphur doping by diffusion through the gallium melt, results in the growth of an n-layer,
 (ii) Zn vapour (from a solid source) to provide a p-layer,
(iii) NH_3 during junction growth to introduce an isoelectronic centre based on nitrogen (to maximize LED efficiency – see section 3.1.3).

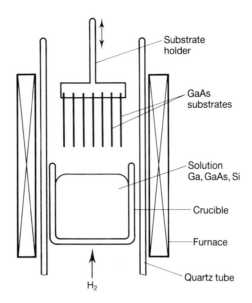

Figure 8.12 Vertical dipping system for LPE.

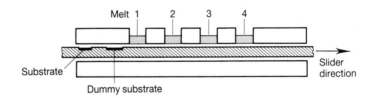

Figure 8.13 Horizontal sliding system for LPE.

8.3.3   Surface morphology

An ideal LPE produced surface should be flat, shiny, featureless and with a low density of underlying dislocations. Deviations away from the ideal growth condition, however, result in undesirable and very visible surface features – these are listed, along with their common causes, in Table 8.4 [18]. It is the myriad of different material surface defects that is the main problem with LPE as a growth technique, as subsequent device processing relies on flat featureless substrates. Defects are usually electrically active as well, leading to unwanted non-radiative recombination centres reducing the device efficiency of both LEDs and lasers.

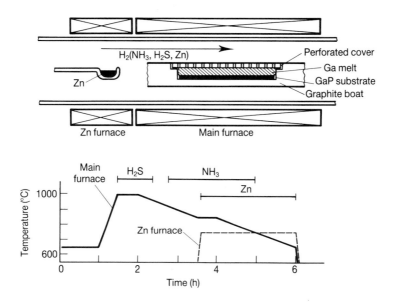

Figure 8.14 Melt-back method for LPE.

8.4 Vapour phase epitaxy (VPE)

Vapour phase epitaxy, also known by its alternative name chemical vapour deposition (CVD), was first reported for the fabrication of III–V material in 1959 [19], and nowadays can be readily split into two distinct areas of research:

(i) chloride transport,

(ii) metalorganic VPE (MOVPE, or MOCVD, or, where the term organo–metallic is preferred, OMVPE or OMCVD). Strictly speaking the suffix VPE rather than CVD should be used in this context, because the latter does not explicitly imply epitaxial growth.

As might be inferred from its title, vapour phase epitaxy involves bringing the constituent atoms of the growth layer to the surface of the substrate in the vapour phase. Reactions take place near the surface which result in atoms being deposited in an epitaxial way. This section looks first at the chloride transport system, and then at the MOVPE method and its associated techniques. Comparisons between the two methods and with LPE are then made.

Fault	Common cause	Cure
Roughness, pinholes	Substrates not covered during high temperature equilibriation in a contaminated tube – uniform nucleation not possible.	Clean growth tube before growth.
Stacking faults	Foreign particles on substrate.	Clean substrate before growth.
Pinholes	Preferential loss of one element of substrate during thermal equilibriation, e.g. As in GaAs – this leads to thermal etching of surface and hence pinholes in grown layer.	Many alternatives – most widely used is growth of a thick buffer layer resulting in smoothing of the etch pits.
Repetitive patterns of terraces (stepped features)	Presence of submicroscopic terrace structure on misoriented substrates after etching.	Correct substrate preparation.
Repetitive pattern of waves (sinusoidal features)	Unclear – possibility is constitutional supercooling.	Control of temperature–time profile. Grow 2° off (100) axis towards (110).
Lines: (i) leading (L) and trailing (T) edge	Circular growth solution (horizontal system) and amount of solution supercooling ΔT_0 being too low ($\sim 0.5\,°C$).	Increase ΔT_0 from $\sim 0.5\,°C$ to $3\,°C$ to promote growth across whole surface.
(ii) Meniscus lines – finer than L and T but parallel to T lines	Unclear – but related to amount of supercooling.	Unclear.
Cross-hatching	Poor lattice matching.	Lattice match growing layer to underlying substrate.

Table 8.4 Commonly observed faults in LPE grown layers.

8.4.1 Chloride transport

Before ion implantation doping (see section 8.7) became a mature technology, chloride transport was the preferred method for making high quality n-doped layers of GaAs for electronic applications. Its use in optoelectronics has been limited to devices based around GaAs and its associated alloys AlGaAs and GaAsP.

A typical system is shown in Figure 8.15, although the reactor can be horizontal or vertical, with open or closed tube systems (but the latter are not very common). $AsCl_3$, which is a liquid, is transferred to the reaction chamber by bubbling hydrogen through it. An initial crust of GaAs is formed on the Ga source as a result of the release of arsenic from the incoming gases:

$$4\,AsCl_3 + 6\,H_2 \rightarrow 12\,HCl + As_4. \tag{8.6}$$

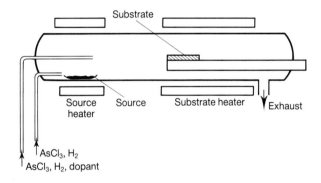

Figure 8.15 Chloride transport system for VPE.

Subsequent reaction of arsenic with gallium forms solid GaAs, and this is transported to the substrate by the reaction

$$4\,GaAs(s) + 4\,HCl(g) \rightarrow 4\,GaCl(g) + As_4(g) + 2\,H_2(g). \tag{8.7}$$

The reverse reaction occurs on the substrate, because this is at a lower temperature than the source. Deposition of solid GaAs then occurs. The crusting of the gallium source is critical, as any non-uniformity in this layer will lead to a non-uniform gas transport and hence epilayer non-stoichiometry. A way to get around this is to use a GaAs source, but generally this is not available in as high a purity as gallium metal.

A variation on this process is to replace the $AsCl_3$ with HCl in the tube passing over the source, and the HCl with AsH_3 for the other gas inlet. This is known as the hydride system. Here, GaCl is generated from the gallium source and As_4 from the pyrolysis of arsine:

$$2\,Ga + 2\,HCl \overset{>800\,^{\circ}C}{\rightarrow} 2\,GaCl + H_2 \tag{8.8}$$

$$4\,AsH_3 \quad \rightarrow \quad As_4 + 6\,H_2. \tag{8.9}$$

The reaction of the substrate is then

$$GaCl + AsH_3 \rightarrow GaAs + HCl + H_2. \tag{8.10}$$

No source saturation step is required, and critical temperature control of the source end of the furnace is unnecessary as at these temperatures the GaCl producing reaction goes to completion. Stoichiometry control can be obtained because of the independent reaction governing GaCl and As_4 production.

To produce GaAsP or GaP, the gas inlet to the gallium source contains H_2 and HCl and the other inlet carries H_2, AsH_3, PH_3 and any doping gases such as NH_3 and H_2S. The relevant reactions, equivalent to that of (8.10) for GaAs, are

$$GaCl + PH_3 \quad \rightarrow \quad GaP + HCl + H_2, \qquad (8.11)$$

$$\text{and} \quad GaCl + (1-x)\,AsH_3 + x\,PH_3 \quad \rightarrow \quad GaAs_{1-x}P_x + HCl + H_2. \text{(8.12)}$$

Hence the $GaAs_{1-x}P_x$ stoichiometry is varied by the arsine/phosgine partial pressures, resulting in material with a varying band gap and hence light emission colour.

Because this is a high temperature process carried out in the vapour phase using generally toxic or explosive materials, extreme care has to be taken in all aspects of the equipment and process procedure, including safe storage of process gases, leak tight gas fittings and proper disposal of unreacted gases and reaction byproducts.

8.4.2   Metalorganic vapour phase epitaxy (MOVPE)

This epitaxial growth technique varies fundamentally from the chloride transport system in that the group III compound is transported to the substrate surface in an organic precursor (trimethylgallium (TMGa, $(CH_3)_3Ga$), triethylgallium (TEGa, $(C_2H_5)_3Ga$), triethylindium (TEIn, $(C_2H_5)_3In$) etc.). Arsine (AsH_3) or phosgine (PH_3) are still used as the carrier for the group V compound. A reaction occurs near a heated substrate surface to form the III–V compound directly from the two carrier gases, e.g.

$$(C_2H_5)_3Ga(g) + AsH_3(g) \rightarrow GaAs(s) + 3\,C_2H_6(g). \qquad (8.13)$$

This system thus avoids the two-stage process and the associated temperature zoning inherent in the chloride transport system. The process was first described in 1969 [20] and an experimental schematic is shown in Figure 8.16. The organic precursors are all liquids at room temperature, and in a similar way to the chlorides in the previous system are transferred to the wafer surface by bubbling hydrogen through the liquid. R.f. heating is provided to make sure that only the graphite susceptor and the substrate are heated. The quartz reaction tube remains cold, and thus the reaction described in (8.13) only occurs in the vicinity of the substrate. Again, dopant carrier gases may be added at the inlet to the reaction tube to produce conducting material.

Once device quality material had been demonstrated by this technique [21], a substantial amount of work was undertaken in many laboratories. MOVPE can now produce multilayered structures of excellent electrical and morphological characteristics over a large area. The technique is then flexible enough to produce a

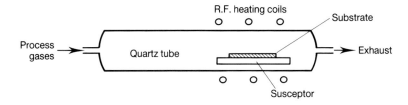

Figure 8.16 Basic arrangement of a MOVPE system.

large area epitaxial layer of any III–V alloy, given the right precursors, and this
has led to it dominating over chloride transport in research applications. The
more common III–V alloys grown by this technique are shown in Table 8.5 [22].
Because of the importance of this technique many different variations on equipment and process procedures have been investigated; some of the more significant
developments are now discussed.

8.4.2.1 *Atmospheric pressure MOVPE*

Gas precursors enter the reaction chamber, transported via individual mass flow
controllers, either in hydrogen or as a single gas. The gas flow in the reactor may
be horizontal, as in Figure 8.16, or vertical. Mixing of the gases occurs, which
can lead to organic polymer formation and deposition on the chamber walls (more
on this in section 8.4.2.2) – this is a parasitic reaction. The desired reaction, as
shown for example in (8.13), happens when the mixed gas reaches the substrate
after passing through a gas boundary layer. It is a feature of MOVPE systems
that the bulk of the gas flow is a constant mixture – near the substrate surface the
characteristics of the gas gradually change in terms of composition. This is the
concept of boundary layer in this application, and such a layer is typically 4 mm
and 20 mm thick for horizontal and vertical MOCVD systems respectively. At the
surface the gases decompose and the elements Ga, As, etc. move around on the hot
substrate until a suitable lattice site for growth is found. Reaction byproducts are
then removed from the surface, where they diffuse back into the main gas mixture
(Figure 8.17). The wafer temperature is generally held in the range of $500-600\,^\circ$C,
depending on the nature of the seed substrate and the chemical reaction causing
the deposition of grown material. It appears that the growth rate is independent
of wafer temperature over a wide range of values. Measurements have also shown
that as long as the vapour phase is arsenic rich, growth rate depends only on the
organic precursor's vapour pressure. As such, growth rates are usually related as
μm mol^{-1} of organic material, with values in the range of 10^3–10^4 being typical for
this process [23]. As with all epitaxial growth techniques, the responsible disposal
of unreacted precursors and reaction byproducts is an important consideration;
this is especially true for the large volumes of gases necessary in an atmospheric
pressure process.

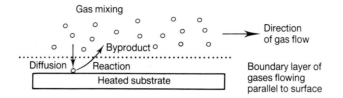

Figure 8.17 Gas kinetics in the MOVPE process.

Semiconductor	Typical precursor (group III)	Typical precursor (group V)
GaP	TMGa, TEGa	PH_3
InP	TMIn, TEIn	PH_3
GaAs	TMGa, TEGa	AsH_3
GaAsP	TMGa	$AsH_3 + PH_3$
AlGaAs	TMAl + TMGa	AsH_3
InGaAs	TEIn + TMGa	AsH_3
AlGaAsP	TMAl + TMGa	$AsH_3 + PH_3$
InGaAsP	TEIn + TEGa	$AsH_3 + PH_3$

Table 8.5 Typical precursors used in the MOVPE growth of common III–V semiconductors.

8.4.2.2　Low pressure MOVPE

Besides the problem of unwanted polymer formation mentioned in the last section, the dynamics of atmospheric pressure MOVPE lead to two other problems:

(i) autodoping, where volatile species originating in the substrate become incorporated in the epitaxial layer, and

(ii) outdiffusion, where impurities diffuse from substrate to active layer or from one layer to another in the case of a multiple-layer growth process.

Autodoping occurs when volatile species are evaporated from the substrate and become trapped in the boundary layer. The nature of this layer provides a relatively high degree of freedom for molecular motion, and dopants originating in one area of the substrate can migrate large distances before reincorporation into an epitaxial layer. The best way to solve this is by modifying the gas dynamics, particularly that of the boundary layer, so that evaporated impurities migrate more readily into the main gas layer. It has been shown for many materials, from Si to InGaAsP, that reducing the pressure in the reaction chamber leads to large decreases in autodoping concentration, e.g. [24]. Gas diffusivity is inversely proportional to pressure and, because a low pressure reduces heat transfer by gas conduction, temperature gradients above the susceptor are less for an atmospheric process. Low pressure also decreases the hydrogen absorption onto the wafer surface. All these factors combine to increase the probability for evaporated dopants to escape from the boundary layer and into the main gas flow. Thus low pressure MOVPE growth works in the 50–100 torr region. It brings with it associated problems. For instance the substrate, located on an r.f. heated graphite susceptor, now has significantly less gaseous convection heating to equate its temperature to that of the substrate; radiant infra-red heating is often preferred. Outgassing from the susceptor is enhanced at low pressure, and so graphite is usually replaced with either high purity polycrystalline silicon or silicon carbide coated with a thick layer of silicon.

The reduced hydrogen absorption means that a lower operating temperature may be used – this results in a substantial reduction in outdiffusion, as diffusivity has an exponential dependence on temperature. It has also been shown that a parasitic reaction deposits unwanted polymers on the inside of the reaction chamber. This is a pressure dependent process which is virtually eliminated using a low pressure technique.

A typical growth procedure would be:

(i) clean the substrate in various etching/rinsing mixtures (see section 8.8),
(ii) place the substrate in the reactor and purge the chamber with nitrogen,
(iii) reduce the operating pressure to 75 torr, but keep the same gas flow rates,
(iv) heat the substrate on a fixed temperature ramp and, at a fixed point, let the hydride gas into the chamber,
(v) raise the temperature further and, again at a fixed growth point, allow an etchant gas into the chamber for a fixed time to allow for final substrate cleaning,
(vi) purge the chamber using N_2 and hydride,
(vii) reduce the nitrogen flow and allow hydrogen into the chamber,
(viii) bubble hydrogen through the metal alkyl precursor at a fixed flow rate, and allow this to enter the chamber for growth.

As for the atmospheric pressure process, growth rates are proportional to the alkyl flow rate, but independent of temperature and hydride flow over a wide range. The low pressure means that growth rates tend to be lower than for atmospheric pressure MOVPE.

Care has to be taken when growing a material using PH_3. For instance, growth of InP requires a reaction temperature $> 500\,°C$, where loss of phosphorus from the surface would occur without a PH_3 overpressure. Unfortunately, at these temperatures PH_3 reacts with $(C_2H_5)_3In$ to form a complex addition compound which is characterized by the appearance of black fumes. So PH_3 is often pyrolized, i.e. reduced to free phosphorus and hydrogen, by adding a furnace to the gas line prior to entry into the chamber. Phosphorus gas is more successful at suppressing loss from an InP surface than is PH_3, and so lower rates of PH_3 can be used in the process than if a furnace was not present [25].

8.4.2.3　*Photo-MOVPE*

The use of lasers to assist MOVPE growth has been investigated. The laser can cause/enhance a reaction in one of two ways:

(i) pyrolytically, where the laser beam heats up the substrate to the required temperature, and
(ii) photolytically, where the wavelength of the laser radiation is of the right value to decompose the carrier gases.

Both methods have been used to grow GaAs, AlGaAs and GaAsP [26]. The technique shows a high growth rate and, moreover, the ability to deposit material only where the laser beam is present. Thus the prospect of an epitaxial layer directly written on to the substrate, or with doped regions similarly defined, becomes a real possibility. Very careful control is needed over the laser-assisted process, however, as the pyrolytic phase can lead to crystalline defects if the surface temperature gradients are too severe, and the photolytic phase can lead to non-uniform deposition of material.

8.4.3　Atomic layer epitaxy (ALE)

In this form of epitaxial growth the boundary between VPE and molecular beam epitaxy (MBE – to be discussed in section 8.5) is less distinct than for the mechanism discussed so far. As will be seen, MBE can deposit atoms one layer at a time. ALE also does this, but by extending and developing the methods of chloride transport and MOVPE already described.

MOVPE based atomic layer epitaxy was first described in 1985 [27], to grow GaAs, with the effects on crystal growth of various illumination techniques also being studied. Chloride transport [28], reported the following year, has also been used to grow GaAs. The process schematic is shown in Figure 8.18 [29]. Trimethylgallium based radicals (MOVPE-like) or GaCl (chloride transport-like) are absorbed on to the substrate. The gas is then purged from the system. AsH_3 is then admitted and reacts with the gallium containing material. This gas is then purged, and the process repeated. Work in this field has noted the following advantages of the process [29]:

(i) accurate thickness control and reproducibility, because of the 'digital' nature of the process, i.e. it is one gas at a time, reacting with one monolayer of surface. There is then no need for precision control of flow rates, temperatures and pressures.
(ii) High quality surface finish, free of many types of defects.

(iii) The ability to dope selectively grown epitaxial layers (through a mask) – this is useful for heavily doped contact regions.

(iv) Sidewall epitaxy, where a previously fabricated multilayer epitaxial wafer can have a different semiconductor grown on the edge, giving three-dimensional confinement.

Other semiconductors have also been grown by this technique, notably InP, InAs and GaP, and GaAs/GaP superlattices [30].

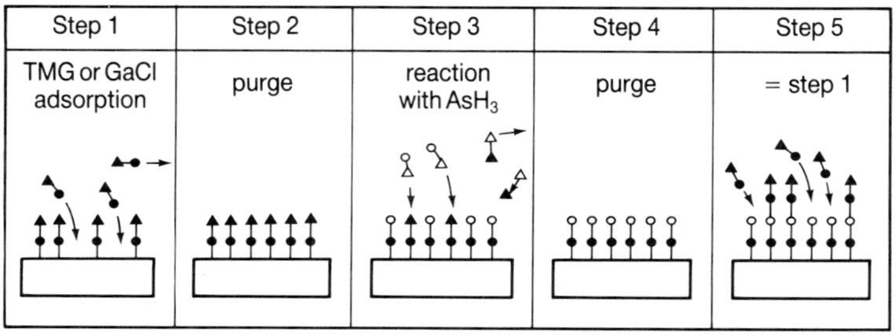

Step 1	Step 2	Step 3	Step 4	Step 5
TMG or GaCl adsorption	purge	reaction with AsH$_3$	purge	= step 1

Figure 8.18 Process schematic of GaAs ALE (©IOP: reproduced by kind permission).

8.4.4 Vapour levitation epitaxy (VLE)

This is a comparatively compact experimental arrangement that uses the increasing gas flow both as a reactant source and as a levitation mechanism to keep the wafer suspended above the growth apparatus [31]. Epitaxial growth then occurs on the underside of the wafer (Figure 8.19). The main advantages of this method are:

(i) there is a uniformity of gas flow over the growth area, promoting thickness uniformity,

(ii) there is a minimal boundary layer, and so transfer of reactants to/products from the growing surface is minimized.

GaAs, InP, InGaAs, InGaP and InGaAsP epitaxial layers, as well as InGaAs/InP heterostructures, have been grown this way.

8.4.5 Comparison of VPE and LPE material

Liquid phase epitaxy (LPE) techniques have a long history, and so it is inevitable that they are the preferred growth method providing the material parameters can be satisfied. For large scale production of non-critical LEDs the obvious choice

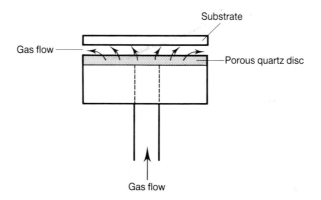

Figure 8.19 Basic arrangement of VLE.

is LPE. However, as was shown in Table 8.4, the quality of the surface finish of LPE material leaves much to be desired, which is a problem for both the definition and operation of fine feature devices. VPE techniques are superior in this respect, but it was the ability to grow thin layers of heterostructure material, and in particular on large area substrates, that was the driving force behind VPE research. Inevitably the initial material quality was inferior to that from LPE, but by the mid-1980s comparisons favoured VPE and the appearance of superlattices confirmed vapour phase techniques as the preferred method for uniformity of growth of advanced structures. Low pressure MOVPE has been shown to reduce all of the problems associated with LPE growth of InP/InGaAsP based alloys, such as carrier concentration levels, anti-melt-back layers and dislocations [32].

As will be seen in the next section, the 'competition' for the best quality growth technique is really between MOVPE and molecular beam epitaxy (MBE) based methods.

8.5 Molecular beam epitaxy (MBE)

After a slow start in the 1960s, principally caused by the lack of good quality substrates but especially by the prohibitive cost of the specialized equipment needed, molecular beam epitaxy (MBE) became rapidly established as the technique for growing thin layers of semiconductor material, especially that containing three or four elements. But by the late 1980s it was being challenged by MOVPE as the 'best' growth technique for this purpose. This section describes the process and its kinetics, before making comparisons with MOVPE which have led to hybrid growth systems.

8.5.1 Process description

In its simplest sense, a molecular beam epitaxy system is a thermal evaporator, but with a degree of temperature control and background pressure not normally associated with such systems (see section 9.2). The evaporation of individual elements of a III–V semiconductor, and the subsequent condensation on a glass substrate to give polycrystalline films, was first described in 1958, but it was only in 1968 [33] that single crystal substrates were used to give monocrystalline films. By the mid-1970s device quality epitaxial AlGaAs/GaAs could be grown; at the same time there was an intense demand for research into growth techniques for other heterostructures, and so MBE began to receive a lot of attention.

The modern MBE system is shown in detail in Figure 8.20(a), with a simpler schematic of the growth chamber in Figure 8.20(b). Substrates are loaded into the growth chamber via a vacuum load lock system, so that the chamber is never let up to air. There are sputter cleaning and high temperature heating stages before the growth process begins. In the growth chamber, the sample is held at a high temperature, whose value depends on the substrate material and epitaxial layer, in an ultra-high vacuum (UHV) system of $\sim 10^{-10}$–10^{-11} torr. In situ analysis includes a mass spectrometer for residual gas analysis (RGA) and reflection high energy electron diffraction (RHEED) to look at the substrate and epitaxial film quality. Evaporated molecular beams are generated from the Knudsen, or effusion, cells, which impinge on the substrate via a rapidly switching shutter mechanism. This enables sharp interfaces to be realized in MBE. The heated sources and substrate in a UHV environment place a tremendous demand on the various pumping mechanisms used. To lessen the possibility of the crucibles outgassing, they are usually placed in a cooled shroud. The substrate, besides being heated, is also usually rotated to improve deposition uniformity. The chemical composition, including any required doping, of the epilayer can be varied either via the temperature of the effusion cell or the aperture of the shutter.

8.5.2 Growth kinetics

This is crucially dependent on effusion cell and substrate temperature. For the most studied system, that of GaAs, there are two effusion cell temperature regimes, one that involves the dimer As_2 and the other the tetramer As_4 [34]. Both, however, involve the same series of events:

(i) evaporation from the source and molecular travel towards the substrate,
(ii) adsorption onto the substrate,
(iii) surface migration and dissociation, leading to incorporation onto the substrate (growth).

Epitaxial films can then be grown that are driven by deposition kinetics, rather than gas phase equilibria. For the growth of GaAs, the dimer form of arsenic was

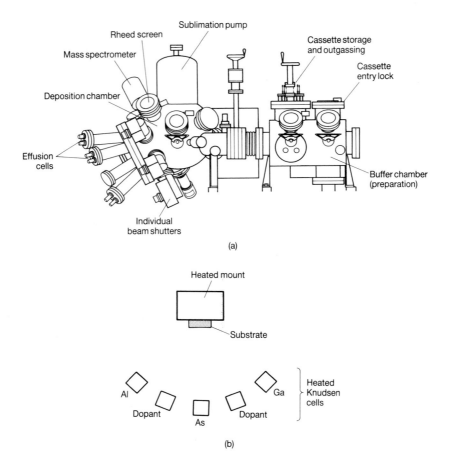

Figure 8.20 (a) Typical apparatus used in MBE (courtesy of VG Semicon). (b) Schematic of the growth chamber.

originally only found using GaAs as a source in the effusion cell. Elemental arsenic produces the tetramer, As_4. This molecule can be used directly in the growth of GaAs or can be 'cracked' at high temperature ($\sim 900\,^\circ$C) to form As_2. The model for growth of GaAs using As_4 is shown in Figure 8.21 [35], and a similar (but not identical) model exists for As_2. Incident As_4 molecules are first adsorbed into a mobile precursor state, whose condensation and reaction is controlled by the Ga adatom population and substrate temperature. Below a substrate temperature of $180\,^\circ$C, there is no dissociation of As_4 and hence GaAs cannot be formed. At higher temperatures ($> 330\,^\circ$C) the GaAs itself begins to desorb As_2 molecules. Material can then be grown in the range 180°–$330\,^\circ$C where the As_4 dissociates to form

GaAs with gallium and there is an insignificant amount of As_2 desorption. Not all the incoming As_4 will stick on the surface (sticking coefficient < 0.5), however, and dissociation of this molecule will occur whatever the growth temperature. Hence there must be an excess of arsenic molecules in the incoming vapour streams; this has to be increased even further if growth temperatures $> 330\,°C$ are used to replace the As_2 lost from the GaAs surface. In fact, electrical and optical measurements via Hall effect, deep level transient spectroscopy and photoluminescence suggest that high temperature growth ($\sim 580\,°C$) should be used, as low temperatures contain a lot of defects. Growth rates are in the range of $1–10\ \mu m\ h^{-1}$, although film quality does not appear to suffer at increased rates.

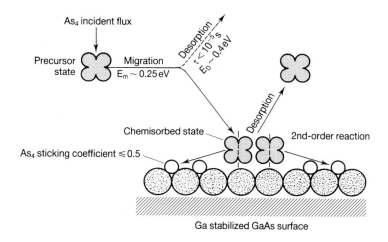

Figure 8.21 Kinetics of GaAs growth using MBE (©North-Holland: reproduced by kind permission).

8.5.2.1 *Other III–V compounds*
Growth kinetics of other group III–V compounds are similar, in that growth rates are determined by the flux of the group III element(s) and an excess of group V elements is necessary to form the semiconductor. The use of the congruant sublimation temperature in determining growth conditions for various III–Vs is shown in Figure 8.22 [36].

Alloys such as AlGaAs were grown as early as 1971, with GaAs/AlGaAs superlattices [37] and heterostructure lasers [38] formed soon afterwards. These and other subsequent results, as well as theoretical studies on growth kinetics, established MBE as the superior growth technique for thin epitaxial systems, especially multiple-layer structures. The growth of AlGaAs has a problem in that aluminium has a strong affinity for both carbon and oxygen, giving a high probability that a growth chamber containing residual amounts of these elements will lead to them being incorporated in an epilayer of AlGaAs. The surface quality of MBE grown

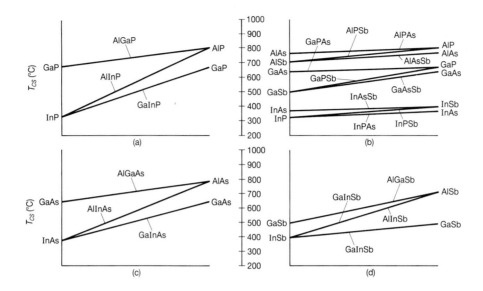

Figure 8.22 Congruent sublimation temperature for: (a) type-I ternary phosphides, (b) type-II ternary alloys, (c) type-I ternary arsenides, (d) type-I ternary antimonides (©T P Pearsall: reproduced by kind permission).

AlGaAs has also been shown to be poor under certain growth conditions; high temperatures and low group V/group III flux ratios can improve this, but lead to associated desorption problems. It has been shown [39] that deliberate misorientation of the substrate by 6° from ⟨100⟩ towards ⟨111⟩A, i.e. where growth occurs on monatomic steps terminated by gallium atoms, can lead to smooth morphologies at low growth temperatures (∼ 620 °C).

Most III–Vs of interest have been grown, with similar process conditions. MBE-grown InP was first demonstrated in 1974 [40]; InGaAs (1976 [41]), GaP and its alloys (1969 [42]) and GaAsSb (1977 [43]) are further examples of first publications on growth of III–V semiconductors. Since these early results many workers have investigated the growth mechanisms and kinetics, with the result that most III–V semiconductors of any composition can be made by MBE with good electrical, optical and surface finish characteristics.

8.5.2.2 Doping

The doping of MBE grown epilayers is generally done at the growth stage to ensure uniformity of impurity incorporation. Separate effusion cells are used for elemental sources of the dopants. Dopant density in the epilayer is a function of incoming flux, which in turn is a function of effusion cell temperature. Figure 8.23 [44] shows a plot of expected carrier concentration in GaAs as a function of dopant effusion cell temperature for common impurities Si and Sn (n-type), Be and Mn (p-type), and Ge (amphoteric). Many other dopants could be used (see section 8.6 on diffusion), but Si is chosen because it has a low diffusion coefficient, and hence resultant films have sharply defined doping profiles. Sn has a high activation level, Be has predictable behaviour, but is toxic to handle, whereas Mn is comparatively safe but has a low level of electrical activity. Other dopants, such as Te and Se for n-type (excessive surface accumulation) and Zn and Cd for p-type (low solubility) tend to have less desirable characteristics than the favoured elements.

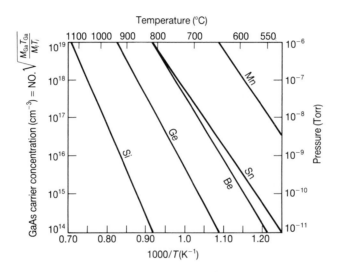

Figure 8.23 Carrier concentration in GaAs vs effusion cell temperature for several dopants (©Academic Press, Inc.: reproduced by kind permission).

8.5.3 Comparisons with MOVPE

MBE was able to make superlattice structures well before MOVPE, and so it has always been regarded as the growth technique for thin multilayer semiconductor devices. Once material quality became equal to that of LPE (from the mid 1970s onwards, depending on material) it began to be used intensively. VPE techniques were always intended to be replacements for LPE, principally to get around the problem of surface morphology, substrate area and melt-back. VPE, and especially MOVPE, made significant improvements above and beyond LPE in the 1980s and soon began to show material quality equal to, and even better than, that of MBE. VPE's substantially cheaper equipment costs were also an advantage. Although superlattices remained a problem for some while, by the late 1980s many groups were reporting such structures using MOVPE. The use of MBE to produce selective growth through a mask, however, remains a significant advantage [45].

As usually happens, hybrid solutions offering the advantages of both systems were put forward. The next section reviews how the hybrid systems developed.

8.5.4   Metalorganic molecular beam epitaxy (MOMBE)

One of the problems with III–V growth using MBE is the group V source. There is a greater flux of this than of the group III element, and so the source is rapidly depleted, leading to regular changes and beam flux variations with time, making it difficult to control. A further problem involving phosphorus is that this element is composed of an arbitrary mixture of allotropes, each with a different vapour pressure–temperature relationship. As a result gas sources for both As and P were proposed [46].

In the first system AsH_3 or PH_3 were admitted, via a leak valve, to a high temperature cracking system such that As_2 or P_2 (along with H_2) were released. Source supply and control are then external to the system, leading to a much longer time between source replenishment and a more even and predictable flux of group V atoms. This gas phase MBE was a noticeable improvement in reproducibility in molecular beam systems, although it is not different in principle.

The real departure from conventional MBE came with the use of gas sources for both group III and group V elements, with a reaction between TMGa or TEGa (and TMIn or TEIn) on the substrate surface with previously cracked As_2 or P_2 [47]. In this system, mass flow controllers determine the flux of gas molecules to the substrate surface through a system of moderate vacuum (5×10^{-4} torr). This is shown in Figure 8.24. The growth kinetics differ from MBE and MOVPE in several ways. In this system the beam of both gas molecules impinges directly onto the heated substrate surface (as in conventional MBE) – there is no boundary layer or collisions because of the low background pressure. After reaching the heated surface, the group III alkyl dissociates to leave a free group III atom on the surface and a desorbed alkyl group. Group V elements can then react readily with the surface group III atoms. This technique, originally known as chemical beam epitaxy (CBE), but now more commonly called metalorganic molecular beam epitaxy (MOMBE), uses the directional nature of MBE to react gas molecules together (like MOVPE), but only on the substrate surface (unlike MOVPE). The kinetics of all three processes MBE, MOVPE and MOMBE, are shown in Figure 8.25 [48]. Advantages of MOMBE over MBE include:

(i)   Greater control over a source that will produce many epilayers before needing refurbishment. Reproducibility and the ability to produce very abrupt interfaces are inherent in the system.

(ii) No oval defects (surface defects).

(iii) A single group III beam, ensuring composition uniformity.

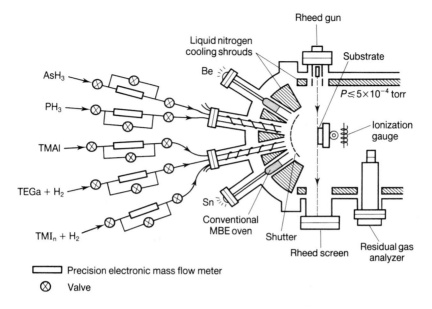

Figure 8.24 MOMBE growth system (©North-Holland Publishing: reproduced by kind permission).

Advantages of MOMBE over MOVPE include:

(i) The use of RHEED and RGA to monitor epilayer growth and gas stoichiometry in situ.
(ii) No flux pattern problems for large area/multi-wafer applications.
(iii) More abrupt interfaces due to the beam nature of the growth.

This technique is still relatively undeveloped, but InGaAs [48], AlGaAs [49], InGaP and AlInP [50] have been grown this way. It has also produced a further spin-off, photo-MOMBE [51], in which the substrate is illuminated with 193 nm radiation from an argon fluoride laser. The experimental assembly bore only a passing resemblance to the MOMBE system, however, especially as an elemental group V source was used, and no mass flow controllers appear to have been utilized.

8.5.5 Migration enhanced epitaxy (MEE)

One of the main reasons why high substrate temperatures are used in MBE growth is to encourage the migration of III–V molecules on the surface to an appropriate lattice site, i.e. because group III or group V atoms can migrate much faster than III–V molecules, much lower substrate temperatures can be used if a molecular beam incident on the surface is a rapidly switched alternating beam of group III

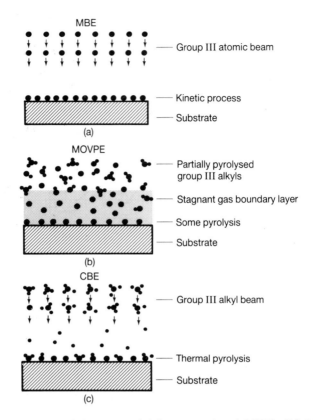

Figure 8.25 Growth kinetics of (a) conventional MBE, (b) MOVPE, (c) MOMBE (©North-Holland Publishing: reproduced by kind permission).

or group V atoms. This was proposed in 1986, and is termed migration enhanced epitaxy (MEE [52]).

8.5.6   Use of Si substrates

Epitaxy of device quality material on Si substrates is a comparatively new phenomenon. It was encouraged for IC applications of GaAs/Si where, if successful, it was hoped the cost of GaAs active layers could be substantially reduced. The other advantages of the system lay in the greater thermal conductivity of Si for heat dissipation, less brittle material, leading to fewer breakages, and the potential to integrate GaAs MESFET and Si CMOS circuits on the same chip. Problems include a 4% lattice mismatch between GaAs and Si (early growth methods relieved this with an intermediate layer of Ge, but this has now been removed), a factor of two difference in thermal expansion coefficient and the formation of antiphase domains, i.e. As on Ga sites and vice versa. Other intermediate layers of III–V material such as an AlP, AlGaP, GaP/GaAsP or GaAsP/GaAs system have been used – lasers have been fabricated with such a system in GaAs/AlGaAs [53].

The first reported growth of GaAs on Si without an intermediate layer was in 1985, using MBE [54]. Si surface preparation, in situ surface desorption and the presence of an arsenic overpressure were all important in realizing the material. Shortly afterwards, MOVPE also reported successful GaAs/Si growth [55].

For InP on Si, the advantages of cost and durability of Si substrates are even more important than for GaAs/Si. But here the lattice mismatch is 8%, although the thermal expansion coefficients are closer. The InP/Si system was first grown in 1987 (by MOVPE [56]), but crystalline quality is improved dramatically if an intermediate layer of GaAs is used [57]. However, large defect densities still occur in the epitaxial layer. It seems that, for both GaAs and InP, the use of intermediate buffer layers to remove the mismatch induced strain is a prerequisite to obtaining the best quality material.

8.6 Diffusion

We have already met the term diffusion when discussing both basic semiconductors and pn junctions: the movement of charge carriers from a region of high concentration to a low concentration region (i.e. diffusion) leads to an associated current, the diffusion current. A similar consideration can be applied to the movement of impurities atoms through a semiconductor. The mechanisms involved are quite different, but the principle of movement from a region of high to one of low concentration is the same (and governed by a similar diffusion law). This section describes the processes and the impurities used in III–V diffusion mechanisms.

8.6.1 Impurity levels

There are four things that need to be considered when choosing an impurity to dope a semiconductor:

  (i) the desired conductivity type, n or p,

  (ii) the solubility of the impurity, i.e. how many dopants can get onto active sites,

 (iii) the activation energy of the impurity – this defines the minimum temperature needed to release electrons to the conduction band (or holes to the valence band),

 (iv) the diffusion characteristics of the dopant.

The latter consideration needs a section on its own (section 8.6.2), but a consideration of the other characteristics (i) and (iii) can be seen from Figure 8.26(a) for GaAs [58], or Figure 8.26(b) for InP [59, 60]. Surprisingly, figures for solid solubility limits of dopants in III–V semiconductors are not available in a collected form. If the characteristics of germanium and silicon are a guide to predicting similar behaviour, then the maximum solubility of any dopant will be at $\sim 700°C$ for Ge and ~ 1100 °C for Si. At room temperature the maximum is much less ($< 10^{20}$ atoms for both Ge and Si). Many dopants, however, have solubility limits that are well below this maximum; one of the main reasons why B, P and As are commonly used in Si IC processing is because of their high value of solid solubility.

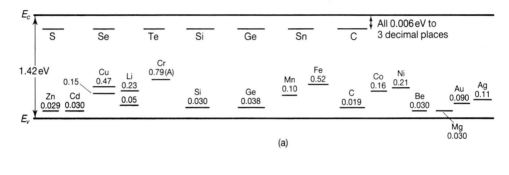

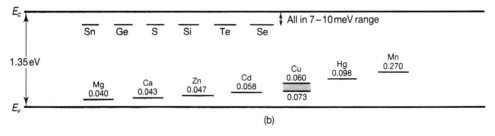

Figure 8.26 Dopant energy levels in the band gap of (a) GaAs, and (b) InP.

8.6.2   Sources

There are basically three types: solid, liquid and gas. The choice depends on the availability of a suitable medium, its handling, especially with regard to toxicity, and the temperatures needed in the diffusion process to release the donor or acceptor impurities. The latter is important not just to determine the time taken for any diffusion process to achieve a desired concentration profile, but also because of the possible need to either encapsulate the III–V semiconductor or provide an overpressure of the more volatile element. Liquid sources are usually only chosen where a carrier gas can be bubbled through the liquid to provide a source of dopant vapour to the semiconductor surface – their mode of operation in diffusion is similar to gaseous sources.

8.6.2.1 Solid source

Three different types of solid source diffusion are shown in Figure 8.27. In Figure 8.27(a) a two-zone furnace contains a diffusion source and the wafers to be doped. A carrier gas, usually inert, flushes the chamber of any residual impurity gases before diffusion takes place, and also acts to promote the movement of diffuser gas to the wafer surfaces. Dummy wafers at the front and back of the device wafers are used to give an even distribution of gas. All wafers in this system must be encapsulated, as it is known as an open-tube diffusion furnace. Figure 8.27(b) shows a similar system, but this time using a dopant in the form of wafers (boron nitride is an example for doping silicon) interleaved in the stack of device wafers. A closed tube furnace is shown in Figure 8.27(c), where either encapsulated wafers or an ambient overpressure can be supplied. An alternative solid source, not shown, is known as doped spin-on glass. This is applied in a similar manner to photoresist (see section 9.1.2) and baked to drive off excess solvents; the resultant film is SiO_2 doped with a particular impurity. Placing the wafer in a furnace drives the dopant out of the oxide and into the wafer. These sources have the great advantage of being relatively safe to use, but there are problems of uniform distribution of dopant within the system; if the glass is spun-on over severe topographical features on the mask thickness variations will occur which can exacerbate dopant uniformity problems.

8.6.2.2 Gas source

Gas source diffusion uses a one-temperature zone open tube furnace. Gases have significant advantages over solid sources in that the use of mass flow controllers to regulate the gas flow results in much more control over dopant supply. Modern manufacturing techniques ensure that gas sources are cleaner than solid sources, as handling is eliminated. Although the basic system is similar to that of Figure 8.27(a), but without the solid source and its associated furnace, many different systems have been tried in order to obtain a uniform distribution of dopants in the furnace. Wafers can be placed vertically as in Figure 8.28(a) to give the greatest production economy, as this enables more wafers to be diffused simultaneously within a given production run. However, it can cause uniformity problems as the wafers act as baffles to the gas flow. A horizontal placement system (Figure 8.28(b)) keeps the laminar flow of the gas as it passes down the tube, but at the expense of lower throughput.

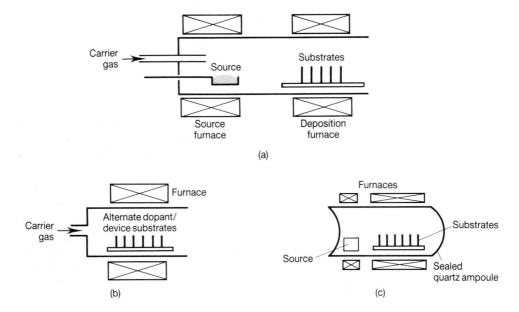

Figure 8.27 Three different methods of solid source diffusion doping (see text for details).

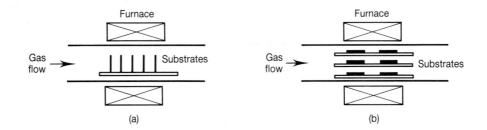

Figure 8.28 Wafer orientation in gas source diffusion: (a) vertical, and (b) horizontal.

8.6.3 Kinetics

Whatever the dopant source or wafer orientation, the diffusion process can be reduced to a consideration of an opening in a mask on a wafer, placed at a uniform temperature in an ambient atmosphere of dopant of uniform concentration. Thus at the surface of the exposed part of the semiconductor the doping concentration will be uniform, at least initially, and dopants will diffuse away from this region in all directions, governed by a diffusion equation similar to that governing electron motion (1.46). If we now describe the motion in terms of a flux F of dopant atoms, a carrier concentration C and a diffusion coefficient D (1.48) becomes

$$F = -D\frac{\partial C}{\partial x} \tag{8.14}$$

in one dimension. Obviously dopants will diffuse under the mask edge, as shown in Figure 8.29(a). This is generally an undesirable feature and can be ignored if the diffusion depth is very much less than the feature size of the mask. Figure 8.29(b) then shows the expected dopant concentration as a function of depth given by (8.14). Considerations of continuity (as in section 1.4.3, only now we have no generation or recombination of dopants) lead to

$$\frac{\partial C}{\partial t} = -\frac{\partial F}{\partial x} \tag{8.15}$$

and hence

$$\frac{\partial C}{\partial t} = D\frac{\partial^2 C}{\partial x^2}. \tag{8.16}$$

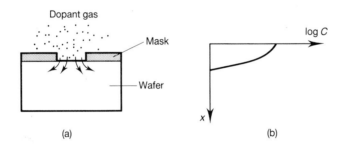

Figure 8.29 (a) Diffusion kinetics. (b) Carrier concentration profile after diffusion.

Equation (8.16) is known as Fick's diffusion equation. Figure 8.30(a) shows the measured diffusion coefficients as a function of temperature of various dopants in GaAs [61]. The straight line nature of such a graph implies that the value of D can be expressed in the form

$$D = D_0 \exp\left(-\frac{E_A}{kT}\right) \tag{8.17}$$

over a wide temperature range, where D_0 is the diffusion coefficient for an extrapolated temperature $(T = \infty)$ and E_A is an activation energy. A similar diagram is shown in Figure 8.30(b) for InP: [62] also contains sufficient data for the same plots to be drawn for GaP, GaSb, InAs and InSb. An observation apparent from Figure 8.30 is that there appear to be two ranges of values for E_A; this implies that there are two types of diffusion mechanisms. Figure 8.31 shows these two

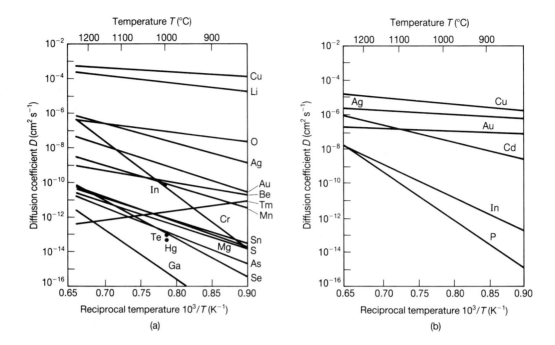

Figure 8.30 Self and impurity diffusion coefficients in (a) GaAs, and (b) InP (©Plenum Publishing Co. Ltd.: reproduced by kind permission).

mechanisms, known as vacancy diffusion (Figure 8.31(a)) and interstitial diffusion (Figure 8.31(b)). For vacancy diffusion, the process involves the movement of a dopant through the crystal by successively hopping from one empty lattice site to the next. Thus the activation energy involved has two functions, to create vacancies and to move dopant atoms. E_A then tends to be large (in the range 2.5–6 eV for GaAs) and D tends to be small at low temperatures. For the other mechanism, interstitial diffusion, the activation energy only provides for dopant motion, because no vacancies are needed for interstitial movement to occur (Figure 8.31(b)). The dopants move between adjacent 'gaps' in the lattice structure; atoms that are much smaller than those of the host often diffuse this way. Hence E_A is much lower (in the range 0.5–1.2 eV for GaAs) and the diffusion coefficient is less sensitive to temperature.

Many atoms do not diffuse by one or other of the two simple mechanisms outlined above. Diffusion profiles can appear quite intricate, depending on dopant concentration, complexes formed with the host atoms/vacancies, impurity complexes, etc. A notable diffuser in this respect is zinc, which has concentration dependent values of D_0 and E_A for all III–V compound semiconductors. Much work was done in the 1960s and 1970s on zinc diffusion in III–Vs because of its technological im-

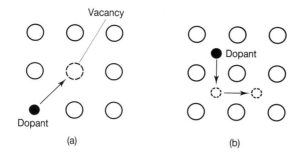

Figure 8.31 (a) Vacancy, and (b) interstitial diffusion mechanisms.

portance in p-doping to create LEDs [63]. It has been determined that in GaAs zinc diffuses interstitially as an ionized donor, reacts with a gallium vacancy and becomes an immobile, substitutional, ionized acceptor. This immobility causes the remaining interstitial zinc to have an enhanced concentration; this is an example of a concentration dependent diffusion coefficient.

The temperature activated nature of diffusion means that any subsequent high temperature process will redistribute a given diffusion profile. This has to be accounted for or, alternatively and far more likely, subsequent processes are undertaken at temperatures well below that of diffusion, so that the small amount of dopant redistribution can be ignored.

Example 8.1

Calculate the value of D_0 and E_A for cadmium in indium phosphide.

Solution: in this example we will need to use (8.17) and Figure 8.30. Equation (8.17) can be rearranged to give

$$\log_e D - \log_e D_0 = \frac{E_A}{k} \times \frac{1}{T}. \tag{8.18}$$

If we take two typical values of D and $1/T$ from Figure 8.30, then we can place these in (8.18). So

$$\text{at } 1/T = 6.5 \times 10^{-4} \text{ K}^{-1}, \ D = 10^{-10} \text{ m}^2 \text{s}^{-1},$$
$$\text{and at } 1/T = 9.0 \times 10^{-4} \text{ K}^{-1}, \ D = 3 \times 10^{-13} \text{ m}^2 \text{s}^{-1}. \tag{8.19}$$

Placing these numbers in (8.18) gives two simultaneous equations from which D_0 can be eliminated. So

$$-23.03 - \log_e D_0 = \frac{6.5 \times 10^{-4} \times E_A}{k}$$

$$-28.83 - \log_e D_0 = \frac{9.0 \times 10^{-4} \times E_A}{k}$$

$$\text{and so} \quad 5.80 = \frac{2.5 \times 10^{-4} \times E_A}{k}. \tag{8.20}$$

From this E_A can be readily isolated to give $E_A = 2.00$ eV. Putting this value in (8.17) gives

$$D_0 = 10^{-6} \exp \left(\frac{2.00 \times e \times 6.5 \times 10^{-4}}{k} \right)$$

$$= 3.5 \text{ cm}^2 \text{s}^{-1}. \tag{8.21}$$

8.6.4   Profiles

Although this is governed by Fick's diffusion equation (8.16), the boundary conditions necessary to determine C as a function of x and t lead to very different solutions. The boundary conditions can be simplified to one of two cases:

(i) constant surface concentration diffusion. This is where, irrespective of the source used, the amount of dopant in the ambient atmosphere is always a constant, and hence needs to be replenished as the dopant diffuses into the semiconductor, and

(ii) fixed source diffusion. This is more applicable to situations where the doping is in a layer of material on the surface, such as spin-on glass (section 8.6.2.1), and hence there is a fixed amount of dopant present. As the impurities diffuse into the semiconductor, the amount of dopant in the source gradually falls.

8.6.4.1   *Constant surface concentration*
If we assume that:

(i) initially there are no dopants in the semiconductor

$$C(x, 0) = 0, \tag{8.22}$$

(ii) the surface concentration of dopants is a constant

$$C(0, t) = C_s, \quad \text{and} \tag{8.23}$$

(iii) the diffusion process never takes impurity atoms through the whole depth of the semiconductor

$$C(\infty, t) = 0, \tag{8.24}$$

then the solution of (8.16) under these conditions is

$$C\left(x,t\right) \;=\; C_s \mathrm{erfc}\left[\frac{x}{2\sqrt{Dt}}\right] \tag{8.25}$$

where erfc is a mathematical term known as the complementary error function. As already seen earlier when discussing electron motion (equation (1.64)), $\sqrt{Dt}$ is known as the diffusion length L. Important properties of the erf and erfc functions are summarized in Table 8.6 for the unfamiliar reader, and a list of values of the error function can be found in any of several books containing mathematical tables, e.g. [64]; these enable diffusion profiles to be plotted as in Figure 8.32.

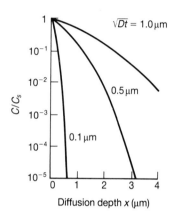

Figure 8.32 Dopant concentration profiles as a function of diffusion length for a constant surface concentration.

Example 8.2

For a p-type GaAs substrate with an initial doping concentration of 5×10^{15} cm^{-3} calculate the junction depth following n-type diffusion at 900 °C for 3 hours using sulphur as a dopant. Assume that the sulphur is in an overpressure of a gaseous source and that the concentration of sulphur atoms on the GaAs surface is 10^{19} cm^{-3}.

Solution: the diffusion coefficient D of sulphur in GaAs can be obtained from Figure 8.30, and is $\sim 10^{-13}$ cm^2 s^{-1}. We can then calculate the diffusion length as

$$\sqrt{Dt} \;=\; \left(10^{-13} \times 3 \times 3600\right)^{1/2}$$
$$=\; 3.29 \times 10^{-5} \text{ cm}. \tag{8.26}$$

The pn junction will be found at a depth when $C = 5 \times 10^{15}$ cm^{-3}, and so from (8.25)

$$\text{erfc}\left[\frac{x}{2\sqrt{Dt}}\right] = \frac{5 \times 10^{15}}{10^{19}}$$

$$= 5 \times 10^{-4}. \tag{8.27}$$

Obviously from Table 8.6 the erf corresponding to this value is 0.9995. This can be cross-checked in mathematical tables to give a value for the $x/\sqrt{Dt}$ term of (2.46). x can then be readily calculated from (8.26) as 1.6 μm.

To determine the total number of dopants $Q(t)$ entering the semiconductor per unit cross-sectional area (i.e. $y \times z$), the area under each of the graphs in Figure 8.32 needs to be calculated. Thus

$$Q(t) = \int_0^\infty C(x,t)\mathrm{d}x. \tag{8.28}$$

Using (8.25) and error function algebra this becomes

$$Q(t) = \frac{2}{\sqrt{\pi}}C_s\sqrt{Dt}. \tag{8.29}$$

8.6.4.2 Fixed source
In this case, we assume that:

   (i) equations (8.22) and (8.24) still apply,
   (ii) the total amount of dopant, and hence total dopant per unit area Q, is fixed

$$\int_0^\infty C(x,t)\mathrm{d}x = Q. \tag{8.30}$$

Note that in this case Q is a constant, and not a function of time as in (8.28). These boundary conditions lead to a solution of (8.16) given by

$$C(x,t) = \frac{Q}{\sqrt{\pi Dt}}\exp\left(\frac{-x^2}{4Dt}\right). \tag{8.31}$$

This is known as a Gaussian distribution. Comparing (8.25) and (8.31), it can be seen that for fixed source diffusion there is no dependency of C on C_s. In fact, putting $x = 0$ in (8.31) gives a value of C_s, which is time dependent. In order for Q to be constant, the surface concentration must decrease as a function of time in fixed source diffusion, unlike for constant surface concentration diffusion. Using this helps to explain the form of the diffusion profiles obtained from this method, as shown in Figure 8.33.

$$\mathrm{erf(x)} \;=\; \tfrac{2}{\sqrt{\pi}} \int_0^x e^{-y^2}\,dy$$

$$\mathrm{erfc(x)} \;=\; 1- \mathrm{erf(x)}$$

$$\mathrm{erf(0)} \;=\; 0$$

$$\mathrm{erf(\infty)} \;=\; 1$$

$$\mathrm{erf(x)} \;=\; \tfrac{2}{\sqrt{\pi}}x \;\; \text{for} \;\; x \ll 1$$

$$\mathrm{erfc(x)} \;=\; \tfrac{1}{\sqrt{\pi}}\frac{e^{-x^2}}{x} \;\; \text{for} \;\; x \gg 1$$

$$\frac{\mathrm{d}(\mathrm{erf}(x))}{\mathrm{d}x} \;=\; \tfrac{2}{\sqrt{\pi}}e^{-x^2}$$

$$\int_0^\infty \mathrm{erfc}(x)\mathrm{d}x \;=\; \tfrac{1}{\sqrt{\pi}}$$

Table 8.6 Important parameters of the error function and its complement.

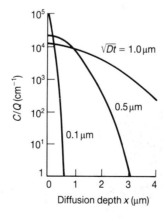

Figure 8.33 Dopant concentration profiles as a function of diffusion length for fixed source diffusion.

Often in device processing, a two-step diffusion process is used. This has a first stage of constant surface concentration diffusion, followed by a further high temperature stage with the dopant source now removed. The initial stage acts to provide dopants, with the second stage giving the diffusion profile. The second stage, known as the drive-in diffusion, is often carried out at a higher temperature and/or longer time than the first, and it is this that largely determines the diffusion profile.

Example 8.3

If we now perform a drive-in diffusion on the material from example 8.2 by removing the sulphur source and raising the processing temperature to 1000 °C for a further 3 hours, calculate the new junction depth.

Solution: in order to do this we must first calculate the total amount of charge per unit area introduced in example 8.2. From (8.29)

$$
\begin{aligned}
Q &= \frac{2}{\sqrt{\pi}} \times 10^{19} \times 3.29 \times 10^{-5} \\
&= 3.71 \times 10^{14} \text{ cm}^{-2}.
\end{aligned}
\tag{8.32}
$$

In the drive-in diffusion this value of Q will remain constant, and can then be used with (8.31) to get the new junction depth. Figure 8.30 can give us a new value of D of $\sim 10^{-12}$ cm^2 s^{-1}. Rearranging (8.31) gives

$$
\begin{aligned}
x &= \left(-4Dt \, \log_e \left[\frac{C\sqrt{\pi Dt}}{Q} \right] \right)^{1/2} \\
&= \left(-4.32 \times 10^{-8} \times \log_e \left[\frac{5 \times 10^{15} \times (\pi \times 10^{-12} \times 10800)^{1/2}}{3.71 \times 10^{14}} \right] \right)^{1/2} \\
&= 5.1 \, \mu\text{m}.
\end{aligned}
\tag{8.33}
$$

This example clearly illustrates the point made in the text about the junction depth being determined largely by the high temperature drive-in diffusion.

8.7   Ion implantation

High temperature diffusion does suffer from several disadvantages which have led to an alternative doping technique being developed. These drawbacks are:

(i) It is an equilibrium process, and so the dopant concentration may never exceed the solubility limit at the diffusion temperature.

(ii) Any impurities in the diffusion ambient will also enter the semiconductor.

(iii) As it is a high temperature process it can introduce additional unwanted defects into the material, and a loss of stoichiometry due to different vapour pressures of the elements of the host semiconductor can occur.

(iv) The depth of diffusion and degree of lateral diffusion under a mask are not very controllable.

(v) Concentration profiles as a function of depth are limited by the diffusion process.

(vi) The choice of dopant is restricted by the magnitude of the diffusion coefficient and the activation energy.

(vii) Total dopant concentration, especially for constant surface concentration diffusion, cannot be accurately monitored during the process.

The first reported work on what is now termed ion implantation was reported in 1952 [65], using ions of such gases as hydrogen, helium, argon and nitrogen, to alter the properties of silicon. Much work has been done since then, with the process now becoming the standard for both IC and optoelectronic applications where shallow, precisely controlled doping concentrations are required.

8.7.1 The implantation process

A schematic of a typical ion implanter is shown in Figure 8.34. The whole assembly is a long vacuum tube with various attachments both inside and outside the system. At the source end is a material containing the element to be implanted. Often this material is a gas, e.g. arsine in the case of implanted arsenic, but can be a solid, heated to create a vapour source, where a gaseous carrier is difficult to find. Atoms released at the source are also ionized at this end of the implanter. These ions are then removed by an accelerating potential (up to 400 keV is common, but machines up to 2 MeV have been built; also ions can obtain double the ionization energy of a single ionization by becoming doubly charged, e.g. $As^+ \rightarrow As^{2+}$). A separator magnet, as used in a mass spectrometer, is used to select only the required ionized species. Contaminants that may have been present in the source can readily be removed at this stage. The separator is usually set for one particular isotope of the element, e.g. $^{29}Si^+$ (this one is chosen instead of the more common $^{28}Si^+$ because 28 is also the atomic mass of ionized molecular carbon monoxide, which is a constituent of the residual gas in an implanter vacuum system). The ion beam leaving the separator constitutes an ion current. This is focused by a lens system and positioned using electrostatic scanning plates on to the wafer target. The ion beam is usually rastered over the wafer, although some systems use a stationary beam and raster the target. Typical beam currents range from ~ 10 μA cm^{-2} for research to ~ 10 mA cm^{-2} for production machines, with total dose (10^{10}–10^{16} ions cm^{-2}) easily monitored as being the integral of current with respect to time. This is a tremendous advantage over chemical diffusion, as is the magnetic separation of impurities. Other advantages are:

(i) The depth of the implanted dopant is controlled by the beam energy and, as the beam is highly directional, lateral spreading of the implanted species is negligible; thus a mask of oxide, photoresist or metal can be used to great effect.

(ii) Accurate control of the concentration profile as a function of depth may be achieved via the beam energy, crystal orientation and implant temperature.

(iii) Implantation is a non-equilibrium process, and impurities may be present in concentrations far exceeding the solid solubility limit.

(iv) Much lower temperatures than are used in chemical diffusion are usually employed, thus reducing the problems of temperature induced defect formation and host sublimation.

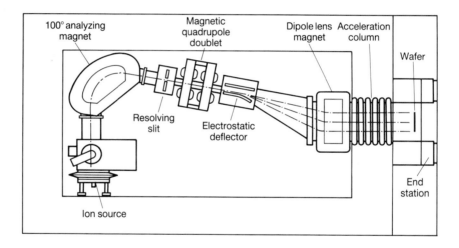

Figure 8.34 A typical ion implanter (courtesy of Varian Associates).

However, ion implantation does introduce additional disadvantages. These are:

(i) As the implanted ions lose energy via collisions with host atoms the crystal lattice becomes damaged, and may even become amorphous.

(ii) The implanted ions are not usually electrically or optically active because they do not come to rest occupying substitutional sites in the lattice.

(iii) An additional heat treatment (annealing) has to be introduced after implantation to restore the crystal structure and incorporate dopants on to active lattice sites.

A further disadvantage, when compared to epitaxial techniques, is that doping profiles are not abrupt.

Example 8.4

Calculate the implanted ion dose per unit area N if a 50 mm diameter GaAs wafer is implanted with 80 keV selenium ions (n-type), using a beam current of $2\mu A$ for 20 minutes.

Solution: the total ion dose is found by integrating the current over time and dividing by the ion charge, which in this case is just equivalent to e. So

$$
\begin{aligned}
\text{total number} \quad &= \quad \frac{I \times t}{e} \\
&= \quad \frac{2 \times 10^{-6} \times 20 \times 60}{e} \\
&= \quad 1.50 \times 10^{16} \text{ ions.}
\end{aligned}
\tag{8.34}
$$

The total number per unit area N is then 7.63×10^{14} ions cm^{-2}.

8.7.2 Energy loss mechanisms

Penetration of the crystal surface by an implanted ion leads to its energy being lost by three processes, with the relative contribution of each component being determined by the particle energy and mass. The dominant energy loss mechanism is electronic stopping, where inelastic collisions occur between the ion and electrons bound within the crystal. Nuclear stopping, which is an elastic collision involving the screened nuclear charges of the ion and target atoms, becomes significant at very low ion velocities, i.e. near the end of the ion track. It is responsible for the deviation of ion trajectories from their original one-dimensional path. Charge exchange between the moving ion and target atoms is the third stopping mechanism which usually has only a small effect on the process.

8.7.2.1 Ion range
The total distance an ion travels before it comes to rest is called its range R, but a more useful parameter is the projected range R_p, which is measured from the crystal surface parallel to the incident ion direction (Figure 8.35). As already mentioned, at high energies electronic stopping dominates; the ion beam is thus

rarely deviated from its original path and R and R_p are approximately equal. Low energy ions, however, are more dominated by nuclear stopping and as such R_p can be considerably less than R.

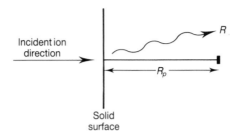

Figure 8.35 Range R and projected range R_p in ion implantation.

The projected range and dose can be calculated from theoretical considerations, details of which were first applied to ion implantation in what has become known as LSS theory (after the authors, J Lindhard, M Scharff and H Schiott). Details of this are quite complex [66] but are based on the fact that the number of collisions per unit path length and the energy lost per collision are random variables. Individual ions will then not have the same range as each other, but collectively will have a range distribution function. Along the angle of incidence, the implanted impurity profile can be approximately given by a Gaussian distribution function

$$n(x) \;=\; \frac{N}{(2\pi)^{1/2}\,\Delta R_p}\,\exp\left[\frac{-\,(x-R_p)^2}{2\,(\Delta R_p)^2}\right] \tag{8.35}$$

where n is the concentration at distance x from the crystal surface, and N is the total ion dose per unit area. At $x = R_p$, the implanted dose reaches a peak value given by

$$n(R_p) \;=\; \frac{N}{(2\pi)^{1/2}\,\Delta R_p}\,. \tag{8.36}$$

Example 8.5

For the material in example 8.4 calculate the peak ion concentration. If the wafer is originally p-type with a doping concentration of 2×10^{15} cm^{-3}, also find the position of the pn junction after implantation. You may assume that the values of R_p and ΔR_p for 80 keV selenium ions in GaAs are 30 nm and 14 nm respectively.

Solution: the peak concentration is given from (8.36), and so

$$n(R_p) = \frac{7.63 \times 10^{14}}{(2\pi)^{1/2} \times 1.4 \times 10^{-6}}$$

$$= 2.17 \times 10^{20} \text{ cm}^{-3}. \tag{8.37}$$

The pn junction will occur at a depth x when $n(x) = 2 \times 10^{15}$ cm^{-3}. Rearranging (8.35) gives (in cm)

$$x = R_p + \left(-2(\Delta R_p)^2 \log_e \left[\frac{(2\pi)^{1/2} \Delta R_p n(x)}{N}\right]\right)^{1/2}$$

$$= 3 \times 10^{-6} + \left(-3.92 \times 10^{-12} \times \log_e \left[\frac{7.03 \times 10^9}{7.63 \times 10^{14}}\right]\right)^{1/2}$$

$$= 9.74 \times 10^{-6} \text{ cm}. \tag{8.38}$$

The junction depth is then approximately 0.1 μm.

LSS theory also shows that, as a general rule, the ratio between R and R_p is approximately given by

$$\frac{\overline{R}}{R_p} = 1 + \frac{M_2}{3M_1} \tag{8.39}$$

where $\overline{R}$ is used instead of R to denote an average range and M_1, M_2 are the masses of the incident ion and host atom respectively. A typical Gaussian profile is shown in Figure 8.36(a). Values of R_p and ΔR_p have been tabulated for various single species and host semiconductors, and these are used to calculate the implant energy/dose needed (e.g. [67, 68]). Experimental profiles are shown in Figure 8.36(b), with two features being noted as differing from the ideal:

(i) an extended tail to the distribution (see next section), and

(ii) a skewness to the distribution as the implant energy is increased. Skewed distribution functions are better modelled using a Pearson type IV function [66] and are especially useful for high energy implantation.

8.7.2.2 *Channelling*

The presence of a long tail to the distribution in Figure 8.36(b) implies that some ions are travelling much further than theory predicts, and this can only occur if the number of collisions occuring at the end of the distribution is less than expected, i.e. nuclear stopping is not having its predicted effect. This happens when the host crystal is oriented such that ions are channelled between rows of atoms, and the incoming ion may 'see' the host crystal as in Figure 8.37 [69]. If the crystal is tilted sufficiently the channelling effect is no longer apparent and this is the reason why wafers are presented at an angle of 7°–10° to the ion beam.

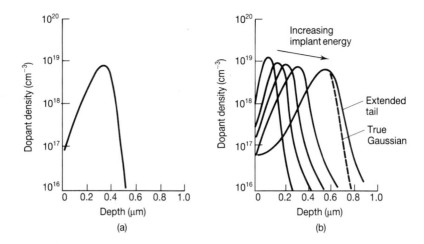

Figure 8.36 Dopant profiles after implantation: (a) Gaussian, and (b) the extended tail, and skewness of the distribution with increasing beam energy.

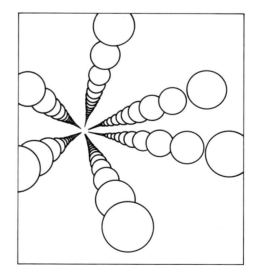

Figure 8.37 Model for a diamond or zincblende structure, viewed along a $\langle 110 \rangle$ axis.

8.7.3   Annealing

As mentioned earlier, the massive amount of crystal damage caused during implantation and the need to locate ions on to active lattice sites leads to the necessity for a post-implantation annealing process. The use of a furnace at 1000 $^-$C for a few hours is the traditional way to do this for silicon devices. However, such high temperatures are unacceptable for III–V compounds because of the high vapour pressure of (usually) the Group V element; loss of stoichiometry would result. Typically around 800–850 $^-$C is used for GaAs (lower for other III–Vs) with annealing carried out in an arsenic overpressure. Sometimes inert gas overpressures or capping layers of silicon dioxide or nitride are used. Besides the stoichiometry problem, thermal annealing has other disadvantages:

(i) It leads to a dopant redistribution; thus lateral spreading under a mask once again becomes a problem. This dopant distribution is given by a Gaussian function similar to that of (8.35):

$$n(x) = \frac{N}{(2\pi)^{1/2} \left(\Delta R_p^2 + 2Dt\right)^{1/2}} \exp\left[\frac{-(x - R_p)^2}{2\left(\Delta R_p\right)^2 + 4Dt}\right]. \qquad (8.40)$$

(ii) It is a time consuming process.

8.7.3.1 Transient annealing

The use of pulsed lasers to anneal ion implanted GaAs was first demonstrated in 1975 [70]. Many different types of transient heating methods have been used but because of reliability and reproducibility problems only one system, rapid thermal annealing (RTA), has survived as still being popular. In fact, the RTA processes have largely replaced furnaces as the standard method of annealing implants, and hence are worth studying in more detail.

The basic RTA apparatus was first described in 1981 [71]. This equipment had just one arc lamp, but modern RTA systems have two banks of lamps above and below the wafer. A schematic is shown in Figure 8.38(a). The d.c. power to the water-cooled lamps is computer controlled via a feedback loop. Initial configurations used a thermocouple on a calibration wafer as the temperature sensor, but most RTA systems now use a pyrometer to measure directly the temperature of the heated wafer. The whole system is purged with nitrogen, or sometimes an annealing overpressure is used. Typical temperature–time graphs are shown in Figure 8.38(b), where there is an initial ramp up to 400 $^-$C before going on to 850 $^-$C; this minimizes the possibility of overshoot at that temperature. Typical process times/temperatures are 2–10 seconds at 800–1050 $^-$C for implants in GaAs, and substantially lower in other III–Vs. The advantages of this system are (compared to furnace annealing):

(i) no or little dopant diffusion,
(ii) shorter processing times,
(iii) little contamination from a quartz chamber, as this is transparent to the wavelength of light used,

and compared to other transient techniques:

(i) shorter times needed to anneal a whole wafer,
(ii) lower electrical energy consumption,
(iii) cheaper to install,
(iv) thermally stable dopant activation.

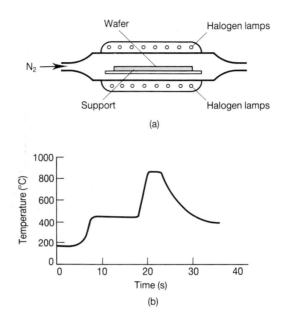

Figure 8.38 (a) Typical RTA system. (b) Typical temperature–time profile of RTA.

Considerable activity has gone into detection and control of the wafer temperature and its uniformity. The emissivity of a semiconductor varies both with its temperature (at least up to 600 $^-$C for silicon) and the detection wavelength, as well as more obvious factors such as surface cleanliness [72]. If the wafer temperature is not uniform and repeatable, then not only does the implant activation vary but slip lines indicating excessive stress appear in the wafer surface. For some devices these lines don't appear to matter, but this is unlikely to be true of, for example, lasers, where line defects are known to be major factors in reducing the operational lifetime.

8.7.4   Implantation related phenomena

The non-equilibrium nature of ion implantation can, with a little ingenuity, lead to the tailoring of a dopant profile to almost any particular requirement. Discussed here are a few examples of the wider exploitation of the implantation technique.

8.7.4.1 *Multiscan implantation*

The implantation profile of Figure 8.36(b) can be used to good effect in producing a constant dose doping profile, as in Figure 8.39, by a series of implants at different energies and doses. This is particularly useful in obtaining a uniform activation over a given volume of the semiconductor.

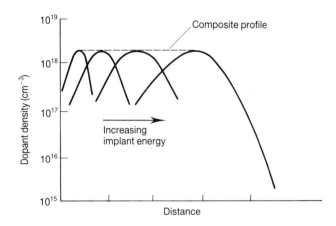

Figure 8.39 Constant doping profile achieved using ion implantation.

8.7.4.2 *Junction creation*

The creation of an abrupt pn junction within a semi-insulating or undoped material relies on at least two implantations. This can be used to create a p-type layer either above or beneath an n-type layer. A use of the former is in a FET (in optoelectronic PINFET receivers the FET is the amplifier) shown in Figure 8.40. A standard FET has two n^+ contact regions, and an n-type channel region. As device sizes shrink, conduction through the substrate becomes an important undesirable phenomenon, as it leads to punchthrough and rapid increase in current on forward bias. To reduce this, a p-type region is created under the channel, which if the p-region is fully depleted will create an abrupt channel on top of a highly resistive region, reducing or even eliminating the punchthrough effect. A second approach to FETs is to implant the p-region close to the gate metal contact [73]. This gives an increased metal–semiconductor barrier height and hence leads to greater allowed noise margins in FETs. This p-type surface implant can also be useful in pin diodes, where the uppermost part of the device needs to be very thin to let light through to the depletion region.

8.7.4.3 *Doping through a mask*

Because of the nature of a typical ion implantation profile, the peak of the distribution can be altered and brought nearer to the surface by implanting through a thin surface capping layer. If this layer thickness (typically a few hundred Å) is

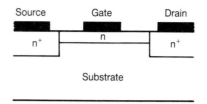

Figure 8.40 Cross-section of a FET.

tailored correctly the peak of the concentration can be at or very near the surface, leading to an extremely thin conducting layer. Also, if the capping material is silicon dioxide or nitride it can be used as a subsequent cap in the anneal process. This technique is used extensively in producing narrow, highly conducting regions such as for thin channels or contact layers.

8.7.4.4 *Molecular implantation*
Another technique to obtain shallow conducting layers is to implant with heavy ions. By implanting molecular ions such as $^{47}SiF^+$ and $^{66}SiF^{2+}$ instead of $^{29}Si^+$, a shallow implant profile is obtained for a given energy, whilst still giving the same dose of dopant [74].

8.7.4.5 *Direct write*
Most implantations are done using a material such as photoresist as the beam mask. However, because an ion beam is scanned electrostatically, it follows that it can also be shut on or off by such means. Thus a similar mechanism to that of electron beam lithography (see section 9.1.10), where an electron beam is positioned under computer control, should be possible with ion implantation, as indeed has been performed. This obviates the need for a mask, and hence an extra processing step is removed. Careful control over beam position needs to be exercised, however, as dimensional tolerances are very tight in implantation for IC production. It is thus the takeup of direct write in silicon ICs that will determine the success of the technique, not optoelectronics.

8.7.4.6 *Proton isolation*
This is the most ironic of applications of ion implantation, a technique originally developed to enhance the conductivity of semiconductors. High energy proton bombardment does exactly the opposite. Proton isolation exploits the crystal damage effects induced by ion implantation to disrupt the lattice so much that no conduction is possible – it is thus a highly effective method of electrically separating adjacent devices by means other than physical etching of the semiconductor, hence maintaining a planar surface for ease of subsequent processing. Protons are light and hence implants are very deep, giving an isolation extending well beyond the conducting layers and into the underlying substrate.

8.8   Wet etching

Etching is an integral part of device manufacture. There are two basic techniques: wet, involving chemicals in a liquid solution, and dry, involving reactive species generated in a plasma. The latter system is considered in section 9.2, because dry etching techniques are usually employed in processing technology after most material aspects of growth, epitaxy and doping have been considered. Wet etching does occur in processing, but also at the basic materials end of device fabrication; hence it is included here. The two techniques have little of any physical or techno- logical commonality except the common aim to remove material, and so it is not inconsistent to split them this way. Also, the first time a wet etch is met in device processing is to give new wafers an initial clean.

8.8.1   The wet etching process

To remove semiconductor materials an etchant usually contains three basic con- stituents; an oxidizing agent, a complexing agent and a dilutant. There are many different types of oxidizing and complexing agents used, depending on the etch rate required and other factors such as mask integrity, crystallographic etching, etc. The dilutant is usually water or methanol. Many reviews containing extensive lists of recipes have been published, e.g. [75–78]. Some examples are given in Table 8.7, for semiconductors, common metals and insulators used in fabrication. Etch rates depend on relative concentration [75, 77, 78].

Let us take as an example the etching of GaAs in a solution of H_2SO_4 (complexing agent): H_2O_2 (oxidizing agent): H_2O (dilutant). The basic mechanism is shown in Figure 8.41. Both H_2SO_4 and H_2O_2 move to the semiconductor surface by diffusion through the dilutant. H_2O_2 oxidizes both Ga and As separately. H_2SO_4 then complexes with the oxides to form a soluble product which is removed. If the oxidation rate is faster than the removal rate then the H_2O_2 has to undergo a solid phase diffusion through an oxidized film to the GaAs–oxide interface.

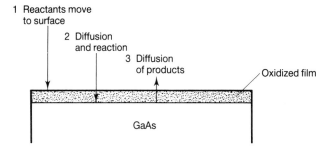

Figure 8.41 Kinetics of oxide removal in GaAs.

Material	Etchant
SiO_2	HF or HF:H_2O:NH_4F (buffered HF) (28 ml:170 ml:113 g)
Si_3N_4	HF:H_2O, Buffered HF, H_3PO_4:H_2O
Al	HNO_3:CH_3COOH:H_3PO_4:H_2O
Ti	HF:H_2O
Pt	HNO_3:HCl:H_2O
Cr	Dilute HCl or HNO_3 (must depassivate by physical contact with electropositive metal, e.g. Al or Zn)
Au	KI:I_2:H_2O (slow) or HCl:HNO_3 (fast)
Mo	HNO_3:CH_3COOH:H_3PO_4:H_2O
Ni	HNO_3:CH_3COOH:H_2SO_4:H_2O
W	KH_2PO_4:KOH:$K_3Fe(CN)_6$:H_2O
GaAs	H_2SO_4:H_2O_2:H_2O (fast) or NaOH:H_2O_2 (slow)
GaP	Br_2:CH_3OH
InP	Br_2:CH_3OH or H_2SO_4:H_2O_2:H_2O
InGaAs	Br_2:CH_3OH
InGaAsP	Br_2:CH_3OH
InSb	I_2:CH_3OH
GaSb	Br_2:CH_3OH

Table 8.7 Commonly used semiconductors, metals and insulators and *examples* of their etchants (many other solutions can be used, depending on etch rate, other materials in the device, i.e. selectivity, mask integrity, degree of crystallographic etching, temperature, availability of electrolytic etching, etc.).

8.8.1.1 *Process variables*

If the oxidizing agent concentration is low, the oxidation rate is low and hence the process is reaction rate limited. Increasing the oxidizer concentration increases the etch rate in a linear fashion, up until a point where the surface is oxidizing faster than it is being removed. The dependence of etch rate on oxidizer concentration will then be sublinear unless the complexing agent concentration is increased (Figure 8.42(a)). However, the solution then becomes viscous, agents cannot reach the reaction surface quickly and the process becomes diffusion limited. Stirring is then needed to increase the reaction rate (Figure 8.42(b)).

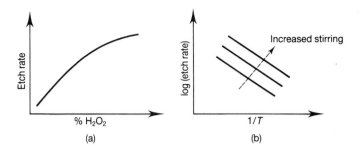

Figure 8.42 Etch rate as a function of (a) complexing agent concentration, and (b) temperature.

The same diagram also shows the effect of temperature: etch rate always increases with this parameter as the key physical phenomena in etching (diffusion, surface adsorption) have an $\exp(-\Delta E_A/kT)$ dependence on temperature, where ΔE_A is an activation energy.

An important difference between a reaction and a diffusion limited etch is the effect of time. For the former case etch rate will be time independent, but for the latter the gradual depletion of the etchant close to the semiconductor surface will lead to a fall-off in etch rate with time.

The nature of the process, i.e. oxidation and removal, makes it sensitive to other external factors. The oxidation takes place at anodic sites and the oxidant is reduced at cathodic sites; anything which changes the supply of electrons or holes at the surface will then change the reaction rate. Examples are doping, illumination and electric current (the latter is considered separately in section 8.8.2, electrolytic etching).

Some etchants can produce bubbles, usually denoting hydrogen, which will prevent etching if left to adhere to the surface. Constant agitation is usually used to alleviate this.

8.8.1.2 Crystallographic etching

The etch rate depends on the density of semiconductor atoms, and for all zincblende or diamond (i.e. most semiconductor) structures the (111) plane is more closely packed than the (100) plane; an orientation dependent etch will then remove atoms faster in the (100) case. An example of this is KOH mixed in water and isopropyl alcohol, which has an etch rate ratio of 100:16:1 for the (100), (110) and (111) planes of silicon respectively. This can lead to different etch profiles as shown in Figure 8.43. for (100) oriented surfaces (Figure 8.43(a)) the etch downwards will be much faster than that along the (111) planes which are oriented at 54.7° to the (100). Narrow mask windows will produce a V-groove etch whereas large windows will have a tapered edge to a flat bottom. For (100) oriented silicon (Figure 8.43(b)) the (110) and (111) planes are perpendicular to each other, and hence rectangular shaped profiles are obtained [79].

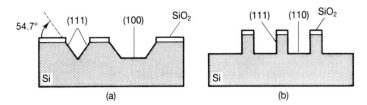

Figure 8.43 Orientation dependent etching: (a) profile on masked (100) Si, and (b) profile on masked (110) Si ©John Wiley & Sons: reproduced by kind permission).

For compound semiconductors the effect of crystal orientation is far more involved. Here there is the consideration of at least two different atomic planes to take into account. What happens in practice can best be seen by considering Figure 8.44. In Figure 8.44(a), an etch mask is oriented at 45° to the [1$\bar{1}$0] and [110] directions. Undercut of the mask occurs, a major limitation of wet etching in III–Vs, but the etch profiles are identical for the two examples shown. Undercut occurs because the preferential etching of different orientations is far less pronounced than for silicon; ratios of 100:70:60 for (100), (110) and (111) planes of GaAs are found in practice, with precise numbers depending on the etch chemicals [77].

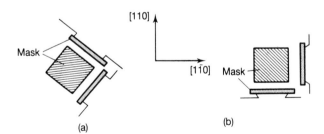

Figure 8.44 Undercut profiles in GaAs, with the mask oriented at (a) 45° to the [110] and [1$\bar{1}$0] directions, and (b) oriented parallel to these directions.

In Figure 8.44(b) the undercut profiles for the [110] or [1$\bar{1}$0] oriented edges of the mask are clearly very different; in the former case profiles are dovetailed and in the latter trapezoidal. The difference can be explained by first of all considering the unit cell of GaAs and its associated crystal planes, as shown in Figure 8.45(a). The zincblende structure consists of two interlocking fcc lattices of Ga and As separated by (1/4 1/4 1/4) of the lattice constant. It can clearly be seen that (111) planes can be made up of solely As or Ga atoms (As$_{21-26}$ from part of a plane, as do Ga_{21-23} and As_{11-13}, etc. beyond the unit cell). The distance between planes is unequal; for instance atom Ga_{21} is much closer to the three atoms it is bonded to in the plane 'underneath' (atoms As_{21}, As_{22}, As_{26}) than to the atom in the plane 'above' (As_{11}). This is true for all atoms in the structure, and it then becomes apparent that, as far as {111} planes are concerned, there are two closely spaced planes ({111}A Ga and {111}B As) held together by three bonds between Ga and As, and these are joined to the next pair of planes by a weaker bond in a perpendicular ⟨111⟩ direction. It is also apparent that, for a [111] direction, a (111) Ga plane is 'exposed' to the open spaces of the crystal, but As atoms are only exposed at the $(\bar{1}\bar{1}\bar{1})$ plane and $[\bar{1}\bar{1}\bar{1}]$ direction. Thus any discontinuity forced on the crystal in a ⟨111⟩ direction, such as by cleavage or etching, causes the crystal to terminate with the strongly bound atoms exposed to the surface as the weaker, perpendicular bond is more readily broken than the three other bonds from the plane; As atoms and Ga atoms are exposed for a free $(\bar{1}\bar{1}\bar{1})$ As and (111) Ga surface respectively.

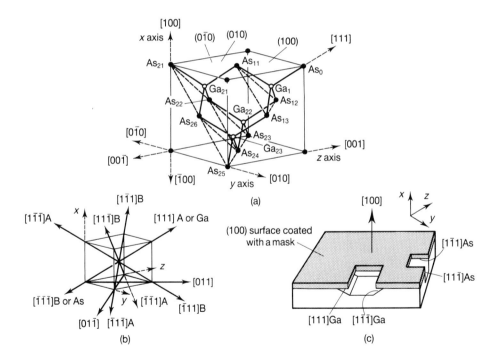

Figure 8.45 (a) Unit cell of GaAs and its associated crystal planes. (b) The family of {111} planes. (©John Wiley & Sons: reproduced by kind permission.) (c) The resultant etch profiles.

If we now consider Figure 8.45(b), which shows the family of $\langle 111 \rangle$ directions, it is clear that there are four A types ($[111]$, $[\bar{1}\bar{1}1]$, $[\bar{1}1\bar{1}]$ and $[1\bar{1}\bar{1}]$) and four B types ($[\bar{1}\bar{1}\bar{1}]$, $[11\bar{1}]$, $[1\bar{1}1]$ and $[\bar{1}11]$). Also consider the valency of the atoms in each type of associated plane; for Ga planes the valency of three is completely satisfied by the three underlying As atoms, but for As planes the valence of five leaves two unbonded electrons. As oxidation involves the loss of electrons, As atoms on a {111} surface react more than equivalent Ga atoms. Once the As atoms have been removed by oxidation, the underlying Ga atoms are readily removed because they only have a single bond holding them in place to the next {111} As surface. So {111} As etch rates are far higher than those for {111} Ga planes. Etch profiles, as shown in Figures 8.44(b) and (c), are then explained.

This phenomenon is true of all compound semiconductors, because of the polar nature of the compounds. Although the above example is described in detail for GaAs, Ga and As can be replaced by any group III and group V element(s) respectively and the principle will still be valid.

8.8.1.3 Surface cleaning

Included in this section are mild etching processes, such as are used prior to a metallization. Surface cleaning in these cases is necessary to remove contaminants such as carbon or native oxides that begin to grow immediately a semiconductor is exposed to air. Although no compound semiconductor oxidizes as readily as silicon, the few tens of angströms of oxide that is typically present on a III–V surface prior to any cleaning can be a major obstacle to a good ohmic or Schottky metallization.

Etchants used here have to take account of the nature of the oxides to be removed. For GaAs, for instance, the native oxides As_2O_3 and $As_2)O_5$ are readily soluble in water, alcohols, acids and alkalis; the oxides Ga_2O_3 and Ga_2O are insoluble in water, slightly soluble in acids and readily soluble in alkali solutions. It would then appear that a solution such as $NH_4OH : H_2O$ is ideal for cleaning GaAs, as it removes both types of oxide and has the added bonus of degreasing the surface of carbon based compounds [77]. However, for InP, although alkali solutions do clean the surface, they are not as effective as acid solutions, which must be used to obtain a totally oxide free material [80].

8.8.2   Electrolytic etching

As mentioned in section 8.8.1.1, etching is affected by the presence of electrons and/or holes, and one way of doing this is by making the wafer to be etched the cathode or anode of an electrolytic cell. A typical apparatus for anodic etching is shown in Figure 8.46(a) [81], and includes an external light source. The cathode is platinum which doesn't react with the electrolyte, usually a fruit acid based system such as one part 3% tartaric acid buffered with NH_4OH, to two parts propylene glycol. For n-GaAs, the current is carried by electrons in the semiconductor and ions in the oxide; thus the interface between the two gives rise to a reverse biased junction and associated depletion region (Figure 8.46(b)). On illumination, a photocurrent is generated in the depletion layer by the avalanche effect (see Chapter 7). The external current measured will be a multiple of this. The avalanche process supplies holes to the oxide–semiconductor surface, which is the equivalent of the removal of electrons. Hence oxidation occurs without an oxidizing chemical. This process is self-limiting, for when the n-region is sufficiently thin as to reach the semi-insulating substrate the depletion region widens. Here no breakdown occurs, no holes are created and hence oxide is no longer formed. When this point occurs, the cell voltage rapidly increases as the in-line resistance becomes very high. On detecting this point, the process is stopped, and the thickness of the remaining n-type material can be readily calculated as being exactly equal to the depletion layer thickness given by (2.79).

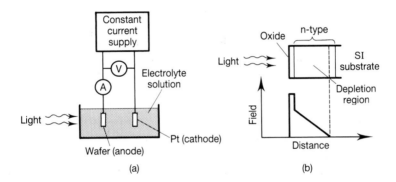

Figure 8.46 (a) Typical anodic etching system. (b) The formation of a depletion region during anodic etching.

It can be shown [81] that the relationship between doping density, layer thickness and incident light flux Φ is given by

$$N_D w = k\Phi \qquad (8.41)$$

where k is a material constant. Hence for any doping density the amount of material left after etching (and hence the amount of material removed) is determined by the light flux. The grown oxide can be removed in any of the chemicals mentioned previously for this purpose.

The same apparatus can be used for p-type GaAs, but in this case the junction 'diode' is forward biased and conducts readily. It is thus all removed in the etching process.

Cathodic etching is not so commonly used as it is not technologically as important; it selectively removes a semi-insulating compound but leaves conductive material. For the semi-insulator exposed to an etchant, no current flows and chemical etching takes place [82]. When conductive material is reached, current flows and provides electrons to satisfy the oxidizing agent; for a sufficiently high current, etching ceases.

8.9   Problems

1. What are the advantages and disadvantages of ever bigger wafer sizes in device production?

2. Comment on the likely result if the pull rate of an LEC boule is non-uniform. Would the same happen in HB growth?

3. If an LEC-grown GaAs boule is pulled at the rate of 7 mm h^{-1}, how many atoms per second recrystallize for a wafer diameter of 50 mm?

4. Explain why most ternary and quaternary III–V semiconductors are unlikely to be made by bulk crystal growth methods. Is this also the case for II–VI compounds?

5. Suggest a reaction based on chloride transport that produces InP.

6. What is the meaning of the term solid solubility in semiconductor doping? Explain how diffusion and ion implantation differ in this respect.

7. Consider a p-type GaAs substrate with a dopant concentration of 10^{15} cm^{-3}. If the wafer is placed in a sulphur containing ambient at 900 °C for 2 hours (with also an arsenic overpressure), calculate the junction depth and the total amount of sulphur introduced into the wafer. Assume that the solid solubility of sulphur in GaAs is 10^{19} cm^{-3} at 900 °C.

8. If the sulphur source was removed from the ambient of problem 7, and the temperature raised to 1000 °C, calculate the new junction depth for a further 5 hours processing.

9. The surface concentration of a particular GaAs dopant is temperature independent, has an activation energy of 3.5 eV and a value of diffusion coefficient at 700 °C of 10^{-16} cm^2 s^{-1}. The diffusion length of all processing should be 10^{-6} cm. Calculate:

    (i) the process time at 700 °C,

    (ii) the area density of impurities in the diffused layer at the same temperature,

    (iii) the change in process time if an elevated temperature of 800 °C is used,

    (iv) the flux of atoms after 30 minutes at 800 °C.

10. InP is diffused with a dopant at 600 °C for 3 hours. A diffusion length of 500 nm is measured and the dopant area density is 3×10^{12} atoms cm^{-2}. Calculate:

    (i) the diffusion coefficient at 600 °C,

(ii) the surface concentration,

(iii) the flux of atoms after 1 hour.

If a similar experiment is performed for the same amount of time at 750 °C, the surface concentration remains constant but the diffusion length doubles. What is the value of the activation energy?

11. For a drive-in diffusion of sulphur in GaAs, estimate the uncertainty in the dopant surface concentration if the process temperature controller has an associated uncertainty of 1% at 900 °C.

12. Why can photoresist be used as a mask against implantation, but not against diffusion?

13. If a 50 mm diameter p-type GaAs wafer is implanted with 80 keV selenium ions for 10 minutes at a beam current of 5 μA, calculate the ion dose per unit area and the peak ion concentration. If the substrate has a doping density of 10^{15} cm^{-3}, find the position of the pn junction if R_p and ΔR_p of 80 keV Se$^+$ ions in GaAs are 30 nm and 14 nm respectively.

14. For a given implant energy, boron ions travel further than phosphorus ions which in turn travel further than those of arsenic. Explain this.

15. For a 100 keV implant of ^{29}Si$^+$ ions, calculate:

(i) the ion velocity,

(ii) the magnetic field required if the separator has a radius of 30 cm.

16. Why is bombardment using H$^+$ ions, as opposed to any other type, the preferred method of disrupting a crystal lattice by implantation?

17. What would you expect to be the main problems associated with transient annealing that have meant that only one technique has been transferred to production?

8.10 References

1. M Hansen, *Constitution of Binary Alloys*, 2nd ed., McGraw Hill, 1958, p. 165.

2. F A Shunk, *Constitution of Binary Alloys*, 2nd supplement, McGraw Hill, 1969, p. 446.

3. See [2], p. 360.

4. J B Mullin, B W Straughan and W S Brickell, 'Liquid Encapsulation Techniques: the Use of an Inert Liquid in Suppressing Dissociation during the Melt-Growth of InAs and GaAs Crystals', *J. Phys. Chem. Solids* **26**, 782 (1965).

5. C G Kirkpatrick, R T Chen, D E Holmes and K R Elliott, 'Growth of Bulk GaAs', in *Gallium Arsenide: Materials, Devices and Circuits*, M J Howes and D V Morgan, eds, Wiley, 1985, p. 39.

6. R N Thomas, H M Hobgood, G W Eldridge, D L Barrett, T T Braggins, L B Ta and S K Wang, 'High Purity LEC Growth and Direct Implantation of GaAs for Monolithic Microwave Circuits', in Semiconductors and Semimetals, vol. 20: *Semi-insulating GaAs*, R K Willardson and A C Beer, eds, Academic Press, 1984, p. 1.

7. R T Chen and D E Holmes, 'Dislocation Studies in 3-inch Diameter Liquid Encapsulated Czochralski GaAs', *J. Crystal Growth* **61**, 111 (1983).

8. S M Sze, *Semiconductor Devices – Physics and Technology*, Wiley, 1985, p. 306–310.

9. See [6], p. 10.

10. S Ozawa, H Nakayama, Y Shiina, E Ohashi and T Kikuta, 'Growth of 4 inch Diameter Semi-insulating LEC GaAs with Applied Magnetic Field', *IOP Conf. Series* **96**, IOPP, 1989, p. 343.

11. W A Bonner, B J Sknomme, E Berry, H L Gilchrist and R E Nahory, 'Bulk Single Crystal $Ga_{1-x}In_xAs$: LEC Growth and Characterisation', in [10], p. 337.

12. J J Hsieh, 'Liquid Phase Epitaxy', in *Handbook of Semiconductors*, vol. 3, S P Keller, ed, North-Holland, 1980, p. 415ff.

13. K Nakajima, 'The Liquid Phase Epitaxial Growth of InGaAsP', in Semiconductors and Semimetals, vol. 22A: *Material Growth Techniques*, W T Tsang, ed., Academic Press, 1985, p. 1ff.

14. H Nelson, 'Epitaxial Growth from the Liquid State and its Applications to the Fabrication of Tunnel and Laser Diodes', *RCA Review* **24**, 603 (1963).

15. K Gillesen and W Schairer, *Light Emitting Diodes: an Introduction*, Prentice-Hall International, 1987, p. 48.

16. M B Panish, I Hayashi and S Sumski, 'A Technique for the Preparation of Low Threshold Room Temperature GaAs Laser Diode Structures', *IEEE J. Quantum Electron.* **QE-5**, 210 (1969).

17. See [15], p. 50.

18. See [12], p. 468ff.

19. G R Antell and D Effer, 'Preparation of Crystals of InAs, InP, GaAs and GaP by a Vapour Phase Reaction', *J. Electrochem. Soc.* **106**, 509 (1959).

20. H M Manasevit and W I Simpson, 'The Use of Metal–Organics in the Preparation of Semiconductor Materials, I. Epitaxial Gallium-V Compounds', *J. Electrochem. Soc.* **116**, 1725 (1969).

21. Y Seki, R Tanno, K Iida and E Ichiki, 'Properties of Epitaxial GaAs Layers from a Triethyl Gallium and Arsine System', *J. Electrochem. Soc.* **122**, 1108 (1975).

22. G B Stringfellow, 'Organometallic Vapour-Phase Epitaxial Growth of III–V Semiconductors', in [13], p. 212.

23. See [22], p. 222.

24. M Razeghi, 'Low Pressure Metallo–Organic Chemical Vapour Deposition of $Ga_xIn_{1-x}As_yP_{1-y}$ Alloys', in [13], p. 299ff.

25. J P Duchemin, M Bonnet, G Beuchet and F Koelsch, 'Organometallic Growth of Device Quality InP by Cracking of In(C$_2$H$_5$)$_3$ and PH$_3$ at Low Pressure', *IOP Conf. Series* **45**, IOPP, 1979, p. 10.

26. N H Karam, N A El-Marry and S M Bedair, 'Laser Selective Deposition and Direct Writing of Single Crystal III–V Compound Films', *IOP Conf. Series* **83**, IOPP, 1987, p. 171.

27. J Nishizawa, H Abe and T Kurabayashi, 'Molecular Layer Epitaxy', *J. Electrochem. Soc.* **132**, 1197 (1985).

28. A Usui and H Sunakawa, 'GaAs Atomic Layer Epitaxy by Hydride VPE', *Jpn. J. Appl. Phys.* **25**, L212 (1986).

29. H Watanabe and A Usui, 'Atomic Layer Epitaxy', in [26], p. 1.

30. M Ozeki, K Mochizuki, Y Sakuma, N Ohtsuka and K Kodama, 'Atomic Layer Epitaxy of III–V Compounds by Metalorganic and Hydride Sources', *IOP Conf. Series* **106**, IOPP, 1990, p. 31.

31. H M Cox, S G Hummel and V G Keramidas, 'Vapour Levitation Epitaxy: System Design and Performance', *J. Crystal Growth* **79**, 900 (1986).

32. See [28], p. 372.

33. J E Davey and T Pankey, 'Epitaxial GaAs Films Deposited by Vacuum Evaporation', *J. Appl. Phys.* **39**, 1941 (1968).

34. W T Tsang, 'MBE for III–V Semiconductors', in [13], p. 100.

35. B A Joyce and C T Foxon, 'Adsorption, Desorption and Migration on Semiconductor Surfaces', in Comprehensive Chemical Kinetics, vol. 19: *Simple Processes at the Gas–Solid Interface*, C H Banford, C F H Tipper and R G Compton, eds, Elsevier, 1984, p. 278.

36. C E C Wood, 'III–V Alloy Growth by Molecular Beam Epitaxy', in *GaInAsP Alloy Semiconductors*, T P Pearsall, ed, Wiley, 1982, p. 87.

37. L L Cheng, L Esaki, W E Howard and R Ludeke, 'The Growth of a GaAs–GaAlAs Superlattice', *J. Vac. Sci. Technol.* **10**, 11 (1973).

38. A Y Cho and H C Casey, Jr, 'GaAs–Al$_x$Ga$_{1-x}$As Double-Heterostructure Lasers Prepared by Molecular Beam Epitaxy', *Appl. Phys. Lett.* **25**, 288 (1974).

39. G D Kramer, R K Tsui, J A Curless and M S Peffley, 'Properties of AlGaAs Grown by Molecular Beam Epitaxy on Lenticular Substrates', in [26], p. 117.

40. R F C Farrow, 'Growth of Indium Phosphide Films from In and P$_2$ Beams in Ultra-High Vacuum', *J. Phys. D: Appl. Phys.* **7**, L121 (1974).

41. K Tateishi, M Naganuma and K Takahashi, 'Graded-Bandgap III–V Ternary Compound Films by Molecular Beam Epitaxy', *Jpn. J. Appl. Phys.* **15**, 785 (1976).

42. J R Arthur and J J LePore, 'GaAs, GaP and GaAs$_x$P$_{1-x}$ Epitaxial Films Grown by Molecular Beam Deposition', *J. Vac. Sci. Technol.* **6**, 545 (1969).

43. H Sakaki, L L Chang, R Ludeke, C-A Chang, G A Sai-Halasz and L Esaki, 'In$_{1-x}$Ga$_x$As–GaSb$_{1-y}$As$_y$ Heterojunctions by Molecular Beam Epitaxy', *Appl. Phys. Lett.* **31**, 211 (1977).

44. A Y Cho, 'Growth of III–V Semiconductors by Molecular Beam Epitaxy and their Properties', *Thin Solid Films* **100**, 291 (1983).

45. W T Tsang and M Ilegems, 'Selective Area Growth of GaAs/AlGaAs Multilayer Structures with Molecular Beam Epitaxy using Si Shadow Masks', *Appl. Phys. Lett.* **31**, 301 (1977).

46. M B Panish, 'Molecular Beam Epitaxy of GaAs and InP with Gas Sources for As and P', *J. Electrochem. Soc.* **127**, 2729 (1980).

47. W T Tsang, 'Chemical Beam Epitaxy of InP and GaAs', *Appl. Phys. Lett.* **45**, 1234 (1984).

48. W T Tsang, 'Chemical Beam Epitaxy of $Ga_{0.47}In_{0.53}As/InP$ Quantum Wells and Heterostructure Devices', *J. Crystal Growth* **81**, 261 (1987).

49. H Ando, A Sandhu, H Ishikawa, Y Sugiyama and T Fujii, 'Gas-Source MBE Growth of $Al_{0.3}Ga_{0.7}As$ Using TEG, TEA and AsH_3', in [30], p. 217.

50. A Takamori, T Yokotsuka, K Uchiyama and M Nakajima, 'Electrical and Optical Properties of Heavily Be-Doped GaInP and AlInP Grown by Gas Source MBE using PH_3', in [30], p. 229.

51. K Tahahashi, 'Future Epitaxial Growth Process: Photo-MOMBE', in [26], p. 73.

52. M Razeghi, 'LP-MOCVD Growth, Characterisation and Application of InP Material', in Semiconductors and Semimetals, vol. 31: *Indium Phosphide: Crystal Growth and Characterisation*, R K Willardson and A C Beer, eds, Academic Press, 1990, p. 263.

53. S Sakai, T Soga, M Takeyasu and M Umeno, 'AlGaAs/GaAs DH Lasers on Si Substrates Grown Using Super Lattice Buffer Layers by MOCVD', *Jpn. J. Appl. Phys.* **24**, L666 (1985).

54. A Christou, B R Wilkins and W F Tseng, 'Low Temperature Epitaxial Growth of GaAs on (100) Silicon Substrates', *Elec. Lett.* **21**, 406 (1985).

55. S K Shastry and S Zemon, 'Low Pressure Organometallic Vapour Phase Epitaxial Growth of Device Quality GaAs Directly on (100) Si', *Appl. Phys. Lett.* **49**, 467 (1986).

56. M K Lee, D S Wuu and H H Tung, 'Heteroepitaxial Growth of InP Directly on Si by Low Pressure Metalorganic Chemical Vapour Deposition', *Appl. Phys. Lett.* **50**, 1725 (1987).

57. S M Vernon, V E Haven, C R Abernathy, S J Pearton, A T Macrander, V M Haegel, V P Mazzi, K T Short and M M Al-Jassim, 'Growth and Characterisation of MOCVD-Grown InP on Si', in [10], p. 211.

58. H C Casey, Jr, 'Diffusion in the III–V Compound Semiconductors', in *Atomic Diffusion in Semiconductors*, D Shaw, ed, Plenum, 1973, p. 370.

59. E W Williams, W Elder, M G Astles, M Webb, J B Mullin, B Straughan and P J Tufton, 'Indium Phosphide: I. A Photoluminescence Materials Study', *J. Electrochem. Soc.* **120**, 1741 (1973).

60. E Kubota, Y Ohmori and K Sugii, 'Electrical and Optical Properties of Mg, Ca and Zn-doped InP Crystals Grown by the Synthesis Solute Diffusion Technique', *J. Appl. Phys.* **55**, 3779 (1984).

61. See [58], p. 418.

62. See [58], p. 419ff.

63. See [58], p. 369ff.

64. L M Milne-Thomson and L J Comrie, *Standard Four Figure Mathematical Tables, (edition B)*, Macmillan & Co., 1948, p. 211.

65. R S Ohl, 'Properties of Ionic Bombarded Silicon', *Bell System Tech. J.* **31**, 104 (1952).

66. J F Gibbons, 'Ion Implantation', in [12], p. 603.

67. J F Gibbons, W S Johnson and S W Mylroie, *Projected Range Statistics, Semiconductors and Related Materials*, 2nd ed., Dowden, Hutchinson and Ross, 1975.

68. G Dearnaley, J H Freeman, R S Nelson and J Stephen, *Ion Implantation*, North Holland, 1971.

69. L Pauling and R Hayward, *The Architecture of Molecules*, W H Freeman, 1964, p. 16.

70. G A Kachurin, N B Pridachin and L S Smirnov, 'Annealing of Radiation Defects by Laser Radiation Pulses', *Sov. Phys. Semicond.* **9**, 946 (1975).

71. A Gat, 'Heatpulse Annealing of Arsenic Implanted Silicon with a CW Arc Lamp', *IEEE Electron. Dev. Lett.* **EDL-2**, 85 (1981).

72. L Peters, 'The Hottest Topic in RTP', *Semiconductor International* **14(9)**, 56 (1991).

73. S P Kwok and S K Cheung, 'A High Effective Barrier Height GaAs M-p$^+$-n SAGFET', *IOP Conf. Series* **91**, IOPP, 1988, p. 677.

74. A Tamura, K Inoue and T Onuma, 'Characterisation of SiF$_x$ and SF$_x$ Molecular Ion Implanted Layers in Semi-insulating GaAs', in [73], p. 459.

75. W Kern and C A Dechert, 'Wet Etching', in *Thin Film Processes*, J L Vossen and W Kern, eds, Academic Press, 1978, p. 401.

76. B Tuck, 'The Chemical Polishing of Semiconductors', *J. Mater. Sci.* **10**, 321 (1975).

77. S D Mukherjee and D W Woodard, 'Etching and Surface Preparation of GaAs for Device Fabrication', in [5], p. 119.

78. R E Williams, *Gallium Arsenide Processing Techniques*, Artech House, 1984, p. 101.

79. K E Bean, 'Anisotropic Etching in Silicon', *IEEE Trans. Electron. Dev.* **ED-25**, 1185 (1978).

80. O Oda, K Katagiri, K Shinohara, S Katsura, Y Takahashi, K Kainosho, K Kohiro and R Hirano, 'InP Crystal Growth, Substrate Preparation and Evaluation', in [52], p. 155.

81. A Shimano, H Takagi and G Kano, 'Light Controlled Anodic Oxidation of n-GaAs and its Application to Preparation of Specified Active Layers for MESFETs', *IEEE Trans. Electron. Dev.* **ED-26**, 1690 (1979).

82. P D Greene, 'Selective Etching of Semi-Insulating Gallium Arsenide', *Solid State Electron.* **19**, 875 (1976).

9

Fabrication technology

The definition of the word 'technology' as applied to semiconductor device fabrication is difficult to phrase in precise terms. In the last chapter we looked at semiconductor materials; how they were grown, etched and doped to suit the purposes of any particular device. In this chapter we are going to examine what subsequently happens to those semiconductor materials; how they are metallized, the importance of dielectrics and, before either of these topics, the patterning techniques used to form the correct feature. Fabrication technology takes the semiconductor material and turns it into devices on wafer, ready for dicing and packaging. We will not be looking at processing schedules for each type of device in this chapter, as these have already been covered. Rather we shall be discussing the general technology of the fabrication process, both current usage and projected trends as seem relevant to the optoelectronics industry.

For technology, and especially the processes involving lithography, a cleanroom is very important. Lithography areas are generally class 100 (a dust count of less than 100 particles of diameter 0.5 μm or larger per cubic foot), with the rest of the processing area class 1000: many laboratories comfortably exceed these specifications. The need for rigorous scientific procedure is essential even though, as we shall see, many areas still remain 'black art' rather than well understood science.

Safety is an important aspect. Many fabrication processes involve handling dangerous or toxic chemicals. This is especially true of plasma processes, where many of the gases used fall into the 'handle with extreme care' category. Evaporation involves the use of high voltage or high current power supplies; sputtering and again plasma processes involve r.f. power, the leakage of which must be avoided. In adition, toxicological effects have been associated with long term exposure to photoresist solvents. As with almost all safety hazards, knowledge of the dangers and good working practice can eliminate most potentially harmful situations.

There is a danger that a chapter on technology can present the processes as 'easy to do' – this is anything but the case in real life. Uniformity, the variation of a particular device parameter across a wafer, and reproducibility, the ability to produce the same results time after time, are far more important to a production line than state of the art technical merit. Optoelectronics is a competitive business, and a major way of improving cash flow is to increase yield, which is why a uniform, reproducible process is so important. Besides giving a significant advance in device performance, any new process developed in a research laboratory should have sufficient latitude to allow it to be transferred to other equipment. Because one or other of the above criteria cannot be met, many of the ideas developed in the research laboratories never get into production.

9.1   Lithography

In the context of semiconductor device fabrication, lithography is the process of applying a previously defined pattern onto a substrate such that only certain areas of the latter receive any subsequent processing. The remaining areas are masked off, and go through the fabrication stage unaffected by processing of the unmasked areas. Although photolithography was invented in 1798, only since 1960 have great advances been made. Pressure from the silicon IC industry has seen a relatively straightforward process turned into a very exacting technology, with great demands being placed on equipment and chemical manufacturers and on the process itself. This has led to the limited introduction of other type of lithography in recent years: principally e-beam and x-ray. Photolithography remains the mainstay of pattern transfer, however, and subsequent reference will assume a photolithographic process unless otherwise stated.

9.1.1   The basic photolithographic process

This is shown schematically in Figure 9.1. After cleaning (usually by boiling in isopropyl alcohol – IPA or propan-2-ol) and drying (in an air oven at 200 °C) of the wafer a polymer material is uniformly applied (Figure 9.1(a)). This is called photoresist, because its properties are sensitive to light. Unexposed, it is resistant to attack from a developing solution (hence the suffix -resist). Exposed, it becomes easily dissolvable in alkaline developer. The photoresist is exposed through a mask (Figure 9.1(b)), which usually has a lifesize pattern on it of the device area to be processed (this depends on the method of pattern transfer, as we shall see in section 9.1.4). The photoresist is developed, removing all exposed areas (Figure 9.1(c)). A further clean of the surface is usually necessary prior to metallization (a mild oxide etch is sufficient) or other processing (Figure 9.1(d)). After processing the whole wafer is immersed in boiling acetone (Figure 9.1(e)) which dissolves the photoresist, leaving a pattern of metal (or other material) on the wafer that is a reproduction of that same pattern on the mask. How faithful that reproduction is, the pattern fidelity, is a complex interaction between many different factors in the lithography process. Other concerns of great importance to the success of the process are cleanliness, reproducibility, limits of performance, process latitude and throughput. All these issues will be addressed as we examine each stage of the lithographic process in more detail.

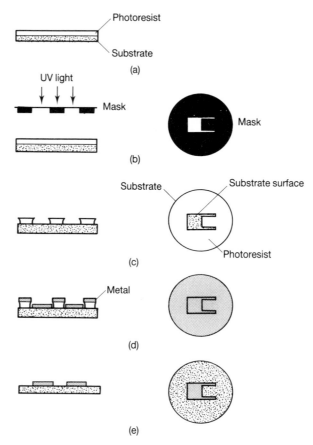

Figure 9.1 The basic steps in evaporation using lithography. (a) Spin and bake photoresist, (b) expose photoresist through a mask, (c) develop, (d) metallize, and (e) remove photoresist.

9.1.2   Resist coating

All photoresists contain three basic chemicals: a photosensitive compound, a base resin and a solvent. There will also be several other components in lower volume that give each resist its unique properties. A good coating of photoresist must satisfy the following requirements: it must be contamination free, pinhole free, have excellent uniformity and adhere well to the surface. As supplied by the manufacturer, the photoresist has a high solvent content to aid its application (even so, most resists have the consistency of syrup). Photoresist can be dispensed on the wafer via a syringe or using an automated system which controls the amount of photoresist applied. The former method is usually applied to a stationary wafer, the latter to a slowly spinning one. The photoresist will spread over the wafer and, on completing the application, the wafer is spun at high speed (several thousand r.p.m. for up to a minute) to ensure that the coating is uniform. During this process most of the photoresist is spun off the edge of the wafer, collected in a catch cup and drained away. There is also usually an exhaust system to remove solvent vapours. The thickness obtained will depend on the viscosity of the resist, its solid content and the spin speed, and a few examples are shown in Figure 9.2 (the spin time is not critical, as past a certain length of time no change in film thickness is obtained. Manufacturers thus usually specify only a minimum spin time).

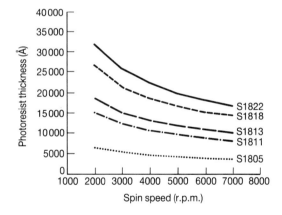

Figure 9.2 Spin speed vs final thickness of Shipley Microposit S1800 Series Photoresist (courtesy of Shipley Europe Limited).

After the resist has been spun the wafer is baked to remove excess solvents, either in an oven for about half an hour or on a hotplate for a minute. In both cases the temperature is in the region of 90–100 °C but must be carefully controlled. After this stage the resist is ready for exposure.

There is a danger of particulate contamination, which can take one of two forms: either a particulate is present on the wafer at the dispense stage and becomes spun into the coating, or the photoresist was the source of contamination. Particulates are a considerable problem, as they introduce defects into the pattern transfer process. Subsequent processing could lead to bridging between metal layers, for instance. In addition, metal ion contamination of the photoresist could lead to early device failure if ions are driven into the devices during a heat treatment.

Adhesion of the photoresist onto clean substrates does not usually present a problem. However, if the wafer has been coated with a metal or dielectric the adhesion of the resist is poor. This can be overcome by applying a thin layer of adhesion promoter before dispensing the resist. The most common adhesion promoter used is hexamethyldisilazane (HMDS). The structure of this molecule contains six methyl groups and a Si_2NH group. The latter radical attaches to anything inorganic, e.g. substrate, metal, dielectric, and the methyl groups similarly attach themselves to anything organic, e.g. photoresist. HMDS can be dispensed and spun in the same way as photoresist, but a better method of application is known as a vacuum vapour prime. A wafer, or several wafers, is heated to above 100 °C in a vacuum of $\sim$ 1 torr, causing rapid evaporation of water from the wafer surface. This is important as any water remaining on the wafer reacts with HMDS to form hexamethyldisiloxane, which reduces the adhesion properties of HMDS. Whilst the wafers are in the vacuum, HMDS fumes are pulled into the wafer surroundings and react with the surface in the same way as liquid HMDS.

There are many other factors in the dispensing stage which affect the resist properties. Clean room temperature and humidity must be carefully controlled (around 20 °C and 45% respectively). Method of application, dispense speed and spin acceleration, vapour exhaust rates and catch cup design all have an input to the final thickness and uniformity obtained, such that the previously simple idea of dispense and spin has now been elevated to the level of a major technology needing a careful consideration of chemistry, mechanics and aerodynamics in the design of equipment [1].

There are many different types of photoresist available, which can be applied in thicknesses ranging from $\sim$ 0.3 μm to $\sim$ 5 μm. The thickness of resist depends on the needs of the subsequent processing, with thin resists used to define narrow lines (section 9.1.4) and thick resists for processes where the polymer itself may be etched. A typical thickness of $\sim$ 1.5 μm can be used routinely to obtain linewidths in the $\sim$ 1.0 μm region.

Although Figure 9.1(c) shows the developer removing exposed regions of resist (a positive photoresist), this is not always the case. Negative photoresists are also available. How these resists work and their exposure characteristics are discussed in section 9.1.4. The technology of photoresists is changing rapidly, as more demands are put on the process, coupled with a need for safer solvents (EGMEA (ethylene glycol monoethyl ether acetate) has been used for most positive photoresists but its toxicological effects have promoted research into, and the gradual acceptance of, alternatives such as those based on PGMEA (propylene glycol monoethyl ether acetate) [2, 3]).

9.1.3 Mask design

The mask is used to define the areas of photoresist to be exposed and hence ultimately the area of wafer to be processed. A mask usually consists of a quartz substrate coated with chromium, with the latter having the desired pattern etched in it. The use of chromium ensures a high reflectivity of unwanted light from the opaque areas of the mask. Because of the reliance on contact printing (section 9.1.4), the substrate must be flat (within ~ 2 μm across its surface) and the chrome film thickness uniform (within 50 Å). The average grain size of chromium coatings is less than ~ 0.1 μm.

The initial stage in mask design is to draw a large scale composite of the complete set of masks, and then to break this down into individual mask layers for metallization, passivation, etc. An example is given in Figure 9.3, where the feature on mask level one is designed to fit inside a feature on level two within a certain nesting tolerance, one of the layout rules of the circuit. The data from each mask level is converted to a computer tape that can be read by a mask making machine. This uses an electron beam to expose a resist pattern on the chromium plated quartz mask (see section 9.1.9 on e-beam lithography). The chromium is then etched away from the areas where the resist has been removed by development. In this way the original artwork for each layer can be transferred to a lifesize pattern on the mask, and the pattern itself can be stepped and repeated across the whole area of the mask [4].

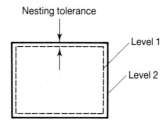

Figure 9.3 Two individual mask levels with nesting tolerance.

Clear or opaque mask defects can be inadvertantly introduced at this stage [5]. Clear defects include chrome or resist pinholes, and opaque defects may be bubbles or pits in the quartz substrate. If necessary masks may be repaired using a focused ion beam system [6]. The final yield obtained from a manufacturing process will depend on minimizing defects at every mask level and the number of levels itself.

The process involved in making masks is very exacting and hence expensive. For features sizes of less than ~ 10 μm a chrome mask is the only alternative. However, if the mask set contains only coarse feature sizes, a much simpler approach can be used. This involves making a large scale image of a mask with a plastic film known as rubylith. The image is then photographed using a high definition camera. Once developed, the image can then be made into a mask using a step and repeat camera to expose a photographic emulsion film on a glass substrate. This method is very cheap, and hence allows masks to be readily made using modest facilities. The limitation on feature size is a big drawback, however.

Inspection and cleaning of masks prior to exposure is very important to achieve a high yield. Often photoresist from previous use in contact printing will adhere to the mask surface and this should be removed before each new use of that mask.

9.1.4   Exposure

9.1.4.1   Principle

The base resin of a photoresist is dissolvable in developer at a rate of about 150 Å s^{-1}, but with the addition of a photoactive compound this decreases to 1 Å s^{-1} – hence the alternative name of inhibitor to describe such a compound. Exposure alters the dissolution rate, and photoresists are most sensitive to light in the ultraviolet part of the spectrum. Hence mercury lamps are a common source of exposing radiation (Figure 9.4). Exposure to UV light affects the photoactive compound in one of two ways, depending on whether the resist is positive or negative.

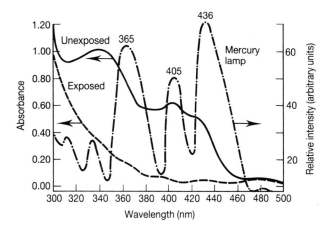

Figure 9.4 Spectral output of a high pressure mercury lamp and relative response of Shipley Microposit S1800 Series Photoresist (courtesy of Shipley Europe Limited).

For a positive resist, absorption of photons by the inhibitor causes the latter to degrade to a ketene which, in the presence of a small amount of water ($\sim 0.5\%$), forms an indene carboxylic acid, a compound highly soluble in the developer. Hence the exposed photoresist removal rate is increased to over 1000 Å s^{-1}. This shows the importance of humidity control in the cleanroom, as in the absence of water the degraded inhibitor crosslinks with identical molecules to decrease the solubility [7].

As a result of the breakdown of the inhibitor the strong absorption characteristics of the resist are significantly reduced and the exposed resist becomes essentially transparent.

Negative resists work by exploiting the crosslinking principle. The increase in molecular weight as a result of such interaction after exposure leads to insolubility in the developer. During the development the resist film swells and the unexposed resist is dissolved. This swelling action limits the resolution of negative resists, (minimum resolvable feature $\sim 3\times$ film thickness) and hence positive resists are almost always used for fine line patterning. Negative resists are very sensitive, however, and so permit a greater throughput of wafers if this is an important factor. Figure 9.5 shows typical exposure characteristics of both types of resist, where E_t is the minimum energy required for complete removal of resist during the development stage.

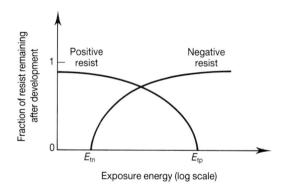

Figure 9.5 Typical photoresist exposure characteristics.

9.1.4.2 Proximity printing

The three main ways of exposing a photoresist are shown in Figure 9.6: these are proximity, contact and projection. The proximity method involves bringing the resist close to, but not touching, the mask. This eliminates most of the defects that result from contact. However, this method is not suitable for small features (minimum feature size quoted varies, but is $\sim 2~\mu$m). This is a result of Fresnel diffraction (occurs when $d < w^2/\lambda$) at the mask edges, as shown in Figure 9.7. This will lead to an effective increase in exposed areas at the edge of the feature. In this region the energy incident on the resist is given by [8]

$$E = kE_i \exp\left(-mx\left(\frac{2}{\lambda d}\right)^{1/2}\right) \tag{9.1}$$

where k and m are respectively the value and the slope of I/I_0 near the mask edge: these depend on the optical system and the mask pattern. The effective edge of the feature will occur at a value of x where $E = E_t$, the exposure threshold energy. Rearrangment of (9.1) gives the value of x as

$$x = \frac{1}{m} \left(\frac{\lambda d}{2}\right)^{1/2} \log_e \left(\frac{kE_i}{E_t}\right). \tag{9.2}$$

Thus δw, the difference between the mask feature size w and the exposed area on the wafer, is $2x$ or

$$\delta w = \left(\frac{2\lambda d}{m^2}\right)^{1/2} \log_e \left(\frac{kE_i}{E_t}\right). \tag{9.3}$$

9.1.4.3 Contact printing

Contact printing is the most widely used technique for optoelectronic devices. In this method the mask and wafer are vacuum clamped together for exposure. Ideally the distance d is thus eliminated and diffraction effects as given by (9.3) will not exist. In practice, contact between mask and wafer does not give $d = 0$ and some small amount of Fresnel diffraction will occur. True contact printing will only take place when $d < \lambda$. However, very high resolution is possible. Again it is difficult to put precise numbers on this, as technologial developments have made previously unattainable resolutions possible. Certainly ~ 1 μm features across a whole wafer are straightforward and submicron features have been readily obtained and reported using standard methods. The use of deep ultra-violet xenon–mercury lamps emitting at 220–240 nm has enabled ~ 0.5 μm lines to be obtained.

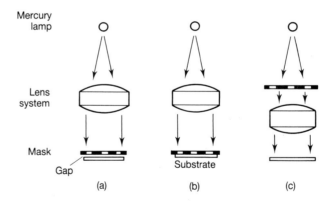

Figure 9.6 The three techniques of photoresist exposure: (a) proximity, (b) contact, and (c) projection.

The great drawback of contact printing is dirt, where a speck of dust on the wafer prior to mask contact could scratch the mask, and not just ruin one device, but all devices subsequently exposed with that area of mask. Contact printing is thus best used for small die-size devices where defect density does not significantly affect yield, and thus it is ideal for optoelectronic device processing.

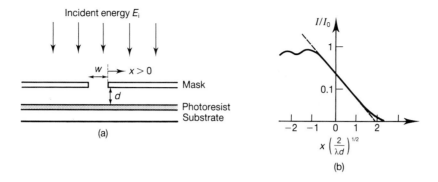

Figure 9.7 (a) Proximity printing. (b) Fresnel diffraction intensity pattern at a mask feature edge (©1975 IEEE: reproduced by kind permission).

9.1.4.4   Projection printing

In projection printing an image of the mask is optically transferred to the photoresist. Masks thus remain free from damage and have a potentially unlimited lifetime. Problems exist with this arrangement, notably the depth of focus of the optical system puts a limit on the flatness of the wafer that can be tolerated (± 10 μm at best). There is also great difficulty in fabricating an optical system with both a uniform light intensity and image quality over a full wafer area. A comparison of the diffraction pattern observed from all three types of printing is shown in Figure 9.8 [9].

In many areas of VLSI processing, where the need is for ever smaller device features and ever more features per chip, all these systems have been replaced by a more sophisticated method, an optical stepper, or DSW (direct step-on wafer). This is similar in its operation to a projection printer, except that in the stepper the mask only contains the image of a few device areas, or even just one. The mask is imaged onto the slice, the slice moved and the exposure repeated. The requirements placed on the optics of a stepper are such that its performance is diffraction, not defect, limited. Such perfection, and the need for a precise step and repeat system, make optical steppers very expensive and as such are only viable in high volume, high device density production. This makes them ideal for VLSI, but not as yet for optoelectronics. The optical considerations influencing the performance of a stepper can be found in [10]. This type of exposure is carried out in the Fraunhofer diffraction region.

9.1.4.5   Interference

In addition to diffraction effects, optical interference within the photoresist can have a significant influence on the energy density received within the resist and hence its dissolution rate in the developer. Interference will occur between the incoming wave and the wave reflected from the photoresist–substrate interface. A

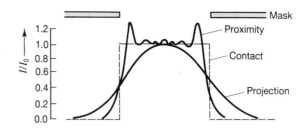

Figure 9.8 A comparison of diffraction patterns achieved using the different methods of lithographic printing.

standing wave pattern will be produced, leading to a series of nodes (minima) and antinodes (maxima) in the intensity distribution, and hence in the inhibitor absorption. The dissolution of the resist is similarly periodic and leads to structures as shown in Figure 9.9. The exact pattern obtained depends on both the resist and the substrate characteristics, with dielectrics giving little reflection and metals a strong reflection with a large phase change. The structure shown in Figure 9.9 can be removed by a post-exposure bake which redistributes the inhibitor prior to development.

9.1.4.6 Alignment

A final word on exposure needs to be saved for alignment. If the mask being used is the first on the wafer, its orientation relative to the wafer flats needs to be assessed. Subsequent masks, however, need to be aligned to the previous ones. Machines that expose patterns on to photoresist through a mask are thus called aligners. Alignment is done by leaving a pattern, an alignment or registration mark, on the wafer at each lithography step. This mark is not part of a device feature but is used for subsequent masks to align to. An example is shown in Figure 9.10 using a system of increasingly sized crosses.

As it is the total energy received by the resist that is important in determining exposure, the output of the lamp should be monitored routinely, both internally by the aligner and externally by an intensity meter. Output uniformity across the slice should also be periodically assessed. Aligners are very sensitive to vibration, and hence are usually mounted on air tables or special foundations for acoustic isolation.

9.1.5 Development

9.1.5.1 Principle

This is the stage that removes the part of the resist where subsequent processing is to take place (photosensitized for positive resists, non-sensitized for negative

Figure 9.9 Standing wave pattern produced by interference in photoresist.

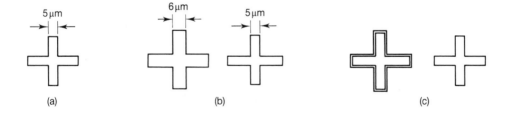

Figure 9.10 A typical series of alignment marks. (a) First mask has a single cross. (b) Second mask has two unequal size crosses. (c) Perfect alignment when large cross on mask two overlaps cross on mask one. Second cross on mask two is for alignment to mask three.

resists). Developer is usually an alkaline solution such as NaOH, though metal-ion-free alternatives such as NH_4OH are available. Development may be either performed on a stationary wafer (puddle development) or by directing a spray of developer solution at a spinning wafer (spray development). In either case the developer should be thoroughly removed after the process time (usually 1–2 minutes), usually by spinning under a spray of deionized water. A further period of spinning without spraying dries the wafer. The wafer is now inspected to ascertain the linewidths obtained, and resist profiles at this stage typically look as in Figure 9.11. If satisfactory the wafer is given a final bake to harden the resist and render any more exposure/development ineffective. If linewidths are not satisfactory the wafer may be developed further or the resist removed and the wafers reworked.

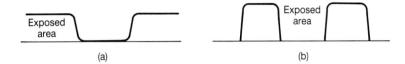

Figure 9.11 Typical edge profiles obtained with photoresist: (a) negative resist, and (b) positive resist.

9.1.5.2   Profiles

The edge profile of the resist is a crucial factor in determining the success of subsequent processing. Profiles as in Figure 9.11 are wholly unsuitable for evaporation sourced metallization, for example. In this case the edge profile needs to look as in Figure 9.12(a), with a lip overhanging the foot of the resist (see section 9.2.6). This is known as a lift-off profile, and is achieved by soaking the photoresist in chlorobenzene (usually prior to exposure but it can be prior to development). This has the effect of retarding the development in the upper layers by removing residual solvents and the low molecular weight components of the resin. A lip is thus produced, the size of which increases with the chlorobenzene soak time [11]. The wafer needs to be baked after the soak to remove the chlorobenzene before subsequent processing.

Another common requirement is for a profile as in Figure 9.12(b). Here the resist has a gently sloped edge, and is being used to define a similar edge in the underlying dielectric by a subsequent etching process. To achieve this profile, the resist is given a high temperature (130 °C for 2 minutes) bake which reflows the resist. The foot of the resist stays in contact with the substrate and hence a sloped edge profile can be obtained. Metallization on top of this dielectric, thus giving a contact window, is the next stage of the process.

It is clear that there are many factors influencing a resist profile. Each fabrication facility will have its own lithography system, and possibly a different process for each mask layer, as the lithography and edge profile are tuned to specific applications. Masks commonly have a 'bias' on them, where the size of the feature in the mask is deliberately larger or smaller than that obtained in the photoresist, because the process is set up that way. This is often the case and, despite the great variety of resist/exposure/developer combinations on the market, it is difficult to get a device manufacturer to change a process they are happy with, as the characterization of a new process in terms of all these variables takes a very long time.

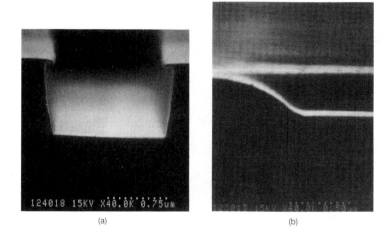

Figure 9.12 Process induced variations in positive photoresist edge profiles: (a) lift-off profile, and (b) 40° edge profile.

9.1.6 Removal

After a wafer has been processed on the areas exposed through the photoresist, the resist itself must be removed to allow the next lithography/processing step to take place. How the resist is removed depends on how it has been affected by the process step. Metal evaporation is usually benign to photoresist, and in this case boiling the wafer in acetone is sufficient to cause resist removal (Figure 9.1(e)). Boiling in IPA is then necessary to ensure residual traces of acetone are removed. If the wafer has undergone a dry etching step (section 9.4) then it is likely that the resist will become impervious to acetone attack and will itself have to be dry etch removed, though using a different etch gas (oxygen) and process conditions.

9.1.7 Multi-level techniques

Two- or three-level techniques find use in very specific applications where single level systems are inappropriate, e.g. planarization, easy production of a lip profile and narrow linewidths using large feature masks. Both multi-level systems rely on a thin resist as the upper layer and thick resist underneath: the three-level system has an intermediate dielectric as a transfer layer [12]. The top layer is used for exposure, and subsequent etching of the underlying layer(s) can create the right resist profile for processing (Figure 9.13(a)). In this way standing wave effects are eliminated in the underlying resist.

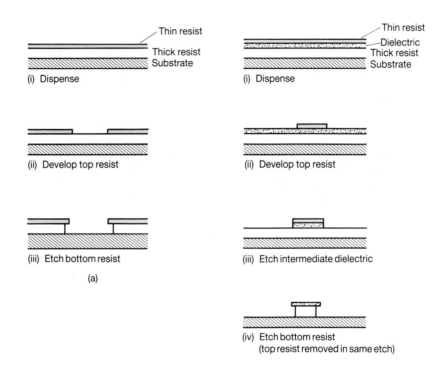

Figure 9.13 The main stages in (a) a two-level, and (b) a three-level multi-level process.

Figure 9.13(b) shows a similar phenomenon in a tri-level structure. The intermediate dielectric and photoresist are selectively etched to produce this profile, illustrated in Figure 9.14. If the area surrounding this feature is coated with a dielectric and the resist removed, there is an area of the wafer open for subsequent metallization that is smaller than the mask feature that produced the original pattern in the resist.

9.1.8   Resolution enhancement

The multi-level techniques mentioned in the last section are examples of this, but there are others. The main reason for wanting to extend the performance of optical lithography beyond its current limits is simple; a new non-optical technique

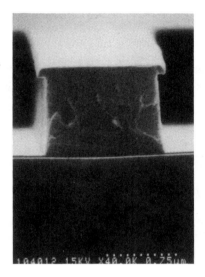

Figure 9.14 Final profile achieved using a tri-level process.

is usually very expensive in terms of capital equipment and running costs, and involves the characterization of a very new process. The comparative simplicity and familiarity of optical lithography makes a compelling case for continued research into more refinement.

Whilst not generally used to such resolution in the optoelectronics industry, optical lithography is employed in the IC industry to below 0.5 μm, and is predicted to still be in use when geometries shrink to 0.2 μm, using a combination of short wavelengths (mercury i-line (365 nm) or deep UV excimer laser source (248 nm)) and sophisticated optical techniques [13, 14]. This section looks in more detail at two of the most promising methods.

9.1.8.1 *Phase shift lithography*
This technique works on a simple application of interference [15], as can be seen in Figure 9.15. As mask apertures get smaller and closer together, diffraction at the aperture edge results in overlapping light intensity patterns on the wafer, giving no clear indication of the mask features. If light passing through an aperture is π out of phase with that from the adjacent aperture, then the resultant addition of light intensity on the wafer will mean that the mask pattern is still distinguishable. The improvement in i-line lithography is an ultimate resolution increased from $\sim$ 0.45 μm to $\sim$ 0.3 μm [16]. Techniques can take one of several forms,

including additional apertures in the chrome patterns on the mask, edge contrast enhancement or an absorptive phase shifter [16, 17]. An alternative is to make the phase shifter in the photoresist [18], thus obviating the need to fabricate special masks. Diffraction effects are even more limited using this approach.

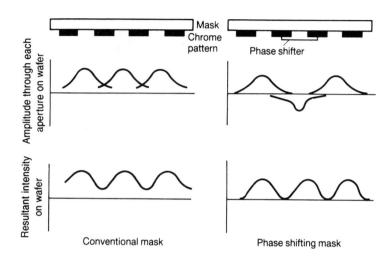

Figure 9.15 The principle of phase shift lithography.

9.1.8.2 Holographic lithography

This is a two-stage process that involves the holographic production of a photomask, and then the reconstruction of the mask image in the wafer plane [19, 20]. Consider Figure 9.16, in which a standard photomask is illuminated from below. Interference with a reference beam (which will be totally reflected at the film/air interface) generates a holographic image in the film. This can then be converted to a pattern by passing a conjugate beam through the hologram – the wafer is exposed by placing it in the image plane. The system has the advantages of no geometrical aberrations, good resolution and optical simplicity, although the process is lengthier than phase shift techniques and mechanical stability of the system needs careful attention. As such the method has not yet proved as popular as phase shift printing, although it has been used in optoelectronics to a certain extent.

9.1.9   E-beam lithography

9.1.9.1   Principle

We noted earlier in section 9.1.3 that electron beam exposure was used to define the pattern in a chromium plated mask. This is the main use of electron beam lithog-

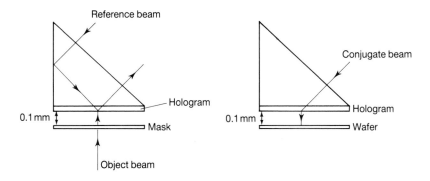

Figure 9.16 The principle of holographic lithography.

raphy throughout the semiconductor industry, where the resist used is sensitive to exposure from electron beams, and not light (though such resists are also sensitive to deep UV radiation at 200–260 nm). As with photoresists, e-beam resists exist with either positive or negative characteristics, and react to the exposing e-beam in a similar way; exposure to electrons in a positive e-beam resist causes molecular breakdown, whereas in negative resists it promotes crosslinking. Similarly, positive resists have better resolution because negative resists tend to swell, but the latter are much more sensitive to exposure.

The main advantages of using exposure with electron beams as opposed to light are better resolution, greater depth of field and a direct write system. Optical lithography will always be wavelength limited and, although features below $\sim 1.0 \ \mu$m can now be obtained, it is becoming ever more difficult to make smaller features with the uniformity and reproducibility that is required. $0.5 \ \mu$m can be produced routinely using an e-beam source, and much lower limits ($< 0.2 \ \mu$m) are available with this technique. This is because it is much easier to focus an electron beam to a small spot size ($\sim 0.01 \ \mu$m) – although the resolution determining factor is electron scattering in the resist layer (see below).

The depth of field of a focused e-beam is much greater ($\sim 25 \ \mu$m) than an optical source, and so wafer flatness is not as important. The main source of defocusing in an electron beam is the Boersch effect [21], a result of significant Coulombic interaction whenever electrons are tightly packed. Aberrations in the focusing system also contribute to the spot size.

9.1.9.2 Exposure
Exposure of the resist is by direct writing of the electron beam by computer. There are thus none of the problems associated with a masking process, such as particulates or diffraction (because of the electron wavelength diffraction effects would be small anyway). The use of a direct write system also enables the pattern to be changed via the control software. This is especially useful in the development

stage of a circuit layout where the time delay and expense of acquiring masks is avoided.

Electron beam lithography has its disadvantages, however (not the least of which are cost and complexity), and these can be appreciated best by first considering how the process is performed. A schematic of an e-beam machine is shown in Figure 9.17. The e-beam is driven via a pattern generator. Electrons are produced by thermionic emission from a tungsten filament or, more usually, one made from high brightness lanthanum hexaboride (LB_6). Electron optics in the upper half of the system are used to focus the spot, and a blanking plate is used to turn the beam on and off. Positioning of the spot on the wafer is performed by electromagnetic deflection just above the wafer position.

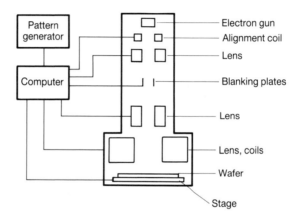

Figure 9.17 The main components of an e-beam exposure system.

9.1.9.3 Scanning

There are two types of scanning modes: raster and vector scan. In the raster scan system the beam is moved continuously across the scan field (see below) and only switched on when the resist is required to be exposed. In a vector scan system the beam jumps from feature to feature, rather than across the whole field, to expose the resist. Raster scan optics are less complicated, but the system is slower than vector scan for repetitive exposure of small patterns and finds primary use in mask making. In either case the range of scanning, the scan field, is limited to an area about 10 mm square and, after completing the scan of this field, the wafer must be mechanically moved to enable another area to be exposed. This makes the whole process of exposing the wafer very slow, and is the major limitation of e-beam lithography. With beam energies of 10–25 kV, currents of < 50 nA and a spot size of ~ 0.01 μm diameter an individual element of resist is exposed in about 10^{-7} s. However, as the process is completed by exposing a series of elements, or pixels, the entire wafer takes several minutes to expose. E-beam lithography is thus only used when reliable sub-micron geometries are absolutely essential, and even then the minimum area of wafer is exposed as the process time is proportional to the exposed area.

An alternative, but more complicated, approach is to use a vector scan beam delivery system with beam shaping optics to control the spot shape and size. In this way large areas can be exposed at the end of one scan. This, of course, makes the e-beam machine even more expensive and complicated than in its original form, as small geometries become difficult to define in a machine that must accommodate variations. Nevertheless writing time can be significantly reduced using this system.

Metal alignment marks have to be placed on the wafer prior to exposure using an e-beam. Well defined edges are essential to ensure registration accuracy. The alignment marks are usually placed in the corner of each scan field.

Semi-insulating substrates such as GaAs can lead to charging problems. If the beam current is not drained away, charge build up on the wafer surface can misplace subsequent patterning. A thin layer of metal on the wafer surface can act as an electrode in this case [22], although this must be removed at a later stage. Because the beam currents involved are small, semiconductive substrates do not create any charging problems.

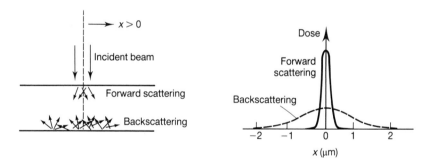

Figure 9.18 The effect of electron scattering on the spot size obtained in e-beam resist.

9.1.9.4   Resolution

Because an incoming electron beam will be forward scattered after entering the resist, the resist will become exposed over an area wider then the spot size (Figure 9.18). A far bigger problem, however, is backscattering from the resist–substrate interface as this creates a much wider spread of the beam, and also gives a greater exposure in the bottom of the resist than at the top. Because the degree of backscattering is proportional to the atomic number of the substrate, different substrate materials cause great variations in exposure. The exposure dosage, i.e. the total charge received by the resist, will thus give a characteristic appearance to the resist profile, with the increasingly higher dosage causing more backscattering from the substrate and hence a profile more suited for lift-off (Figure 9.19). Increasing the electron energy has a similar effect. The increase in exposure width due to backscattering is called the proximity effect and is the major factor limiting both e-beam linewidth and the minimum spacing between exposed areas.

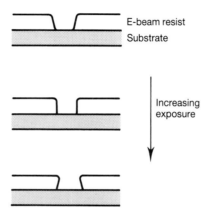

Figure 9.19 The effect of increased e-beam exposure on the edge profile of e-beam resist.

9.1.9.5 Resists

PMMA (polymethylmethacrylate) is a commonly used positive e-beam resist although, as with optical resists, there are many types available. It can be developed in MIBK (methylisobutylketone) and, again as in the optical case, the development time affects the resist profile, with longer times leading to a more pronounced undercut profile as the larger volume of exposed resist closer to the substrate is dissolved.

E-beam lithography finds a particular use in optoelectronics in defining the phase grating of a DFB laser (0.23 μm periodicity – see Figure 9.20). It is too expensive to be put into general use, and even the silicon IC manufacturers would prefer to push the limits of optical lithography ever further before they use e-beam.

9.1.9.6 Other particle beams

Focused ion beams can also be used. These have the advantage of comparatively minimal backscattering, leading to an increased resolution capability. Because accelerated ions can supply a greater energy to the resist than electrons, exposure times are a lot shorter, overcoming e-beam lithography's other main problem of throughput [23].

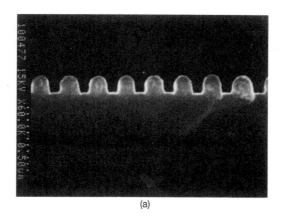

(a)

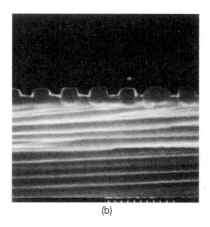

(b)

Figure 9.20 (a) Resist profile of a first-order DFB grating (0.23 μm pitch). (b) Dry etched first-order grating profile (©Northern Telecom 1993: photos courtesy of BNR-Europe Limited).

9.1.10   X-ray lithography

This was first proposed in 1972 [22] and the 1980s saw intensive research and limited introduction into silicon processing, though not as yet into optoelectronics (this review is thus a lot shorter than many others, e.g. [24]). Soft x-rays with a wavelength between 1 and 50 Å (although common usage is in the 2–20 Å range) offer an attractive alternative to photon exposure because the very short wavelength makes diffraction effects negligible, thus potentially giving a very high resolution. X-ray lithography systems have much in common with optical ones in their mode of operation in that both have a fixed position exposing source with the slice exposed through a mask.

An x-ray system is shown in Figure 9.21. X-rays from the source (see below) pass through a window into a helium filled exposure chamber (helium is transparent to x-rays; air isn't). The mask is placed as in a proximity aligner. There are no backscattering effects, hence the proximity effect of e-beam resists is not a problem, and dust is largely transparent to x-rays, minimizing mask/wafer cleanliness problems. No focusing of the x-ray beam is needed and, because x-ray resists are weakly absorbing, the amount of absorption throughout the exposed area is fairly constant leading to straight sidewalls on development.

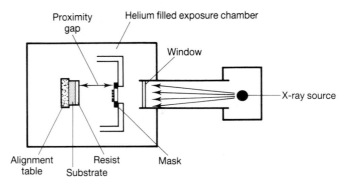

Figure 9.21 The main features of an x-ray aligner.

Although high resolution is a potential capability of this technique, masks are still made using e-beam lithography and so practical limits are much higher than ideal. The masks themselves are quite complex and very fragile.

Early x-ray sources used high energy electrons to bombard metal targets. X-rays are produced as the electrons are decelerated, and major emission lines in a broad spectrum of x-ray energies are the usual characteristic of these sources. The source is thus not collimated, which leads to a geometrical limitation on optimum linewidth. This is known as penumbral blur, and the geometry of the system needs to be designed to reduce this. Another problem is run out or lateral magnification error. This is zero at the centre of the wafer but increases towards the edge because the x-ray beam is no longer at normal incidence to the mask. This latter error can be compensated for in the mask making or can be reduced by using a reduced field size exposure and moving the slice under the x-ray beam. Such x-ray steppers are now available.

A collimated x-ray source is available in the form of synchrotron radiation. This is emitted when electrons are accelerated normal to their direction of motion by a magnetic field. At relativistic speeds synchrotron radiation is in the x-ray region.

Not only is the source collimated but it is also highly intense, allowing shorter exposure times (currently used x-ray resists, of which DCOPA (dichloropropy-lacrylate) is a popular choice, are very weakly absorbing). The main drawback is that currently such machines are very expensive, but an intense effort is being made by many companies to try and make compact, and thus cheaper, synchrotron sources. Their adoption by silicon fabrication plants may lead to applications in the optoelectronics industry.

Laser induced pulsed plasma x-ray sources are also an alternative, although research is at a much less advanced stage. These offer a high intensity x-ray pulse from what could be a significantly less expensive source than synchrotron radiation.

9.2 Metallization

Whilst it is true that the techniques for metallizing compound semiconductors have broadly followed those of the silicon IC industry in their development, the technologies employed have been quite different. For ICs based on GaAs, metallization schemes have evolved not only because of the obvious difference of Si vs GaAs and the MOSFET vs MESFET (the active device in Si CMOS and GaAs circuits respectively), but also different processing constraints, particularly with regard to temperature cycles. The GaAs IC requires an understanding of both ohmic and Schottky contacts. Optoelectronic devices largely require a consideration of ohmic contacts only; Schottky, MIS and JFET structures are only needed in integration of processing circuitry or in the case of the Schottky photodiode. The requirements of ohmic or Schottky contact formation, good conductivity and adhesion, chemical inertness and the lack of undesirable interaction with the substrate, especially important over the long operating lifetime now expected of these devices, have led to the development of different metallization schemes to suit each particular purpose, whilst ensuring compatibility with subsequent processing.

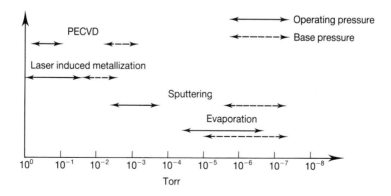

Figure 9.22 The vacuum requirements of various metallization schemes.

The different methods of metallizing semiconductors are given in Figure 9.22, together with their associated vacuum requirements. Note that evaporation is the only method that does not significantly increase the base pressure of the chamber. This is because, as we shall shortly see, it does not rely on filling the whole chamber with a gas, either as a sputtering element or as a metal percursor. Table 9.1 lists the main properties of both the metallizing equipment and some of the resultant film properties. We will now explore the individual metallization techniques a little further.

9.2.1   Thermal evaporation

Thermal evaporation involves heating a small evaporation 'boat' containing a charge of material. This boat is made of a refractory metal, usually tungsten or tantalum, and formed into the shape of a strip of metal with a dimple in it to contain the material. Such a boat is shown in Figure 9.23, although there are many designs available. A high current is passed through the boat, causing a temperature rise due to the power dissipated in the boat's resistance. Heat is conducted from boat to charge, causing the latter to melt and eventually boil. This system is cheap, applicable to a lot of materials and produces no adverse effects on the substrate. However, because the boat is always hotter than the charge, contamination can occur. It is also very difficult to evaporate certain metals this way, i.e. those that have a high (> 2200 °C) melting point. Coevaporation from the same source is to be undertaken with care, as even with an alloy of different metals such as AuGe one or other, in this case germanium, will evaporate first giving a film of stoichiometry varying with thickness.

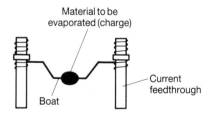

Figure 9.23 A typical evaporation boat.

9.2.2   E-beam evaporation

Electron beam evaporation overcomes the contamination problems of thermal evaporation by using a focused electron beam accelerated electrostatically towards the charge. Such a system is shown in Figure 9.24. A low voltage power supply (10 V)

Process	Equipment	Film properties
Evaporation: – both types	Vacuum chamber needs to be 'tall' (source–substrate distance large compared to substrate diameter. Load lock an advantage.	High purity. Little control of film stress and resistivity (though usually neither is a problem). Deposit at 5–30 Å s^{-1}. Coating is directional – ideal for lift-off process. Applicable to all metals – care must be taken with some high melting point materials.
– thermal	High current (up to 200 A, 5 V) supply.	Calibrated thickness measured in situ. Uniformity depends on system design, but generally good.
– e-beam	High voltage (up to 10 kV, 1 A) supply.	
Sputtering	d.c. and/or 13.56 MHz (up to 2 kW) supply. 'Tall' chamber not required. Load lock an advantage.	Usually some sputtering gas incorporated. Some control over stress and resistivity. Deposition rate is 10–50 Å s^{-1} to minimize gas incorporation. Coating is near or fully conformal, depending on pressure.
PECVD (Plasma enhanced chemical vapour deposition)	13.56 MHz (up to 1 kW) supply. Small chamber. Load lock optional. Overall cheapest system.	Film purity poor because of impure source and gas incorporation. Wide control of stress and resistivity. Film type depends on availability of gaseous precursors. Deposition rate 0.5–5 Å s^{-1}. Coating is fully conformal. Poor uniformity.
Laser enhanced deposition.	C.w. laser operating in near or deep UV. Smallest chamber. Computer control of deposition area.	Film purity problems as for PECVD, but not as severe. Fair control over resistivity (stress not well reported). Film type and deposition rate as for PECVD. Directly written, fully conformal (in exposed areas), with potentially good uniformity.

Table 9.1 The main characteristics of metal deposition techniques.

heats a tungsten filament, causing thermionic emission of electrons. The filament also forms the cathode in a –10 kV power supply. An anode is positioned a few mm away from the filament. Emitted electrons are accelerated under a strong electric field to the anode, which has an aperture of the same size (but rectangular in shape, $\sim 10\times3$ mm) as the filament. Electrons pass through the aperture, are bent under the influence of an external magnetic field, and come to rest in the evaporant. Their kinetic energy is dissipated through the metal, causing it to heat up. Once a sufficient beam current has been established the metal will melt and eventually start to evaporate. The shape of the aperture will cause the electron beam spot on the metal to be a crescent shape, and smaller in magnitude than the diameter of the evaporant (usually disc shaped, 30 mm diameter and 5 mm thick, but dependent on the crucible design). By placing a coil parallel to the filament and in the existing magnetic field an additional component to the field can be created. This gives control over the position of the electron spot in one dimension. Position control in a second axis is obtained by a coil arranged perpendicular to the one above. By varying the d.c. current through these coils in a regular fashion the electron beam can be made to 'scan' across most of the metal surface, giving more even evaporation and minimizing the production of a 'hot spot' on the metal or even burning a hole through it.

This system has several advantages over thermal evaporation. All metals, given an appropriate beam current supply, may be evaporated this way. Only the surface of the metal is heated, so there is a minimal chance of impurities migrating from the crucible. High evaporation rates can be obtained, and the source metal usually lasts for many evaporation runs.

The prime disadvantage of this system is cost. The use of high voltage power supplies and their associated control, and the design and construction of water cooled crucibles point to a more expensive system to purchase and operate than thermal evaporation. Some of this expense can be minimized by using a multi-metal electron beam system, where that part of the crucible containing the evaporant (the hearth) forms part of a multi-component system that is rotatable under the path of the electron beam. Thus several metals can be evaporated sequentially from one power supply. A second problem is the production of secondary electrons from the primary electron impact. These can be bent out of harm's way by extending the influence of the magnetic field. There is a chance of vapourized metal becoming ionized by the incoming electrons, but yields are small and are only of concern for easily ionized metals from groups I and II. An additional problem is caused by the electrons coming to rest in the metal and producing x-rays (bremsstrahlung – braking radiation). These will provide a serious health hazard at accelerating voltages above ~ 15 kV unless lead shielding is provided on the evaporation chamber. X-rays can also damage device surfaces, but this is usually more of a problem for charge sensitive devices such as MOSFETs, where the production of K-shell x-rays from 10 kV electrons heating an aluminium target is well known [25]. In this case devices require a subsequent mild annealing treatment to restore their capacitor characteristics.

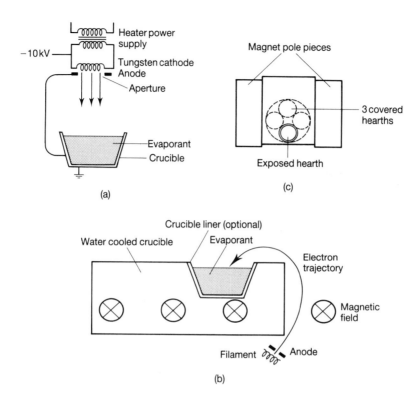

Figure 9.24 The components of an electron beam evaporation system: (a) power supply, (b) crucible arrangement, and (c) multi-hearth system.

9.2.3   The evaporation system

A basic design of an evaporation system is as in Figure 9.25. It consists of a single thermal or e-beam source in an evaporation chamber evacuated by a rotary/diffusion pump combination with the deposition controlled by a computer. After loading the source and substrates into the chamber all valves except the foreline (valve 1) are closed. The chamber is brought down from atmospheric pressure to 3×10^{-2} torr in a few minutes. Heating of the chamber walls during this time will aid the process of evacuation by desorbing the inner surfaces of the chamber, particularly of water vapour. There will be a large degree of turbulence in the chamber near the foreline outlet, leading to a particulate swirl in this region. It is important, therefore, to have the foreline as far away as possible from the substrate to minimize the number of particulates sticking to the latter.

The foreline valve is now closed and the backing line valve (2) opened. The diffusion pump will attain its backing pressure very rapidly, upon which the high

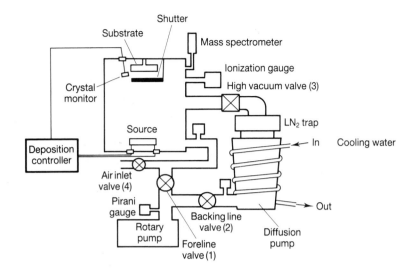

Figure 9.25 The main components of an evaporation chamber.

vacuum valve (3) opens. The chamber is now being pumped by the diffusion pump, and the time taken to obtain the evaporation pressure (typically 10^{-6} to 10^{-7} torr, but in some systems up to 10^{-5} torr is used) will depend on pumping speed, chamber size and chamber wall desorption – typical pump down times are in the 30–60 minute region. To minimize wall desorption the chamber is now usually cooled. A mass spectrometer head can give a residual gas analysis (RGA) inside the chamber.

Once a suitable pressure has been reached evaporation can begin. Initially the shutter is closed over the substrate and power is applied slowly to the source. This will degas the metal surface of water vapour, possible vacuum pump oils and any other contaminants that may have adsorbed on the source since the previous evaporation. There is then usually a slight rise in the partial pressure of water vapour in the chamber. For some refractory metals such as titanium the partial pressure of water vapour then starts to fall dramatically. This is because some titanium is being evaporated, which acts as a 'getter' for water. Water vapour is the dominant constituent of the residual gas at 10^{-6} torr, and so titanium evaporation acts to lower the chamber pressure by up to an order of magnitude. Power is then ramped up to the level required for a given evaporation rate. Once the rate has stabilized the shutter is opened, metal then starts to condense on the substrate and the controller accumulates the total metal deposited. Once the appropriate metal thickness is reached the shutter is closed back over the substrate and the e-beam power is gradually reduced to zero. The metal source is then allowed to cool before any subsequent processes are begun.

Another factor besides residual gas analysis to consider during evaporation is substrate temperature. The metallization is almost always being performed over a photoresist pattern on the substrate, and if the photoresist becomes too hot as a result of high melting point metals such as platinum the pattern may lose definition and the resist may even crack. Generally a well baked photoresist can be allowed to rise to around 100 °C for a few minutes without degradation.

There may be more than one type of metal to be evaporated in a given process run. This can be achieved by using either a multi-hearth e-beam or rotating the position of the sample above more than one evaporation source.

After all evaporations have been completed and the sources cooled down valve 3 is closed. It is a good idea at this point to heat the chamber walls again as the next stage is to open the air inlet valve (4). Water vapour in the air will condense on the inside of the chamber if the walls are not hot. The use of dry nitrogen as the inlet gas will prevent this, but will not stop water condensation from the ambient air once the chamber is opened. It is important to remove substrates and return the chamber under vacuum as quickly as possible to minimize condensation and impurity problems.

9.2.4 Deposition characteristics

9.2.4.1 Principle

Whatever metal we are using, and by whatever means it is being evaporated, we need to be able to predict the amount of metal being deposited on the substrates. For this we need a reference substrate (section 9.2.5) and knowledge of the evaporation/deposition characteristics of the source/substrate system. The amount of metal deposited per unit area on the substrate will be given by:

(i) source emission characteristics,
(ii) source to substrate distance,
(iii) substrate orientation relative to the source.

The following assumptions are made about the evaporation environment:

(i) Molecules emitted from the metal surface behave as if they were part of a gas.
(ii) The background pressure is sufficiently low, $\sim 10^{-6}$ torr, such that collisions between metal vapour and residual gas molecules are unlikely. The mean free path of the dominant residual gas, water vapour, at 10^{-6} torr is 3.4 m – a significant number of collisions is thus unlikely given the typical source to substrate distances used in most modern evaporators (0.2–1.0 m).
(iii) The metal vapour intensity immediately above the source is so low that the effect of collisions between similar molecules can be neglected (typically 10^{-3}–10^{-2} torr immediately above the source but decreases rapidly to base pressure away from it).

(iv) On striking the substrate the vapour molecule immediately condenses, i.e. has a sticking coefficient of 1.

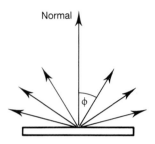

Figure 9.26 Evaporation from a directed area source.

9.2.4.2   *Directed surface source*

Consider first the source emission characteristics. There are three basic types: point, directed surface and wire sources. There are analogies here with light emitters, where a point source emits over all directions and is thus isotropic, and a Lambertian source which emits light whose intensity is proportional to the cosine of the viewing angle. This is the emission characteristic of an ideal planar LED. Point sources of evaporation are isotropic and directed surface sources evaporate according to the Knudsen cosine law [26] similarly to a perfect Lambertian (we shall not concern ourselves here with wire sources as these are not commonly used). Directed surface sources are the best approximation to realistic evaporation systems, assumed to be a small plane emitting surface of uniform temperature. Thus material will be evaporated in all directions from the source, with the amount evaporated in any one direction being proportional to the cosine of the angle to the source normal (Figure 9.26). The mass m or rate of material deposited is also proportional to the solid angle subtended at the source. Thus

$$\begin{array}{ll} \text{fraction of mass/rate} & = \cos\phi \times \text{fraction of total} \\ \text{evaporated through a} & \text{solid angle of a} \\ \text{given solid angle} & \text{plane described by} \\ & \text{the given solid angle} \end{array} \qquad (9.4)$$

where ϕ is the angle subtended by the given solid angle to the source normal. This can be more clearly seen in Figure 9.27(a), and thus leads to, in terms of m,

$$\frac{\mathrm{d}m}{m} = \cos\phi\,\frac{\mathrm{d}\Omega}{\pi} \qquad (9.5)$$

because π is the total solid angle of a plane. Suppose we have a substrate of area S, inclined at an angle θ to the normal to $d\Omega$, and let dS be the area of the substrate intercepted by the cone described by $d\Omega$. Then

$$d\Omega = \frac{dS \cos \theta}{r^2} \qquad (9.6)$$

by solid angle geometry. From (9.5) and (9.6)

$$\frac{dm}{m} = \frac{dS \cos \theta \, \cos \phi}{\pi r^2} . \qquad (9.7)$$

Mass can be converted to thickness, the usual required parameter, from the density ρ and deposited area. Thus thickness t is given by

$$t = \frac{dm}{\rho \, dS} . \qquad (9.8)$$

Using (9.7) and (9.8)

$$t = \frac{m \cos \theta \, \cos \phi}{\rho \pi r^2} . \qquad (9.9)$$

If the areas of both source and substrate are parallel, then $\theta = \phi$. Consider the case of Figure 9.27(b), where l is the distance from source to substrate centre and x is the substrate radius. The thickness of material deposited at **O** is given by

$$t_O = \frac{m}{\rho \pi l^2} \qquad (9.10)$$

and at a point on the perimeter **P** by

$$t_P = \frac{m \cos^2 \theta}{\rho \pi r^2} \qquad (9.11)$$

$$= \frac{m}{\rho \pi r^2} \frac{l^2}{r^2} \qquad (9.12)$$

or, in terms of more accurately measurable distances,

$$t_P = \frac{m l^2}{\rho \pi \left(l^2 + x^2 \right)^2} . \qquad (9.13)$$

From (9.10) and (9.13) the variation in thickness across the substrate from centre to edge is

$$\frac{t_P}{t_O} = \frac{l^4}{\left(l^2 + x^2 \right)^2} \qquad (9.14)$$

or $$\frac{t_P}{t_O} = \frac{1}{\left[1 + (x/l)^2 \right]^2} . \qquad (9.15)$$

Example 9.1

Calculate the minimum evaporation chamber height needed to give a film thickness uniformity of (i) 99%, and (ii) 99.9% on a substrate of 50 mm diameter.

Solution: (i) rearranging (9.15) gives

$$l = \frac{x}{\left[\left(\frac{t_Q}{t_P}\right)^{1/2} - 1\right]^{1/2}}$$

$$= \frac{25}{[1.005 - 1]^{1/2}}$$

$$= 352\,\text{mm}.$$

(ii) Similarly $l = \dfrac{25}{[1.0005 - 1]^{1/2}}$

$$= 1118\,\text{mm}. \tag{9.16}$$

It can readily be seen that most evaporation chambers in use, where l is in the range 0.2–1.0 m, will give a very uniform film deposition. A theoretical uniformity of > 99% is usually more than sufficient for most metallizations because, as we shall see in section 9.2.5, metallization thicknesses are only calibrated and the measuring instruments used to determine final thickness are not accurate to the above-mentioned tolerances.

9.2.4.3   Point source

A brief word about point sources is appropriate here. These can occur if the metal does not wet the evaporation boat in a thermal system. The metal will thus 'ball up' and act as a point source. In this case (9.5) becomes

$$\frac{\mathrm{d}m}{m} = \frac{\mathrm{d}\Omega}{4\pi} \tag{9.17}$$

where the $\cos\phi$ dependence is dropped because a sphere emits equally over all space (isotropic) and the 4π is introduced to describe the total solid angle when describing a sphere, not a plane surface. In this case, and following through the same arguments as above, (9.9) and (9.15) become

$$t = \frac{m\cos\theta}{4\rho\pi r^2} \tag{9.18}$$

and $\dfrac{t_P}{t_o} = \dfrac{1}{\left[1 + (x/l)^2\right]^{3/2}}$ \hfill (9.19)

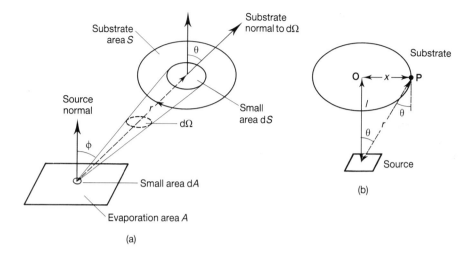

Figure 9.27 Evaporation characteristics of a directed surface source: (a) evaporation through a solid angle $d\Omega$, (b) source and substrate parallel.

respectively. Assuming that an evaporation does not result in metal exhaustion, inspection of the evaporation boat will soon indicate whether the evaporant was a point or directed area source.

Example 9.2

Recalculate the result of example 9.1 (part (i)) for a metal which behaves as a point source when being evaporated.

Solution: in this case rearranging (9.15) gives

$$
\begin{aligned}
l &= \frac{x}{\left[\left(\frac{t_Q}{t_P}\right)^{2/3} - 1\right]^{1/2}} \\
&= \frac{25}{[1.0067 - 1]^{1/2}} \\
&= 305\,\text{mm}.
\end{aligned}
\tag{9.20}
$$

This shows that for a given chamber height a point source will give a more even deposition that a directed area source.

A way to get around uniformity problems, regardless of the source emission characteristics, is to move the substrates around. This is particularly effective when many substrates are involved, and commonly these are mounted in a dome which is subsequently traversed around the evaporation chamber with its perimeter edge in a circular groove (Figure 9.28). If the evaporation is carried out over a sufficiently long period of time, large scale uniformity of coatings can be obtained. This method is expensive, and has one other disadvantage when coating easily oxidizable metals such as titanium: the substrates are continually moving in and out of the vapour stream, and thus the deposited hot titanium is being regularly exposed to the residual gas in the vacuum chamber. This will readily oxidize the titanium, leading to an impure metallization of increased resistivity. A fixed substrate position well inside the main evaporation region ensures that the deposited titanium is prevented from oxidizing by the rest of the evaporant picking up any residual gas.

Figure 9.28 A planetary coating system (photo courtesy of Leybold AG).

9.2.5   Thickness measurement

There are several techniques that can be used for thin film thickness measurement. An example is stylus profilometry, a popular choice for checking thickness after deposition and lift-off. A stylus traverses across the substrate and, on encountering a discontinuity due to a metallized layer, is vertically displaced. This can be picked up by electromagnetic induction in much the same way as in the principles of a record player. Further details on this, and other, techniques are given in [27].

However the most useful, and hence most common, form of thickness measurement is an in situ method. This is done via a crystal monitor, which can be calibrated for any metallization and, using the equations developed in the last section, the amount of metal depositing on the substrate can be assessed. All the calculations are usually performed electronically by an external deposition controller.

A crystal monitor is based on the principle that the resonant frequency of a piezoelectric crystal such as quartz is proportional to its thickness, and hence its mass. By depositing material on the crystal we change its mass, and hence its resonant frequency, and the change in frequency can be correlated back to a given metal thickness if we know the deposited area and the metal density. Disc shaped quartz crystals are cut along a certain direction (usually an AT cut). Electrodes are attached either side of the disc and, when the disc is placed in an oscillating circuit, resonance occurs at a frequency f given by

$$f = \frac{v_Q}{2t} \tag{9.21}$$

where t is the disc thickness and v_Q the velocity of sound in the quartz. For an AT cut the resonant frequency is 1.67 MHz mm and crystals supplied for most crystal monitors have a resonant frequency of 5 or 6 MHz. Depositing material on the crystal will increase its mass by dm, and the effective increase in film thickness is given by

$$dt = \frac{dm}{\rho_Q A} \tag{9.22}$$

where ρ_Q is the density of quartz and A the deposited area. From 9.21 and 9.22

$$df = \frac{v_Q \, dt}{2t^2} \tag{9.23}$$

$$= \frac{-2dm \, f^2}{\rho_Q A v_Q} \tag{9.24}$$

$$\text{and so} \quad dm = \frac{df \, \rho_Q A v_Q}{2f^2}. \tag{9.25}$$

Example 9.3

Calculate the thickness of gold (density $= 1.93 \times 10^4$ kg m^{-3}) deposited on a quartz crystal monitor of cross-sectional area 1 cm^2 for a 1% change in a resonant frequency of 6 MHz. The velocity of sound in quartz is 3.34×10^3 m s^{-1} and the density of quartz is 2.21×10^3 kg m^{-3}.

Solution: we first need to use (9.25) to calculate dm:

$$dm = \frac{6 \times 10^4 \times 2.21 \times 10^3 \times 10^{-4} \times 3.34 \times 10^3}{2 \times 36 \times 10^{12}}$$
$$= 6.15 \times 10^{-7}\,\text{kg}. \qquad (9.26)$$

This result can now be put in (9.8) to get the film thickness – in this example A in (9.25) is equivalent to dS in (9.8):

$$t = \frac{6.15 \times 10^{-7}}{1.93 \times 10^4 \times 10^{-4}}$$
$$= 3.19 \times 10^{-7}\,\text{m}. \qquad (9.27)$$

The film thickness on the crystal monitor is then 3190 Å, in the unit most commonly used for metallization thicknesses. A consideration of (9.9) will give the relative thicknesses of metal deposited on substrate and crystal monitor (the tooling factor).

Although the monitoring technique is very accurate, it is only a calibration and does not measure directly the mass condensing on the substrate. It assumes emissions are from an ideal source, whether point or directed area, and also assumes that the sticking coefficient on both crystal monitor and substrate are equal. The crystal monitor is also affected by heat, and the head has to be cooled to avoid frequency drift with temperature. The crystal itself has to be changed regularly as, when a certain amount of material has been deposited, the mass of the metal become comparable to that of the quartz. In this case we now have two oscillators, complicating any thickness calculation. At this stage it is wise to remove the crystal and either clean off the deposited metal or, when that option is not appropriate, use a new crystal.

9.2.6   Sputtering

This method of film deposition has been known for over a century and led from the earlier work of glow discharges (plasmas) in gases. Early discoveries showed that when an electrical discharge is passed between two electrodes in a low pressure atmosphere, the ambient gas is ionized, giving rise to a particular colour to the discharge, dependent on the gas, whenever ions and electrons recombine. The positively charged gaseous ions will be attracted to the cathode and, if they have sufficient energy, will cause material to be liberated from the cathode by ionic bombardment. The term cathodic sputtering was used to describe this phenomenon of free atom liberation; if the freed atoms subsequently react with the gas the process is called reactive sputtering (reviewed, as well as reactive evaporation, in [28]). The physics of atomic liberation has been well covered, e.g. [29], as have the properties of plasmas, e.g. [30]. A cross-section of a typical glow discharge is shown in Figure 9.29 for a diode sputtering arrangement with an external d.c. power supply. Of the various regions the cathode dark space is the most important, as it is across here that most of the applied voltage is dropped. Ions created in the plasma are accelerated in this region towards the cathode, as shown in Figure 9.30(a). Similarly, electrons are accelerated towards the anode, where the substrates are located, potentially causing damage or excessive heating. In a magnetron sputtering process, Figure 9.30(b), the plasma is concentrated close to the cathode surface by magnetic confinement. This increases the electron density around the cathode, leading to high gas ionization rates and subsequently a higher cathode sputtering rate. Problems due to electron bombardment of the substrates are minimized. The principles of magnetron operation, showing electron confinement and subsequent material erosion, are shown in Figure 9.31.

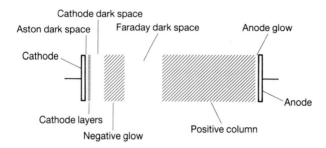

Figure 9.29 The major features of a low pressure gas discharge.

There are many variations on the basic theme of sputtering, reactive and magnetron being two of the more important examples. Another important variation is to use an r.f. power supply instead of d.c. This is to get around the problems of using d.c. when sputtering materials of high resistivity, such as silicon. In this case the target could build up a charge and hence degrade the sputtering process. In r.f. sputtering a matching network, mounted as close to the sputtering assembly as possible, is provided to match the impedance between the power supply (usually 50 Ω at 13.56 MHz) and plasma. An example is shown in Figure 9.32.

Other important variations involve physical changes, e.g. the substrates may be positioned above the target (sputter up), as opposed to the sputter down arrangement of Figure 9.30. Alternatively, the cathode may be aligned vertically within the chamber. Both of these positions are intended to alleviate problems of particulates originating from the cathode and settling on the substrates.

Chamber design and pumping arrangements are not that dissimilar to an evaporation system, where a rotary/diffusion pump combination can be used. Alternatively, for elimination of pump oils from the chamber, a cryopump is a popular choice. Base pressures (10^{-7}–10^{-6} torr) are similar, but the system is operated at a gas pressure of 10^{-3}–10^{-2} torr. The gas used is usually inert, either argon

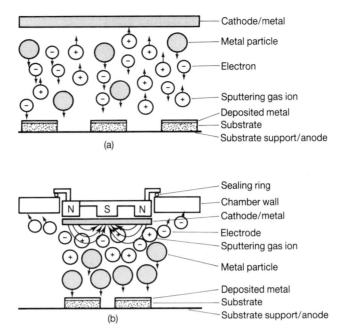

Figure 9.30 The sputtering process for (a) normal cathodic, and (b) magnetron systems. Note that in both cases the sputtered metal would cover the substrate support as well as the substrates (courtesy of Balzers High Vacuum).

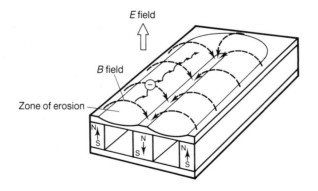

Figure 9.31 A planar magnetron sputtering target (courtesy of Balzers High Vacuum).

or xenon, but for reactive sputtering nitrogen is often used. The film resulting from the sputtering process, including deposition rates, is a complex interaction

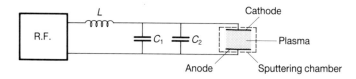

Figure 9.32 R.f. power supply for a sputtering system.

of gas pressure, source–substrate distance, plasma power and material sputtering rates [31]. By varying these it is possible to alter the film thickness, resistivity and stress (the latter two as a result of gas incorporation in the film). What can't be changed to any great extent, however, is the conformal nature of the coating. This is unlike evaporation, which is carried out at low pressure and hence there is a low probability of evaporated atoms colliding with residual gas molecules. This means that evaporated atoms impinging on the substrate surface are essentially travelling in one direction, and a lift-off profile in photoresist can be used effectively (Figure 9.33(a)). Sputtering is carried out at a much higher chamber pressure than evaporation, and so impinging atoms arrive at all angles and tend to deposit in all possible places, despite the use of a lift-off profile in the photoresist (Figure 9.33(b)). This conformal coating means that the resist is very difficult to remove, as the acetone solvent has no point of attack. An ultrasonic bath may sometimes be of use in these circumstances, and a lowering of the gas pressure can produce some degree of non-conformal coating (Figure 9.33(c)). However, sputtering is best used when the whole substrate area is to be metallized, either as a finished coating or for subsequent etching using a wet or dry (plasma) technique. Sputtering rates for various metals are shown in Table 9.2 [32].

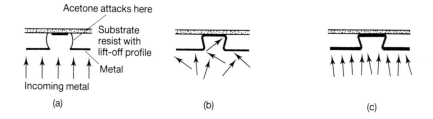

Figure 9.33 The types of coating achieved as a result of different metallization schemes: (a) non-conformal (directional), (b) conformal, and (c) degree of non-conformality.

Metal	Yield (atoms/ion)
Ag	3.4
Al	1.2
Au	2.8
Cr	1.3
Mo	0.9
Ni	1.5
Pd	2.4
Pt	1.6
Rh	1.5
Ta	0.6
Ti	0.6
W	0.6

Table 9.2 Sputtering yield of various metals for an argon ion bombardment energy of 600 eV.

9.2.7   PECVD

The principles of plasma enhanced chemical vapour deposition (PECVD) are discussed in the next section (9.3) on dielectrics, where the technique has found most use in depositing insulators such as silicon dioxide or silicon nitride. PECVD of metals grew out of the use of the technique to deposit silicides in the VLSI industry. Advantages of the technique over CVD are:

(i) lower substrate temperatures are needed because reactions are in the plasma phase,

(ii) smaller grain size and hence smoother layers.

Compared with evaporation and sputtering the metallizations produced by PECVD are:

(i) conformal. Typical base and process pressures are 10 and 500 mT respectively,

(ii) non-uniform. It is difficult to achieve across the chamber, and even across the wafer, uniformity to within 2–3%,

(iii) variable in stress and resistivity – these factors are essentially controlled by the reaction rates and kinetics [33],

(iv) impure. The principle problem is the source gas/liquid/solid, where purities of 99% were typical for early samples, although this has improved substantially. Metals that have been deposited this way include tungsten (from liquid WF_6) and molybdenum (liquid MoF_6). A typical reaction involves the breakdown of the vapour from these sources in a hydrogen atmosphere, e.g.

$$WF_6 + 3H_2 \rightarrow W + 6HF\,. \qquad (9.28)$$

The release of HF is not as big a problem as it might first appear, as only about 0.001% of gas molecules introduced into the chamber actually react (section 9.3). The HF is heavily diluted on evacuation from the process chamber. It should be noted that the addition of hydrogen to scavenge the free fluorine ions is essential; otherwise the deposited tungsten will be etched by these radicals [34].

The technique involves much less capital expenditure than with evaporation or sputtering, and similarly running costs are low. However, the reproducibility and metal purity are major problem areas, as is the availability of suitable gaseous precursors for a wider variety of metal films.

9.2.8 Laser-induced deposition

Lasers have found many uses in semiconductor processing technology since they were first used for fabricating pn diodes in 1968 [35]. As with most of the other examples, laser induced metallization was first performed on silicon substrates, but since then there have been many reports of almost all types of metals being deposited on compound semiconductor substrates, e.g. [36] (and references therein). Although there are two possible types of processes involved in metal deposition, the experimental arrangement is largely similar in both cases (Figure 9.34). A laser beam is scanned across a fixed position substrate (alternatively a moving substrate is placed in the path of a stationary beam) that is inside a reaction chamber. A gaseous precursor, containing the metal to be deposited, is passed over the substrate where an interaction with the laser takes place resulting in metal deposition. The metal deposit is directly written only in the vicinity of the laser beam, giving no need for a photoresist pattern to define the metallized areas. Using a suitable scanning system directly written patterns can be obtained.

There are two basic types of deposition processes involved in using a c.w. laser; pyrolytic and photolytic, although hybrid versions of these are becoming common. A pyrolytic process involves the substrate absorbing the laser beam, increasing its local temperature and hence giving a surface on which the gas may decompose. This type of process is sensitive to the substrate surface conditions, over which great care should be taken with regard to cleanliness and surface appearance. The process involves localized heating of the substrate, and so care must also be taken with fragile or volatile materials. Low resistivity metal films can be obtained, but the metal is relatively impure [37].

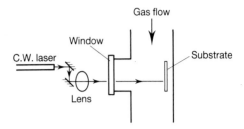

Figure 9.34 Direct write laser assisted deposition from a metalorganic precursor.

A photolytic process involves the gaseous precursor decomposing after photon absorption. A problem with this technique has been the availability of suitable carrier gases. Although the situation is constantly improving, most precursors only strongly absorb in the deep UV, where continuous lasers are not readily available. Deposition is not as sensitive as the pyrolytic method to substrate preparation, which allows uniform metal lines to be deposited over different materials. Fine line deposition is not possible, however, because of the need to focus the beam away from the plane of the substrate. A hybrid process [37], using low temperature (200–300 °C) surface heating and a near UV (350 nm) laser source, has given some results for important metallizations such as tungsten and platinum.

9.2.9   Metallization systems

9.2.9.1   Schottky contact

Up to now we have considered only the metal deposition methods. The choice of metallization itself, although important, is not as vital as might be expected from the theoretical considerations detailed in Chapter 2. As noted previously there are two distinct types of contact needed in optoelectronic devices; ohmic (section 2.2.3), where the series resistance at the metal-semiconductor interface is so small that it can be ignored, giving a linear I–V plot, and Schottky (rectifying – section 2.2.1), where the I–V characteristics are similar to that of a pn junction. However, this ideal behaviour is rarely observed; metal–semiconductor contacts always need to be alloyed to produce ohmic behaviour, and the barrier height of the most actively studied III–V system, metal/GaAs, is only weakly dependent on metal work function, unlike the case of the metal/Si system [38]. This was originally thought to be due to 'Fermi level pinning' at the semiconductor surface, where a high density ($> 10^{13}$ cm^{-2}) of surface states prevents significant band bending at the metal–semiconductor interface [39]. These states were originally considered to be intrinsic [40], but it is now thought that there are no detectable intrinsic surface states in the GaAs band gap and that the Fermi level pinning at about

0.8 eV below the conduction band minimum ($\equiv \phi_{bn}$) results from submonolayer coverage of contamination such as metals or oxygen [41]. Surface states are now more associated with native acceptor or donor defects produced by the interaction of GaAs and contaminant [42]. Similar results are obtained on other III–V semiconductors, but with ϕ_{bn} being pinned at different levels (e.g. 0.5 eV for InP, 0.2 eV for $In_{0.53}Ga_{0.47}As$ and 0.2–0.5 eV for $y = 0$–1 in $In_{0.53}Ga_{0.47}As_{1-y}P_y$). These low barrier heights are of concern when fabricating a MESFET out of these materials, as might be desirable for an integrated receiver/amplifier. A low barrier height increases the drain output conductance and the pinch-off drain current. This is especially serious for the InGaAsP alloys where a decreasing band gap, giving a lower barrier height, also gives increased mobility. The use of a thin, interfacial oxide layer between metal and semiconductor to create a MIS structure gives a quasi-Schottky barrier and an increase in effective barrier height, in the case of InGaAs and InGaAsP to 0.5 eV and 0.72 eV respectively [43].

Even with the most careful chemical preparation of the semiconductor surface and UHV (ultra-high vacuum) metal deposition, there will still be a thin layer of contamination of the surface prior to metallization. This is also likely to be non-uniform, giving potential reproducibility problems.

Other factors to consider in choosing a metal for a Schottky contact are:

(i) long term stability, particularly with regard to electromigration,
(ii) stable operating characteristics, e.g. vs. temperature,
(iii) ability to be wire bonded,
(iv) adherance to the semiconductor surface.

Rarely does one metallization match all these criteria. This has led to the development of multi-level systems, where each element has a role to play in producing the ideal contact. A classic example is the GaAs/Ti/Pt/Au system. Gold itself does not stick very well to GaAs, but titanium does. Gold, however, is easily bonded to but titanium isn't. Unfortunately the two metals interact, and the gold will diffuse into the GaAs at a temperature as low as 200 °C, producing a very visible phenomenon called the 'purple plague'. The use of a platinum interfacial layer postpones the onset of this interaction to beyond 350 °C, where devices would not be expected to operate anyway.

There are many schemes, especially multi-level ones, for producing Schottky metallizations to III–V compounds. References [43] (InGaAs and InGaAsP), [44] and [45] (GaAs) and [46] (GaAs, GaP and InP) are a few examples of collected works on this topic.

9.2.9.2 Ohmic contact

Despite what might be predicted, for many years no metal deposited directly on to a III–V semiconductor surface could produce an ohmic contact; the junction had to be subsequently alloyed to obtain linear *I–V* behaviour with low resistance. Again this is due to the problems of surface state pinning. A thin layer of germanium epitaxially grown on a GaAs surface and subsequently metallized can produce an ohmic contact [47]. InAs, which does not have a Fermi pinned surface, can also be used instead of germanium. Here there is an abrupt InAs/GaAs interface, as the two semiconductors have a 7% lattice mismatch. The use of a graded InGaAs interfacial layer, to produce a final structure as in Figure 9.35, of metal/InAs/graded InGaAs/GaAs, has been used to overcome this problem [48]. Low barrier height ohmic contacts have largely been confined to the research laboratories, as the technique of epitaxy and immediate metal evaporation is incompatible with other processing requirements such as metal area definition. The use of a direct write metallization process, such as one of the laser assisted techniques, would help this type of contact gain greater acceptance.

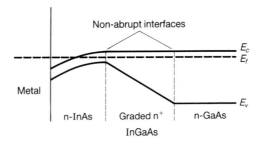

Figure 9.35 The use of a graded structure to overcome lattice mismatch in InAs/GaAs.

A tunnelling contact, based on alloying or sintering (liquid or solid phase reaction respectively, with the former being far more common) has been the basis of most routine ohmic contacts to III–V semiconductors. Although the precise mechanism of contact formation is unclear, a basic understanding has emerged. A typical example is the Au/Ge/Ni contact to GaAs. Gold and germanium are evaporated in the form of a low melting point eutectic alloy, AuGe, of a stoichiometric mass ratio of 88:12. This has a melting point of 356 °C, well below that of either gold (1063 °C) or germanium (958 °C). After deposition the contact is alloyed at a temperature in excess of 356 °C (usually in the range 360–600 °C) for a short period of time (5 s to 15 minutes, depending on the alloying procedure – see section 8.7.3 for a discussion of thermal and RTA techniques). During the alloy the AuGe melts and GaAs is dissolved in this melt. Gallium preferentially outdiffuses, and germanium moves on to vacant gallium sites. After alloying the contact regrows as a highly n-doped semiconductor (because of the Ga–Ge substitution) in proximity to the metal which consists largely of gold. Here, as with the Schottky contact, adhesion is important. If deposited and alloyed as described above the contact will not stick to the GaAs surface and will 'ball up'. The addition of a nickel capping layer, deposited after the AuGe, prevents this. There is also evidence that a thin layer of Ni deposited before the AuGe helps locate the Ge onto vacant Ga sites.

The contact resistance obtained using this technique will depend on the complex interaction between five elements, of which two form a compound semiconductor, two are in the liquid phase and one is a solid metal. It is not surprising that the scheme is not precisely understood, and that many laboratories each have their own processing technique which they have determined to be the best for their own contacts. Process variables that will have a strong bearing on the contact resistance obtained are:

(i) initial doping density of the III–V surface,
(ii) total and relative amounts of AuGe and Ni, and the order of evaporation,
(iii) the presence of any capping layer or ambient gas during the alloy cycle,
(iv) the temperature–time characteristics of the alloy itself.

Whatever the variables chosen from the above list, a good ohmic contact can be visibly assessed after the alloy cycle, as it changes its surface appearance from a uniform smoothness to a very non-uniform mottled and rough-looking structure (Figure 9.36). A rough-looking ohmic contact is shown in Figure 9.37, contrasted alongside a very smooth Schottky contact.

(a)   (b)

Figure 9.36 An AuGe/Ni ohmic contact to GaAs, (a) before, and (b) after alloying (photos courtesy of BNR Europe Limited).

Tin is often used instead of germanium to contact to n-type III–Vs, particularly to InP and InGaAs. For p-type III–Vs the dopant is commonly zinc. A full list of the many different metallurgies employed to make ohmic contacts to III–Vs can be found in [49] and [50] (GaAs), [51] and [52] (GaAs, AlGaAs, GaAsP and InP).

Figure 9.37 Comparison of the surface appearance of ohmic and Schottky contacts to GaAs (photos courtesy of BNR Europe Limited).

9.3   Dielectric deposition

Dielectrics are useful in optoelectronic devices as a diffusion barrier, a metal crossover insulator, a capacitor material, an active surface passivation layer (where all subsequent processing is done by etching holes in the dielectric) and as a scratch protection for the finished device.

The most commonly used dielectric materials are silicon dioxide, silicon nitride and polyimide. Silicon dioxide is usually stoichiometric SiO_2, silicon nitride is commonly written as SiN_x as the deposition method usually used (PECVD) results in a material of variable stoichiometry, and polyimide is a generic name covering a family of high molecular weight organic compounds. Evaporation of these materials is generally undesirable (SiO_2 – loss of stoichiometry, SiN_x, polyimide – decomposition) and, although sputtering of SiO_2 is quite common, the normal method of depositing inorganic dielectrics is by some form of chemical vapour deposition, either thermal (CVD), plasma ehanced (PECVD) or photo-assisted (photo-CVD). Polyimides are usually deposited by a spin-on technique, similar to photoresist (section 9.1.2). We will look at each of these techniques in more detail, with most emphasis on PECVD, the most commonly used CVD method. We first of all examine the basic CVD system.

9.3.1 Chemical vapour deposition (CVD)

This is a popular method in the silicon IC industry for depositing poly-Si, SiO_2 and Si_3N_4 (stoichiometric silicon nitride). Its use in the optoelectronics sector is governed by the suitability of the substrates for withstanding a high temperature process. CVD is essentially a pyrolytic decomposition of gaseous precursors at temperatures up to 950 °C. Above 600 °C most compound semiconductors are unstable; ohmic contacts degrade on reheating above their alloy temperature and Schottky contacts have a stability limit dependent on the metallization used (see section 9.2.9). Thus the equipment and reaction used is not only dependent on the layer to be deposited, but also on the processing history of the wafer. A typical reaction might be

$$SiH_4 + 2O_2 \overset{400-450°C}{\rightarrow} SiO_2 + 2H_2O \tag{9.29}$$

for depositing SiO_2. Although there are many reaction chamber designs available, based largely on a consideration of gas flows and/or temperature gradients, two basic types are in common use; the horizontal atmospheric pressure reactor and the low pressure CVD (LPCVD) arrangement. The former system is shown in Figure 9.38. The substrates are held on a wafer holder (susceptor) which is subsequently heated. The method of heating has an important influence on the decomposition characteristics. If the whole reaction chamber is placed inside a furnace, the walls of the quartz tube become hot and material is deposited there (hence, a hot wall system). If the susceptor is heated by other means, such as r.f. induction heating, then the reactor walls stay cold and much less deposition occurs there. This cold wall system has the added advantage of a small thermal mass, enabling the temperature cycle involved in CVD to be undertaken much more rapidly.

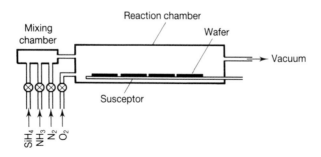

Figure 9.38 The main components of a horizontal CVD reaction chamber (the external heating method varies).

Whichever heating system is used, reactor gases are usually diluted in an inert carrier gas and mixed before entering the reactor; an exception is oxygen where some reaction may occur in the mixing chamber. How the process of CVD works has been described previously when discussing MOVPE, section 8.4.2.1. The diffusion rate of the reactants, and hence the resultant film properties and uniformity, depend upon the substrate temperature (proportional to $T^{3/2}$), total pressure $(1/P)$ and partial pressure of the reactant (e.g. P_{SiH_4}). The thickness of the boundary layer depends on the distance in the direction of the gas flow $(x^{1/2})$ and the gas velocity $(1/v)$ [53].

Low pressure CVD is an important technique where good step coverage is important. The experimental arrangement is not too dissimilar to Figure 9.38, with the major difference being that the substrates are oriented vertically rather than horizontally. Typical pressures used are 0.2–2 torr at a flow rate of 100–1000 s.c.c.m. (standard cubic centimetres per minute). This system has the additional advantage of a large load size and very good uniformity. The main disadvantage is a low deposition rate as the reactant species is depleted as it flows inside the reaction chamber. Typical deposition rates are 20–200 Å/min.

CVD produced films are characterized by having a high density, as a result of minimal inclusion of carrier gases because of the high temperature nature of the process.. Pinhole and crack densities are low, and adhesion is very good because of the low stress inherent in the films.

9.3.2   Plasma enhanced chemical vapour deposition (PECVD)

9.3.2.1   Principle

As was noted in the last section, compound semiconductor materials are generally unstable above 600 °C; this rules out the transfer of many CVD reactions from the IC to the optoelectronic industry because of the low temperature limit available. Plasma enhanced reactions are a way of causing the same chemistry as in (9.29) but at a much lower temperature. This is especially useful for silicon nitride, where a low temperature CVD process is not easy to obtain.

In a plasma the gaseous reactants, at low pressure, are ionized by the application of an external field. Although the ions are at an ambient temperature within the plasma, the free electrons have sufficient energy to break molecular bonds and hence form reaction byproducts. The ionization rate is small (of the order of 1 in 10^5) but sufficient to create a reasonable deposition rate.

All PECVD equipment follows the same basic structure, outlined in Figure 9.39(a), with Figure 9.39(b) showing the potential difference between the two chamber electrodes. A reactor such as this is, for obvious reasons, called a parallel plate reactor. Mixed or unmixed gases are entered into the chamber at the top via a showerhead. The gas pressure is usually in the range 100–1000 mT (base pressure 10–50 mT) at a flow rate of 1–200 s.c.c.m. For silicon nitride the gas stoichiometry is chosen from a mixture of SiH_4, NH_3 and N_2. Deposition rates are similar to those of CVD, i.e. 20–200 Å/min, and because of the high operating pressure coatings are fully conformal. An example of this is shown in Figure 9.40, where

SiO_2 deposition has covered above and underneath an aluminium lip on a silicon substrate.

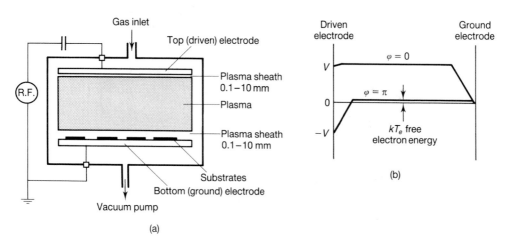

Figure 9.39 (a) PECVD reaction chamber. (b) Plasma voltage response.

The top electrode of a parallel plate reactor is driven by the r.f. field and, as the plasma is largely neutral, all the potential drop is across the plasma sheath at the ground electrode for the positive half cycle. For the negative half cycle the potential is dropped across the plasma sheath at the driven electrode. The use of r.f. power of a suitable frequency minimizes ion bombardment damage of the substrates. This can be seen by considering Figure 9.39(b), and assuming that there is an ion at the edge of the plasma closest to the substrates on the positive half cycle. If an ion can move across the plasma sheath and reach the ground electrode before the next negative half cycle, its maximum energy is the maximum plasma potential ($\sim V$). If the ion does not respond quicker than the r.f. frequency, the average potential is V/π (assuming a sinusoidal response in the positive half cycle, plasma potential grounded in the negative) [54]. There will be a transition range of frequencies where the average potential will be between V and V/π. The range will depend on the gases concerned, but the selected r.f. frequency of 13.56 MHz is comfortably above the transition region.

9.3.2.2 Film characteristics
The film properties as a result of PECVD are a complex interaction of many variables; gas stoichiometry, pressure and flow rate, r.f. power, frequency and electrode spacing, substrate temperature (normally heated to 100–300 °C) and substrate type all have an effect on film stoichiometry, thickness, uniformity, stress, refractive index and etching rate. There are many possible chemical reactions because the plasma nature of the process increases the availability of many different radicals.

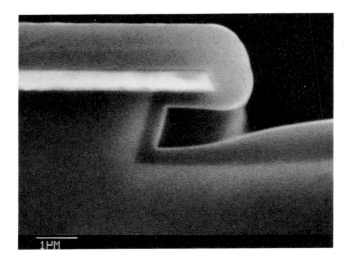

Figure 9.40 Conformal coating of PECVD deposited SiO_2 (photo courtesy of GEC–Marconi Materials Technology Limited).

Although the nature of plasmas and their reactivity have been well investigated in the past, e.g. [55], the transfer of this knowledge to predict the properties of PECVD films specific to individual reactors has proved difficult. As a consequence, most plasma processes are developed on a slow empirical basis, with a carefully controlled set of experiments around the above mentioned parameters leading to an investigation of film properties. This form of experimentation is limited in its scope because:

   (i) results are only appropriate to one specific reactor,

  (ii) variables do not always act independently – quite often there is interaction,

 (iii) complications arise because of the past history of the chamber. Reaction chambers need frequent cleaning because the build up of deposited dielectric on the electrodes can lead to a stress-induced flaking of silicon nitride particles, giving a high concentration of dust in any deposited film. Cleaning of the chamber is performed by operating it in the plasma etching mode (see section 9.4.1),

 (iv) in all cases the operating base pressure must be the same and successive wafers must be placed on the same part of the grounded electrode. This is emphasized in Figure 9.41, which shows the deposition thickness increasing from the centre of the electrode (position 0) to the edge; for the outer one-third area of the electrode the film thickness increases rapidly.

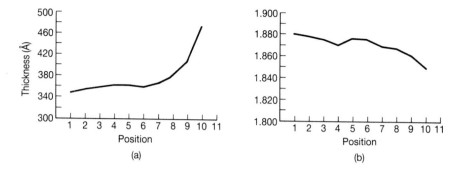

Figure 9.41 The variation in (a) film thickness, and (b) refractive index with substrate position on the grounded electrode for a typical non-uniform PECVD silicon nitride process.

Silicon nitride deposited by PECVD is unlikely to be stoichiometric Si_3N_4 produced by CVD, and hence is given the formula SiN_x. The departure from stoichiometry is indicated by the etch rate in hydrofluoric acid (HF), typically 10–20 times faster for PECVD than for CVD films. Etch rates for PECVD films are also a function of hydrogen incorporation (itself a function of substrate temperature) and can vary over more than two orders of magnitude. General trends for how SiN_x film properties vary with deposition conditions are given in [56].

An accepted method of optimizing film properties is to use a designed set of experiments based on response surface methodology (RSM) [57] (although the article is about plasma etching, the same principles apply). RSM uses a statistical approach which models a process according to empirically derived mathematical expressions. Specific experiments are designed around a dimensional structure, and then interactions between various parameters are studied to arrive at a final parametric model which can be used in process optimization. The experiments with one variable (the level) and the number of variables in any experiment (the factor) determine the total number of experiments to be performed (the trials). Polynomial solutions can usually be found to predict the resultant film properties. Although popular in the chemical manufacturing industry for decades, RSM has only been used since the mid-1980s in the microelectronics industry, as traditional approaches to experimentation became less and less satisfactory as more was demanded of a process in a shorter lead time.

9.3.2.3 Thickness measurement

Whichever approach is used to determine film properties, the thickness has to be measured after deposition; placing a 6 MHz driven crystal monitor in a 13.56 MHz r.f. field would lead to spurious results of film thickness being obtained. A quick guide to an approximate thickness can be obtained by observing the colour of the wafer obtained by interference effects. This is how Table 9.3 was devised

Order	Colour	Silicon dioxide thickness range (Å)	Silicon nitride thickness range (Å)
1st	Silicon	0–270	0–200
	Brown	270–530	200–400
	Golden brown	530–730	400–550
	Red	730–970	550–730
	Deep blue	970–1000	730–770
	Blue	1000–1200	770–930
	Pale blue	1200–1300	930–1000
	Very pale blue	1300–1500	1000–1100
	Silicon	1500–1600	1100–1200
	Light yellow	1600–1700	1200–1300
	Yellow	1700–2000	1300–1500
	Orange-red	2000–2400	1500–1800
	Red	2400–2500	1800–1900
	Dark red	2500–2800	1900–2100
2nd	Blue	2800–3100	2100–2300
	Blue-green	3100–3300	2300–2500
	Light green	3300–3700	2500–2800
	Orange-yellow	3700–4000	2800–3000
	Red	4000–4400	3000–3300

Table 9.3 The colour of silicon oxide and nitride films as a function of thickness.

[58]. Although the data is for a silicon wafer, III–V substrates have the same visual appearance and so the table broadly correlates with optoelectronic materials. Note also that a colour can mean one of several thickness ranges.

For a more accurate guide to thickness, ellipsometry must be used. This is based on evaluating a change in the polarization state of light, usually from a He–Ne laser, reflected from the substrate-film interface. The state of polarization is determined by the relative amplitudes of the parallel ($E_{\parallel}$) and perpendicular ($E_{\perp}$) components of the laser and the phase difference between them (ϕ). On reflection from a surface these components undergo changes dependent upon the real and imaginary optical components of the substrate (n_s and k_s respectively), the angle of incidence θ, the constants of the film (n_f and k_f) and the film thickness t. If n_s and k_s are known and the film is transparent ($k_f = 0$) then n_f and t can be determined. An ellipsometric system is shown in Figure 9.42. Ellipticity is produced at the film–

substrate interface, which is compensated by rotating the polarizer and analyzer until beam extinction is shown by the detector. From the polarizer and analyzer angles the phase difference ϕ and amplitude ratio $\tan \psi$ can be obtained. n_f and t can then be determined [59].

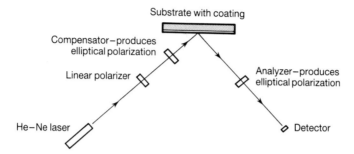

Figure 9.42 The main components of an ellipsometric thin film measurment system.

9.3.2.4 Composition

Infra-red spectroscopy is useful in determining film composition. SiN_x and SiO_2 absorb some radiation in the infra-red part of the spectrum, but the greater part of the absorption is by specific resonance peaks (see Table 9.4). The presence and relative magnitude of these peaks can be used as a guide to the film composition and quality. An example is shown in Figure 9.43 where, in addition to the main Si-N peak at 850 cm^{-1}, there is a small peak at 2160 cm^{-1} corresponding to Si-H. Other important things to note from IR spectroscopy are that the Si–N peak position shifts with deposition temperature, the sharpness of the Si–N peak is related to hydrogen content, and peaks at 1050 cm^{-1}, 1405 cm^{-1} and 2905 cm^{-1} indicate a C–H bond, implying hydrocarbon contamination.

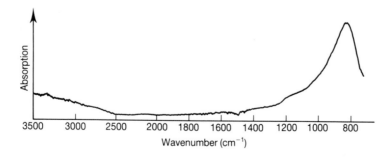

Figure 9.43 A typical infra-red absorption spectrum of PECVD silicon nitride.

Wavenumber (cm^{-1})	Wavelength (μm)	Bond
610	16.39	Si lattice
650	15.39	a-Si
850	11.77	Si–N
1107	9.03	Si–O
1170	8.55	N–H
2141	4.67	Si–H
2160	4.63	Si–H
3340	2.99	N–H

Table 9.4 The main absorption peaks observed in infra-red spectroscopy of SiN$_x$.

9.3.3 Other CVD systems

Photo-CVD is the most common of these. Lasers or UV lamps can be used to initiate a CVD reaction in much the same way as a plasma system. The advantages of a photo-enhanced system are even lower substrate temperature, and no ion bombardment damage. Maintaining a uniform deposition using this technique is much more difficult however.

PECVD alternating with argon sputtering of SiO$_2$ (a technique known as bias CVD) has been used to overcome the conformality of a conventional PECVD coating [60]. It has demonstrated films varying from fully conformal in nature, to 45° sloped, to fully planarized.

Three techniques discussed in more detail in section 9.4 have also been explored. A downstream plasma reactor has been used to deposit SiO$_2$ [61]. In this system a microwave plasma at 2.45 GHz is used to liberate atomic oxygen from nitrous oxide; the oxygen is mixed with silane in an afterglow region downstream of the main plasma. The polysiloxane precursors formed by this reaction convert to SiO$_2$ on the wafer surface.

Electron cyclotron resonance (ECR) plasmas use the same microwave frequency, but additionally have magnetic field coils surrounding the resonant cavity [62]. The effect of the coils is to contain electrons within the plasma. High ion densities at a much lower operating pressure (10^{-4} to 10^{-5} torr) can be achieved this way. Both downstream plasma reactors and ECR reactors have been successful in reducing the hydrogen content of films from 5–20% for a typical PECVD process to less than 1%. This gives a much denser, more evenly coated film than PECVD, and deposition rates are much greater due to the high ion density in the plasma.

A magnetron system, similar to magnetron sputter deposition, (section 9.2.6) has also been used to produce SiO_2 [63]. The magnetic confinement of electrons near the substrate acts to increase the probability of collisions between electrons and gas atoms, releasing ions to react together. This happens without any increase in ion potential, and hence possible substrate damage, which would occur if the power delivered to the plasma increased. As in ECR, a plasma can be maintained at much lower pressure (1–10 mT) than in conventional PECVD.

9.3.4 Polyimide

This is used primarily as a final passivation layer for scratch protection. Its use as an interlayer dielectric has been limited because of question marks in the past over its long term reliability, but in recent years these have been identified as more of a processing than material problem.

Polyimide's greatest advantage over SiO_2 or SiN_x as an interlayer dielectric is its planarizing properties. It is spun on to a wafer in much the same fashion as photoresist (see section 9.1.2) although, depending on the thickness required, alternative deposition techniques such as spraying, rolling or screen printing may be more appropriate. As such it planarizes over any surface features (Figures 9.44(a) and (b)). The surface of the polyimide may then be etched back uniformly to produce a surface ideal for subsequent metallization (Figures 9.44(c) and (d)). This is not possible with a conformal coating such as is achieved by any of the CVD methods. After deposition the polyimide is cured in a vacuum oven. The curing process itself is crucial to the subsequent stability of the polyimide. A typical process involves three stages: a ramp up to a given temperature, a hold at this temperature for a fixed time and then a ramp down again. The aim is to drive off all solvents from the polyimide and set it against ingress of contaminants such as water. If the initial ramp-up is too fast, solvent from the lower layers will not have time to be driven off before the surface polyimide hardens. If the hold time is too short, again incomplete solvent evaporation could occur and the polyimide may be completely thermally stabilized. If the ramp down is too quick the subsequent stress associated with differential cooling could cause adhesion problems or even crack the polyimide.

Sometimes a further high temperature stage is added after the first to ensure complete stabilization of the polyimide. Typical temperatures for this process are 200–400 °C.

A further problem on curing is that the polyimide shrinks, resulting in a profile that looks more like Figure 9.45 than Figure 9.44(b). The degree of planarization, a figure of merit of the process is given by

$$DOP = 1 - h/t. \tag{9.30}$$

Typical values for DOP are in the 0.5–0.7 region; a second polyimide layer raises the DOP to much closer to 1. The planarity is important for subsequent metal-

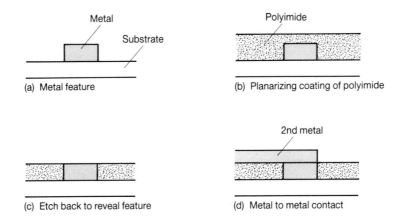

Figure 9.44 The steps in producing a metal to metal contact using polyimide as an insulator.

lization as it leads to more uniform thicknesses, giving uniform current densities and reducing the chances of failure due to electromigration.

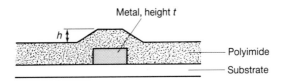

Figure 9.45 Shrinkage of polyimide after curing.

Polyimides generally have a dielectric constant in the range 3.2–3.4, although some specific products have a value as low as 2.4 [64]. Good insulating properties are noted from the high value of the dielectric breakdown field ($> 2 \times 10^8$ V m^{-1}) and volume resistivity ($> 10^{15}$ Ω cm). The thermal properties of polyimide depend on the success of the curing process. Properly cured, polyimides can withstand subsequent processing at temperatures in the range 300–500 °C, again dependent on the individual product, before decomposing; this is more than enough to remove any concerns about polyimide stability during subsequent metallization. In addition, polyimide coated circuits have been cycled down to 77 K with no adverse effect on the dielectric.

Windows are formed in a polyimide by dry etching using an O_2 or CF_4/O_2 plasma with a photoresist mask. Photosensitive polyimides are also available, where the patterning of the polyimide layer is done in much the same way as if the material was a photoresist. This eliminates the additional processing steps of the photoresist masking layer and the dry etching. Such polyimides tend to act as negative resists;

fine line definition is then generally ruled out, but for polyimide windows this is rarely a problem anyway.

9.4 Dry etching

Etching processes using corrosive or sputtering gases in the plasma state come under the general heading of dry etching. There are many variations, and new ones are being invented all the time, based around a simple plasma etching system. New systems are introduced to improve on the basic process in terms of directionality, throughput or reproducibility. Details of new etch gases/combinations of gases are published at a prodigious rate, and a section here is devoted to etch chemistries.

Dry etching was introduced when IC lateral dimensions began to shrink to the same order as vertical dimensions: around the 1 μm region. Greater control is provided by dry etching, the degree of undercutting of masks can be controlled (particularly important for deep etches) and the degree of selectivity between substrate materials can be varied with the process parameters. Because a basic plasma etch process relies on the same principles as plasma enhanced CVD, except that the gases used produce etching radicals rather than a deposited film, the result of any etch is similarly dependent on all the process variables inherent in the system; response surface methodology [57] can again be used to great effect.

9.4.1 Plasma etching

The process chamber can be configured as in Figure 9.46 (barrel reactor) or as in Figure 9.39(a) (parallel plate reactor). The latter system has already been described, and the former consists of a quartz tube surrounded by capacitive electrodes or inductive coils which generate a plasma within the tube. The slice is placed inside a perforated metal cylinder. This acts as an equipotential surface, and the size of the perforations ensures that no plasma can penetrate into the central region. Plasma byproducts can diffuse in, however, and any reaction on the wafer surface is then a result of non-ionized gaseous species only. The system is not often found in laboratories these days, as uniform etch rates are almost impossible to obtain because of plasma and gas flow non-uniformities. It is still used in resist stripping if an acetone rinse is inappropriate, as this is not a critical process step providing the resist is overetched significantly to allow for any local irregularities.

Parallel plate reactors are much more common and, besides the electrode arrangements, have much in common with PECVD. Gas flows and pressure are the same, as is the design of the gas inlet system. In fact the basic differences from an operational point of view are that:

(i) substrates are not generally heated above 100 °C, if at all, except for etching III–V materials.

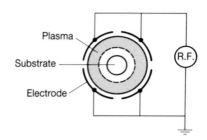

Figure 9.46 Schematic of a capacitively coupled barrel reactor.

(ii) gases used are entirely different from PECVD.

It is, of course, this latter aspect that is crucial to plasma etching. The gases involved usually include a highly reactive species such as hydrogen, oxygen or one of the halogens (Br, Cl, F). Plasma generated reactions then release radicals via, for example

$$O_2 \;\rightarrow\; 2O \tag{9.31}$$

$$\text{or} \quad CF_4 \;\rightarrow\; CF_3 + F\,. \tag{9.32}$$

The addition of oxygen to this latter reaction results in even more fluorine being formed (and hence faster etch rates for certain materials) by

$$2CF_3 + O_2 \;\rightarrow\; 2CO_3 + 6F \tag{9.33}$$

$$\text{or} \quad 2CF_3 + O_2 \;\rightarrow\; 2COF_2 + 2F\,. \tag{9.34}$$

The use of one or other gases depends on whether oxidation produces a volatile product (as with photoresists) or a stable product (as with metals), and which of the oxidation/halogenation reactions is more favoured. It is possible that too much oxygen in the plasma would decrease etch rates by passivating the material with an oxide layer.

Often a process is called upon to etch material under a mask; it is important that the mask itself is not eroded in this process. The selectivity between mask and material is an important process variable and will strongly depend, amongst other things, on the gas stoichiometry. Whatever the selectivity, because of the high (0.1–1 torr) operating pressure and low ion energy, plasma etch processes are near or fully isotropic and etch by chemical reaction only.

Plasma etching can generate heat on the wafer surface, but there is usually enough convective heat transfer through the chamber gases to maintain a steady wafer temperature. Another consideration is the 'loading effect', where empirically it has been found that etch rates decrease as more material is exposed to the etch [64], either through a bigger area on the substrates, or more substrates themselves in one process run. This can be overcome by keeping the amount of material etched in every run constant via dummy wafers – or by only etching one wafer at a time, as is increasingly being done in the IC industry. This has the severe disadvantage of a low throughput, and etch pressures must be kept high to counteract this. A vacuum load lock is a standard feature of a single wafer etcher. The loading effect implies that, because of the low ionization rates, the etching process can potentially consume more free radicals than are produced in the plasma, and that very few of those radicals are pumped away before etching the surface.

The end point of an etch can be detected in one of three ways. If the material to be etched is a different colour from the substrate, a visual inspection can suffice. If it is transparent, then ellipsometry (see section 9.3.2) may be used. The use of emission spectroscopy, however, is a common approach where neither of these methods is suitable. It has the advantage that the measurements are in situ, and the process does not have to be stopped to monitor progress. A spectrometer system is used to look at various emissions in the plasma; an increase in emissions from an etch species such as fluorine, or a decrease from a volatile product such as SiF_4, indicate the end of an etch as fewer species are being consumed, or fewer products are being formed, in the former and latter cases respectively. This can be a useful technique where the mask itself may be etching in the process, and the engineer is concerned about overetching causing mask erosion. Otherwise a 100% overetch is not uncommon in plasma etching to ensure that any process irregularities do not affect the ultimate removal of unwanted material.

9.4.2   Reactive ion etching (RIE)

As mentioned in section 9.3.2, most of the plasma potential is dropped across the sheath to whichever electrode is the more negative. This potential accelerates ions towards the substrate causing bombardment damage; it was shown how this could be minimized. RIE takes advantage of this bombardment to direct etching radicals towards the substrate surface. The process exploits the fact that the voltage dropped at each electrode V is proportional to the electrode's area A, a relationship given by

$$\frac{V_1}{V_2} = \left(\frac{A_2}{A_1}\right)^n \tag{9.35}$$

where $1.2 < n < 4$, depending on chamber design. An RIE chamber is shown in Figure 9.47(a), where the major differences to plasma etching are that the wafers are placed on the driven electrode and the ground electrode is very much the larger of the two. This means that most of the potential is dropped to the driven electrode (Figure 9.47(b)) – this causes ion acceleration towards the substrates resulting in bombardment. An average self-bias is generated across the plasma – this is an indication of the ion bombardment energy. If the operating pressure is reduced, all etching radicals will be travelling in the same direction and directionality can be introduced into the etching process: this is the key advantage of RIE over plasma etching. Typical etching processes and resultant profiles for plasma and RIE are given in Figure 9.48. Base pressures needed are usually lower than in plasma etching, as are the operating pressures (1–10 mT and 10–100 mT respectively); once the pressure begins to rise the etching begins to lose its directionality. This can be used to an advantage if a T-shaped profile is required, where low pressure (anisotropic) RIE is followed by high pressure (isotropic) RIE. A general RIE process will have some degree of non-directionality, and as with plasma etching and PECVD, the end results depend on a number of process variables; a typical trend of directionality vs self-bias and gas flow rate is given in Figure 9.49.

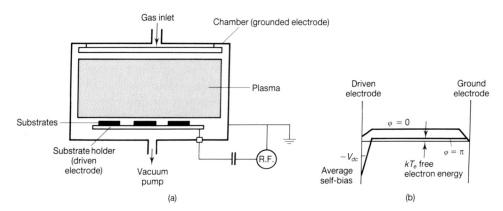

Figure 9.47 (a) RIE process chamber. (b) Plasma voltage response.

The low pressure nature of most RIE processes means that it is sometimes difficult to cause a plasma to 'strike' when the r.f. power is applied; for this reason a plasma should be initiated as soon as etching gases are let into the chamber. This initial surge of pressure is sufficient to enable a plasma to strike without unduly affecting the etching profiles obtained. A reduction in pressure to normal operating conditions ensues as the pumping system and mass flow controllers reach equilibrium; the plasma will then be sustained in the low pressure mode.

There are several other points to note about RIE processes. The directionality is achieved by kinetically assisting the chemical etching – there is no sputtering in RIE. Beacuse of the directionality, it is not as easy as for plasma etching to alter selectivity between different materials. Because of the lower operating pressure, three other factors besides directionality are inherent in the process:

(i) convective cooling is less effective than in plasma etching – substrates are often placed on a water cooled electrode,

(ii) slower etch rates are usual,

(iii) directionality makes the loading effect less of a problem (see section 9.4.1).

The driven electrode should be made of, or coated with, a material which does not etch in any RIE process envisaged for the chamber. For the ground electrode

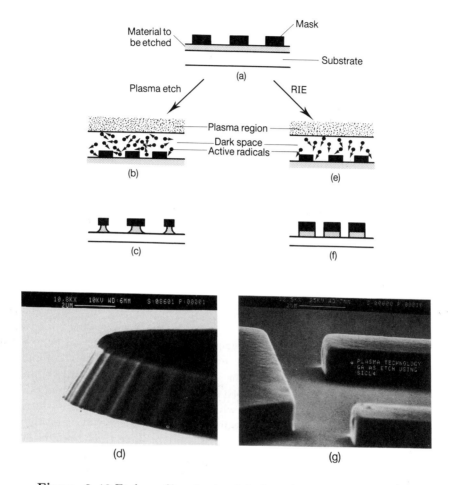

Figure 9.48 Etch profiles obtained during plasma etch and RIE processes. (a) Original profile, (b) plasma etch process, (c) resultant etch profile, (d) photoresist removed, (e) RIE process, (f) resultant etch profile, (g) photoresist removed (photos courtesy of Oxford Plasma Technology).

this is unnecessary, receiving as it does ions with a very low energy. Finally, the RIE process itself can help to create its own anisotropy. For gases such as CF_4 or C_2F_6, molecular breakdown in the plasma can create radicals such as CF_2, which do not etch but readily polymerize to form a highly stable compound. Deposited on the sidewalls of an RIE produced well, this can act as an irremovable coating on previously etchable material. This may be desirable in certain processes, but if not steps should be taken to avoid this happening, e.g. the use of oxygen to scavenge excess fluorocarbons, or alternative etch gases such as SF_6 or NF_3.

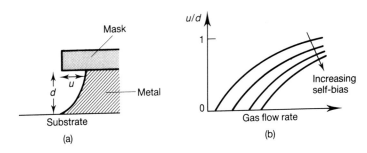

Figure 9.49 The dependence of undercutting on self-bias and gas flow · rate in an RIE system: (a) undercut definition, (b) undercut dependence.

9.4.3   Dry etching gases

A study of all the literature available on etching would quickly reveal an enormous number of potential gases that can etch semiconductor processing materials. A review of all the possible variants is beyond the scope of this section, which limits itself very much to being a review of reviews. However, a close examination of available systems shows that most of the variations in etch gas chemistry are more subtle than substantial. If we remember the criteria for etching to take place, i.e. the plasma must create free radicals which, on reaction with the surface to be etched, form a volatile product that is subsequently pumped away, then the differences between alternative gases become of less importance than the etch method itself. Thus CF_4, CCl_4 or CF_3Br may be chosen because the material to be etched produces a volatile component with F, Cl or Br respectively. Another consideration is that chlorine radicals are usually very short lived and their etching action is enhanced by the UV radiation within the plasma; for these reasons some chlorine based etches are carried out with the wafers in the plasma itself. Adding of O_2 to CF_4 can increase the etch rates, as noted in section 9.4.1. Polymerization of sidewalls can occur in RIE with CF_4, which is eliminated with NF_3 (section 9.4.2). However, this gas is so reactive that very low pressures (< 10 mT) are needed to obtain controllable etches and anisotropic profiles.

The choice of gas is also dependent on the material to be etched. Materials basically fall into four categories: dielectric, metal, semiconductor and organic; a comprehensive review of the etching of three of these is given in [64], and for III–V materials in [65].

Noble metals such as Ni, Au and Pt are difficult to etch, and are usually used as etch masks in fluorine plasmas. Gold can be etched in a chlorine plasma, however

[66]. Refractory metals such as Cr, Ti, Mo and W can be etched in most halogen based chemistries.

For III–V materials there are few dry etching processes in production as wet etching techniques still dominate. The situation is rapidly changing, however, and the greater fidelity and control will begin to make dry etching the dominant technology. Unlike the etching of metals and dielectrics, where only isotropic and anisotropic (and variations thereof) profiles exist, the structure of III–V materials usually introduces another variable: crystallographic etching. For a semiconductor made from two or more unlike elements, the preferential etching of one or the other by the etch radical leads to profiles following crystallographic directions: this dosen't happen in silicon. Chlorine and bromine plasmas are usually used to etch GaAs and InP, as fluorine is ineffective. Group III halides have a lower volatility than those of group V: it is the removal of the former that governs the overall etch rate and an increase in temperature can have a dramatic effect on this [67]. Thus RIE etched III–V materials tend to show 'overcutting', a phenomenon where profiles slope outward from the mask edge (Figure 9.50). Low pressures can increase the anisotropy and restore a sidewall profile; however, this is usually at the expense of surface roughness, making the process unsuitable for generating phase gratings or mirror facets. A further problem is standard etch mask selectivities tend to be low against chlorine. The use of a CH_4/H_2 mixture has been shown to be a good choice in countering these difficulties [68].

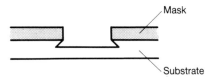

Mask

Substrate

Figure 9.50 The crystallographic (overcutting) profile achieved in etching III–Vs using chlorine based RIE.

Resists, polyimides and other organics are effectively etched in oxygen based systems, although the addition of halogen radicals can sometimes assist the etching process.

The choice of etch gas can depend on other factors, such as using the underlying layer as an end stop. A common example is the etching of windows in silicon nitride on III–Vs using CF_4 or CF_4/O_2; the underlying substrate will not be etched by the fluorine released in the plasma. A natural etch stop like this is highly desirable in any process, even one that determines the end of an etch by spectroscopy (section 9.4.1).

Safety is another factor. The rules of handling compressed gases apply to all chemistries, but additional safety factors need to be considered. Oxygen is a familiar material and, apart from its ability to promote a fire, is fairly innocuous. CF_4 is chemically inert and non-toxic. SF_6 and particulary NF_3 must be prevented from escaping to air; such gases have low safe exposure limits which must not be exceeded. Similarly most chlorine and bromine based systems should be handled with care. These gases are also associated with 'poisoning' vacuum systems, especially the more commonly used chlorine-based gases. Corrosion of vacuum lines and pumps can occur if free chlorine is allowed to interact with aluminium components. Concern over the effects on the ozone layer raises a question mark over the long term availability of the chlorine containing gases.

9.4.4   Ion beam etching

To increase the ion energy in reactive ion etching further than can be obtained by altering the relative areas of the two electrodes, an accelerating grid (500–1000 V) can be introduced between plasma and substrates (Figure 9.51). This, and the use of lower operating pressures (10^{-4} torr), leads to a greater degree of anisotropy in the etching. This is the reactive ion beam etching (RIBE) system and, because ion energies are greater than in RIE, material removed by physical sputtering can contribute to the etching process. Because of this partially physical nature, the process does not rely on the chemical production of a volatile species to etch, as material can be removed just by bombardment.

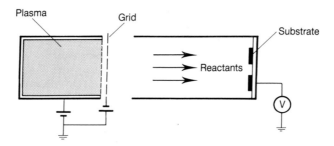

Figure 9.51 Schematic of reactive ion beam etching (RIBE) apparatus.

A mechanism that is purely physical is ion milling, where an ion beam is produced from an inert gas as in Figure 9.52. No volatile species are produced, etch rates are a function of beam angle and there is no undercutting of any etch mask. The mask will be etched, however, and should be carefully chosen so that the substrate will reach the required etch depth before the mask has eroded completely. Further details on both RIBE and ion beam milling can be found in [69].

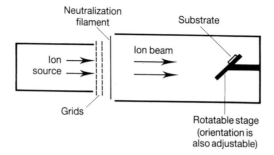

Figure 9.52 Schematic of ion milling apparatus.

9.4.5 Other etching techniques

As with magnetron sputtering or magnetron assisted PECVD, the effect of a magnetic field in an RIE system is to provide a high electron concentration in the region of most etching/deposition activity. In the case of magnetron ion etching (MIE), the electron concentration is highest near the driven electrode, leading to increased reactions with the etching gas and hence increased etch rates. Etch rates up to 1 μm per minute have been reported with SiO_2 [63]; single wafer etchers become much more economical using this method.

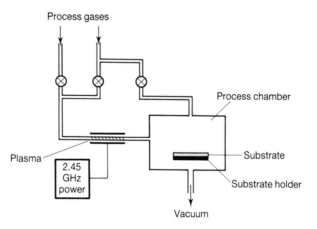

Figure 9.53 Experimental arrangement for downstream plasma etching.

Figure 9.53 shows the experimental arrangement for downstream plasma etching. The great advantage of this system, for deposition as well as etching, is that the wafer is out of the plasma region; radicals generated in the plasma region travel 'downstream' and react with the wafer in a different part of the apparatus. Damage to the surface due to ion bombardment is then avoided.

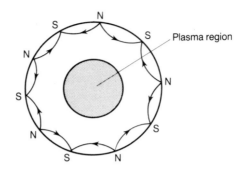

Figure 9.54 Plasma confinement using a ring of permanent magnets.

Microwave multipolar plasma etching takes the advantages of both MIE and downstream plasma etching to produce high etching rates away from the plasma. The plasma is generated at 2.45 GHz out of the etching chamber, as in a downstream plasma reactor, and magnetically confined by an external field to produce high ionization rates. There is more than one way of doing this, and an early development is shown in Figure 9.54 [70]. A ring of permanent magnets surrounds the chamber, producing confinement rather like a magnetic bottle.

More recently electron cyclotron resonance (ECR) has been introduced (Figure 9.55). Microwave power is transmitted to the plasma down a waveguide, and the plasma generating region has surrounding it coils producing a magnetic field of 0.0875 T, the cyclotron resonance condition at the chamber orifice [71]. This greatly increases the rate of ionization with the plasma, as electrons are permanently held within it. Thus even low operating pressures ($\sim 10^{-5}$ torr) can lead to greatly increased etch rates (up to 10 times that of plasma etching). The promise of low plasma damage is also of great interest in III–V devices, where the semiconductor is more sensitive than silicon to a hostile processing environment. Whilst ECR shows some results that promise low damage, it is still too new a technique to win unanimous approval from the industry [72].

A combination of multipolar magnetic field and ECR, distributed ECR, has been used where a set of cylindrical conductors within the plasma chamber are used to apply the 2.45 GHz power to the plasma [73]. These conductors are placed a few millimetres away from the surface of a permanent magnet, at a point where the magnetic field exceeds the resonance condition (Figure 9.56). A magnetically confined reactor (MCR) has also been developed, where the same r.f. frequency as in RIE is used and an external magnetic field (as in Figure 9.54) acts to confine the plasma [74]. It is then different from microwave multipolar plasma etching in the use of a much lower frequency and the fact that the plasma is generated within the confinement region.

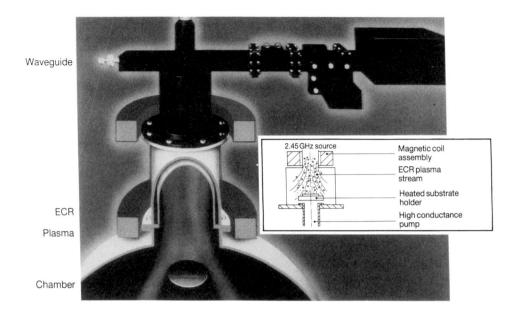

Figure 9.55 Generation of an ECR plasma (photo courtesy of Oxford Plasma Technology).

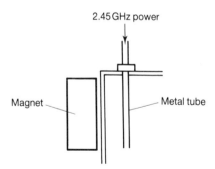

Figure 9.56 Apparatus for introducing distributed ECR to the plasma process.

Although plasma and reactive ion etching remain the mainstay of dry processing techniques at present, developments in other areas will lead more and more to the situation where techniques are individually tailored to the process, not as at present where the process requirement searches for a technique. A review of the newer and more speculative techniques is given in [75].

9.5   Problems

1. If a 50 mm diameter GaAs wafer is left under a class 1000 laminar flow hood for 1 minute, calculate the number of dust particles that will land on the wafer for an airflow of 0.5 m s^{-1}. If the sticking coefficient of these particles is 0.05, and they are uniformly distributed, calculate the likely yield from devices with a surface area of 1 mm^2 if one adhering particle is enough to cause a device to fail.

2. Does lithography require a more or less clean environment than other processing? Why?

3. Explain the role of UV light in lithography.

4. Where would you use a negative photoresist in preference to a positive photoresist?

5. Descibe what happens if photoresist films are underdeveloped.

6. Often the cross-sectional profile of a photoresist pattern shows a sloped edge after development. If instead vertical sidewalls were required, and asuming the process could be started again, what would be the best way of achieving this?

7. Calculate the wavelength of 25 keV electrons. Compare the linewidth limitations due to diffraction when comparing an e-beam with a UV optical source at 365 nm.

8. Why should metal evaporation be performed in a high vacuum?

9. What is the role of the magnetic field in e-beam evaporation?

10. Why would a lift-off profile be generally unsuitable for patterning sputtered metal? Are there ways to overcome this limitation?

11. When should r.f., as opposed to d.c., sputtering be used?

12. Which metal deposition technique is likely to be most applicable to direct write metallization, i.e. pattern definition without a mask?

13. What is meant by the terms isotropic and anisotropic when applied to etching?

14. Sketch the cross-sectional profile of an isotropically etched feature in a film under a non-erodable mask for:

    (i) etching to completion,

    (ii) 100% overetch.

15. Suggest how 0.5 μm features in an etchable material could be made using a mask with 1 μm features.

16. When would silicon nitride be used as an insulator on silicon based devices, instead of silicon dioxide?

17. Suggest reasons why CVD deposited oxide and nitride are termed SiO_2 and Si_3N_4 respectively, whilst PECVD materials are usually denoted SiO_x and SiN_x.

9.6 References

1. K Skidmore, 'Applying Photoresist for Optimal Coatings', *Semiconductor International* **11(2)**, 56 (1988).

2. P Burggraaf, 'Positive Photoresists: 1988 Trends', *Semiconductor International* **11(5)**, 128 (1988).

3. R Iscoff, 'SIA Study Links Glycol Ethers to Miscarriages', *Semiconductor International* **16(1)**, 21 (1993).

4. J A Reynolds, 'An Overview of E-Beam Mask Making', *Solid State Technology* **22(8)**, 87 (1979).

5. K Kagaya, 'Chrome Photomasks', *Solid State Technology* **31(5)**, 144 (1988).

6. T D Kambria and N P Economou, 'Mask and Circuit Repair with Focused Ion Beams', *Solid State Technology* **30(9)**, 133 (1987).

7. T Batchelder and J Platt, 'Bake Effects in Positive Photoresist', *Solid State Technology* **26(8)**, 211 (1983).

8. D A McGillis and D L Fehrs, 'Photographic Linewidth Control', *IEEE Trans. Electron. Dev.* **ED-22**, 471 (1975).

9. D A McGillis, 'Lithography', in *VLSI Technology*, S M Sze, ed., McGraw Hill, 1983, p. 277.

10. I Brodie and J J Murray, *The Physics of Microfabrication*, Plenum, 1982, p. 272.

11. Y Mimura, 'The Mechanism of Overhang Formation in Diazide/Novalak Photoresist Film by Chlorobenzene Soak Process', *J. Vac. Sci. Technol.* **B4**, 15 (1986).

12. B J Lin, 'Multilayer Resist Systems and Processing', *Solid State Technology* **26(5)**, 105 (1983).

13. P M Wood, 'i-Line Lithography in the 1990s', *Solid State Technology* **34(9)**, 41 (1991).

14. P Burggraaf, 'Lithography's Next Step-per', *Semiconductor International* **16(2)**, 38 (1993).

15. M D Levenson, N S Viswanathan and R A Simpson, 'Improving Resolution in Photolithography with a Phase-Shifting Mask', *IEEE Trans. Electron. Dev.* **29**, 1828 (1982).

16. S Okazaki, 'Lithography Technology for Future ULSIs', *Solid State Technology* **34(11)**, 77 (1991).

17. B J Lin, 'The Attenuated Phase-Shifting Mask', *Solid State Technology* **35(1)**, 43 (1992).

18. 'Sharp Wafer Level Phase-Shift Technology', *Semiconductor International* **15(6)**, 40 (1992).

19. J Brook and R Dändliker, 'Submicrometer Holographic Photolithography', *Solid State Technology* **32(11)**, 91 (1989).

20. B A Omar, F Clube, M Hamidi, D Struchen and S Gray, 'Advances in Holographic Lithography', *Solid State Technology* **34(9)**, 89 (1991).

21. See [10], p. 107ff.

22. D L Spears and H I Smith, 'High Resolution Pattern Replication Using Soft X-Rays', *Elec. Lett.* **8**, 102 (1972).

23. D W Peters, 'Examining Competitive Submicron Lithography', *Semiconductor International* **11(2)**, 96 (1988).

24. See [10], p. 294ff.

25. D B Fraser, 'Metallisation', in *VLSI Technology*, S M Sze, ed., McGraw Hill, 1983, p. 357.

26. M Knudsen, *The Kinetic Theory of Gases*, Methuen & Co. Ltd., 1934.

27. A Piegari and E Masetti, 'Thin Film Thickness Measurement: a Comparison of Various Techniques', *Thin Solid Films* **124**, 249 (1985).

28. R F Bunshah and C V Deshpandey, Plasma Assisted Physical Vapour Deposition Processes: a Review, *J. Vac. Sci. Technol.* **A3**, 553 (1985).

29. See [10], p. 210.

30. L I Maissel and R Glang, *Handbook of Thin Film Technology*, McGraw Hill, 1970, p. 4–2.

31. K L Chopra, *Thin Film Phenomena*, McGraw Hill, 1969, p. 31.

32. See [30], p. 4–40.

33. J K Chu, C C Tang and D W Hess, 'Plasma-Enhanced Chemical Vapour Deposition of Tungsten Films', *Appl. Phys. Lett.* **41**, 75 (1982).

34. D W Hess, 'Plasma-Enhanced CVD: Oxides, Nitrides, Transition Metals and Transition Metal Silicides', *J. Vac. Sci. Technol.* **A2**, 244 (1984).

35. J M Fairfield and G H Schwuttke, 'Silicon Diodes made by Laser Irradiation', *Solid State Electron.* **11**, 1175 (1968).

36. Y Rytz-Froidevaux, R P Salathé and H H Gilgen, 'Laser Generated Microstructures', *Appl. Phys.* **A37**, 121 (1985).

37. H H Gilgen, T Cacouris, P S Shaw, R R Krchnavek and R M Osgood, 'Direct Writing of Metal Conductors with Near-UV Light', *Appl. Phys.* **B42**, 55 (1987).

38. S M Sze, *Semiconductor Devices – Physics and Technology*, Wiley, 1985, p. 163.

39. J Bardeen, 'Surface States and Rectification at a Metal–Semiconductor Contact', *Phys. Rev.* **71**, 717 (1947).

40. W Schockley, 'On the Surface States Associated with a Periodic Potential', *Phys. Rev.* **56**, 317 (1939).

41. W E Spicer, I Lindau, P Skeath and C Y Su, 'Unified Defect Model and Beyond', *J. Vac. Sci. Technol.* **17**, 1019 (1980).

42. R W Grant, J R Waldrop, S P Kowalczyk and E A Kraut, 'Correlation of GaAs Surface Chemistry and Interface Fermi Level Position in a Single Defect Model Interpretation', *J. Vac. Sci. Technol.* **19**, 477 (1981).

43. H Ohno and J Barnard, 'Field Effect Transistors', in *GaInAsP Alloy Semiconductors*, T P Pearsall, ed., Wiley, 1982, p. 443.

44. R E Williams, *Gallium Arsenide Processing Techniques*, Artech House, 1984, p. 232.

45. C J Palmstrom and D V Morgan, 'Metallisations for GaAs Devices and Circuits', in *Gallium Arsenide: Materials, Devices and Circuits*, M J Howes and D V Morgan, eds, Wiley, 1985, p. 210.

46. A G Milnes and D L Feucht, *Heterojunctions and Metal–Semiconductor Junctions*, Academic Press, 1972, p. 163.

47. See [45], p. 219.

48. J M Woodall, J L Freeouf, G D Pettit, T Jackson and P Kirchner, 'Ohmic Contacts to n-GaAs Using Graded Band Gap Layers of $Ga_{1-x}In_xAs$ Grown by Molecular Beam Epitaxy', *J. Vac. Sci. Technol.* **19**, 626 (1981).

49. See [44], p. 233.

50. See [45], p. 230.

51. See [46], p. 297.

52. K Gillesen and W Schairer, *Light Emitting Diodes – an Introduction*, Prentice-Hall International, 1987, p. 91.

53. P Gise and R Blanchard, *Modern Semiconductor Fabrication Technology*, Prentice-Hall, 1986, p. 126.

54. R H Bruce, 'Ion Response to Plasma Excitation Frequency', *J. Appl. Phys.* **52**, 7064 (1981).

55. R F Gould, ed., *Chemical Reactions in Electric Discharges*, Advances in Chemistry Series, **80**, Am. Chem. Soc. Publ., 1969.

56. See [44], p. 174.

57. M W Jenkins, M T Mocella, K D Allen and H H Sawin, 'The Modelling of Plasma Etching Processes Using Response Surface Methodology', *Solid State Technology* **29(4)**, 175 (1986).

58. See [44], p. 299.

59. W A Pliskin and S J Zanin, *Film Thickness and Composition*, in *Handbook of Thin Film Technology*, McGraw Hill, 1970, p. 11–21.

60. E J McInerney and S C Avanzino, 'A Planarised SiO_2 Interlayer Dielectric with Bias CVD', *IEEE Trans. Elec. Dev.* **ED-34**, 615 (1987).

61. R L Jackson, J E Spencer, J L McGuire and A M Hoff, 'Afterglow Chemical Vapour Deposition of SiO_2', *Solid State Technology* **30(4)**, 107 (1987).

62. S Matsuo and M Kiuchi, 'Low Temperature Chemical Vapour Deposition Method Utilising an Electron Cyclotron Resonance Plasma', *Jpn. J. Appl. Phys.* **22**, L210 (1983).

63. M F Leahy and G Kagonowicz, 'Magnetically Enhanced Plasma Deposition and Etching', *Solid State Technology* **30(4)**, 99 (1987).

64. J W Coburn, 'Plasma-Assisted Etching', *Plasma Chemistry and Plasma Processing* **2**, 1 (1982).

65. D E Ibbotson and D L Flamm, 'Plasma Etching for III–V Compound Devices: Part II', *Solid State Technology* **31(11)**, 105 (1988).

66. R L Bersin, 'A Survey of Plasma Etching Processes', *Solid State Technology* **19(5)**, 31 (1976).

67. D E Ibbotson and D L Flamm, 'Plasma Etching for III–V Compound Devices: Part I', *Solid State Technology* **31(10)**, 77 (1988).

68. U ·Niggebrugge, M Klug and G Garus, 'A Novel Process for Reactive Ion Etching on InP, Using CH_4/H_2', *IOP Conf. Series* **79**, IOPP, 1985, p. 367.
69. See [44], p. 197ff.
70. R R Burke and C Pomot, 'Microwave Multipolar Plasma for Etching and Deposition', *Solid State Technology* **31(2)**, 67 (1988).
71. S Matsuo and Yo Adachi, 'Reactive Ion Beam Etching Using a Broad Beam ECR Ion Source', *Jpn. J. Appl. Phys.* **21**, L4 (1982).
72. P H Singer, 'ECR: Is the Magic Gone?', *Semiconductor International* **14(8)**, 46 (1991).
73. M G Pichot, 'Microwave Multipolar Plasma Etching at Low Pressure: A Novel Reactor Concept', *Microelectronic Engineering* **3**, 411 (1985).
74. M Engelhardt, 'MCR: An ECR Alternative', in [72], p. 52.
75. P Singer, 'Trends in Plasma Sources: The Search Continues', *Semiconductor International* **15(8)**, 52 (1992).

10

Packaging and testing

No less important than the other main aspects of device fabrication, i.e. materials and technology, is the transformation of a wafer containing many active devices into a large number of well characterized and reliable packaged products, either for sale or incorporation into other systems. This procedure involves a lot of mechanical aspects, and unlike the microelectronics industry a lot of optoelectronic device packaging is done by hand. The combination of the extremely small size of optoelectronic devices, their comparative fragility and the need for optical alignment in the case of source/fiber or detector/fiber assemblies does not lend itself well to full automation. The added aspect that many optoelectronic devices are not made in large volumes contributes another factor in terms of assembly cost; there simply may not be enough of a particular device needed to justify the expense of high throughput automation.

The testing of devices has largely followed the procedures of the microelectronics industry with techniques such as burn-in, current stressing and lead fatigue all important features of optoelectronic device qualifications. Although this chapter, like the last two, tries to be general when talking about packaging and testing techniques, inevitably some examples will only be relevant to one particular type of device; this is especially true of the many specialist aspects of laser packaging and testing.

We start this chapter by looking at the concept of device packaging and its importance in the manufacturing chain. As we have seen in previous chapters, and in particular Chapter 4 on semiconductor lasers, many advanced optoelectronic devices have been reported. This trend will continue for some time yet, as advances in material growth techniques and quality, coupled with ever more sophisticated processing procedures, lead to demonstrations of devices with performance characteristics close to physical predictions. Unfortunately many of these devices never get beyond a demonstration. This is largely because the device performance as a chip becomes significantly degraded when packaged, because the technology of the latter has tended to be regarded as somewhat peripheral compared to materials and processing. Packaging has been seen as a manufacturing problem, a 'low tech' area, whereas all the application of scientists and device engineers 'should be' only up to the unpackaged stage. This attitude has changed in recent years, and needed to: high performance devices are largely useless if they are limited by the package and its assembly.

Packages are large compared to the devices; combine this with the hand assembly and, depending on the device concerned, packaging can then take up to 75% of the final component cost. The challenge of advanced packaging design and assembly has now been taken up by many manufacturers. Techniques common with the microelectronics industry are encapsulation, bonding, lead attachment, headers, microwave layout and multichip; an obvious exception is optical alignment to a fiber, where techniques have been developed solely for optoelectronics. The packaging sections of this chapter are then split along the lines of common techniques in section 10.1 and optical alignment in section 10.2.

10.1   General packaging techniques

This section starts with the assumption that a wafer consists of a series of finished devices, that now await breaking up into individual die and packaging.

10.1.1   Back-wafer lapping

Substrates of III–V semiconductors are much thicker than silicon substrates, because of the much higher fragility of the compound semiconductor materials. A III–V substrate may be typically 2-3 times thicker than a silicon wafer of the same diameter. This thickness, whilst necessary to limit the number of breakages during processing, may not be desirable in the finished package; it will, for example, introduce an extra series resistance with the device. The extra thickness can be removed by lapping the back of the wafer. In this process a wafer is placed, back side down, on a large grinding area in a solution of an abrasive powder such as carborundum (silicon carbide). The finish produced on the back of the wafer is not particularly critical, as long as it is no worse than when the lapping started. The abrasive is thoroughly rinsed off and the wafer dried, ready for back side metallization. After this, the die on the wafer will undergo a functional test to identify the working and non-working devices.

10.1.2   Wafer probing

This is liable to be of short duration and automated, and obviously the nature of the test will depend on the device concerned. Photodetectors may be tested for dark current, and LEDs and lasers for light emission (surface emitters only). On testing a diode, a bad one may be marked with a blob of ink, or its data stored in a computer for later analysis. Every device on a wafer needs to be tested, and so the procedure must be short and not particularly rigorous. Typical test times per device will be around half a second, with about the same time taken to move on to the next device.

10.1.3 Device separation

This is a process known as dicing, and it can be done by one of two main methods: mechanical scribing and sawing, although laser scribing techniques have sometimes been used on an experimental basis.

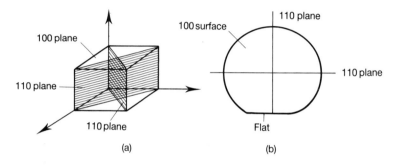

Figure 10.1 (a) Relative orientation of (100) and (110) planes. (b) Their orientation relative to the wafer flat.

10.1.3.1 Mechanical scribing

This technique takes advantage of the crystallographic nature of semiconductor wafers. Most III–V devices are made on ⟨100⟩ oriented substrates. As shown in Figure 10.1(a), this gives two {110} planes oriented perpendicular to each other, and to the (100) surface. When looking at a circular wafer there is no way to tell where these {110} planes are oriented, but a flat ground from the edge of the wafer will show their direction, as in Figure 10.1(b). This flat is introduced during the wafer shaping process (see section 8.1.4) and is determined by x-ray crystallography. (Note: in reality a wafer has its surface cut 2° off (100) to reduce the defect density, but this doesn't affect the principle of the scribing process.)

An area around each device is usually left clear of any processing to allow for the scribing procedure; as an example Figure 10.2 shows contacts made to a wafer of photodetector die. The gap between the edge of the metal contact and the 'scribe line' is an important feature: too small a gap, and there is a risk of device destruction in the scribing process; too large a gap means fewer devices per wafer.

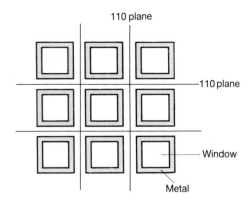

Figure 10.2 Scribe lines in a typical wafer of photodetector die.

Before scribing, the wafers are placed under tension on a stretched adhesive foil. A diamond scribe is then passed along a {110} scribe plane, cutting into the wafer a certain amount, but not through it. The scriber then steps and repeats the process across all parallel planes until the end of the wafer is reached; the wafer is then turned through 90° and the scribing process repeated. A quick inspection of Figure 10.1(a) will show that {100} scribe planes could equally well be chosen, at least in theory; in practice, the partially ionic nature of III–V semiconductors mean that they break a lot easier along the {110} planes. Trying to force against this natural phenomenon by scribing {100} could only lead to inadvertant cleavage along {110}; in any case there is no advantage in doing so.

The purpose of the scribe process is to weaken the structure along the {110} cleavage, but not to break it. If the wafer started to break up the perpendicular scribing could not take place. Die separation is performed by covering the scribed wafer with a scratch protection foil, and applying pressure on the foil via a cylindrical roller. This process introduces stress in the structure. If the scribe lines have been correctly drawn, the already weak crystal bonds along these directions will lead to a sudden fault appearing along the whole plane. The wafer is then separated into individual strips. Rolling along a perpendicular direction will then break the strips into square or rectangular die. Because of the tension introduced by the adhesive foil, the die will tend to separate very readily, but will stay attached to the foil and not 'ping' off in an unpredictable manner. Stretching of the foil will then separate the die even further. The die can then be picked off the foil for mounting, either by hand or automatically.

The scribe process creates a device with {110} planes at its periphery; because these are cleaved they are perfect crystal planes, and act as good end mirrors in a semiconductor laser. They also act as additional outlets for an LED, useful if the LED is simply an indicator, where all that is required is high brightness rather than directionality. For a photodetector using surface entry, the cleavage planes are unlikely to have much effect on device performance.

There are drawbacks with this system. There is a fine balance to be determined when scribing the wafer, so as to introduce enough damage to weaken the structure, but not to split it. If the wafer is not weakened the subsequent rolling process may not result in 100% device separation, causing havoc with any automatic handling system. The second major limitation is the suitability of substrates. There is often a need in liquid phase epitaxy for [111] orientated wafers, and it is clear from a consideration of the relevant crystal planes that these could not be broken into orthogonally sided structures, only triangular ones.

10.1.3.2 Laser scribing

In this process the diamond scribe is replaced by a c.w. or pulsed laser source. The expected advantage is that the finer control offered by a focused laser spot should lead to less 'dead space' being needed around an active device. The focused, high intensity spot is passed along one of the cleavage planes of Figure 10.2. If a c.w. laser is used, the result will be a trench due to the semiconductor being vapourized; a pulsed laser will leave a series of holes. Either way, a vapourized semiconductor can recondense and solidify along the edge of the trench/hole, as in Figure 10.3; this is know as the kerf. The reliability problems inherent due to this redeposition, plus the health hazards associated with the presence of elemental group V vapour, have not led to widespread adoption of this technique. Mechanical scribers also appear to be more reproducible. Laser techniques have been used to create holes straight through wafers, however; this technique is known as photoablation, and is being increasingly used in micro and optoelectronics to create holes of several tens of μm in diameter for such applications as multichip interconnect.

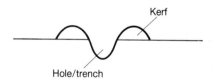

Figure 10.3 A kerf formed after laser scribing.

10.1.3.3 Sawing

Besides mechanical scribing, the second main die separation technique is sawing. Circular rotating diamond blades, of about 30 μm thickness, are passed along the scribe lines of Figure 10.2. In this case the saw blades cut straight through the substrate (the wafer is initially placed on the same adhesive foil as for the scriber). After sawing, the die are separated by the width of the blade and there is no need for rolling and stretching. The yield of the process is then very high as the die separation is done in one step. Another great advantage is that the 'forced' nature of the separation (rather than using natural cleavage planes as for scribing) means that substrates of any orientation can be used, with resultant die separation made in any direction.

The big disadvantage of sawing is also related to its forced nature; the fully mechanical process of die separation results in massive crystal damage to the sawn planes. This manifests itself as strain within the device, which leads to a severely reduced operating lifetime. The saw damage is usually removed by a light chemical etch in one of the appropriate solutions (see section 8.8). Most saw damage is removed within an etch depth of 0.5 μm.

10.1.4   Chip bonding

Considered in this section are the processes whereby diced devices are mounted onto suitable headers. Factors to be taken into account in this process are orientation of the device to ensure good alignment to a fiber (where needed) and the possibility of heat sinking, especially true for semiconductor lasers and avalanche photodetectors: both are very temperature sensitive in their operation.

The first step is usually to mount the chip on a header using indium solder. This should be done in an inert atmosphere, of say Ar/6% H_2, and a typical process temperature is 175 °C. The mounting is done with the contact pads face up for subsequent wire bonding, but as we shall see in section 10.1.6 flip chip arrangements are becoming more important. The chip should be designed, if it is a laser or avalanche diode, such that the thinnest region (usually p-type, as it is normal to perform p-epitaxy on n-substrates) is facing down on to the header. This is because essentially all the heat in a laser is generated in the active region, and hence the ability to conduct that heat away is enhanced by the small thermal resistance of a thin layer between heat source and sink. The p-region should not be too thin, however, as significant optical losses could occur. Also, the thermal conductivity of a system such as GaAs/AlGaAs decreases with increasing aluminium content. It is usual, then, for such a device to contain a 1 μm AlGaAs confinement layer before the GaAs contact layer.

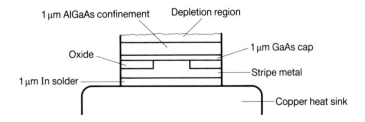

Figure 10.4 A semiconductor laser solder bonded to a heatsink.

The copper heatsink is much more massive than the chip itself, and the better thermal conductivity of diamond has led to the use of this material as a more effective heatsink. For devices where temperature control and heat dissipation are not a major problem, the header can be as small as possible.

Example 10.1

Calculations of typical thermal resistivity [1] show that for a laser of stripe width 12 μm and an effective width of 20 μm the contributions of the various elements shown in Figure 10.4 are as follows: AlGaAs confinement 13 K W^{-1}, GaAs cap 2 K W^{-1}, indium solder 3 K W^{-1} and copper heatsink 5.5 K W^{-1}. Calculate the power input which will give a junction temperature 10 °C above the heatsink temperature.

Solution: the power required to raise the temperature by each degree is simply the reciprocal of the sum of the thermal resistivities, which is $1/23.5 = 0.043$ W. For a temperature rise of 10 °C the power input is then obviously 0.43 W.

10.1.4.1 *Forced cooling*

For some applications, such as precise temperature control for wavelength or gain stability, or where the device generates a large amount of heat, such as in a laser array, a heatsink is not able to cope with the demand of providing a reasonably low and stable temperature. The normal way to get around this is to provide a thermoelectric cooler attached to the heatsink, which uses the well-known Peltier effect [2]. This is one application of thermoelectricity, where electrons at the hot end of a material can find states of lower energy at the cold end to which they diffuse, creating a potential difference.

Thermoelectric coolers in practice are an array of systems as shown in Figure 10.5. As current is passed through the material, electrons transferring from the top metal plate to the n-type semiconductor must obtain an energy kT, thus cooling the plate. This energy is then released at the bottom plate as the electron moves back into the metal. A similar process occurs for hole transfer through the p-type semiconductor. Placing an array of the devices in Figure 10.5 in series, with a plate placed on the top and the bottom, can transfer heat from the top plate to the bottom simply by passing a current through the array.

Thermoelectric junctions are, however, limited by the fact that they require a fairly large current and cannot effectively heatsink large thermal masses. In recent years silicon micromachining has been used to fabricate a familiar looking

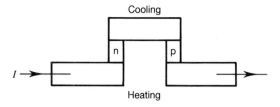

Figure 10.5 One element of a Peltier cooler.

finned heatsink structure on a scale comparable to optoelectronic device sizes. A concept for the use of such a structure is shown in cross-section in Figure 10.6(a) [3]. A flow of water coolant over this structure is used to keep the system cool. A complete assembly of laser arrays, diamond heat sinks and silicon microchannels is shown in Figure 10.6(b). The laser arrays are alternated with synthetic diamonds as chip carriers. A more detailed close-up of a real laser/diamond assembly is shown in Figure 10.6(c). Here just one array is used, and the negative electrode is made of copper. The open microchannel structure of Figure 10.6(a) is bonded to borosilicate glass to create a sealed channel arrangement, with each channel being 1 cm long. Other device arrangements have since been made, e.g. [4], and the approach has been extremely successful in realizing high power semiconductor laser arrays. So much so that these devices are potential replacements for flash lamps when pumping solid state lasers such as Nd^+:YAG.

10.1.5 Wire bonding

The active device, now secured on its header and with or without associated cooling, now needs to be contacted to the outside world. One contact is usually provided via the header itself, but a second contact pad (or several for any level of integration) needs to be provided on the top of the device to complete the circuit. The pad is usually ~ 100 μm square, but can be less if space is a problem, and can be made of aluminium (more usual for integrated circuits) or gold.

The standard method of connection is a gold wire about 25 μm thick which has one end connected to a package lead-out. The other end is connected to the contact pad(s) in a process known as ultrasonic bonding, which was discovered more by accident than design in the 1940s. There is an additional, less used process known as thermal compression bonding. The ultrasonic process and its variations will now be studied in more detail.

10.1.5.1 *Ultrasonic bonding*
This technique has become the standard for bonding wires to chips. It has led to several variations, where the additional use of heat gives rise to the term thermosonic bonding, and the use of a 'flame-off' can lead to different bond profiles,

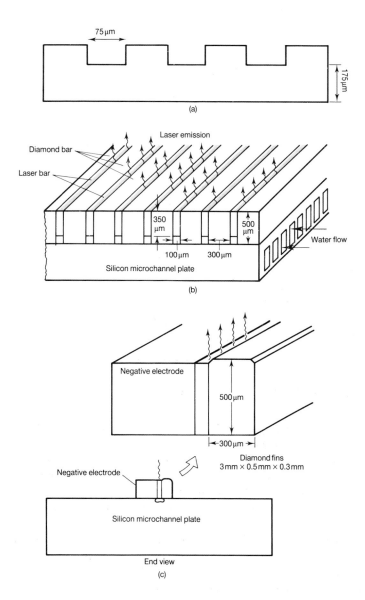

Figure 10.6 (a) A silicon micromachined heat sink. (b) Design for an array of lasers with heat sinks. (c) Assembly used to demonstrate heat sink performance (©AIP: reproduced by kind permission).

either wedge or ball. A basic system is shown in Figure 10.7. An ultrasonically driven vacuum collet is brought down onto a die with the wire end already in place over the contact pad. The end of the wire extends out from underneath a wedge tool. Ultrasonic energy is then provided to promote wire-pad bonding, with the nitrogen used to prevent oxidation. If the metals used are different, e.g. gold wire to an aluminium pad, then several intermetallic phases are possible. There are many factors involved in creating a good bond, such as frequency, time, temperature, surface cleanliness and the metals themselves. As described above, the process will provide for a wedge bond, as shown in Figure 10.8(a) [5]. The mechanics of this process are not clear, as the interface temperature is too low for it to be considered a thermal process. The various explanations of ultrasonic bonding are given in [6], and a review of observed behaviour against process parameters is given in [7].

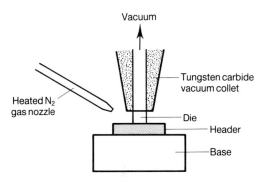

Figure 10.7 The basic bonding system.

The wedge profile of Figure 10.8(a) can be made to appear as the ball contact of Figure 10.8(b) (in reality more like a filled torus than a ball) by altering the process parameters. If the bond wire is cut by a high voltage spark or oxyhydrogen torch (hence the term 'flame-off') the wire will ball up at its end. The ultrasonic process will now lead to a bond profile appearing as in Figure 10.8(b). Only gold wire can do this, as the surface tension of other materials is not sufficient to produce a good ball.

After either wedge or ball bonding, the other end of the wire is taken out to a lead post on the package and bonded there. At present wedge bonding can achieve a closer lead pitch because of the narrower profile of the wedge tool [8].

Modern bonding machines can perform their tasks automatically at speeds up to 10–15 bonds per second; this is important for the IC industry where the need for an ever increasing number of leads per chip and the sheer volume of devices requires a fast automated process. Most production lines are set up for one device, lending itself to ease of automation. For the optoelectronics industry, comparatively few connections are needed; this and the lower volume nature of the business combine to make high speed bonding more difficult to justify.

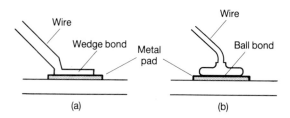

Figure 10.8 Typical profiles of (a) a wedge bond, and (b) a ball bond.

10.1.5.2 Thermocompression bonding

The apparatus and bond profiles produced by this technique are very similar to those of ultrasonic bonding. The difference is in the way the bond is made; as might be inferred from the title, thermocompression bonding involves a combination of heat and a slight mechanical vibration normal to the bonding surfaces.

10.1.5.3 Bond testing and failure mechanisms

The type of bond test used to assess the process integrity depends on the bond itself; as can be seen from Figure 10.8, the geometries of the bond and its associated area are quite different. The wire in a wedge bond has a concave approach, and the width of the bond is of the order of the wire diameter. In contrast, a ball bonded wire has a convex approach, with a bond width several times that of the wire. The standard pull test for wedge bonds would then be of limited use for a ball bond, because in the latter case the wire itself is likely to break before the bond integrity fails, unless the bond is of an exceptionally poor quality.

The pull test is effected by placing a small hook under the wire in the middle of the lead and pulling. The amount of pull force exerted before failure is set by standards, either national or military. Typical values are 2 gf (gram-force) for aluminium wires and 3 gf for gold wires. Failure of the wire is usually due to underbonding (insufficient contact), overbonding (too much contact, leading to squashing) or undesirable intermetallic formations (purple plague, an Au–Al generated reaction giving vacancies which collect at microcracks, leading to voids and hence a reduction in bond strength). The forces involved in this test, although initially looking quite simple, are fiddly to manipulate algebraically and so it is important that comparisons made between different pull-tested devices are done under the same experimental conditions [9].

For a ball bond, it has been shown [10] that a shear test apparatus is needed. This involves bringing a chisel shaped ram against the ball bond and applying a shearing force sufficient to cause the bond to break, as in Figure 10.9. The nature of the bond failure as well as the force needed provides a lot of the information needed to rectify any bonding problem.

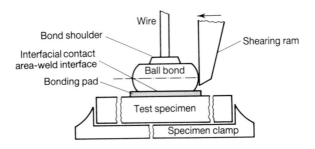

Figure 10.9 A ball bond test assembly (©ASTM: reprinted with permission).

10.1.6   Other bonding techniques

Most of the methods here are aimed at combining the die and wire bond requirements in one process; the first of these, and the one most likely to be used in optoelectronic integrated circuits (OEICs), is flip-chip bonding.

10.1.6.1   Flip-chip bonding

A flip-chip process, as the name implies, involves taking a device and mounting it upside down compared to a 'normal' mounting process, i.e. the contact pads are on the underside. Flip-chips have their bond pads covered by bumps of conductive material. The whole chip can then be soldered ultrasonically to similar bumps on the header in one process, reducing process time, space and the potential of failure due to multiple wire interconnects. Reliability is then improved. A conventional way to enact the technology is by solder bumps – this is shown in Figure 10.10 [11]. The bump consists of three layers of metal on the bond pad with a solder bump on top. The process is not easy, and requires strict cleanliness in its operation. A polymer bump flip-chip process has been reported, which is considerably simpler [11]. Flip-chips are not likely to be ever used in optoelectronics where the device is made using the whole depth of the wafer, as is the case for most single operation devices. However, OEICs which combine several functions on a chip often use a thin top part of the substrate. In this case the flip-chip process could be a means of increasing the production rate of transmitter/receiver modules.

10.1.6.2   Tape automated bonding

Tape automated bonding (or TAB as it is commonly called) was introduced in the late 1960s as a competitor for wire bonding, but because of the maturity of the latter technique, TAB was not really developed until the 1980s. It is now being applied extensively in the IC industry, but as yet has little demand in optoelectronics largely due to the low pin count of these devices.

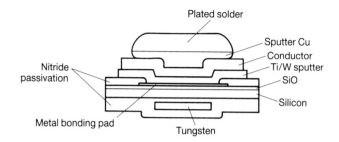

Figure 10.10 Solder bump technology for bump formation (©Angel Publishing: reproduced by kind permission of European Semiconductor magazine).

TAB is a wire-less process, using a metal (usually copper) etched pattern of beam leads, that terminate at specific points, which line up with similar beams or, more likely, bumps on the circuits to be attached. The other end of the beam lead then mates up with a printed circuit board. Attachment of the tape to the chip or to the PCB is traditionally done in a similar way to wire bonding, i.e. ultrasonically or by thermocompression. Bonding may be single point or all simultaneously (gang-bonding). There are several variations on the TAB process technology, but all are characterized by a bonding projection between the chip and the beam lead. The advantages of TAB over wire bonding are [12, 13]:

(i) smaller bonding pad and pitch on chip, giving a greater potential pin count, and a smaller PCB area,
(ii) no wire loops, giving a low profile assembly suitable for thin outline packages,
(iii) greater precision,
(iv) less moulding and lower labour costs,
(v) stronger leads – typically the pull strength will be five times higher than for ball bonds,
(vi) better heat transfer,
(viii) less gold and hence cheaper materials cost.

10.1.7 Multichip modules

A lot of research effort in microelectronics has gone into multichip modules (MCMs) in the search for an improvement in board area utilization. The idea is simple in concept – stack more than one chip on top of each other, and if the interconnect problem can be solved, then a tremendous benefit in terms of usable area will be realized. The interconnect problem is, of course, the key difficult issue. A typical schematic of an MCM is shown in Figure 10.11. The common interconnects would be power rails, ground planes and clock signals, and it is clear than an MCM has to be designed as a complete chip-set from the start, thus maximizing the functionality of each chip and minimizing the number of (and hence associated area of) interconnections between chips. The use of MCMs in optoelectronics is debatable unless complex processing circuitry is required; future 'optical MCMs' are more likely to be interconnected by some means such as holography.

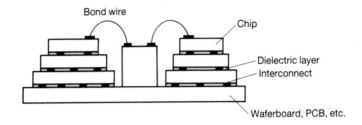

Figure 10.11 A typical MCM (multichip module) schematic.

10.1.8   High frequency packaging

Of principle interest to high bit rate photoreceivers, the design of a package to eliminate parasitics such as wire capacitance to optimize performance is an important issue in high speed optical communications. A common ground plane is essential, bends are minimal to eliminate stray inductances, multiple wire bonds are used to minimize resistances and packages are shielded. The circuit that contains a photodetector and amplifier is usually a submount chip in a hybrid circuit. Similar techniques can be used to increase the high frequency performance of laser diodes.

10.2   Optical alignment

The big difference between optical and electrical devices/integrated circuits in terms of input/output is the need in the former to couple light from/to a fiber. Not all devices need this; display LEDs being an obvious example, but most communication devices are connected in this way. We start this section by looking at fiber coupling, the techniques used for alignment and finally a hybrid device system that promises to be able to enhance both the performance and manufacturability of optoelectronic components.

10.2.1   Optical coupling

This has been covered in the relevant sections on LEDs (section 3.3.4) and lasers (section 4.1.3). An LED can be considered as a Lambertian emitter, giving off light at all angles and with an angular intensity distribution function $I(\theta)$ given by (3.27). An optical fiber placed close to the LED will receive this light, but only that incident within the acceptance angle θ_a will be coupled to the fiber.

However, a laser is much more directional in its output, although without good designs the diffraction limited output can be several tens of degrees. This was covered in section 4.1.3.4, and a laser output can be considered to be less affected by fiber acceptance angle, as the incident light is largely normal to the fiber end. Only reflection losses then occur.

For a detector, the fiber end acts as a source emitting light as a Lambertian emitter, but only up to its acceptance angle θ_a. As for the light sources, some collecting lens and/or close proximity of the detector to the fiber is then necessary. This coupling problem and how it is overcome is now considered in more detail.

10.2.1.1   Source–fiber coupling

One consideration to be noted straightaway is the physical size of the source in relation to the fiber core. Two examples are shown in Figure 10.12, for a source diameter both smaller and larger than that of the fiber core. For the former case, Figure 10.12(a) shows that a coupling lens can refract some of the source output to within the acceptance angle of the fiber core, thus increasing the amount of light coupled to the fiber compared to a lens-less design.

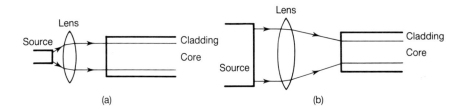

Figure 10.12 Source to fiber coupling for (a) source area smaller and (b) bigger than fiber end area.

Figure 10.12(b), where the source has a larger diameter than the fiber core, apparently shows that again a lens can couple more light to a fiber. However, this violates the conservation of brightness (power/(area × solid angle) = a constant [14]) and all the extra 'coupled' light is not guided by the fiber because it must be incident outside the acceptance angle.

This conservation of brightness can be translated to a design rule for optical coupling via a lens (or some other means); the coupling efficiency will only be enhanced if

$$A_s\Omega_s \leq A_f\Omega_f \tag{10.1}$$

where A and Ω represent cross-sectional area and solid angle respectively, and the subscripts s and f refer to source and fiber core respectively. The lens then magnifies the souce area in the same proportion as it collimates the solid angular distribution of the radiation. The maximum value of the fiber coupling efficiency η_c' is then [15]

$$\eta_c' = (NA)^2\frac{A_f}{A_s} \tag{10.2}$$

where NA is the fiber numerical aperture, given by $NA = \sin\theta_a$. Simple considerations of geometrical optics, e.g. [16], will show that

$$\sin\theta_a = (n_1^2 - n_2^2)^{1/2} \tag{10.3}$$

where n_1 and n_2 are the fiber core and cladding refractive indices respectively, and so from (10.2) and (10.3)

$$\eta_c' = (n_1^2 - n_2^2)\frac{A_f}{A_s} \tag{10.4}$$

in terms of simple parameters of the system. Equation (10.4) clearly indicates that a small area source (compared to the fiber) will couple much more efficiently than a large area one. However, a small area device implies lower total object power, and for this to remain constant the brightness must be increased.

Example 10.2

Calculate the coupling efficiency of an LED to a 50 μm core diameter fiber if the LED has a surface area of 10^3 μm^2 and the LED can be assumed to be a perfect Lambertian emitter. The core and cladding refractive indices are 1.465 and 1.452 respectively.

Solution: from (10.4)

$$\begin{aligned}
\eta_c' &= (2.146 - 2.108) \times \frac{\pi \times 625}{10^3} \\
&= 0.07.
\end{aligned} \tag{10.5}$$

It can be seen from this that coupling efficiencies are generally very low for simple systems.

Many different types of lens designs have been proposed and used. The simplest type is a ball lens, although cylindrical and hemispherical systems have also been used. The fiber end can also be tapered, and additionally a lens can be placed on the end of this. Table 10.1 [17] summarizes many different types of coupling, along with loss tests on selected systems. The combination of a tapered fiber with a high index 'microbead' lens attached to its end would appear to be the most efficient design.

The principle of the tapered fiber approach can be seen from (10.4) and Figure 10.13. If a_t is the radius of the tapered end and a_f the radius of the constant diameter fiber, then (10.4) shows that for a source of diameter less than $2a_t$ the improvement in coupling efficiency of a taper over normal fibers is $(a_f/a_t)^2$.

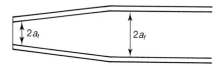

Figure 10.13 The tapered fiber.

10.2.1.2 *Fiber alignment*

Of course, all of the coupling methods in Table 10.1 rely crucially on the ability to make idealized structures. Imperfections, such as lens aberrations, can have a dramatic effect on performance. Calculations on this aspect are given in [18]. Obviously no lens system will be able to couple two badly aligned components together, and so the initial positioning of source and fiber in terms of x, y, z and angular position in two dimensions θ and ϕ is critical. The amount of misalignment that can be tolerated depends on the individual devices concerned. If the source area is substantially smaller than the fiber core cross-section, then lateral misalignment may not be too big a problem. This explains why single mode fiber (typical core diameter $\sim 10~\mu$m) is far less forgiving in this respect than multi-mode fiber (typical core diameter 50–100 μm). Misalignments of ± 1–1.5 μm are sufficient to cause 1 dB of loss in single mode, but the error can be as large as ± 5–10 μm for multimode [19]. For longitudinal misalignment, i.e. increasing the distance between source and fiber, the tolerances are greater, typically doubling the figures quoted above for 1 dB losses. Alignment to planar optoelectronic integrated circuits is usually done differently. In this case, a fiber is brought in parallel to the chip surface, and its end polished to a 40° angle. Total internal reflection then couples the light from fiber to device (Figure 10.14 [20]).

Alignment is usually done via micrometer based stages, and once maximized the fiber is fixed in position via a large blob of epoxy resin, which is then cured. This is normally an acceptable method, but shrinking of the epoxy can cause future alignment problems – this is especially true for critical single mode systems. Vibration

Method	Description	Notes	Minimum loss (dB)	
			Bench	Package
Cylindrical lens	Separate lens	a,e		
Hemispherical taper end	Fiber tapered and rounded	a,c	4.1	4
Ball and GRIN lens	Two separate lenses	f	3.5	3
Plano-convex GRIN lens	Separate lenses	f	3.3	5
Cylindrical and GRIN lens	Two separate lenses	e		
Etched conical end	Core end shaped by etching	a,b	2.8	
Hemispherical tipped lens	Glass droplet attached to fiber end	a		
Quadrangular end	End face polished to special shape	a,e		
High index microbead	Bead attached to inside of cap window	f	1.6	2.1
High index taper end	Taper tip dipped into high index glass melt	a,c	2.1	
Etched end with lens	Fiber etched around and lens formed on end	a,d		2.5

Table 10.1 A selection of ways of improving the coupling efficiency of a source/detector to a fiber. Notes: (a) fiber seal is required, (b) lens is exactly aligned to core, (c) lens is adequately aligned to core, (d) lens is adequately aligned if the core is concentric to the cladding, (e) asymmetric configuration, (f) no fiber seal is required.

isolation can also be a problem. The alignment of a fiber and its subsequent stability then becomes a packaging problem, and several package designs have been generated to minimize this.

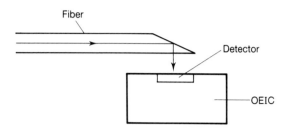

Figure 10.14 Alignment of a fiber to a planar device.

10.3   Packages

In this section we will look at the basic packages for devices, the TO- cans, and then discuss the more detailed pigtail arrangement and its subassembly for high performance optoelectronic devices. The encapsulation/packaging of LEDs as display devices is not covered here, as it was detailed in section 3.5.5, and is specific to that type of device.

10.3.1   TO- can

A TO- can is very simple in its construction, and the TO number (TO-3, TO-5, TO-18, etc.) represents a variation on the basic theme of the structure, which is illustrated in Figure 10.15. The device is bonded to a header and wires attached. A metal can with a window is then affixed by resistance welding, in an inert atmosphere if a hermetic seal is required. The window must obviously not affect the characteristics of the device. Antireflection coatings are sometimes used, and if the device contained in the package is to be a UV-sensitive photodetector the window should be made of mica rather than the more usual glass or plastic. The TO- can is a simple, low cost package that provides a high degree of environmental protection for the device, and many systems are sold using this type of package. What can't be achieved, however, is close alignment with a fiber, and if this is necessary a different packaging method is needed.

Axially symmetric packages are available, where lenses are used between the source/detector and fiber. Here a TO- can is used to incorporate the device and a first lens. A fiber and second lens is then aligned to the can and locked in place. Great attention is needed to minimize the reflections from the many optical interfaces, and any thermoelectric cooling is usually applied externally [21].

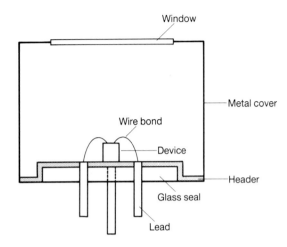

Figure 10.15 The basic TO- can.

10.3.2   Fiber pigtail

For precise alignment of a fiber with a source/detector, the fiber itself needs to be brought inside the package, aligned and fixed in position as close as possible to the semiconductor device. A TO- can does not allow for this, and the whole system is redesigned to look more like the familiar DIL (dual in-line) package used for integrated circuits. The main differences between an electronic DIL package and an optoelectronic one are:

(i) in an electronic DIL, most of the volume is not needed for the device, which occupies a very small part near the centre. The reason why the package is comparatively big is to accomodate the output connections to a standard pitch. An optoelectronic component and its associated circuitry does actually occupy most of the surface area available within a DIL.

(ii) An optoelectronic DIL has a fiber entering the package through a hermetic seal in addition to the given number of electrical pins (see Figure 4.91).

(iii) All optoelectronic DILs are metal encapsulated; most electronic packages are plastic (although an increasing number are becoming metal).

As well as the dual in-line package of Figure 4.91, a single in-line (SIL) system is available.

10.3.3   Grooved silicon substrates

Many of the fabrication techniques used in optoelectronic device technology are adaptations of work that has its origins in silicon processing. Sometimes, however, not only the techniques but the material and its mechanical properties can be taken. Research in the late 1980s pointed to silicon as a suitable mechanical substrate; in particular to align fibers precisely to a source/detector by way of a V-grooved channel [22]. The use of silicon waferboards, as the method has come to be known, has the following advantages:

(i) low toxicity, compared to BeO substrates and GRIN lenses using thallium,

(ii) unaffected by organic solvents,

(iii) tolerance to high temperatures used in subsequent processing,

(iv) control of electrical properties, with resistivities available over several orders of magnitude,

(v) good mechanical stability, especially with regard to temperature induced changes,

(vi) familiarity with techniques used for patterning, obtained from IC manufacture,

(vii) ability to make an optical bench by crystallographic etching (see section 8.8.1.2).

It is the precision of the latter that is of the greatest importance. Silicon can be micromachined to dimension tolerances much less than 1 μm, which compares favourably with most device active dimensions and very well with the smallest diameter single mode waveguide ($\sim$ 6 μm). Once etched, the silicon is also very stable, meaning long term reliability is to be expected from a system that is used to hold optical components in precise alignment.

The different shapes naturally obtained from crystallographic etching are another advantage. Inverted pyramid shaped parts can hold lenses, whilst V-grooves are usually used to hold the fiber. In addition, the active devices themselves can be die bonded on to mesas or in troughs. The subsequent integration of silicon electronic circuits or silicon dioxide/nitride based waveguides is a further possibility. In fact, many ideas have been proposed that use silicon as a large area optical bench/supporting substrate for a complete optoelectronic component. An example is shown in Figure 10.16 [23], which is a drop/insert multiplexer. This device reads information from one fiber input and, if necessary, can substitute different information into the output data stream.

10.4   Testing

Testing encompasses many different aspects of device qualification. We have already looked at one aspect of mechanical testing in section 10.1.5 on wire bonding,

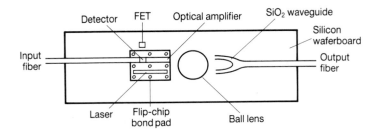

Figure 10.16 A proposed optoelectronic component (a drop/insert multiplexer) utilizing a silicon waferboard (©Pennwell Publishing: adapted by kind permission from Figure 4 in R A Boudreau, 'Innovative Packaging Enhances Performance of OE Components', *Laser Focus World* **27(11)**, 149 (1991)).

where the strength of the bond itself was tested either via a pull test (wedge bond) or a shear test (ball bond). Electrical and, for light transmitters, optical performance testing are also necessary, and each manufacturer and/or customer will have their own specification for performance. Lengthy test periods under harsh environmental conditions (burn-in) add to the screening procedures. In this section we will look at each of the testing methods in turn, but first consideration needs to be given to predictions of likely failure modes, independent of the testing technique.

10.4.1 Testing strategy

All the devices discussed in Chapters 3–7 have associated failure modes due to a range of time and temperature associated defect mechanisms. To a certain extent these can be predicted empirically, if not always well understood in a scientific sense. What is far more difficult, if not impossible, to predict for an individual device is a short term failure due to some fault in the fabrication or packaging. Testing strategy should be to accomodate both the long and short term failure modes, as well as the medium term mechanisms, on a statistical sample basis. The object is to eliminate the devices that will/do suffer short or medium term failure, and keep those whose predicted lifetime is not likely to be the limiting factor in system performance. Hence there is a great emphasis on harsh testing of new devices to 'weed out' the ones not likely to meet the system lifetime criteria.

Fortunately, the failure modes of optoelectronic devices when judged on a statistical basis are like many other manufactured products, whether semiconductors, light bulbs, engines or whatever. This section is based upon the data in [24].

10.4.1.1 The bathtub curve

This has become a standard depiction of failure for many devices, and it is made up of basically three modes of failure, independent of the device concerned. These are shown in Figure 10.17.

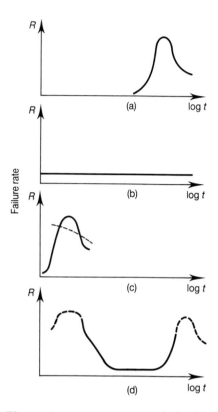

Figure 10.17 The various components of the bathtub curve: (a) long term failure, (b) random failure, (c) short term failure, and (d) the final shape using (a), (b) and (c).

Long term failure is shown in Figure 10.17(a). The distribution is Gaussian in time, but with a positive skew and an asymmetry because the independent variable is the logarithm of time. The device to device variations are a result of different growth and processing conditions that cannot be ascertained once the device is ready for testing. The curve is known as lognormal.

Figure 10.17(b) shows a graph of random failure modes vs time. Examples are mechanical shock, high currents due to external circuitry failure, etc. Because these modes are random, they will induce a constant failure rate with time, and will affect all devices equally. The number of survivors is given by a Poisson distribution, and hence the failure rate R is a constant given by the reciprocal of the lifetime against chance failure.

Short term failure is shown in Figure 10.17(c), and typical mechanisms are cracked chips or weak wire bonds. Short term, or infant, failure is not as well characterized as the other modes for several reasons:

(i) the $t = 0$ point is arbitrary,
(ii) it is difficult to monitor very short lifetimes, and
(iii) many origins are possible.

For these reasons, short term failure is usually characterized by a lognormal curve as in Figure 10.17(a), but with the curve shifted down the time axis, and superimposed on top an exponential function which represents the failure time distribution of some mechanical defects whose distribution is random and extrinsic to the device. Short term failures are then characterized by Figure 10.17(c). A composite of Figures 10.17(a)–(c) is shown in Figure 10.17(d), where the bathtub shape can be clearly seen. The maximum point in the hazard rate for short term failure may be at such a short time that it would not be detected. The maximum point for long term failure is ideally so far off into the future for high quality devices that it is unlikely to ever be seen.

The bathtub shape then suggests the following testing strategy: operate all the devices until the failure rate falls to a constant value, or falls below some acceptable level, or becomes immeasurably small. The remaining devices will then fail primarily by wear out, i.e. long term ageing.

10.4.1.2 *Accelerated thermal ageing*
The problem with the approach outlined above is that it doesn't determine the average lifetime of a device. If the components have a very long lifetime, then testing in the laboratory is not practical. On the assumption that failure is temperature as well as time dependent, operation at elevated temperatures can give evidence of predicted lifetimes. For instance, following from (3.76) and (3.77), where

$$\frac{P}{P_0} = \exp\left[-\beta_0 t \exp\left(-E_A/kT\right)\right] \tag{10.6}$$

for a light emitter, then testing the output power at two different temperatures can give a value of the activation energy. This data can then be extrapolated back to device operational temperature and the lifetime predicted.

Accelerated ageing doesn't pick out infant failures, however, and typical lifetime plots show a characteristic as in Figure 10.18. Infant failures are shown as the 'freak' population with low life expectancy. The 'S' shape is shown as a bimodal distribution, because of the occurance of two failure mechanisms.

There are problems with this kind of testing, of which the following two considerations are the most important:

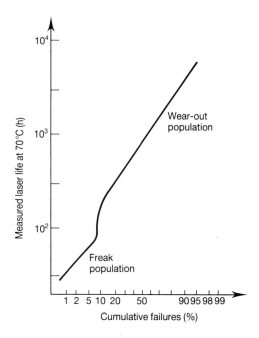

Figure 10.18 Wear out and freak distributions of the failures observed in 70 °C ambient ageing of AlGaAs lasers.

(i) if the two lognormal distributions of Figure 10.17(d) overlap because of a large dispersion on one or other, or both, distributions, then the bathtub will never flatten out. Testing to eliminate the infant failures will continue into the region where wear out begins to occur.

(ii) Many infant failures have low activation energies, and so their effect is largely temperature independent. This is not true for the large activation energies of wear-out failures, typically 0.5 to 1.5 eV.

Example 10.3

A particular type of LED has two independent failure mechanisms, denoted M_1 and M_2, with the relevant physical parameters given in Table 10.2.

Calculate the time taken, to the nearest convenient unit, for the power output of the device to fall to half its original value for each of the failure mechanisms at an operating temperature of 20°C.

After fabrication a sample batch of the diodes was tested at an elevated temperature of 150°C. Successful LEDs emitted more than half their original power

	β_0 (per hour)	E_A (eV)
M_1	0.8	0.2
M_2	5.5×10^7	0.8

Table 10.2 The physical parameters associated with example 10.3.

after one week of testing. If the expected lifetime of the diodes in operation at 20°C is 70 years, and the lifetime is defined as a further 50% fall in output power, prove that the testing procedure is invalid because it misses the short term failure mechanism (assuming that each diode will fail by only one of M_1 or M_2).

Solution: the expected lifetime associated with M_1 and M_2 can be calculated by rearranging (10.6):

$$t = \frac{\log_e (P/P_0)}{-\beta_0 \exp (-E_A/kT)} .$$

$$\text{For } M_1 \quad t = \frac{\log_e 0.5}{-0.8 \exp (-0.2 \times e/k \times 293)}$$

$$\sim 3 \text{ months},$$

$$\text{and for } M_2 \quad t = \frac{\log_e 0.5}{-5.5 \times 10^7 \exp (-0.8 \times e/k \times 293)}$$

$$\sim 83 \text{ years}. \tag{10.7}$$

These results suggest that M_1 and M_2 are short and long term failure modes respectively. If we now perform some accelerated testing at an elevated temperature of 150 °C for 1 week (168 hours), then (10.6) will now give us:

$$\text{for } M_1 \quad \frac{P(t)}{P_0} = \exp \left(-0.8 \times 168 \times \exp \left(\frac{-0.2 \times e}{k \times 423} \right) \right)$$

$$= 0.57$$

$$\text{and for } M_2 \quad \frac{P(t)}{P_0} = \exp \left(-5.5 \times 10^7 \times 168 \times \exp \left(\frac{-0.8 \times e}{k \times 423} \right) \right)$$

$$= 0.07. \tag{10.8}$$

In this case all devices with failure mode M_1 pass, whereas all those that fail by M_2 are rejected. This example shows the catastrophically misleading effect of accelerated thermal ageing with a temperature independent early failure mode; indeed, as this example shows, long term failure (with reference to normal operating conditions) occurs before short term failure in accelerated thermal testing! A combination of burn-in and accelerated ageing can then be used, such that the former is used to screen out the early failures and the latter used to predict the wear-out lifetime. A detailed strategy based on this approach is given in [24].

10.4.2 Mechanical testing

We have already considered the testing of bond wires in section 10.1.5. Other mechanical tests include measuring the performance during and after shock (i.e. striking the assembly with a severe, measured blow), acceleration, solderability, terminal strength, bonding stress and vibration amplitude and frequency. Further details of specific test procedures are given in [25].

10.4.3 Environmental testing

During its lifetime, an optoelectronic component may be deliberately or inadvertantly used in a severe environment. Operating temperatures may be high, or the device could be on the ocean floor where the whole assembly is under great pressure and also susceptible to salt water attack. These would be steady state conditions, but it is also possible that the device may be operating in a fluctuating environment where, for instance, a given temperature range is likely to be encountered.

To test over a wide temperature range, large environmental chambers are used that can accomodate many devices simultaneously. There are three basic uses for this kind of chamber:

(i) accelerated thermal ageing, typically operating at 70–100 °C,
(ii) high temperature storage testing, typically 150 °C for 1000 h, and
(iii) thermal shock cycling, typically over a temperature range of –65 to 150 °C.

The environmental chambers can also add humidity at levels up to 98%; again, this can be done on a steady state or cyclical basis. Moisture can be a real problem in optoelectronic devices, as in integrated circuits. Unwanted water vapour leads to metal corrosion, decomposition of organics and increases in absorption in an optical fiber. If moisture cycling is used in conjunction with thermal and vibrational stressing, most minor defects in otherwise hermetically sealed structures are likely to be found. An example of this is the stress induced in cracks by the freezing and subsequent melting of embedded moisture. A salt atmosphere will produce an accelerated effect in any corrosion problems. Finally, environmental chambers can also be used to increase or reduce the operating pressure, again looking to find any weak points in the packaging of components.

10.4.4   Electrical testing

There is very little to test electrically with optoelectronic devices other than their $I–V$ characteristic – is it changing with operating conditions? If the device forms part of an encapsulated circuit which, for instance, may contain a laser driver or a photodetector/amplifier, then other electrical tests on this additional circuitry should be independently performed. Other electrical considerations largely relate to insulation resistance, freedom from electromagnetic interference, and grounding of high frequency devices.

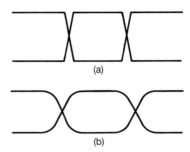

(a)

(b)

Figure 10.19 The 'eye' pattern used to test the high speed performance of emitters or detectors: (a) ideal, and (b) observed patterns.

10.4.5   Optical testing

An LED or laser's light output power vs drive current $(L–I)$ characteristic is its most important parameter. Both power stability and linewidth should be closely monitored. Power stability is usually determined using 1010 data patterns over the operating range. Other tests include looking at the 'eye' pattern (Figure 10.19). A fast photodetector is used to pick up the light output, which is obtained by driving the emitter with a pseudo random bit pattern. The oscilloscope is synchronized with the basic clock rate and so the eye is composed of all possible sequences of '1' and '0'. Ideally, the eye should be as in Figure 10.19(a), but from the real display of Figure 10.19(b) the rise and fall times, along with any jitter or overshoot, can be determined and monitored under the test conditions. Of course, this method can also be used to monitor detector performance if this is the device to be tested, and the light source is assumed constant.

The spectral width of an emitter output can be monitored using an optical spectrum analyzer, which in principle is no different from its equivalent electrical device except that the operational frequency range is much higher.

10.5   Problems

1. If III–V wafers are too thick for the desired operating characteristics of the finished device, why aren't the original substrates specified to the ideal thickness, instead of lapping the substrate after the rest of the processing has been completed?

2. What would you expect to be the mechanism of material removal in photoablation, where a high energy (e.g. 193 nm ArF) pulsed laser is fired at a target?

3. Consider a 500 μm laser diode bonded onto a substrate at a temperature of 175 °C. If the linear expansion coefficient of the diode is 2.5×10^{-6}/°C, and of the substrate double this figure, how much does one end of the diode move relative to the other once the assembly has cooled to room temperature, assuming that one end is fixed? Compare this distance with the diameter of a typical wedge or ball bond.

4. What are the silicon wafer orientations and type of etchants needed to make:

   (i) a heatsink with water channels,

   (ii) V-grooves for fiber alignment,

   (iii) an inverted pyramid for lens alignment?

10.6   References

1. H Kressel, M Ettenberg, J P Wittke and I Ladany, 'Laser Diodes and LEDs for Fiber Optical Communication', in Topics in Applied Physics, vol. 39: *Semiconductor Devices for Optical Communication*, 2nd ed., Springer Verlag, 1980, p. 27.

2. R D Barnard, *Thermoelectricity in Metals and Alloys*, Taylor and Francis, 1972.

3. D Mundinger, R Beach, W Benett, R Solarz, W Krupke, R Staver and D Tuckerman, 'Demonstration of High Performance Silicon Microchannel Heat Exchangers for Laser Diode Array Cooling', *Appl. Phys. Lett.* **53**, 1030 (1988).

4. R Beach, D Mundinger, W Benett, V Sperry, B Comaskey and R Solarz, 'High Reliability Silicon Microchannel Submount for High Average Power Laser Diode Arrays', *Appl. Phys. Lett.* **56**, 2065 (1990).

5. W C Till and J T Luxon, *Integrated Circuits: Materials, Devices and Fabrication*, Prentice-Hall International, 1982, p. 360.

6. V H Winchell, II and H M Berg, 'Enhancing Ultrasonic Bond Development', *IEEE Trans. Components, Hybrids and Manuf. Technol.* **CHMT-1**, 211 (1978).

7. T H Ramsey and C Alfaro, 'The Effect of Ultrasonic Frequency on Intermetallic Reactivity of Au–Al Bonds', *Solid State Technology* **34(12)**, 37 (1991).

8. R Bidin, 'High Pin Count Wirebonding: The Challenge for Packaging', *Solid State Technology* **35(5)**, 75 (1992).

9. G G Harman and C A Cannon, 'The Microelectronic Wire Bond Pull Test – How to Use it, How to Abuse it', *IEEE Trans. Components, Hybrids and Manuf. Technol.* **CHMT-1**, 203 (1978).

10. H K Charles, Jr, G V Clatterbaugh and J A Weiner, 'The Ball Bond Shear Test', in *Semiconductor Processing* **ASTM STP 850**, D C Gupta, ed., American Society for Testing and Materials, 1984, p. 429.

11. 'Die Bonding', *European Semiconductor* **14(7)**, 17 (1992).

12. J H Lau, D W Rice and C G Harkins, 'Thermal Stress Analysis of Tape Automated Bonding Packages and Interconnections', *IEEE Trans. Components, Hybrids and Manuf. Technol.* **CHMT-13**, 182 (1990).

13. 'Tape Automated Bonding', *European Semiconductor* **13(10)**, 29 (1991).

14. M Born and E Wolf, *Principles of Optics*, 5th ed., Pergamon Press, 1975, p. 188.

15. M C Hudson, 'Calculation of the Maximum Optical Coupling Efficiency into Multimode Optical Waveguides', *Appl. Opt.* **13**, 1029 (1974).

16. J Senior, *Optical Fiber Communications: Principles and Practice*, 2nd ed., Prentice Hall International, 1992, p. 18.

17. G-D Khoe, H G Kock, D Küppers, J H F M Poulissen and H M de Vrieze, 'Progress in Monomode Optical-Fiber Interconnection Devices', *J. Lightwave Technol.* **LT-2**, 217 (1984).

18. M Sumida and K Takemoto, 'Lens Coupling of Laser Diodes to Single-Mode Fibers', *J. Lightwave Technol.* **LT-2**, 305 (1984).

19. P W Shumate, 'Semiconductor Laser Transmitters', in *Optoelectronic Technology and Lightwave Communication Systems*, C. Lin, ed., Van Nostrand Reinhold, 1989, p. 424.

20. T Horimatsu and M Sasaki, 'OEIC Technology and its Application to Subscriber Loops', *J. Lightwave Technol.* **7**, 1612 (1989).

21. See [19], p. 426.

22. C H Henry, G E Blonder and R F Kazarinov, 'Glass Waveguides on Silicon for Hybrid Optical Packaging', *J. Lightwave Technol.* **7**, 1530 (1989).

23. R A Boudreau, 'Innovative Packaging Enhances Performance of OE Components', *Laser Focus World* **27(11)**, 149 (1991).

24. F R Nash, W B Joyce, R L Hartman, E I Gordon and R W Dixon, 'Selection of a Laser Reliability Assurance Strategy for a Long-Life Application', *AT & T Tech. J.* **64**, 671 (1985).

25. C E Jowett, *Semiconductor Testing Technology*, October Press, 1982, pp. 39–50.

Index